INTRODUCTION TO
Aircraft Structures, Systems, and Powerplants

A HANDBOOK FOR PILOTS, MECHANICS, AND MANAGERS

Edited by Kevin High and David Jones

Production Staff

Designer/Photographer Dustin Blyer
Designer/Production Coordinator Roberta Byerly
Production Artists Christy Kauffman and Paul Johnson
Contributor Jeff Strong
Editors Kevin High and David Jones

International Standard Book Number 1-933189-79-7
ISBN 13: 978-1-933189-79-6
Order # T-INAIST-0101
For Sale by: Avotek
A Select Aerospace Industries, Inc., company

Mail to:
P.O. Box 219
Weyers Cave, VA 24486
USA

Ship to:
200 Packaging Drive
Weyers Cave, VA 24486
USA

Toll Free: 800-828-6835
Telephone: 540-234-9090
Fax: 540-234-9399

First Edition
First Printing
Printed in the USA

www.avotek.com

Preface

Introduction to Aircraft Structures, Systems, and Powerplants serves as an introductory text for students in any aviation-related track of study: future mechanics/technicians, pilots, or aviation managers. It gives them an introduction to aircraft construction and systems, providing a foundation of knowledge and understanding needed for advanced classes. Text that is easy to understand and uses many figures offers the perfect level of detail for anyone new to aviation. Readers get an excellent overview of aircraft structures and systems. To complement the aircraft topics, the book also discusses aircraft powerplants—both reciprocating and turbine—and the systems that support them. Throughout, this text describes both newer technology and the tried-and-true, older ones that are still widely used.

Textbooks must be of a general nature in their coverage of subject areas. The aircraft manufacturer is the sole source of operation, maintenance, repair, and overhaul information. The manufacturer manuals are approved by the FAA and must always be followed. You may not use any material presented in this textbook as a manual for actual operation, maintenance, or repairs.

The writers, individuals, and companies who contributed to this textbook have done so in the spirit of cooperation for the good of the industry. To the best of their abilities, they have tried to present the material with accuracy, honesty, and pertinence. As with all human endeavors, errors and omissions can show up in the most unexpected places. If any exist, they are unintentional. Please bring them to our attention. ➣

To make comments or suggestions, email us at comments@avotek.com.

Avotek® Aircraft Maintenance Series
Introduction to Aircraft Maintenance
Aircraft Structural Maintenance
Aircraft System Maintenance
Aircraft Powerplant Maintenance

Avotek Avionics Series
Avionics: Fundamentals of Aircraft Electronics
Avionics: Beyond the AET
Avionics: Instruments and Auxiliary Systems
Avionics: Systems and Troubleshooting

Other Books by Avotek
Advanced Composites
Aircraft Corrosion Control Guide
Aircraft Hydraulics
Aircraft Structural Technician
Aircraft Turbine Engines
Aircraft Wiring & Electrical Installation
AMT Reference Handbook
Avotek Aeronautical Dictionary
Fundamentals of Modern Aviation
Light Sport Aircraft Inspection Procedures
Structural Composites: Advanced Composites in Aviation
Transport Category Aircraft Systems

Acknowledgments

AT&T Archives and History Center

Avotek

Electronics International, Inc.

Federal Aviation Administration

GE Aviation

National Aeronautics and Space Administration

Mark Stoltzfus

Select Airparts

Sporty's Pilot Shop

Textron Aviation

United Technologies Corp., Pratt & Whitney Division

U.S. Air Force

U.S. Navy

Contents

Aircraft Structures

The term *aircraft* is appropriate for any device that is used for, or is intended to be used for, flight in the air. This covers a great many flying machines of all types and sizes. This term applies to everything from the largest wide-bodied jet airliners to the small drones that have become the fastest growing segment of aviation today. Each of these designs incorporates some sort of structure to ensure that it can meet its goal of flight.

The most familiar type of aircraft is the fixed-wing airplane. As the name implies, the wings on this type of flying machine are attached to the fuselage and are not intended to move independently in a way that creates lift. This is where we focus our instruction.

The first of its kind to carry a person aloft was the Wright Flyer. It had thin, cloth-covered wings attached to a wood truss structure, with wires providing additional support.

Powered heavier-than-air flight grew from this early Wright design. Inventors and fledgling aviators began building their own aircraft. Early on, many designs were similar to those constructed by the Wrights, using wood and fabric with wires.

With the desire for better performance, more powerful engines were developed, and airframe structures changed to be able to withstand the additional stress.

In the 1920s, metal, instead of wood, was increasingly used in aircraft construction. Fuselages capable of carrying cargo and passengers were developed. The early flying boats with their hull-type construction borrowed from the shipbuilding industry provided the blueprints for fuselage construction. Construction methods also changed with the shift from wood to metal.

Left: The Cessna 206 is a popular single-engine, high-wing aircraft with fixed landing gear.

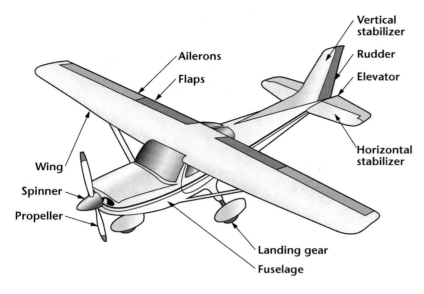

Figure 1-1-1. The parts of an airplane.

Into the 1930s, all-metal aircraft accompanied new lighter and more powerful engines. All-metal aircraft with an aluminum *stressed skin* construction were developed, and fewer truss and fabric aircraft were built.

After WWII, the development of turbine engines led to higher altitude flight. The need for pressurized aircraft pervaded aviation. In a pressurized aircraft, air is pumped into the cabin after takeoff, and a difference in pressure between the air inside the cabin and the air outside the cabin is established. This ensures that enough oxygen is available for passengers to breathe normally and move about the cabin without special equipment when flying at high altitudes. Pressurization causes significant stress on the fuselage structure and adds complexity to the design.

Cycling from unpressurized to pressurized and back again with each flight also causes metal fatigue. The all-metal, stressed skin aircraft construction methods needed to be made even stronger as a result. Refinements were made to increase strength and combat metal fatigue caused by this cycle. Rounded window and door openings were developed to avoid weak areas where cracks could form.

In the 1960s, even larger aircraft were developed to carry passengers. As engine technology improved, the jumbo jet was designed and built. Still constructed primarily of aluminum, the sheer size of the airliners of the day initiated a search for lighter and stronger materials from which to build them. Introducing composites saved weight without compromising strength. A wide variety of composite construction materials led to a steady increase in composites used for aviation structures from

the 1970s to the present. Advanced manufacturing techniques and materials have resulted in a gradual shift from aluminum to carbon fiber and other strong, lightweight materials. Many airframe structures today are made of more than 50 percent composites, with some airframes approaching 100 percent.

Section 1

Parts of the Airplane/Part Location

In this section we look at each of the major parts, and their functions, individually. The illustration in Figure 1-1-1 identifies the major parts of an airplane.

Fuselage

The fuselage is the primary structure of an aircraft to which all other components are attached. The fuselage provides cabin space for the pilot, passengers, and cargo and is made in many configurations. We explore fuselage structures later in this chapter.

Wings

Wings provide the lift that permits an airplane to fly. The forward motion of the aircraft provides airflow over the wings and creates the forces necessary to provide lift. Depending on the desired flight characteristics, wings can be built in many shapes and sizes. Because of their excellent low-speed performance and stability, you are more likely to find the straight wing designs on smaller aircraft, and the swept wing designs on larger, faster aircraft. Figure 1-1-2 shows several leading and trailing edge shapes; these are referred to as the planform of the aircraft.

In addition to the configuration of the leading and trailing edges, wings are also mounted in different positions relative to the fuselage. The aircraft shown in Figures 1-1-3, 1-1-4, and 1-1-5 illustrate some common wing locations.

You might notice that the wing tips can angle up or down from the wing root to the tip. The term *dihedral* is a reference to the angle of the wings compared to the horizon for wing tips that point upward. Dihedral adds lateral (roll) stability. This helps the aircraft come back to a wings-level condition if the aircraft starts to roll.

Figures 1-1-2 through 1-1-5

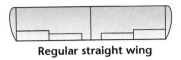

Regular straight wing

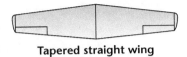

Tapered straight wing

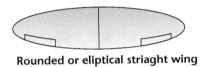

Rounded or eliptical striaght wing

Slight sweepback wing

Moderate sweepback wing

Great sweepback wing

Forward sweep wing

Figure 1-1-2. A variety of wing shapes are made.

Figure 1-1-3. High wing.

Figure 1-1-4. Mid-wing.

Figure 1-1-5. Low wing.

Figure 1-1-6. Some aircraft use anhedral to increase controllability.

Full cantilever

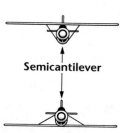

Semicantilever

Figure 1-1-7. Externally braced wings have wires or struts to support the wing. Full cantilever wings have no external bracing and are supported internally.

Low-winged aircraft generally have much more dihedral than high winged aircraft. This can be seen when comparing the aircraft shown in Figure 1-1-3 to the one in Figure 1-1-5. This is the result of the relative position of the aircraft's wings to its center of gravity. On a low-wing aircraft, the center of gravity is above the wing. This results in a design that is less stable on the lateral axis. By introducing a few degrees of dihedral, roll stability can be increased. High-wing aircraft have a center of gravity that is lower than the wings, and the resulting design is more stable on the lateral axis. These aircraft need much less dihedral to give the desired control characteristics.

Anhedral or negative dihedral refers to wings that point down. This design is used on some very large aircraft such as the transport aircraft shown in Figure 1-1-6. The size of the airplane, the sweepback of the wings, and the totality of the design features result in such a stable aircraft that without introducing anhedral there would not be enough roll control available to the flight crew. Anhedral is added here to make the aircraft less stable, and more controllable.

Wings can be built so that no external bracing is needed. They are supported internally by structural members assisted by the skin of the aircraft. These are known as full cantilever wings. Other aircraft wings use external struts to help support the wing and carry the aerodynamic and landing loads. Figure 1-1-7 shows samples of wings using external struts, also known as semi-cantilever wings. Cantilever wings built with no external bracing are also shown.

Fixed-wing aircraft are not limited to one set of wings; biplanes and triplanes are also made (Figure 1-1-8). Over the years, many combinations have been tried, but the monoplane seems to be the most popular.

Ailerons

As we continue our look at the parts of an airplane, refer to Figure 1-1-9. The ailerons mounted on the outboard end of the wing are one of the primary flight control surfaces. This is the control that causes the airplane to *roll* (a motion that lifts one wing and lowers the opposite).

Flaps

Flaps are used to modify the lift of the wings. They are an important safety feature when operating at low speeds and high angle of attack, as in takeoff and landing. A more detailed discussion of the different types of flaps and their effect is given later in this book.

Empennage (Tail Structure)

The empennage is also called the tail section, and most aircraft designs consist of a tail cone, fixed surfaces, and movable surfaces. The fixed surfaces are known as stabilizers and further identified by their position, (a) horizontal stabilizer and (b) vertical stabilizer. The moveable control attached to the vertical stabilizer is the rudder and moves the aircraft's nose left and

Figure 1-1-8. A monoplane, biplane and triplane.

Figure 1-1-9. The aileron is one of the primary control surfaces.

Figure 1-1-10. An aircraft with a tailwheel.

Figure 1-1-11. Aircraft with a nosewheel.

right. The moveable control attached to the horizontal stabilizer is known as the elevator and moves the aircraft's nose up and down while in flight.

Landing Gear

The assembly that supports the aircraft during landing, or while it is resting or moving about on the ground, is known as the landing gear. The landing gear can also incorporate shock struts to absorb the shock of landing and taxiing. Brakes installed in the wheels enable the aircraft to be slowed or stopped while on the ground.

The landing gear arrangement normally includes either a tailwheel or a nosewheel. Aircraft with a tailwheel are said to have *conventional* landing gear. This is a holdover from the time when most aircraft had tailwheels. An aircraft with a tailwheel is shown in Figure 1-1-10.

Aircraft with a nosewheel are referred to as having tricycle landing gear. Figure 1-1-11 shows an aircraft that uses a nosewheel. With either of these configurations, skis or floats can be installed to permit aircraft operations from snow or water.

On many aircraft, the landing gear are mounted in a fixed position that remains unchanged in all modes of flight. This arrangement is the lightest, least prone to failure, and has the lowest manufacturing and maintenance costs. However, having the landing gear in position under the aircraft introduces a large amount of drag. When an aircraft is designed for high speed flight, one of the easiest ways to reduce drag is to change the configuration of the landing gear.

To reduce wind resistance during flight, the landing gear of most high-speed or large aircraft is retracted (drawn up into streamlined

Figure 1-1-12. The aircraft's landing gear are retracting.

enclosures). An aircraft with the gear retracting is shown in Figure 1-1-12. This configuration adds the weight of the retraction mechanism, but the benefits gained by the reduced drag make the design successful.

Cowling

Cowling usually refers to the detachable covering of those areas into which access must be gained regularly, such as engines, accessory sections, and engine mount or firewall areas. Figure 1-1-13 labels the pieces of cowling for a horizontally opposed engine on a light aircraft.

The final component on the front of most propeller driven aircraft is known as the spinner. This is also shown in Figure 1-1-13. The spinner serves to streamline the propeller assembly and to protect the mechanism of propellers incorporating pitch change capability. Spinners also serve to help smooth the airflow into the cowling to provide engine cooling.

Powerplant

Many types of engines have been used on aircraft over the years; however, the most common applications today fall into one of two categories. Most light aircraft use a reciprocating engine, and larger business and transport category aircraft use turbine engines.

Engine design and efficiency has been a constant quest since the first powered flight and continues today. Some of the recent developments include a newer design for diesel cycle engines, electric power, and a new generation of ultra-high bypass turbofan engines.

Propellers

Although turbojet and turbofan engines can produce thrust without using a propeller, piston and turboprop engines use a propeller to convert the power produced by the engine to the thrust needed to move the aircraft forward. Propellers operate on the same aerodynamic principles that allow a wing to create lift. They are, in all aspects, rotating airfoils.

The design and construction of propellers is ever changing. Newer propellers are lighter, quieter, and produce less vibration than previous designs. This is especially true on the larger piston engine applications. Figure 1-1-14 shows one of the modern propeller designs that have increased efficiency.

Streamlining

Aircraft designers and manufacturers are always looking for ways to smooth the airflow and reduce drag. The objective is to make the aircraft faster and more efficient. The term fairing is broadly applied to the nonstructural components that are added to smooth airflow. One common location for these fairings is at the wing root (where it attaches to the fuselage), as shown in Figure 1-1-15.

Other locations for fairings include front of the vertical stabilizer, and around the wheels on fixed-gear aircraft. The fairings on landing gear are commonly referred to as *wheel pants* (Figure 1-1-16).

Section 2

Getting Around the Airplane

Basic Directions

To make certain that we can understand each other when discussing aircraft, there must be a common method of determining which direction we are referring to, and common terms to describe our actions. From the earliest days of aviation, the language used has been mostly adapted from nautical terms. The idea of an airplane moving through the sky does resemble a ship moving through the water

Figure 1-1-13. Cowling for a horizontally opposed engine.

Figure 1-1-15. A fairing is used here to streamline the point where the wings attach to the fuselage.

Figure 1-1-14. Modern propeller design increases efficiency.

Figure 1-1-16. Wheel pants are installed to streamline the landing gear.

and many of the same terms apply. Following nautical traditions, you might even hear left referred to as *port* and right referred to as *starboard*.

Basic directions all begin from the pilot's seat. If you are sitting in the pilot's seat looking toward the nose of the aircraft, forward is

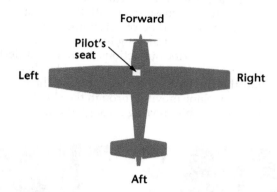

Figure 1-2-1. Directions are relative to someone sitting in the pilot's seat.

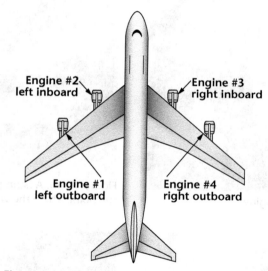

Figure 1-2-2. Boeing 747 engine designations.

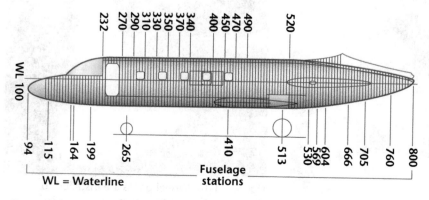

Figure 1-2-3. Fuselage stations.

ahead of you, and aft is behind you. Left is to your left, and right is to your right. These are illustrated in Figure 1-2-1.

If you are standing in front of the aircraft, looking toward the tail, you are said to be "forward, looking aft." If you are near the tail of the aircraft looking forward, you are said to be "aft, looking forward." Items closer to the fuselage are referred to as "inboard," and items closer to the wing tip are referred to as "outboard."

On multiengine aircraft, the engine positions are numbered from left to right, as viewed from the pilot's seat. Figure 1-2-2 shows the engine numbers and common designations for a Boeing 747.

Location Numbering Systems

Although the basic directions—left, right, forward, aft—are understood to be relative to the position of the pilot's seat, distance in any of those directions needs additional explanation.

Various numbering systems are used to facilitate location of specific wing frames, fuselage bulkheads, or any other structural members on an aircraft. Most manufacturers use some system of station marking; for example, the nose of the aircraft might be designated zero station, and all other stations are at measured distances in inches behind the zero station. Thus, when a blueprint reads "fuselage frame station 137," that frame station is found 137 in. behind the nose of the aircraft. Figure 1-2-3 is a typical station diagram.

To locate structures to the right or left of the center line of an aircraft, many manufacturers consider the center line as a zero station for structural member location to its right or left. With such a system, the stabilizer frames can be designated as being so many inches right or left of the aircraft center line.

The applicable manufacturer's numbering system and abbreviated designations or symbols should always be reviewed before attempting to locate a structural member. The following list includes location designations typical of those used by many manufacturers.

1. Fuselage stations (Fus. Sta. or FS) are numbered in inches from a reference or zero point known as the reference datum. The reference datum is an imaginary vertical plane at or near the nose of the aircraft from which all horizontal distances are measured. The distance to a given point is measured in inches parallel to a center line extending through the

aircraft from the nose through the center of the tail cone. Some manufacturers might call the fuselage station a body station (BS).

2. Buttock line or butt line (BL) is a width measurement left or right of, and parallel to, the vertical center line.

3. Water line (WL) is the measurement of height in inches perpendicular from a horizontal plane a fixed number of inches below the bottom of the aircraft fuselage.

4. Aileron station (AS) is measured outboard from, and parallel to, the inboard edge of the aileron, perpendicular to the rear beam of the wing.

5. Flap station (FS) is measured perpendicular to the rear beam of the wing and parallel to, and outboard from, the inboard edge of the flap.

6. Nacelle station (NC or Nac. Sta.) is measured either forward of or behind the front spar of the wing and perpendicular to a designated water line.

In addition to the location stations listed above, other measurements are used, especially on large aircraft. Thus, there might be horizontal stabilizer stations (HSS), vertical stabilizer stations (VSS) or powerplant stations (PPS). In every case, before you locate a point on an aircraft, refer to the manufacturer's terminology and station location system.

Section 3
Fuselage Structures

Because it serves as the structure that connects the wings, the empennage, the engine, and the landing gear, it is very important that the fuselage structure be designed to withstand the anticipated loads that can occur during all aspects of flight and ground operations. Three general types of fuselage construction are used: the truss type, the monocoque type, and the semi-monocoque type. Each type has its advantages and disadvantages, and all three have been in use for many years.

Truss Type

A truss is a rigid framework made up of members such as beams, struts, and bars to resist deformation by applied loads. The truss-framed fuselage is generally covered with fabric.

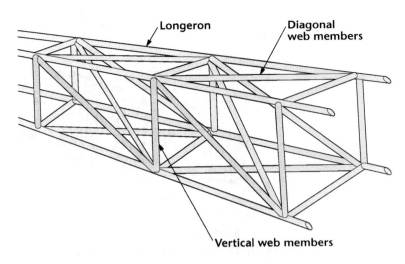

Figure 1-3-1 A truss-type, welded, tubular-steel fuselage.

The truss type fuselage frame (Figure 1-3-1) is often constructed of steel tubing welded together in such a manner that all members of the truss can carry both tension and compression loads. In other aircraft, principally the light, single-engine models, the truss fuselage frames are constructed of aluminum alloy and can be riveted or bolted into one piece, with cross-bracing achieved by using solid rods or tubes.

Monocoque Type

A monocoque (single shell) fuselage relies largely on the strength of the skin or covering to carry the primary stresses. However, this design is usually divided into two classes: 1. Monocoque, or 2. Semi-monocoque. Most aircraft are of semi-monocoque-type construction.

The true monocoque construction (Figure 1-3-2) uses formers, frame assemblies, and bulkheads to give shape to the fuselage, but

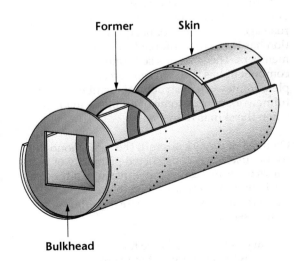

Figure 1-3-2. Monocoque construction.

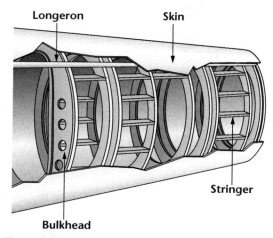

Figure 1-3-3. Semi-monocoque construction.

the skin carries the primary stresses. Because no bracing members are used, the skin must be strong enough to keep the fuselage rigid. Thus, the biggest problem involved in monocoque construction is maintaining enough strength while keeping the weight within allowable limits.

Because it is the skin that carries the load, any damage to the outer skin can quickly result in a failure of the entire structure. Consider an aluminum drink can. In its original condition, it is very strong and can resist a large pressure when the top is pushed on. However, even slight damage to the skin results in the can being crushed easily when the top is pushed on.

Semi-Monocoque Type

To overcome the strength/weight problem associated with monocoque construction, a modification called semi-monocoque construction (Figure 1-3-3) was developed.

In addition to the formers, frame assemblies, and bulkheads associated with monocoque fuselages, the semi-monocoque construction has the skin reinforced by longitudinal members. The shell of a semi-monocoque component has the skin reinforced by a complete framework of structural members. This framework carries some of or all the load, even when the skin is damaged.

On most of today's aircraft, the semi-monocoque fuselage is constructed primarily of the alloys of aluminum and magnesium, although steel and titanium are found in areas of high temperatures. Also, composite materials are being used increasingly.

Primary bending loads are taken by the longerons, which usually extend across several points of support. The longerons are supple-

mented by other longitudinal members, called stringers. Stringers are more numerous and lighter than longerons. The vertical structural members are referred to as bulkheads, frames, and formers. The heaviest of these vertical members are placed at intervals to carry concentrated loads and at points where fittings are used to attach other units, such as the wings, powerplants, and stabilizers.

By themselves, the structural members discussed do not give strength to a fuselage. They must first be joined together. This is done using connective devices as gussets, rivets, nuts and bolts, or metal screws. The metal skin or covering is then riveted to the longerons, bulkheads, and other structural members and carries part of the load. The fuselage skin thickness varies with the load carried and the stresses sustained at a location.

The semi-monocoque fuselage has many advantages. The bulkheads, frames, stringers, and longerons facilitate the design and construction of a streamlined fuselage and add to the strength and rigidity of the structure. The main advantage, however, lies in the fact that it does not depend on a few members for strength and rigidity. This means that a semi-monocoque fuselage can withstand considerable damage and still be strong enough to hold together.

Section 4
Wing Structure

Aircraft wings are designed to produce lift when moved rapidly through the air. The design depends on several factors, such as size, weight, use of the aircraft, desired speed in flight and at landing, and the desired rate of climb.

Spars

The principal structural member of the wing is the spar. They run parallel to the lateral axis, or toward the tip of the wing, and are usually attached to the fuselage by wing fittings. The spars support all distributed loads and concentrated weights, such as fuselage, landing gear, and, on multiengine aircraft, the nacelles or pylons.

Most aircraft today have multi-spar wings. The multi-spar wing incorporates more than one main longitudinal member in its construction. To give the wing contour, ribs or bulkheads are often included.

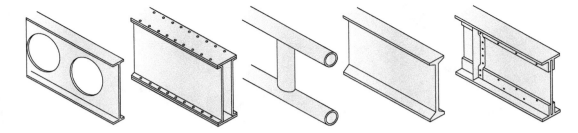

Figure 1-4-1. Examples of metal wing spar shapes.

Most modern aircraft have wing spars made of solid extruded aluminum or aluminum extrusions riveted together to form the spar. However, the increased use of composites, and the combining of materials is becoming more common. Figure 1-4-1 shows examples of metal wing spar cross-sections

Composite materials are also used for spar construction. Among the modern aircraft to incorporate composite material for spar construction is the Airbus A350 (Figure 1-4-2). This airliner uses tapered C-shaped channels to make up the front and rear of the wing-box.

Ribs

Ribs are the structural crosspieces that make up the framework of the wing. They usually extend from the wing leading edge to the rear spar or to the trailing edge of the wing. This is the component that gives the wing its cambered shape and transmits the load from the skin and stringers to the spars. Ribs are also found in ailerons, elevators, rudders, and stabilizers.

Ribs can be made from wood, metal or composite material. Either wood or metal ribs are used with wooden spars, but metal ribs are usually used with metal spars. A typical aluminum rib, of the type used on many light aircraft, is shown in Figure 1-4-3.

The position of the ribs, spars, and other wing structures is shown in Figure 1-4-4. In addition to the front and rear spars and stringers, various types of ribs are also illustrated.

A nose rib is also called a false rib, because it usually extends from the wing leading edge to the front spar or slightly beyond. The nose ribs give the wing leading edge area the necessary curvature and support. The wing rib, or plain rib, extends from the leading edge of the wing to the rear spar and in some cases to the trailing edge of the wing.

Figure 1-4-2. Airbus A350.

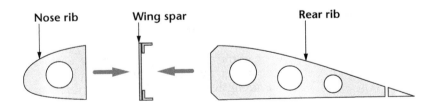

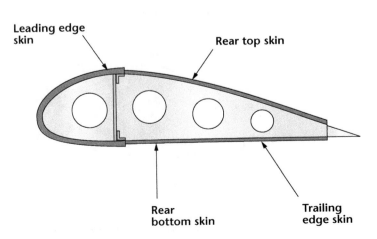

Figure 1-4-3. Examples of wing rib constructed of aluminum.

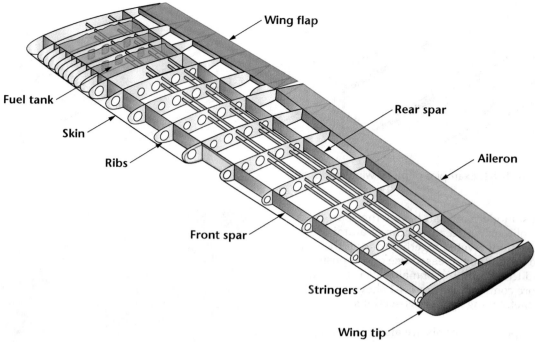

Figure 1-4-4. Basic wing structure and components.

Wing Attachment

Although a few aircraft designs incorporate one-piece wing assemblies, most aircraft wings are built separately and bolted to the fuselage. To carry the entire load of the aircraft, the structural member that ties the two wings together is of very heavy construction. This is often referred to as the spar carry through, or wing carry through. It can be a steel tube truss structure, a heavy aluminum structure, or, on some newer designs, a composite structure.

The wing attachment fittings, shown in Figure 1-4-5, illustrate one means of attaching the wing to the aircraft fuselage. This is a common design for light aircraft. Depending on the strength of the wing, a wing could require external support. This is referred to as a semi-cantilever wing. Wings that do not need external support are referred to as cantilever wings.

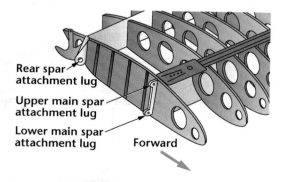

Figure 1-4-5. Wing attach lugs are used to connect the wing to the fuselage.

Section 5

Materials

Selecting the materials used for constructing aircraft is a constantly evolving process. As new materials and manufacturing processes become popular, the aviation industry seeks to find those that possess the properties important to flight. Generally, this depends on how strong and how light the material is.

Wood

Early aircraft builders relied on wood for the primary structure. While several species of wood have demonstrated the required strength-to-weight ratio, Sitka Spruce has become the standard for aircraft use. You might see solid wood, laminated wood, or plywood used on aircraft.

Solid wood is exactly that—pieces of wood that have been sawn from the tree. Generally, to get the best quality product, these are pieces that have been *quarter sawn*. This describes the location on the cross section of the tree that was used to get this board. This gives the best grain structure and strongest product. Figure 1-5-1 shows the traditional method of quarter sawing.

Both laminated wood and plywood are made by gluing very thin sheets of wood together.

The difference lies in the direction of the grain of each layer. Laminated wood has the grain of each layer positioned in the same direction. This gives it good strength in only one direction, but because the grain is all in the same direction, it can also bend (but only in one direction). This is very handy when you want to shape the wood around a curve. Plywood, on the other hand, has its layers glued together with the grain perpendicular to the adjacent layers. This means that it has equal strength in both directions, but it cannot be bent so easily.

Lightweight woods such as balsa have also been used as the core for a sandwich type structure. The wooden core is laminated between two pieces of thin aluminum or composite material. This can be used to increase the strength and keep the weight to a minimum. You might see this type of sandwich construction in floorboards of larger aircraft.

Fabric

On early aircraft, builders covered the wings, the control surfaces, and sometimes the fuselage with cotton or linen fabric. This made for a very lightweight covering, but it was not very durable. To address the durability issue, builders began treating the fabric with a cellulose nitrate mixture referred to as *dope*. This reduced the porosity of the fabric and made it waterproof. The fabric life was extended by this process. This combination of load-bearing fibers and a plastic-like matrix constitutes the first application of composite technology to aircraft.

Even under the best of conditions, the organic fabrics did not have a long life, and replacing the fabric on an airplane is an expensive and time-consuming activity. New fabrics, mostly consisting of Dacron®, were introduced and are still in use today. Although fabrics are not as commonly used as they once were, new aircraft are still being manufactured with truss type structures and fabric covering. These are generally either aircraft designed for recreational flying, or those used in extreme back-country operations. Many aircraft in the Light Sport Aircraft (LSA) category use fabric covering.

Manufacturers continue to design and build aircraft using fabric covering because it still offers several advantages over other materials. Although we do not often think of fabric being a structural material, that is exactly the case when we use it to cover an aircraft wing. The tensile strength of the fibers transmit the lift generated by the wing to the ribs and spars, and then on to the fuselage. It is the favorable strength-to-weight ratio that makes fabric a viable choice in aircraft construction. Also, the

Figure 1-5-1. Traditional pattern of quarter sawing to get the best lumber.

cost and repairability of fabric surfaces keep them competitive with other materials. Figure 1-5-2 shows fabric being used to cover a fuselage.

Steel

Although it sometimes loses in the strength-to-weight battle, steel is still an important material for aircraft construction. Many assemblies require the strength that steel can provide and cannot be made from a lighter material. This is especially true in high-stress areas like engines, engine mounts, and landing gear construction. Steel is also a very common material for high-strength fasteners such as bolts, nuts, and screws.

Figure 1-5-2. Fabric covering being applied to a fuselage.

The term steel is used for many types of materials, but the properties of these metals vary a lot. Although they all use iron as the base metal, many different alloying agents are added to give specific properties. A numerical index, supported by the Society of Automotive Engineers (SAE) and the American Iron and Steel Institute (AISI), is used to identify the chemical compositions of the structural steels.

In this system, a four-digit series is used to designate the plain carbon and alloy steels; five digits are used to designate certain types of alloy steels. The first two digits indicate the type of steel, the second digit also generally (but not always) gives the approximate amount of the major alloying element, and the last two (or three) digits usually indicate the approximate middle of the carbon range. However, a deviation from the rule of indicating the carbon range is sometimes necessary.

Steel containing carbon in percentages ranging from 0.10 to 0.30 percent is classed as low-carbon steel. The equivalent SAE numbers range from 1010 to 1030. Steels of this grade are used for making items such as safety wire, certain nuts, cable bushings, or threaded rod ends. This steel in sheet form is used for secondary structural parts and clamps and in tubular form for moderately stressed structural parts.

Steel-containing carbon in percentages ranging from 0.30 to 0.50 percent is classed as medium carbon steel. This steel is especially adaptable for machining or forging and where surface hardness is desirable.

Steel containing carbon in percentages ranging from 0.50 to 1.05 percent is classed as high-carbon steel. Adding other elements in varying quantities hardens this steel. In the fully heat-treated condition, it is very hard, withstands high shear and wear, and has little deformation. It has limited use in aircraft.

The various nickel steels are produced by combining nickel with carbon steel. Steels containing from 3 to 3.75 percent nickels are commonly used. Nickel increases the hardness, tensile strength, and elastic limit of steel without appreciably decreasing the ductility. It also intensifies the hardening effect of heat treatment. SAE 2330 steel is used extensively for aircraft parts, such as bolts, terminals, keys, clevises, and pins.

Chromium steel is high in hardness, strength, and corrosion resistant properties, and it is especially adaptable for heat-treated forgings, which require greater toughness and strength than can be obtained in plain carbon steel. It can be used for articles such as the balls and rollers of antifriction bearings. Chrome-nickel or stainless steels are corrosion-resistant metals.

The anticorrosive degree of this steel is determined by the surface condition of the metal and by the composition, temperature, and concentration of the corrosive agent. The principal alloy of stainless steel is chromium. The corrosion resistant steel most often used in aircraft construction is known as 18-8 steel because its content is 18 percent chromium and 8 percent nickel. One of the distinctive features of 18-8 steel is that cold working can increase its strength.

Stainless steel can be rolled, drawn, bent, or formed to any shape. Because these steels expand about 50 percent more than mild steel and conduct heat only about 40 percent as rapidly, they are more difficult to weld. Stainless steel can be used for almost any part of an aircraft. Some of its common applications are in exhaust collectors, stacks and manifolds, structural and machined parts, springs, castings, tie rods, and control cables (Figure 1-5-3).

The chrome-vanadium steels are made of about 18 percent vanadium and about 1 percent chromium. When heat-treated, they have strength, toughness, and resistance to wear and fatigue. A special grade of this steel in sheet form can be cold formed into intricate shapes. It can be folded and flattened without signs of breaking or failure. SAE 6150 is used for making springs; chrome-vanadium with high carbon content, SAE 6195, is used for ball and roller bearings.

Control cables

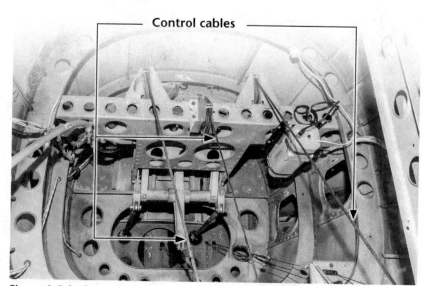

Figure 1-5-3. Control cables are commonly made of stainless steel.

Molybdenum in small percentages is used in combination with chromium to form chrome-molybdenum steel, which has various uses in aircraft. Molybdenum is a strong alloying element. It raises the ultimate strength of steel without affecting ductility or workability. Molybdenum steels are tough and wear resistant, and they harden throughout when heat-treated. They are especially adaptable for welding and, for this reason, are used principally for welded structural parts and assemblies. This type steel has practically replaced carbon steel in the fabrication of fuselage tubing, engine mounts, landing gears, and other structural parts. For example, a heat-treated SAE X4130 tube is approximately four times as strong as an SAE 1025 tube of the same weight and size.

Aluminum

Aluminum has been flying since the days of the Wright brothers. The engine on the Wright Flyer was built using a cast aluminum crankcase. Piston engines today still primarily rely on cast aluminum crankcases. Aluminum has also been a primary structural material for aircraft use for many years. Its excellent strength-to-weight ratio makes sheet aluminum very popular for constructing wings, fuselages, and other primary structures (Figure 1-5-4).

Commercially pure aluminum is a white, lustrous metal that stands second in the scale of malleability, sixth in ductility, and ranks high in its resistance to corrosion. Aluminum is combined with various percentages of other metals to form alloys that are used in aircraft construction.

Aluminum alloys with principal alloying ingredients are manganese, chromium, or magnesium and silicon show little attack in corrosive environments. Alloys with substantial percentages of copper are more susceptible to corrosive action. The total percentage of alloying elements is seldom more than 6 or 7 percent in the wrought alloys.

Aluminum is one of the most widely used metals in modern aircraft construction. It is vital to the aviation industry because of its high strength-to-weight ratio and its comparative ease of fabrication. The outstanding characteristic of aluminum is its light weight. Aluminum melts at the relatively low temperature of 1,250°F. It is nonmagnetic and is an excellent conductor.

Commercially pure aluminum has a tensile strength of about 13,000 pounds per square inch (p.s.i.), but rolling or other cold-working

Figure 1-5-4. The primary structures of these Cessna aircraft are made of aluminum.

processes can roughly double its strength. By alloying with other metals, or by using heat-treating processes, the tensile strength can be raised to as high as 65,000 p.s.i. or to within the strength range of structural steel.

Aluminum alloys, although strong, are easily worked because they are malleable and ductile. They can be rolled into sheets as thin as 0.0017 in. or drawn into wire 0.004 in. in diameter. Most aluminum alloy sheet stock used in aircraft construction range from 0.016 to 0.096 in. thick; however, some of the larger aircraft use sheet stock that could be as thick as 0.356 in.

The various types of aluminum can be divided into two general classes: (1) Casting alloys (those suitable for casting in sand, permanent mold, or die castings), and (2) Wrought alloys (those that can be shaped by rolling, drawing, or forging).

Aluminum casting alloys are divided into two basic groups. In one, the physical properties of the alloys are determined by the alloying elements and cannot be changed after the metal is cast. In the other, the alloying elements make it possible to heat treat the casting to produce the desired physical properties.

Of the two general classes, the wrought alloys are the most widely used in aircraft construction, being used for stringers, bulkheads, skin, rivets, and extruded sections. Wrought aluminum and wrought aluminum alloys are designated by a four-digit index system. The system is broken into three distinct groups: 1xxx group, 2xxx through 8xxx group, and 9xxx group (which is unused).

The first digit of a designation identifies the alloy type. The second digit indicates specific alloy modifications. If the second number is zero, it indicates no special control over individual impurities. Digits 1 through 9, however, when assigned consecutively as needed for the second number in this group, indicate the number of controls over individual impurities in the metal.

The last two digits of the 1xxx group are used to indicate the hundredths of 1 percent above the original 99 percent designated by the first digit. Thus, if the last two digits were 30, the alloy would contain 99 percent plus 0.30 percent of pure aluminum, or a total of 99.30 percent pure aluminum.

Below are some examples of alloys in this group:

- 1100—99.00 percent pure aluminum with one control over individual impurities
- 1130—99.30 percent pure aluminum with one control over individual impurities
- 1275—99.75 percent pure aluminum with two controls over individual impurities

In the 2xxx through 8xxx groups, the first digit indicates the major alloying element used in the formation of the alloy. The benefits of these alloying agents are described here.

1000 series: 99 percent aluminum or higher, excellent corrosion resistance, high thermal and electrical conductivity, low mechanical properties, excellent workability. Iron and silicon are major impurities.

2000 series: Copper is the principal alloying element. Solution heat treatment, optimum properties equal to mild steel, poor corrosion resistance unclad. It is usually clad with 6000 or high-purity alloy. Its best-known alloy is 2024.

3000 series: Manganese is the principal alloying element of this group, which is generally non-heat treatable. The percentage of manganese that is alloy effective is 1.5 percent.

4000 series: Silicon is the principal alloying element of this group and lowers melting temperature. Its primary use is in welding and brazing. When used in welding heat treatable alloys, this group responds to a limited amount of heat treatment.

5000 series: Magnesium is the principal alloying element. It has good welding and corrosion resistant characteristics. High temperatures (over 150°F) or excessive cold working increases susceptibility to corrosion.

6000 series: Silicon and magnesium form magnesium silicide, which makes alloys heat treatable. It is of medium strength, good forming qualities, and has corrosion resistant characteristics.

7000 series: Zinc is the principal alloying element. When coupled with magnesium, it results in heat-treatable alloys of very high strength. It usually has copper and chromium added. The principal alloy of this group is 7075.

Plastic

Plastics are used in many applications throughout modern aircraft. These applications range from structural components of plastics reinforced with fiberglass, to decorative trim, to windows.

Today's plastics come in many forms and are suitable for many functions. Reinforced plastics are usually grouped with other composites, and what we refer to as *plastic* is used for secondary structure, trim, and transparent plastics for windows and windshields. Typical plastic overlays used on the instrument panel of a general aviation aircraft are shown in Figure 1-5-5.

Transparent plastic materials used in aircraft canopies, such as windshields, windows and other similar transparent enclosures, can be divided into two major classes or groups: thermoplastic and thermosetting. These plastics are classified according to their reaction to heat.

Thermoplastic materials soften when heated and harden when cooled. These materials can be heated until soft and then formed into the desired shape. When cooled, they retain this shape. The same piece of plastic can be reheated and reshaped any number of times without changing the chemical composition of the materials.

Thermosetting plastics harden upon heating, and reheating has no softening effect. These plastics cannot be reshaped once being fully cured by applying heat.

In addition to the above classes, transparent plastics are manufactured in two forms: monolithic (solid) and laminated. Laminated transparent plastics are made from transpar-

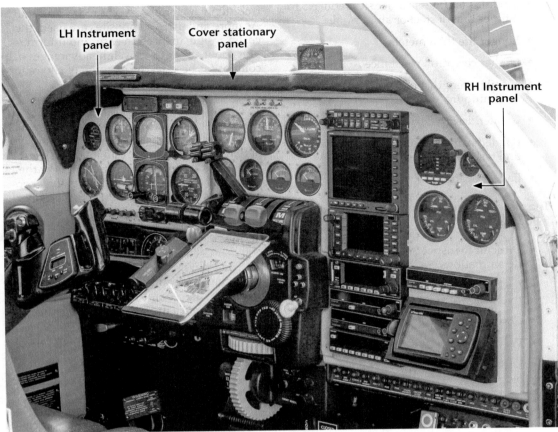

Figure 1-5-5. Plastic components in the pilot compartment of a popular twin-engine aircraft.

ent plastic face sheets bonded by an inner layer material, usually polyvinyl butyryl. Because of its shatter-resistant qualities, laminated plastic is superior to solid plastics and is used in many pressurized aircraft.

Composites

Composites use is not new in aircraft construction. The development of new materials and manufacturing processes has kept them in the forefront of the search for ways to build a better aircraft. The first all-composite aircraft—the Windecker Eagle (Figure 1-5-6)—was awarded Type Certificate #A75SW in 1969. Using composite structure has increased over the years and is now a major portion of many new aircraft, both large and small.

A *composite* material is defined as a mixture of different materials or things. Composite materials are a combination of reinforcement, such as a fiber, whisker, or particle, surrounded and held in place by a resin forming a structure. Separately, the reinforcement and the resin are very different from their combined state. Even in their combined state, they can still be individually identified and mechanically separated.

Following are many advantages for using composite materials:

- High strength-to-weight ratio
- Fiber-to-fiber transfer of stress allowed by chemical bonding

Figure 1-5-6. The Windecker Eagle was the first Type Certificated all-composite aircraft.

- Modulus (stiffness-to-density ratio) 3.5 to 5 times that of steel or aluminum

- Longer life than metals

- Higher corrosion resistance

- Tensile strength 4 to 6 times that of steel or aluminum

- Greater design flexibility

- Bonded construction eliminates joints and fasteners

- Easily repairable

The disadvantages of composites include the following:

- Difficult to inspect, especially to detect delaminations

- Lack of long-term design database, relatively new technology methods

- Costly

- Very expensive processing equipment

- Lack of standardized system of methodology

- Great variety of materials, processes, and techniques

- General lack of repair knowledge and expertise

- Products are often toxic and hazardous

- Lack of standardized methodology for construction and repairs

The increased strength and the ability to design for the performance needs of the product makes composites much superior to the traditional materials used in today's aircraft. As more and more composites are used, the costs, design, inspection ease, and information about strength-to-weight advantages help composites become the material of choice for aircraft construction.

Two main types of composite construction are used: laminated and sandwich. Laminate structures are made by embedding some type of fibrous material in a resin matrix. The fiber is the primary load-carrying element of the structure, and the matrix supports the fibers and bonds them together. Structural properties such as stiffness and strength depend on the number and direction of the fabric layers. Resin is a generic term used to designate the polymer used. The resin, its chemical composition, and physical properties fundamentally affect the processing, fabrication, and ultimate properties of a composite material. The resin, in a sense, glues the fabric fibers together.

Several types of fiber are used for aircraft composite construction. Figure 1-5-7 shows the three most common ones: fiberglass, aramid (such as Kevlar®), and carbon fiber.

Fiberglass. Fiberglass is made by melting glass and shaping it into thin fibers. The fibers are woven together to make a fiberglass cloth or mat. Advantages of fiberglass are lower cost than other composite materials, chemical or galvanic corrosion resistance, and electrical properties (fiberglass does not conduct electricity). Fiberglass is white.

Aramid. Kevlar is DuPont's name for aramid fibers. Aramid fibers are light, strong, and tough. Aramid has high resistance to impact

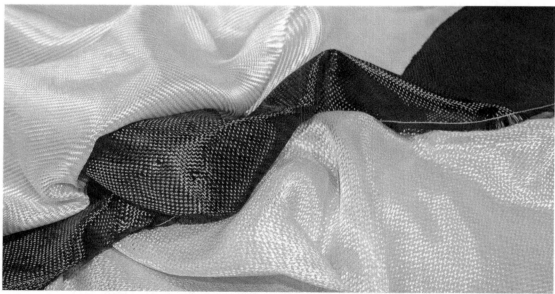

Figure 1-5-7. Fiberglass (left), carbon fiber material (middle), and Kevlar (right).

damage, so it is often used in areas prone to impact damage. Aramid fibers are yellow.

Carbon fiber. Carbon fiber is very stiff and very strong. It is 3 to 10 times stiffer than glass fibers. Carbon fiber is used for structural aircraft applications such as floor beams, stabilizers, flight controls, and primary fuselage and wing structure. Advantages include high strength and corrosion resistance. Carbon fiber is black.

The second type of composite construction you might encounter is called sandwich construction (Figure 1-5-8). Sandwich construction is a structural panel concept that consists in its simplest form of two relatively thin, parallel face sheets bonded to and separated by a relatively thick, lightweight core. The sandwich consists of *facing* and *core* materials. Sandwich construction resists bending and has minimal weight. Facing materials used in aircraft construction include aluminum, fiberglass, aramid, and carbon fiber. Examples of core materials include balsa wood, foam, and honeycomb. Honeycomb is made of many types of materials, and each material gives the finished product specific benefits.

Other materials

We have discussed the primary aircraft construction materials, but some other materials might have in the past been referred to as *exotic metals* but are now found in more applications than ever before.

Magnesium. Magnesium is the world's lightest structural metal. It is a silvery white material weighing only two-thirds as much as aluminum. Magnesium does not possess sufficient strength in its pure state for structural uses, but when alloyed with zinc, aluminum, and manganese, it produces an alloy having the highest strength-to-weight ratio of any of the commonly used metals.

Among the aircraft parts that have been made from magnesium with a substantial savings in weight are nose wheel doors, flap cover skin, aileron cover skin, oil tanks, floorings, fuselage parts, wingtips, engine nacelles, instrument panels, radio masts, hydraulic fluid tanks, oxygen bottle cases, ducts, and seats.

Magnesium's formability also makes it a very versatile material. Magnesium alloys possess good casting characteristics. The properties of these castings compare favorably with those of cast aluminum. In forging, hydraulic presses are ordinarily used, although, under certain

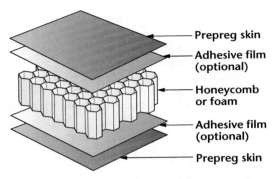

Figure 1-5-8. Honeycomb sandwich construction.

conditions, forging can be accomplished in mechanical presses or with drop hammers.

Titanium. Titanium has been in commercial use since the middle of the twentieth century. The use of titanium is widespread. It is used in many commercial enterprises and is in constant demand for such items as pumps, screens, and other tools and fixtures where corrosion attack is prevalent.

In aircraft construction and repair, titanium is used for fuselage skins, engine shrouds, firewalls, longerons, frames, fittings, air ducts, and fasteners. Titanium is also used for making compressor disks, spacer rings, compressor blades and vanes, through bolts, turbine housings and liners, and miscellaneous hardware for turbine engines.

The corrosion resistance of titanium deserves special mention. The resistance of the metal to corrosion is caused by the formation of a protective surface film of stable oxide or chemi-absorbed oxygen. The corrosion of titanium is uniform. There is little evidence of pitting or other serious forms of localized attack. Normally, it is not subject to stress corrosion, corrosion fatigue, intergranular corrosion, or galvanic corrosion. Its corrosion resistance is equal or superior to 18-8 stainless steel.

Nickel-based alloys. Basically, two nickel alloys are used in aircraft: Monel® and Inconel®.

Monel contains about 68 percent nickel and 29 percent copper, plus small amounts of iron and manganese. It is adaptable to casting and hot or cold working. It can also be welded. Monel has been used in gears and chains to operate retractable landing gear and for structural parts subject to corrosion. On aircraft, Monel is used for parts demanding both strength and high resistance to corrosion. This can include items such as exhaust manifolds and carburetor needle valves and sleeves.

Inconel alloys are high-strength and withstand high temperatures. They contain about 80 percent nickel, 14 percent chromium, and small amounts of other elements. Inconel is frequently used in turbine engines because of its ability to maintain its strength and corrosion resistance under extremely high-temperature conditions.

Section 6

Stresses

The aircraft components are composed of various parts called structural members (i.e., stringers, longerons, ribs, bulkheads). Each aircraft structural member is designed to carry a load, or to resist stress. A single member of the structure might be subjected to a combination of stresses. In most cases the structural members are designed to carry end loads rather than side loads: that is, to be subjected to tension or compression rather than bending. Strength could be the principal requirement in certain aircraft structures, while others need entirely different qualities.

The term *stress* is often used interchangeably with the word *strain*; however, there is a difference. Stress is a force that opposes or resists deformation. Strain is the deformation of a material or substance. Stress, the internal force, can cause strain.

All aircraft are subjected to five major stresses:

1. Tension
2. Compression
3. Torsion
4. Shear
5. Bending

These stresses are illustrated in Figure 1-6-1.

Tension. Tension (Figure 1-6-1 view A) is the stress that resists a force that tends to pull apart. The engine pulls the aircraft forward, but air resistance tries to hold it back. The result is tension, which tries to stretch the aircraft. The tensile strength of a material is measured in p.s.i. and is calculated by dividing the load (in pounds) required to pull the material apart by its cross-sectional area (in square inches).

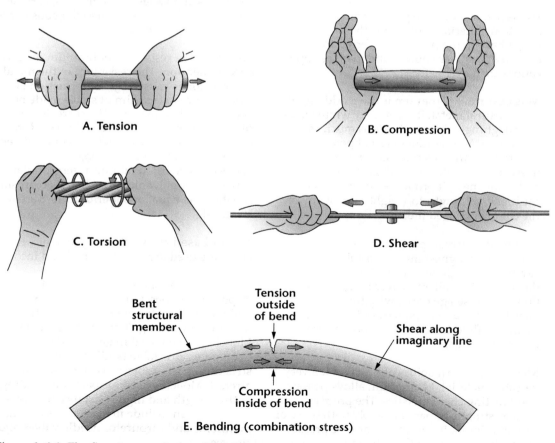

A. Tension

B. Compression

C. Torsion

D. Shear

Bent structural member

Tension outside of bend

Shear along imaginary line

Compression inside of bend

E. Bending (combination stress)

Figure 1-6-1. The five stresses all aircraft experience.

Compression. Compression (Figure 1-6-1 view B) is the stress that resists a crushing force. The compressive strength of a material is also measured in p.s.i. Compression is the stress that tends to shorten or squeeze aircraft parts.

Torsion. Torsion is the stress that produces twisting (Figure 1-6-1 view C). While moving the aircraft forward, the engine also tends to twist it to one side, but other aircraft components hold it on course. Thus, torsion is created. The torsional strength of a material is its resistance to twisting or torque.

Shear. Shear is the stress that resists the force tending to cause one layer of a material to slide over an adjacent layer. Two riveted plates in tension (Figure 1-6-1 view D) subject the rivets to a shearing force. Usually, the shearing strength of a material is either equal to or less than its tensile or compressive strength. Aircraft parts, especially screws, bolts, and rivets, are often subject to a shearing force.

Bending. Bending stress is a combination of compression and tension. The rod in Figure 1-6-1 view E has been shortened (compressed) on the inside of the bend and stretched on the outside of the bend.

Section 7

Mechanical Properties

Strength, weight, and reliability are three factors that determine the requirements to be met by any material used in airframe construction and repair. Airframes must be strong and yet as light as possible. There are very definite limits to which increases in strength can be accompanied by increases in weight. An airframe so heavy that it could not support a few hundred pounds of additional weight would be of little use.

All metals, in addition to having a good strength/weight ratio, must be thoroughly reliable, thus minimizing the possibility of dangerous and unexpected failures. In addition to these general properties, the material selected for a definite application must possess specific qualities suitable for the purpose.

Plasticity. Plasticity is the quality of being easily shaped or molded. This is very important when considering the manufacture of components.

Brittleness. Brittleness is the property of a material that permits little bending or deformation without fracture. Brittleness and hardness are closely associated.

Elasticity. Elasticity is the property of solid materials to return to their original shape and size after the forces deforming them have been removed. The elastic limit is the maximum stress to which the material could be subjected without any permanent strain remaining upon complete release of the stress.

Hardness. Hardness is a measure of how resistant a material is to various kinds of permanent shape change when a compressive force is applied. This is the resistance of a material to deformation, indentation, or penetration by any combination of abrasion, drilling, impact, scratching, or wear.

Toughness. Toughness is the ability of a material to absorb energy and deform plastically without breaking. It is usually measured by the energy absorbed in a notch impact test, but the area under the stress-strain curve in tensile testing is also a measure of toughness.

Strength. Strength is the capacity of an object or substance to withstand great force or pressure.

Strain. Strain is the deformation of a material or substance under applied forces. A normal strain is caused by forces perpendicular to planes or cross-sectional areas of the material, such as in a rod that is pulled or compressed lengthwise. A shear strain is caused by forces that are parallel to, and lie in, planes or cross-sectional areas, such as in a short metal tube that is twisted about its longitudinal axis.

Malleability. Malleability is the state of being malleable, or capable of being shaped, as by hammering or pressing. This is an important property of metals used in many manufacturing processes.

Ductility. Ductility is a measure of a metal's ability to withstand tensile stress, which is a force pulling the two ends of a material away from each other. For example, most common steels are quite ductile and can accommodate local stress concentrations. Brittle materials, such as glass, cannot accommodate concentrations of stress because they lack ductility, and break easily.

Corrosion. Corrosion is the eating away or pitting of the surface or the internal structure

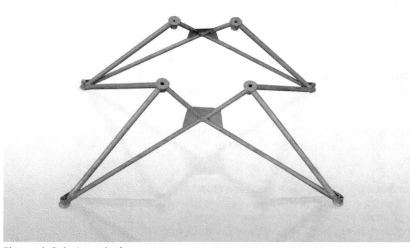

Figure 1-8-1. A conical mount.

Figure 1-8-2. A dynafocal mount.

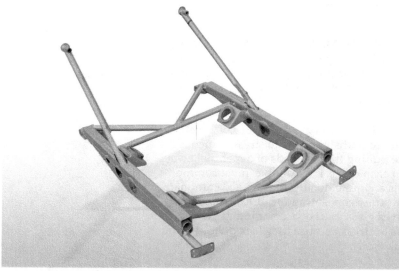

Figure 1-8-3. A bed mount.

of metals. Because of the thin sections and the safety factors used in aircraft design and construction, it would be dangerous to select a material possessing poor corrosion-resistant characteristics.

Formability. Another significant factor to consider in maintenance and repair is the ability of a material to be formed, bent, or machined to required shapes. The hardening of metals by cold-working or forming is termed work-hardening. If a piece of metal is formed (shaped or bent) while cold, it is said to be cold-worked. Practically all the work an aviation mechanic does on metal is cold-work. While this is convenient, it causes the metal to become harder and more brittle.

If the metal is cold-worked too much, that is, if it is bent back and forth or hammered at the same place too often, it cracks or breaks. Usually, the more malleable and ductile a metal is, the more cold-working it can stand.

Section 8

Other Structures

Engine Mount

Engine mounts are designed to meet the specific conditions of an engine installation, such as the location and the method of attachment of the engine mount and the size, type, and characteristics of the engine it is intended to support. An engine mount is usually constructed as a single unit that can be detached quickly and easily from the remaining structure. Engine mounts are commonly made of welded chrome/molybdenum steel tubing, and forgings of chrome/nickel/molybdenum are used for the highly stressed fittings.

Conical Mount

The simplest form of an engine mount and the easiest to fabricate is the conical mount. It has four attach points for the engine, and usually four points to bolt the mount to the firewall. A conical mount is shown in Figure 1-8-1. The mount points are parallel to the firewall so there is no awkward angle when installing the bolts and shock mounts. This type of mount is most often used with small engines.

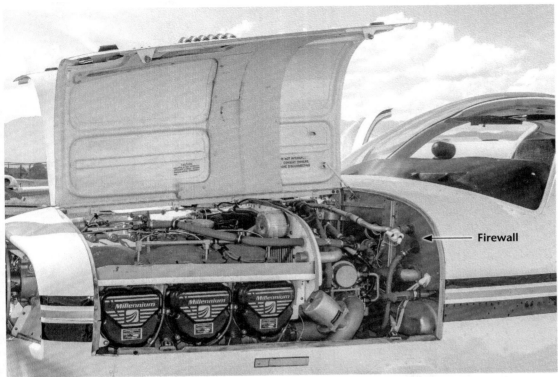

Figure 1-8-4. With the cowling open, the number of components mounted on the firewall can be seen.

Dynafocal Mount

The dynafocal mount (Figure 1-8-2) probably does the best job of cushioning engine movement and vibrations. This results in a lower noise level in the cabin and contributes to reduced crew fatigue. This mount holds the engine in four attach points (formed in a ring) that are arranged at such an angle that they point to the engine's center of gravity. Because of the need for precision alignment, these mounts are much more difficult to manufacture and cost more.

Bed Mount

The bed mount holds the engine at four points underneath the crankcase. These mountings could require special legs to provide the required clearance for accessories and aircraft structure. A typical bed mount is shown in Figure 1-8-3. Some bed mounts are made from steel tube, and some are part of the nacelle structure and are manufactured from aluminum sheet metal components.

Firewall

The firewall provides a separation between the aircraft's engine compartment and the cabin or the rest of the aircraft. The regulations at Title 14 of the *Code of Federal Regulations* (CFR) section 23.1191 establish very specific criteria regarding the design and material requirements for firewalls. These requirements stipulate that the firewall must be able to withstand 2,000°F and must resist flame penetration for at least 15 minutes.

Materials that meet these requirements and can be used without further testing include stainless steel, mild steel (coated with aluminum or otherwise protected against corrosion), terne plate (a thin steel sheet coated with an alloy of lead and tin), Monel, or titanium sheet.

A secondary function of the firewall is to provide a convenient surface on which essential components for engine operation can be mounted. The firewall can become quite a crowded area, but each penetration of the firewall must meet the same high standards for fire prevention as the firewall itself. Figure 1-8-4 shows how many items can be mounted on, or penetrate, the firewall.

2

Flight Controls and Flaps

Section 1

The Axes of an Aircraft

Whenever an aircraft changes its attitude in flight, it must turn about one or more of three axes (Figure 2-1-1). The three axes are imaginary lines passing through the center of the aircraft. The axes of an aircraft can be considered as axles around which the aircraft turns like a wheel. At the center, where all three axes intersect, each is perpendicular to the other two. This point is known as the *center of gravity* (CG). Motions about the axes resemble the movement of a ship, and common nautical terms have been adopted to describe them.

- **Vertical axis**. The axis that passes through the center, from top to bottom, is called the vertical, or yaw, axis. An aircraft moves about its vertical axis in a motion that is called yaw. This is a horizontal movement of the nose of the aircraft.

- **Longitudinal axis.** The axis that extends lengthwise through the fuselage from the nose to the tail is called the longitudinal axis. Motion about the longitudinal axis resembles the roll of a ship from side to side. Thus, the motion about the longitudinal axis is called roll.

- **Lateral axis**. The axis that extends crosswise, from wing tip to wing tip, is the lateral axis. Motion about the lateral axis is called pitch.

An airplane in flight can be maneuvered using one or more of its primary control surfaces. Deflection of a control surface causes rotation of the aircraft about the CG according to whichever control is moved.

Left: A venerable Beechcraft Model 18 is flaps down and ready to land. More than 9,000 of these aircraft were built between 1937 and 1970, making it one of the most widely used light aircraft in the world. Many are still in service for both passengers and freight.

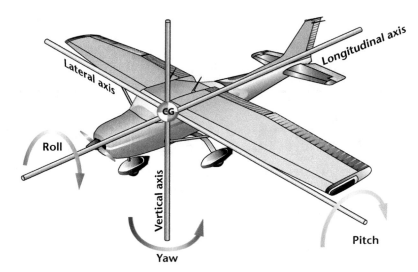

Figure 2-1-1. The axes of an aircraft.

Section 2

Primary Controls

Roll, pitch, and yaw—the motions an aircraft makes about its longitudinal, lateral, and vertical axes—are controlled by the primary control surfaces. These are movable surfaces that are hinged to a fixed surface. The primary control surfaces are identified in Figure 2-2-1. The three axes of motion and the control used to initiate movement are yaw, roll, and pitch.

- Yaw is controlled by the rudder, the rear portion of the vertical tail assembly.

- Roll is produced by the ailerons, which are at the trailing edges of the wings.

- Pitch is affected by the elevator, at the rear portion of the horizontal tail assembly.

Moving any of the three primary flight control surfaces changes the airflow and pressure distribution over and around the airfoil. These changes affect the lift and drag produced by the airfoil/control surface combination and allow a pilot to control the aircraft about the corresponding axis of rotation.

The ailerons are attached to the outboard trailing edge of both wings and when moved, rotate the aircraft around the longitudinal axis. The ailerons move in the opposite direction from each other. Moving the control wheel, or control stick, to the right causes the right aileron to deflect upward and the left aileron to deflect downward (Figure 2-2-2). The upward deflection of the right aileron decreases the camber, resulting in decreased lift on the right wing. The corresponding downward deflection of the left aileron increases the camber resulting in increased lift on the left wing. Thus, the increased lift on the left wing and the decreased lift on the right wing causes the aircraft to roll to the right.

The elevator is attached to the trailing edge of the horizontal stabilizer. When it moves, it alters aircraft pitch, which is movement around the lateral axis. Aft movement of the control column (pulling it back) deflects the trailing edge of the elevator surface up. This is referred to as the up-elevator position.

The up-elevator position decreases the camber of the elevator and creates a downward aerodynamic force, which is greater than the normal tail-down force that exists in straight-and-level flight. The overall effect causes the tail of the aircraft to move down and the nose to pitch up as in Figure 2-2-3.

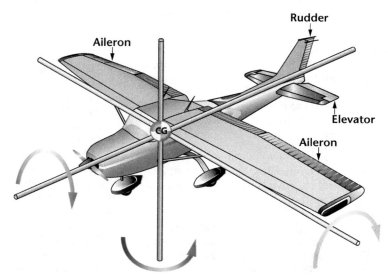

Figure 2-2-1. The primary control surfaces.

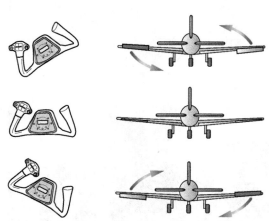

Figure 2-2-2. Moving the control wheel left or right deflects the ailerons in opposite directions.

The rudder is a movable surface that is hinged to the vertical stabilizer. When the rudder changes position, the aircraft rotates about the vertical axis (yaw). The rudder is controlled by the left and right rudder pedals. When the rudder is deflected into the airflow, a horizontal force is exerted in the opposite direction (Figure 2-2-4).

By pushing the left pedal, the rudder moves left. This alters the airflow around the vertical stabilizer/rudder and creates a sideward lift that moves the tail to the right and yaws the nose of the airplane to the left.

Table 2-2-1 serves as a brief reminder of the function of each of the primary control surfaces.

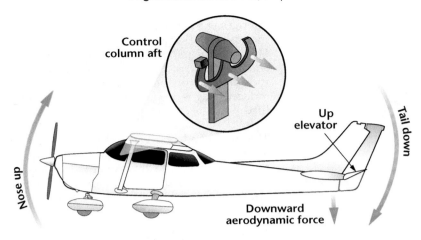

Figure 2-2-3. The elevator is the primary control for changing the pitch attitude of an aircraft.

Section 3

Adverse Yaw

One of the first things people notice when watching the ailerons of an aircraft move is that when one goes up, the other goes down. This is done to initiate the rolling action required for a turn. Consider the situation when the ailerons are moved.

One aileron is deflected downward while the other is deflected upward. On the side with the downward-deflected aileron, lift increases as the deflection effectively increases the camber of that portion of the wing. The opposite happens in the other side. However, drag is also affected by aileron deflection. This includes both induced and profile drags.

Induced drag is a form of drag that is created by any surface that generates lift. The more lift a surface produces the more induced drag it causes (for a given wingspan and wing area). Thus, the wing on which the aileron is deflected downward to generate more lift also experiences more induced drag than the other wing.

Profile drag includes all other forms of drag generated by the wing, primarily skin friction and pressure drag. An increase in profile drag occurs on both wings when the ailerons are deflected. The increase is equal when the ailerons are deflected by the same amount. However, the induced drag on each side is not equal, and a larger total drag force exists on the wing with the down aileron. This difference in drag creates a yawing motion in the opposite direction of the roll. Because the yaw motion partially counteracts the desired roll motion, we call this effect adverse yaw.

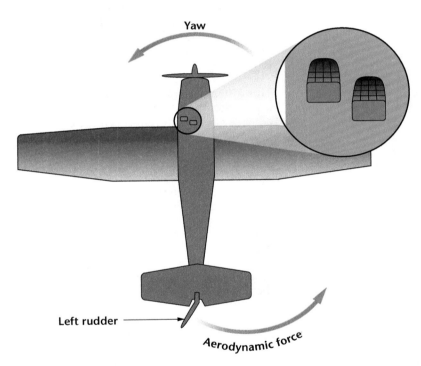

Figure 2-2-4. The effect of left rudder pressure

Primary surface control	Airplane movement	Axis of rotation
Aileron	Roll	Longitudinal
Elevator	Pitch	Lateral
Rudder	Yaw	Vertical

Table 2-2-1. The relationship between the primary controls and their function.

For the same deflection, the profile drag increase is the same in both the wings. However, the induced drag on both sides is not equal, with a larger amount on the wing with the down aileron (because the lift is more and induced drag is proportional to the square of lift).

The effect of adverse yaw can be compensated for by deflecting the ailerons differentially, that is, to deflect the down aileron by a lesser amount than the up aileron. Adverse yaw can also be prevented by using frise ailerons.

Differential Ailerons

One approach to solving adverse yaw is to deflect the ailerons by differing amounts with differential ailerons. The deflection of the down aileron is typically much less than the up aileron so that the additional profile drag is very small compared to that on the up aileron (Figure 2-3-1).

This differential profile drag produces a yawing motion that at least partially offsets the adverse yaw, but the effect is limited.

Frise Ailerons

Another approach to solving adverse yaw is with frise ailerons. The concept behind frise ailerons is to minimize the profile drag on the wing with the down aileron while increasing the profile drag on the wing with the up aileron (Figure 2-3-2). This difference in profile drag counteracts the effect of induced drag, thereby creating a yawing motion that at least partially cancels the adverse yaw effect.

Frise ailerons perform this differential profile drag by maintaining a smooth contour between the upper surfaces of the wing and aileron, causing very little drag, while the

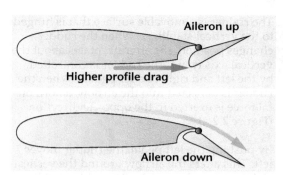

Figure 2-3-2. Frise ailerons are designed to help reduce adverse yaw.

bottom surface of the aileron juts downward to create a large increase in profile drag. Although this approach is simple and provides some relief, the performance of frise ailerons is very dependent on operating conditions. For this reason, such ailerons are often only partially effective at overcoming adverse yaw.

Coupled Ailerons and Rudder (Interconnected)

Coupled ailerons and rudder are linked controls used to overcome adverse yaw. They are connected by using rudder-aileron interconnect springs. This helps correct for aileron drag by automatically deflecting the rudder at the same time the ailerons are deflected. For example, when the control wheel, or control stick, is moved to produce a left roll, the interconnect cable and spring pull forward on the left rudder pedal just enough to prevent the aircraft nose from yawing to the right. The force applied to the rudder by the springs can be overridden if it becomes necessary to slip the aircraft.

Section 4

Other Control Configurations

Stabilator

Some aircraft use a movable horizontal surface called a stabilator (Figure 2-4-1). The stabilator serves the same purpose as the horizontal stabilizer and elevator combined. When the flight deck control is moved, the complete stabilator is moved to raise or lower the leading edge, thus changing the aerodynamic force and the amount of lift on the tail surfaces.

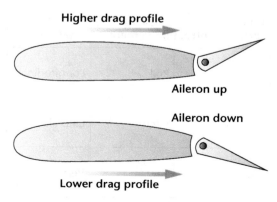

Figure 2-3-1. Differential ailerons move different amounts.

Ruddervator

Some aircraft empennages have been designed that combine the vertical and horizontal stabilizers. Such aircraft have the stabilizers set at an angle as shown in Figure 2-4-2. This arrangement is referred to as a butterfly or v-tail.

The control surfaces are hinged to the stabilizers at the trailing edges. The moveable portion is called the ruddervator. Ruddervators can be operated both up or both down at the same time. When used in this manner, the result is the same as with any other type of elevator. This action is controlled by the control stick or wheel.

The ruddervators can also be made to move opposite each other by pushing the left or right rudder pedal. If the right rudder pedal is pushed, the right ruddervator moves down and the left ruddervator moves up. This produces turning moments (forces) to move the nose of the aircraft to the right.

Flaperon

Flaperons are airfoils with a dual purpose that is normally served by the combination of ailerons and flaps. Flaperons on small planes are single airfoil devices on the trailing edge of each wing that usually extend for most of or all the length of the wing (Figure 2-4-3). They have complex controls that allow for differential movement to produce the action normally performed by ailerons and to move together to produce the effect normally produced by flaps.

On a plane with flaperons, the pilot still has the standard separate controls for ailerons and flaps, but the flap control also varies the flaperon's range of movement. A mechanical device called a *mixer* is used to combine the pilot's input into the flaperons.

Elevon

Delta winged aircraft cannot use conventional flight control systems because of their unique shape. Therefore, they use control surfaces called elevons. The elevons on a military jet are shown in Figure 2-4-4. Elevons are control surfaces that combine the functions of the elevator (used for pitch control) and the aileron (used for roll control), hence the name.

T-Tail

In a T-tail configuration, the elevator is above most of the effects of the propeller downwash

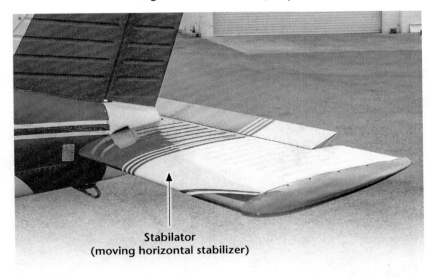

Stabilator (moving horizontal stabilizer)

Figure 2-4-1. The Piper Cherokee is a popular type of aircraft that uses a stabilator.

Ruddervators

Figure 2-4-2. The Beechcraft Bonanza incorporates ruddervators.

G-FOXC

Flaperons

Figure 2-4-3. Flaperons on a popular kit-built aircraft.

Courtesy of Arpingstone, Wikipedia

Figure 2-4-4. Elevons on a delta wing aircraft.

Figure 2-4-5. The King Air 200 is a popular business aircraft with a T-tail design.

Figure 2-4-6. The Beechcraft Starship is a business aircraft design that incorporated a canard.

and airflow around the fuselage and wings during normal flight conditions (Figure 2-4-5). Operating the elevators in this undisturbed air allows control movements that are consistent throughout most flight regimes.

T-tail designs have become popular on many light and large aircraft, especially those with aft fuselage-mounted engines because the T-tail configuration removes the tail from the exhaust blast of the engines. Seaplanes and amphibians often have T-tails to keep the horizontal surfaces as far from the water as possible.

Canard

The canard design uses the concept of two lifting surfaces. The canard functions as a horizontal stabilizer in front of the main wings (Figure 2-4-6). In effect, the canard is an airfoil like the horizontal surface on a conventional aft-tail design. The difference is that the canard creates lift and holds the nose up, as opposed to the aft-tail design, which exerts downward force on the tail to prevent the nose from rotating downward.

Section 5

Stability

An aircraft must be sufficiently stable to maintain a uniform flight path and recover from various upsetting forces. Three terms that appear in any discussion of stability and control are stability, maneuverability, and controllability.

Stability is the characteristic of an aircraft that tends to cause it to fly (hands off) in a straight and level flight path. *Maneuverability* is the ability of an aircraft to be directed along a desired flight path and to withstand the stresses imposed. *Controllability* is the quality of the response of an aircraft to the pilot's commands while maneuvering the aircraft.

Static Stability

An aircraft is in a state of equilibrium when the sum of all the forces acting on the aircraft and all the moments is equal to zero. An aircraft in equilibrium experiences no accelerations, and the aircraft continues in a steady condition of flight. A gust of wind or a deflection of the controls disturbs the equilibrium, and the aircraft experiences oscillation because of the unbalance of moment or force.

The three types of static stability are defined by the character of movement following some disturbance from equilibrium.

- Positive static stability exists when the disturbed object tends to return to equilibrium.

- Negative static stability or static instability exists when the disturbed object tends to continue in the direction of disturbance.

- Neutral static stability exists when the disturbed object has neither the tendency to return nor continue in the displacement direction but remains in equilibrium in the direction of disturbance.

These three types of stability are illustrated in Figure 2-5-1.

Dynamic Stability

Static stability deals with the tendency of a displaced body to return to equilibrium, and dynamic stability deals with the resulting motion with time. If an object is disturbed from equilibrium, the time history of the resulting motion defines the dynamic stability of the object. In general, an object demonstrates positive dynamic stability if the amplitude of motion decreases with time. If the amplitude of motion increases with time, the object is said to have dynamic instability.

Any aircraft must demonstrate the required degrees of static and dynamic stability. If an aircraft were designed with static instability and a rapid rate of dynamic instability, the aircraft would be very difficult, if not impossible, to fly. Usually, positive dynamic stability is required in an aircraft design to prevent objectionable continued oscillations of the aircraft.

Longitudinal Stability

When an aircraft tends to keep a constant angle of attack with reference to the relative wind—that is, when it does not tend to put its nose down and dive or lift its nose and stall—it is said to have *longitudinal stability*. Longitudinal stability refers to motion in pitch. The horizontal stabilizer is the primary surface that controls longitudinal stability. The action of the stabilizer depends on the speed and angle of attack of the aircraft.

Under certain conditions of speed, load, and angle of attack, the flow of air over the horizontal stabilizer creates a force that pushes the tail up or down. When conditions are such that the airflow creates equal forces up and down, the forces are said to be in equilibrium. This condition is usually found in level flight in calm air.

Directional Stability

Stability about the vertical axis is referred to as *directional stability*. The aircraft should be designed so that when it is in straight and level flight, it remains on its course heading even though the pilot takes his or her hands and feet off the controls. If an aircraft recovers automatically from an upset, it has been well designed and has good directional balance. The vertical stabilizer is the primary surface that controls directional stability. Directional stability is also aided by using a large dorsal fin and a long fuselage.

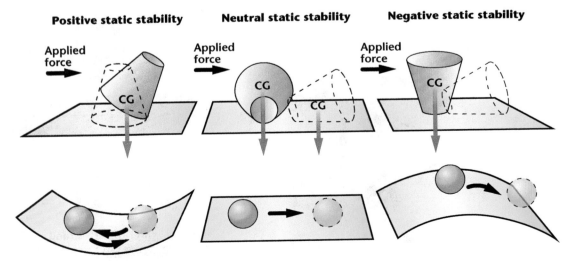

Figure 2-5-1. Three types of static stability.

Lateral Stability

We have seen that pitching is motion about the aircraft's lateral axis and yawing is motion about its vertical axis. Motion about its longitudinal (fore and aft) axis is a lateral or rolling motion. The tendency to return to the original attitude from such motion is called *lateral stability*.

The surface contributing most to the lateral stability of an airplane is the wing. The dihedral of a wing is a powerful contribution to lateral stability. The amount of effective dihedral necessary to produce satisfactory flying qualities varies greatly with the type and purpose of the aircraft. Generally, the effective dihedral is low.

the aircraft could break up in flight. To solve that problem, the control must be balanced, so that its CG is in line with the hinge.

The exact distribution of weight on a control surface is very important. For this reason, when a control surface is repainted, repaired or component parts replaced, it is essential to check for proper balance and have it rebalanced if necessary. To do this, the control surface is removed, placed in a jig, and the position of the CG is checked against the manufacturer's specifications. The setup commonly used to perform this check is shown in Figure 2-6-1. Without any airflow over the control surface, it must balance about its specified CG. This is known as static balance.

Section 6

Flutter

Flutter is an unstable oscillation that can lead to the aircraft's destruction. Flutter can occur on fixed surfaces, such as the wing or the stabilizer, and on control surfaces such as the aileron or the elevator.

When a control surface is moved, a low-pressure area forms on the cambered side. This tends to pull the control back into alignment with the wing, stabilizer, or fin. However, the control surface has mass and therefore momentum. If the CG of the control surface is behind the hinge, the control tends to overshoot the point of alignment. The result is a tendency for the control surface to flutter. Flutter could become sufficiently severe that

Section 7

Control Operating Systems

Although the newest turbine-powered aircraft might use electrically operated servos to move the control surfaces, most aircraft flying today use much less sophisticated methods to convert the pilot's control wheel motion into movements of the flight control surfaces. We begin here by looking at mechanically operated control components as they can be seen on light aircraft.

Cables and Pulleys

By far, the most common control system used on aircraft uses a network of cables and pulleys to transfer the motion of the control wheel to the flight controls. The basic component of a

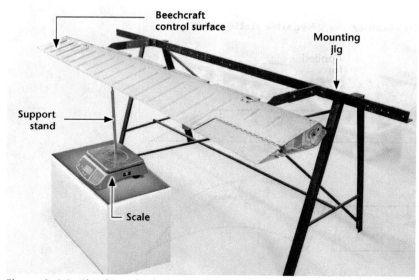

Figure 2-6-1. Checking the balance of a control surface.

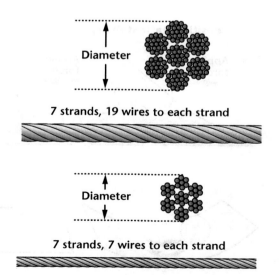

Figure 2-7-1. Cable construction and cross-section.

Flight Controls and Flaps | 2-9

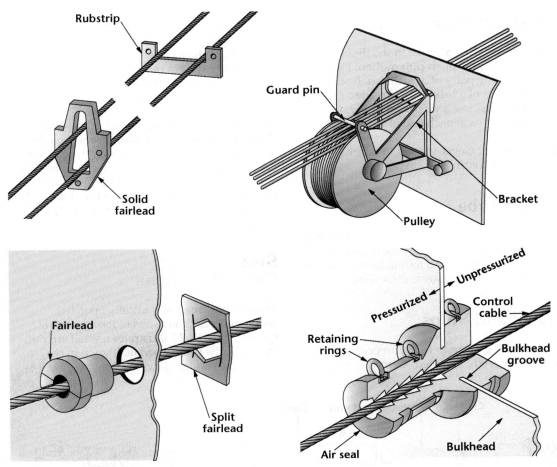

Figure 2-7-2. Cable guides.

cable is a wire. The diameter of the wire determines the total diameter of the cable.

A set number of wires are preformed into a helical or spiral shape and then formed into a strand. These preformed strands are laid around a straight center strand to form a cable (Figure 2-7-1).

Cables are quite efficient at transmitting motion, and they work best in a straight line. Technicians must take great care to guide the cables and prevent chafing. To change the cable's direction, you need to add another component to the system. Pulleys are used to guide cables and to change the direction of cable movement. Brackets fastened to the structure of the aircraft support the pulleys. Cables passing over pulleys are kept in place by guards. Figure 2-7-2 shows typical cable guides.

Cable Tension

For the aircraft to operate as it was designed, the cable tension for the flight controls must be correct. To determine the amount of tension on a cable, a tensiometer is used. Figure 2-7-3 shows a common type of cable tensiometer.

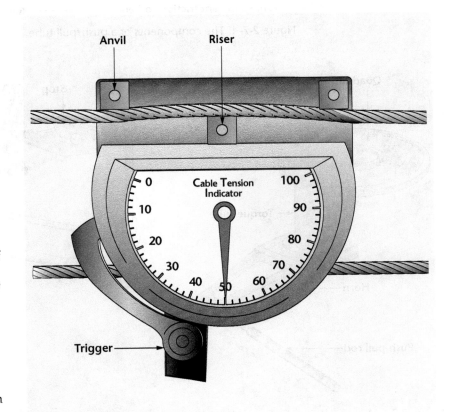

Figure 2-7-3. Cable tensiometer.

Push/Pull Tube

Push rods are used as links in the flight control system to give push-pull motion. Figure 2-7-4 shows the parts of a push rod. Notice that it consists of a tube with threaded rod ends. An adjustable antifriction rod end, or rod end clevis, is at each end of the tube.

The rod end, or clevis, is used to attach the tube to flight control system parts.

Torque Tube

Where an angular or twisting motion is needed in a control system, a torque tube is installed. Figure 2-7-5 shows how a torque tube is used to transmit motion in opposite directions.

Travel and Stops

For a control system to function properly, it must be correctly adjusted. Correctly rigged control surfaces travel through a prescribed arc and are synchronized with the movement of the flight deck operating controls. Rigging any control system requires that you follow the aircraft manufacturer's instructions in the maintenance manual.

To ensure that controls do not go beyond their design limits, manufacturers provide mechanical stops beyond which the control cannot move (Figure 2-7-6). These can be fixed structures that prevent control movement, or they could include some sort of threaded fastener that can be adjusted to meet factory specifications.

Small-Aircraft Control Systems

To show how the mechanically operated components are combined to form a control system, Figure 2-7-7 illustrates a small aircraft. Typically, the rudder pedals (shown in red) control the rudder, the control column's front

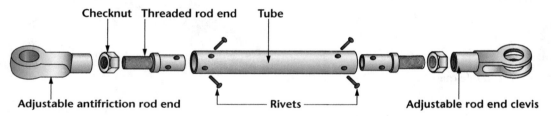

Figure 2-7-4. The components of a push/pull tube.

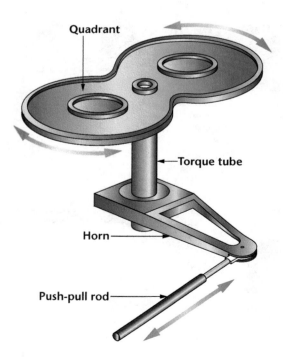

Figure 2-7-5. A torque tube can be used to change direction of force.

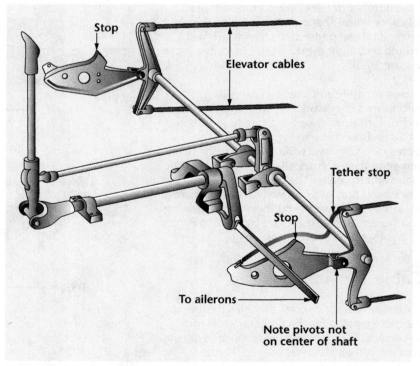

Figure 2-7-6. A stop limits how far a control surface can move.

and back motion controls the elevator (shown in green), and the wheel turning on the control column controls the ailerons (shown in blue).

Other Types of Control Systems

Most small aircraft use mechanical connections to move the control surfaces, but larger and faster aircraft introduced new challenges. Different methods of moving the control surfaces were needed as the force required to move the controls became greater. To make the control force required by pilots manageable, more complex control systems were designed.

First, hydromechanical designs, consisting of a mechanical circuit and a hydraulic circuit (Figure 2-7-8), were developed to overcome the limitations of mechanical flight controls systems. They are capable of providing the force needed to move the controls, but they are heavy and have design limitations.

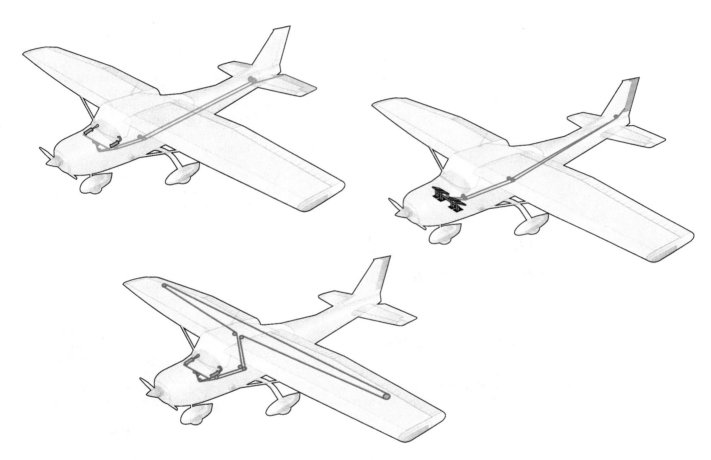

Figure 2-7-7. Small aircraft primary control system.

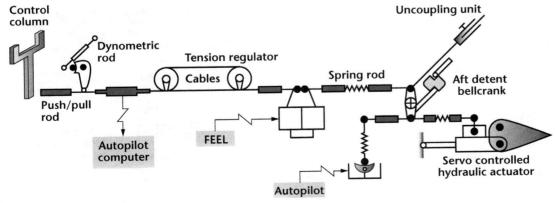

Figure 2-7-8. A hydromechanical control system for large aircraft.

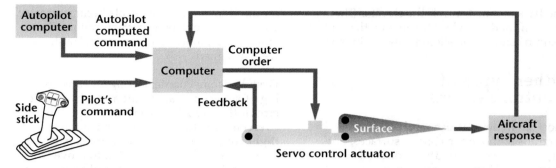

Figures 2-7-9. A fly-by-wire/light control system uses an electrical interface.

As aircraft became more sophisticated, control surfaces were designed to be actuated by electric motors. Control of these motors come from digital signals and are transmitted by wire (Figure 2-7-9) (called *fly-by-wire* systems) or, more recently, by fiber-optic cables (*fly-by-light* systems). Such flight control systems replace the physical connection between pilot controls and the flight control surfaces with an electrical interface. In such systems, the feel of the control reaction is fed back to the pilot by simulated means.

Simply put, the hinge moment is the force that must be overcome to move a control surface. At any given dynamic pressure and airspeed, the hinge moment varies with angle of attack and surface deflection. The study of hinge moments is important to be able to predict the forces (moments) required by the pilot. Additionally, the feedback provided by the required force is an additional cue to help the pilot fly the aircraft.

One device that compensates for this is an inset hinge. The hinge is set back so that the air striking the surface in front of the hinge

Section 8

Dynamic Pressure and Flight Controls

Aerodynamic Balance

Devices are used to achieve aerodynamic balance, or to reduce the hinge movement and thereby the physical effort needed to control an aircraft. If control surfaces were hinged at their leading edge and allowed to trail from that position in flight, the forces required to change the angle on all except light and slow aircraft would be prohibitive. Some form of aerodynamic balancing is required to help the pilot move controls easily without power-assisted controls. The most common forms of balancing are inset hinges, horn balances, internal balances, and tab balances (next section). Some different types of balancing are shown in Figure 2-8-1.

Hinge Moment/Inset Hinge

Each control surface on an aircraft has a hinge of some sort. By deflecting the control, there is an aerodynamic torque about that hinge. The *hinge moment* is the moment acting about the hinge line of a control surface.

Horn Balance

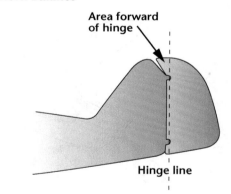

Inset Hinge Balance

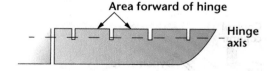

Mass Balance Weight

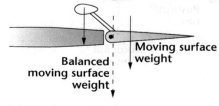

Figure 2-8-1. Balancing applications.

causes a force that tends to make the control move over still further. This partially balances the effect of the air that strikes the rear portion. This is effective, but it must not be overdone. Overbalancing can remove all feeling of control from the pilot, losing the valuable feedback.

Section 9

Secondary Controls: Tabs

The force of the air against a control surface in high-speed flight can make it difficult to move and hold that control surface in the deflected position. A control surface might also be too sensitive for similar reasons. Several types of tabs are used to help with such problems.

Fixed Tabs

A simple, light aircraft might have a stationary metal plate attached to the trailing edge of a primary flight control, often the rudder or aileron. This type of ground-adjustable tab is called a fixed tab (Figure 2-9-1). It can be bent slightly while the aircraft is on the ground to trim the aircraft to a hands-off condition when flying straight and level. The correct amount of bend can be determined only by flying the aircraft after an adjustment. Note that a small amount of bending is usually sufficient.

Adjustable Trim Tab

It is desirable for the flight crew to be able to take their hands and feet off the controls while in flight and have the aircraft maintain its flight condition. Trim tabs are designed to allow this.

Most trim tabs are small, movable surfaces on the trailing edge of a primary flight control surface (Figure 2-9-2). Moving the tab slightly in the opposite direction as the flight control surface deflection causes air to strike the tab and produces a force that helps maintain the flight control surface in the desired position.

Through linkage set from the flight deck (Figure 2-9-3), the tab can be positioned so that it is holding the control surface in position rather than the pilot. Therefore, elevator tabs are used to maintain the speed of the aircraft because they help maintain the selected pitch. Rudder tabs can be set to hold yaw in check and maintain heading. Aileron tabs can help keep the wings level.

Figure 2-9-1. Example of a fixed tab.

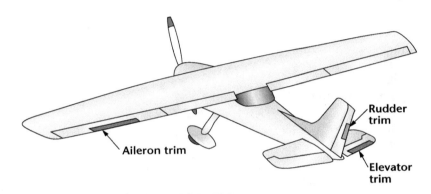

Figure 2-9-2. Adjustable trim tabs on the primary control surfaces.

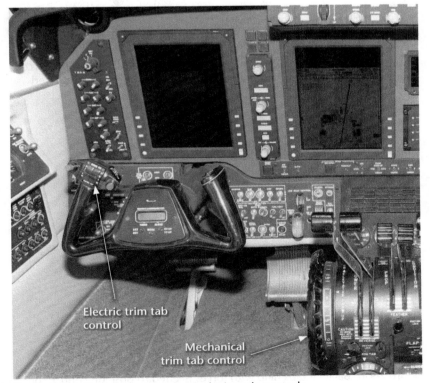

Figure 2-9-3. Electric and mechanical trim tab controls.

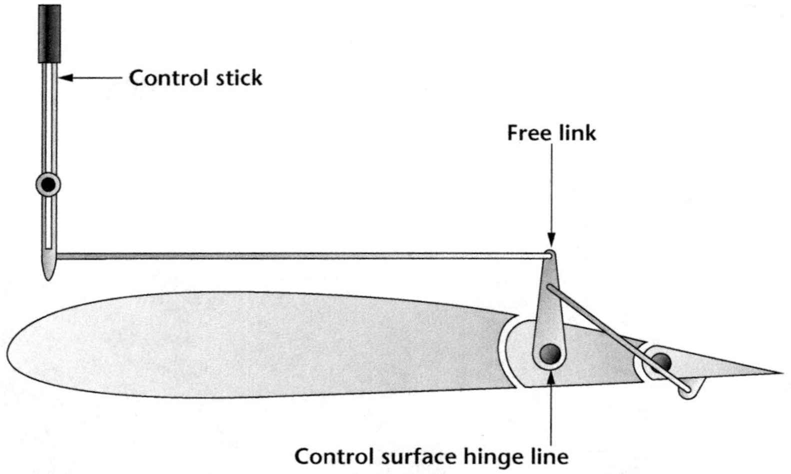

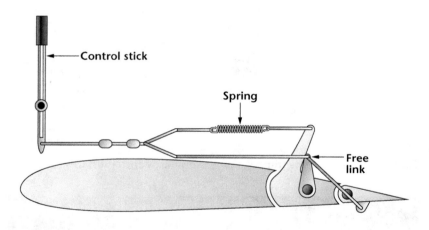

Figure 2-9-4. Servo tabs can position flight control surfaces if hydraulic failure occurs.

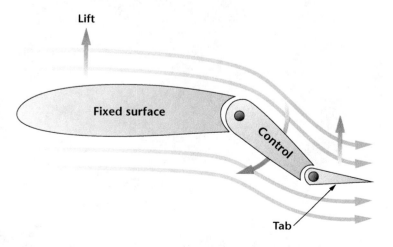

Figure 2-9-5. Many tab linkages have a spring tab that kicks in as the forces needed to deflect a control increase with speed and the angle of desired deflection.

Figure 2-9-6. Balance tabs help with forces needed to position control surfaces.

Servo Tab

A servo tab is designed to operate the primary flight control surface, not just reduce the force needed to do so. It is usually used to back up the primary control of the flight control surfaces. A servo tab is illustrated in Figure 2-9-4.

On heavy aircraft, large control surfaces require too much force to be moved manually and are usually deflected out of the neutral position by hydraulic actuators. These power control units are signaled via a system of hydraulic valves connected to the yoke and rudder pedals. On fly-by-wire aircraft, the hydraulic actuators that move the flight control surfaces are signaled by electric input. In the case of hydraulic system failures, manual linkage to a servo tab can be used to deflect the tab. This, in turn, provides an aerodynamic force that moves the primary control surface.

Spring Tab

A control surface could require excessive force to move only in the final stages of travel, or at higher airspeeds. When this is the case, a spring tab can be used (Figure 2-9-5). This is essentially a servo tab that does not activate until an effort is made to move the control surface beyond a certain point. When reached, a spring in line of the control linkage helps move the control surface through the remainder of its travel.

Balance Tabs

A balance tab is a small a trim tab that moves in one direction to cause the larger control surface to experience a force moving in the opposite direction. This action is illustrated in Figure 2-9-6.

Often, it is difficult to move a primary control surface because of its surface area and the speed of the air rushing over it. A balance tab is hinged at the trailing edge of the control surface and is deflected in the opposite direction. This causes a force that moves the control surface into the desired position and reduces the effort required by the pilot. Balance tabs are usually linked so that they move automatically when there is an input for control surface movement. If the balance tabs are adjustable from the flight deck, they also can serve as trim tabs.

Antiservo Tabs

Antiservo tabs are similar to balance tabs but move in the same direction as the primary control surface. On some aircraft, especially those with a movable horizontal stabilizer, the input to the control surface can be too sensitive.

An antiservo tab tied through the control linkage creates an aerodynamic force that increases the effort needed to move the control surface. This makes flying the aircraft more stable for the pilot. Figure 2-9-7 shows an antiservo tab in the up position. Deflected in the same direction as the desired stabilator movement, it increases the required control surface input. Table 2-9-1 summarizes the types of tabs and their uses.

Section 10
Secondary Controls: Flaps

The size and lifting capacity of a fixed wing design is always a compromise. A larger wing provides more lift and reduces the distance and speeds required for takeoff and landing, but it also increases drag, which reduces the aircraft's performance at cruise. Most aircraft are optimized for

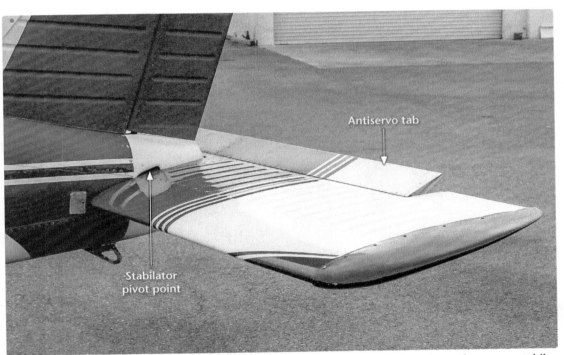

Figure 2-9-7. An antiservo tab moves in the same direction as the control tab. Shown here on a stabilator, it desensitizes the pitch control.

Type	Direction of motion, in relation to control surface	Activation	Effect
Trim	Opposite	Set by the flight crew from the flight deck. Uses independent linkage.	Statically balances the aircraft in flight. Allows *hands-off* maintenance of flight condition.
Balance	Opposite	Moves when the flight crew moves control surface. Coupled to a control surface linkage.	Helps flight crew overcome the force needed to move the control surface.
Servo	Opposite	Directly linked to flight control input device. Can be primary or backup means of control.	Aerodynamically positions control surfaces that require too much force to move manually.
Anti-balance or antiservo	Same	Directly linked to a flight control input device.	Increases force needed by pilot to change flight control position. Desensitizes flight controls.
Spring	Opposite	In line of direct linkage to servo tab. Spring helps when control forces become too high in high-speed flight.	Enables moving control surfaces when forces are high. Inactive in slow flight.

Table 2-9-1. Flight control tabs and their effect.

speed and efficiency during cruise, because this is where the aircraft spends most of its flight time. High-lift devices compensate for smaller wings by adding lift during takeoff and landing. They also reduce the landing distance and speed.

Flaps are probably the most common high-lift device and are found on most aircraft. They are usually inboard on the wing's trailing edge next to the fuselage. Leading-edge flaps are also common. They extend forward and down from the inboard wing leading edge.

Flaps are deployed to increase the camber of the wings and provide greater lift and control at slow speeds. They enable landing at slower speeds and reduce the amount of runway required for takeoff and landing. The amount that the flaps extend and the angle they form with the wing can be selected from the flight deck. Various kinds of flaps are used, and we examine a few common designs here.

Plain

Plain flaps form the trailing edge of the wing when the flap is in the retracted position. The airflow over the wing continues over the upper and lower surfaces of the flap, making the trailing edge of the flap essentially the trailing edge of the wing. As shown in Figure 2-10-1 view A, the plain flap is hinged so that the trailing edge can be lowered. This increases wing camber and provides greater lift.

Split

A split flap is normally housed under the trailing edge of the wing. It is usually just a braced flat metal plate hinged at several places along its leading edge. The upper surface of the wing extends to the trailing edge of the flap. When deployed, the split flap trailing edge lowers away from the trailing edge of the wing (Figure 2-10-1 view B). Airflow over the top of the wing remains the same. Airflow under the wing now follows the camber created by the lowered split flap, increasing lift.

Fowler

When deployed, Fowler flaps lower the trailing edge of the wing, and they slide aft, effectively increasing the wing's area. This action can be seen in Figure 2-10-1 view C. The Fowler flap creates more lift via the increased surface area and the wing camber. When stowed, the Fowler flap typically retracts up under the wing trailing edge like a split flap.

Slotted

Slotted flaps are commonly used on both small and large aircraft. When deployed, they increase wing camber, like other flaps, and also they open a slot between the wing and

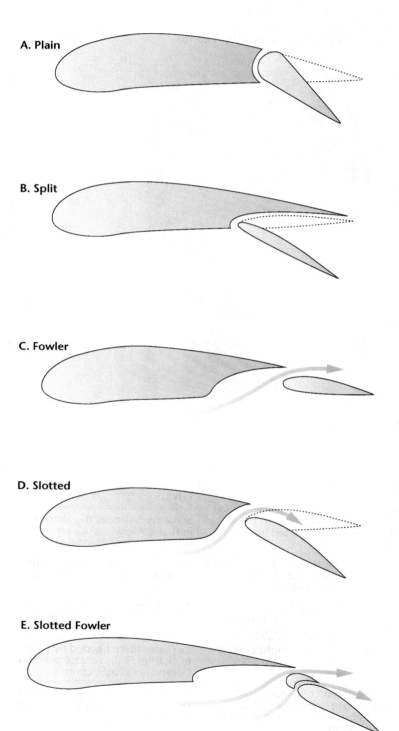

A. Plain

B. Split

C. Fowler

D. Slotted

E. Slotted Fowler

Figure 2-10-1. Types of flaps

the flap (Figure 2-10-1 view D). By opening this slot, high-pressure air from the bottom of the wing flows through the slot into the upper surface. This adds energy to the wing's boundary layer that delays airflow separation and produces less drag. This results in additional lift, without the excessive drag.

Slotted Fowler

An enhanced version of the Fowler flap is a set of flaps that contains more than one aerodynamic surface. Figure 2-10-1 view E shows a slotted Fowler flap. When deployed, each flap section slides aft on tracks as it lowers. The flap sections also separate, leaving an open slot between the wing and the fore flap, as well as between each of the flap sections. Air from under the wing flows through these slots. The result is that the laminar flow on the upper surfaces is enhanced. The greater camber and effective wing area increase overall lift.

Leading-Edge Flaps

Larger aircraft can have leading-edge flaps that are used in conjunction with the trailing-edge flaps. Although they are not installed or operated independently, their use with trailing-edge flaps can greatly increase wing camber and lift. When stowed, leading-edge flaps retract into the leading edge of the wing. One example of this design is seen in Figure 2-10-2.

The differing designs of leading-edge flaps essentially provide the same effect. Activating the trailing-edge flaps automatically deploys the leading-edge flaps, which are driven out of the leading edge and downward, extending the camber of the wing.

Section 11

Other Devices

Trailing-edge flaps are not the only high-lift devices used on aircraft. Other design features are used to help improve performance when operating at lower speeds and with a higher angle of attack. This includes both fixed and moveable designs.

Slots and Slats

Essentially slots and slats have the same effect on the aircraft. Both provide a small

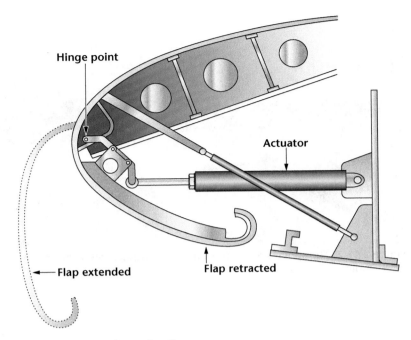

Figure 2-10-2. A leading-edge flap.

airfoil-shaped device attached just in front of the wing's leading edge. This unit redirects the airflow in front of the wing, allowing it to flow more smoothly over the wing. This increases the angle of attack at which the wing maintains its laminar airflow, resulting in the ability to fly the aircraft slower, and still maintain control.

A slat or slot can be either full span or they can be on only part of the wing, usually the outboard section. Slots and slats are sometimes only in front of the ailerons to ensure that the ailerons remain effective as long as possible when the wing is approaching a stall. Airflow across slots and slats is illustrated in Figure 2-11-1.

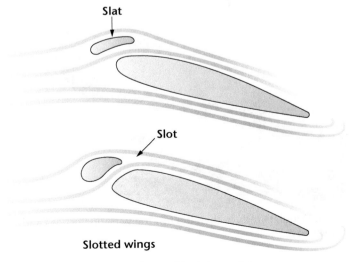

Figure 2-11-1. Airflow over wings with slots or slats.

Figure 2-11-2. The spoilers are deployed on a transport category aircraft after landing.

Figure 2-11-3. Speed brakes can be installed on both large and small aircraft.

Figure 2-11-4. Winglets reduce the effect of the wingtip vortices and increase efficiency.

The primary difference between the two is that slots are fixed surfaces, and slats are moveable—deploying only when they are needed. Deployment can be initiated by the flight crew or initiated automatically according to flight conditions. Automatic operation can use airflow pressure against the slat to close it and small springs to open it at slower speeds when the dynamic pressure is reduced, for example when the speed falls below a certain point or the airflow reaches a predetermined angle-of-attack on the wing.

Spoilers

Spoilers are auxiliary wing flight control surfaces, mounted on the upper surface of each wing. They might be seen on aircraft as small as gliders and as large as the widebody transport jets, and they are very versatile.

On some aircraft, they might operate in conjunction with the ailerons to provide lateral control. Other systems are equipped with separate ground and flight spoilers. Figure 2-11-2 shows the spoilers on a large aircraft.

Speed Brakes

Speed brakes, sometimes called dive flaps or dive brakes, serve to slow an aircraft in flight. These brakes are used when descending at a steep angle or when approaching the runway for a landing. The brakes themselves are made in many shapes, and their location depends on the design of the aircraft and the purpose of the brakes. Speed brakes installed on a light aircraft are shown in Figure 2-11-3.

Winglets

Winglets are the near-vertical extension of the wingtip that reduce the aerodynamic drag associated with vortices that develop at the wingtips as the airplane moves through the air (Figure 2-11-4). By reducing the induced drag at the tips of the wings, fuel consumption goes down and range is extended. Largely because of the fuel savings, this has become a very popular feature of new aircraft and a common retrofit for older aircraft both large and small.

Vortex Generators

Vortex generators are small blades placed in a spanwise line aft of the leading edge of the wing and tail surfaces. They control airflow over the lifting surface of the airfoil by creating vortices that energize the boundary layer. This results in improved performance and control at low airspeeds and high angles of attack.

These consist of small, angled plates attached on the surface of the airfoil (Figure 2-11-5). The angle of this plate causes the air to swirl, creating a vortex behind it. Hence the name, vortex generator. This vortex effect allows the airflow to remain "attached" to the surface even at points where the flow without a vortex would separate from the surface. These plates are mounted in complementary pairs. This causes the vortices being developed to add one another, thus increasing the effect.

As seen with other boundary layer devices, one of the most common locations for vortex generators is on the aircraft's wing, forward of the ailerons. When the aircraft wing stalls, the airflow detaches from the wings. This means that the flow detaches before it reaches the ailerons, making them ineffective. Vortex generators help provide aileron control even if the rest of the wing is stalled.

Stall Fences

A chordwise barrier on the top of the wing, called a stall fence, is used to halt the spanwise flow of air. This barrier can be seen in Figure 2-11-6. In low-speed flight, this maintains proper chordwise airflow reducing the tendency for the wing to stall.

Gap Seals

Because of design and manufacturing considerations, a gap often exists between the trailing edge of a wing or stabilizer and the control surfaces. This creates a situation where, at high angles of attack, high pressure air from the lower wing surface can be disrupted at this gap. The result can be turbulent airflow, which increases drag. There is also a tendency for some lower wing boundary air to enter the gap and disrupt the upper wing surface airflow, which in turn reduces lift and control surface responsiveness. Gap seals are used to promote smooth airflow in these gap areas. Gap seals can be made of a wide variety of materials ranging from aluminum and impregnated fabric to foam and plastic. Figure 2-11-7 shows how gap seals work.

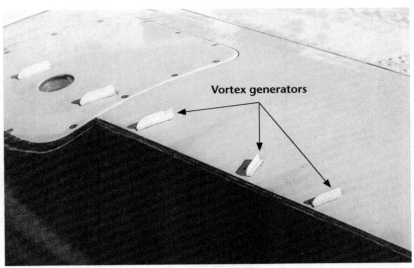

Figure 2-11-5. Vortex generators on a light aircraft wing.

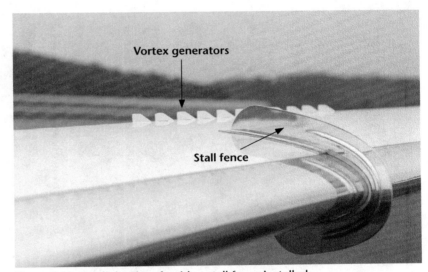

Figure 2-11-6. A light aircraft with a stall fence installed.

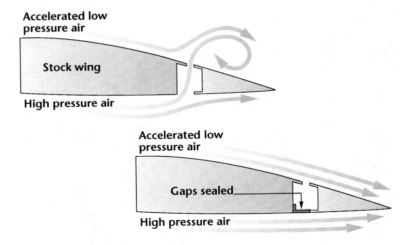

Figure 2-11-7. The effect on airflow with gap seals.

3

Electrical Systems

Section 1

Electrical Principles

Anyone with even a passing interest in aviation is aware of the increasing use of electricity in modern aircraft systems. Functions that were once accomplished mechanically are now performed electrically. Perhaps the most obvious is starting the engine. Rarely do you see anyone start an aircraft by pulling on the propeller. On most aircraft, that job is now done using an electric starting motor.

Using electricity today is so common it would be easy for it to be taken for granted. However, its widespread use in aircraft electrical systems emphasizes the importance of at least a basic understanding of electrical theory and components is necessary for anyone involved in aviation.

Electron Flow

Any understanding of electricity must begin by understanding where this energy comes from, and to do that we must begin with the atom.

Matter can be defined as anything that has mass (weight) and occupies space. Thus, matter is everything that exists. It can exist in the form of solids, liquids, or gases. The smallest particle of matter in any state or form, that still possesses its identity, is called a molecule. Molecules are composed of one of more types of atoms.

Substances composed of only one type of atom are called elements. However, most substances occur in nature as compounds, that is, combi-

Learning Objectives

IDENTIFY
• Electrical components on a schematic

EXPLAIN
• Ohm's Law

DISCUSS
• Basic electrical principles

• Types of aircraft batteries and their operation

Left: Today's aircraft have become increasingly dependent on electrical systems that serve many functions. Many jobs that were accomplished mechanically on earlier aircraft are now done with electrical components.

nations of two or more types of atoms. Water, for example, is a compound of two atoms of hydrogen and one atom of oxygen. A molecule of water is illustrated in Figure 3-1-1. Adding, taking away, or changing anything in this atomic structure results in a substance that is not water.

The atom is considered the basic building block of all matter. It is the smallest possible particle that an element can be divided into and still retain its chemical properties. In its simplest form, it consists of one or more electrons orbiting at a high speed around a center, or nucleus, made up of one or more protons, and, in most atoms, one or more neutrons. Because an atom is so small that some 200,000 could be placed side by side in a line 1-in. long, it cannot be seen, of course. Nevertheless, a great deal is known about its behavior from various tests and experiments.

The simplest atom is that of hydrogen, which is one electron orbiting around one proton, as shown in Figure 3-1-2. A more complex atom is that of oxygen (Figure 3-1-3), which consists of eight electrons rotating in two different orbits around a nucleus made up of eight protons and eight neutrons.

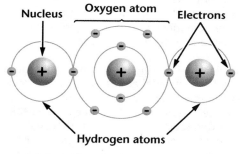

Figure 3-1-1. A water molecule.

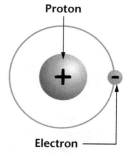

Figure 3-1-2. A hydrogen atom.

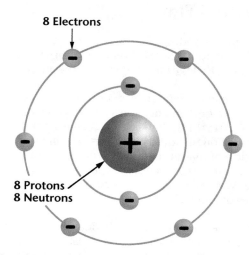

Figure 3-1-3. An oxygen atom.

An electron is the basic negative charge of electricity and cannot be divided further. Some electrons are more tightly bound to the nucleus of their atom than others and rotate in an imaginary shell or sphere closer to the nucleus; others are more loosely bound and orbit farther away from the nucleus. These loosely bound electrons are called *free* electrons because they can be freed easily from the positive attraction of the protons in the nucleus to make up the flow of electrons in a practical electrical circuit.

The neutrons in a nucleus have no electrical charge. They are neither positive nor negative but are equal in size and weight to the proton. Because a proton weighs about 1,845 times as much as an electron, the overall weight of an atom is determined by the number of protons and neutrons in its nucleus. The weight of an electron is not considered in determining the weight of an atom. Indeed, the nature of electricity cannot be defined clearly because it is not certain whether the electron is a negative charge with no mass (weight) or a particle of matter with a negative charge.

Electricity is best understood in terms of its behavior, which is based in part on the charge an atom carries. When the total positive charge of the protons in the nucleus equals the total negative charge of the electrons in orbit around the nucleus, the atom is said to have a neutral charge. If an atom has a shortage of electrons, or negative charges, it is positively charged. If it has too many electrons, it is said to be negatively charged.

In a state of neutral charge, an atom has one electron for each proton in the nucleus. Thus, the number of electrons held by the atoms making up the various elements varies from one, in the case of hydrogen, to 92 for uranium and some rare elements going even higher.

The periodic table of the elements (Figure 3-1-4) is a standardized chart showing the basic data associated with the known elements. They have been organized on this chart by the atomic number of each chemical element. This is the number of protons found in the nucleus of a single atom of that element. We discuss protons and the nucleus of an atom later in this section. This atomic number uniquely identifies each chemical element.

The electrons revolving around a nucleus travel in orbits, sometimes called shells or layers. Each shell can contain a certain maximum number of electrons. If this number is exceeded, the extra electrons are forced into the next higher, or outer, shell.

Group →	1	2	3	4	5	6	7	8	9	10	11	12	13	14	15	16	17	18
Period																		
1	1 H																	2 He
2	3 Li	4 Be											5 B	6 C	7 N	8 O	9 F	10 Ne
3	11 Na	12 Mg											13 Al	14 Si	15 P	16 S	17 Cl	18 Ar
4	19 K	20 Ca	21 Sc	22 Ti	23 V	24 Cr	25 Mn	26 Fe	27 Co	28 Ni	29 Cu	30 Zn	31 Ga	32 Ge	33 As	34 Se	35 Br	36 kr
5	37 Rb	38 Sr	39 Y	40 Zr	41 Nb	42 Mo	43 Tc	44 Ru	45 Rh	46 Pd	47 Ag	48 Cd	49 In	50 Sn	51 Sb	52 Te	53 I	54 Xe
6	55 Cs	56 Ba		72 Hf	73 Ta	74 W	75 Re	76 Os	77 Ir	78 Pt	79 Au	80 Hg	81 Tl	82 Pb	83 Bi	84 Po	85 At	86 Rn
7	87 Fr	88 Ra		104 Rf	105 Db	106 Sg	107 Bh	108 Hs	109 Mt	110 Ds	111 Rg	112 Cn	113 Uut	114 Uuq	115 Uup	116 Uuh	117 Uus	118 Uuo

Lanthanides	57 La	58 Ce	59 Pr	60 Nd	61 Pm	62 Sm	63 Eu	64 Gd	65 Tb	66 Dy	67 Ho	68 Er	69 Tm	70 Yb	71 Lu
Actinides	89 Ac	90 Th	91 Pa	92 U	93 Np	94 Pu	95 Am	96 Cm	97 Bk	98 Cf	99 Es	100 Fm	101 Md	102 No	103 Lr

Figure 3-1-4. Periodic table of the elements.

The number of electrons in the outermost shell determines the *valence* of an atom. For this reason, the outer shell of an atom is called the valence shell, and the electrons in this shell are called valence electrons.

The valence composition determines its ability to gain or lose an electron, which in turn determines the chemical and electrical properties of the atom. An atom that is lacking only one or two electrons from its outer shell easily gains electrons to complete its shell, but a large amount of energy is required to free any of its electrons. An atom with relatively few electrons in its outer shell in comparison to the number of electrons required to fill the shell easily loses these valence electrons. The valence shell always refers to the outermost shell.

When the atom loses electrons or gains electrons in this process of electron exchange, it is said to be *ionized*. For ionization to take place, a transfer of energy must take place that results in a change in the internal energy of the atom.

An atom with more than its normal number of electrons acquires a negative charge and is called a negative ion. The atom that gives up some of its normal electrons is left with fewer negative charges than positive charges and is called a positive ion. Thus, ionization is the process by which an atom loses or gains electrons.

The valence electrons are the most important in electricity. These electrons are the easiest to break loose from their parent atom. Normally, conductors have three or fewer valence electrons; insulators have five or more valence electrons; and semiconductors usually have four valence electrons.

The electrical conductivity of matter is dependent upon the atomic structure of the material from which the conductor is made. In any solid material, such as copper, the atoms that make up the molecular structure are bound firmly together. At room temperature, copper contains a considerable amount of heat energy.

Because heat energy is one method of removing electrons from their orbits, copper contains many free electrons that can move from atom to atom. When not under the influence of an external force, these electrons move haphazardly in the conductor. This movement is equal in all directions so that electrons are not lost or gained by any part of the conductor.

When controlled by an external force, the electrons move generally in the same direction. The effect of this movement is felt almost instantly from one end of the conductor to the other. This electron movement is called an electric current. This movement of electrons through various materials is the foundation of our study of electricity. This movement is like pushing a group of balls through a long tube. Once full, each time a new ball is added to one

Figure 3-1-5. Electron flow.

end, one comes out the other end. This is illustrated in Figure 3-1-5. With this analogy, we can see how electrical current can be viewed as instantaneous, even though it is the reaction of many electrons.

To develop an understanding of electron movement and what we can do with it, we need to study the terms and quantities associated with electron flow. The charge of one electron might be used as the unit of electrical charge, but the charge of one electron is so small that it is impractical to use. The practical unit adopted for measuring the charge is the coulomb (C), named after the scientist Charles Coulomb. One coulomb is equal to the charge of approximately 6.24×10^{18} electrons.

If a charge of one coulomb exists between two bodies, one unit of electrical potential energy exists. This is called the difference in potential between two bodies and is referred to as electromotive force (emf) or voltage. The unit of measurement is the volt (V).

Electrical charges are created by displacing electrons, so that an excess of electrons exists at one point and a deficiency exists at another point. Consequently, a charge must always have either a negative or positive polarity. A body with an excess of electrons is negative, and a body with a deficiency of electrons is positive.

A difference of potential can exist between two points, or bodies, only if they have different charges. In other words, there is no difference in potential between two bodies if both have a deficiency of electrons to the same degree. If, however, one body is deficient of 6 coulombs (representing 6 V), and the other is deficient by 12 coulombs (representing 12 V), there is a difference of potential of 6 V. The body with the greater deficiency is positive with respect to the other.

In most electrical circuits only the difference of potential between two points is of importance. The absolute potentials of the points are of little concern. Very often it is convenient to use one standard reference for all the various potentials throughout an aircraft or a piece of equipment. For this reason, the potentials at various points in a circuit are generally measured with respect to the metal structure on which all components are mounted. This could be the chassis of a piece of equipment, or the aircraft itself.

The aircraft or chassis is considered to be at zero potential and all other potentials are either positive or negative with respect to that structure. When used as the reference point, the aircraft or chassis is said to be at ground potential. This becomes very important when installing electrical equipment as the structure of the airplane often serves as the common ground for all electrical equipment. The practice of using the aircraft as the return path for electrical current means that only half of the amount of wiring that would otherwise be used is necessary. This practice results in lighter aircraft because of the weight savings.

When a difference in potential exists between two charged bodies that are connected by a conductor, electrons flow along the conductor. This flow is from the negatively charged body to the positively charged body, until the two charges are equalized, and the potential difference no longer exists. This flow is known as electrical current.

Electron movement through an electric circuit is directly proportional to the difference in potential, or emf, across the circuit, just as the flow of water through the pipe in Figure 3-1-6 is directly proportional to the difference in water level in the two tanks.

A fundamental law of electricity is that the electron flow (current) is directly proportional to the applied voltage. If the voltage is increased, the current is increased. If the voltage is decreased, the current is decreased.

The amount of current flowing is measured in amperes (A). A current of one ampere is said to flow when one coulomb of charge passes a point in one second. Remember, one coulomb is equal to the charge of 6.24×10^{18} electrons.

We have already mentioned that the number of electrons in the valence shell of certain atoms affects how easily electrons move. This places them in the category of conductor, semiconductor, or insulator. Some materials offer little opposition to current flow, but others greatly oppose current flow.

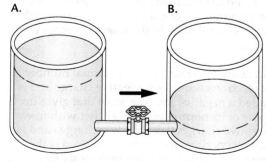

Figure 3-1-6. Water analogy for current flow.

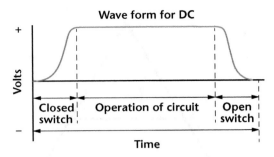
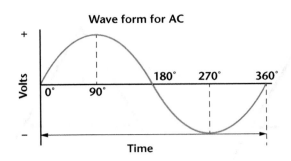

Figure 3-1-7. DC and AC voltage curves.

The opposition to current flow is known as *resistance* (R), and the unit of measure is the *ohm*. One ohm is the amount of resistance required to allow one ampere of current to flow when one volt of potential is applied to the circuit. A conductor has one ohm of resistance when an applied potential of one volt produces a current of one ampere. The symbol used to represent the ohm is the Greek letter omega (Ω).

As you study electricity, you will find two competing schools of thought and analytical practices regarding the flow of electricity. The two are called the conventional current theory and the electron theory.

Of the two, the conventional current theory was the first to be developed and, through many years of use, this method has become ingrained in electrical texts. The theory was initially advanced by Benjamin Franklin who reasoned that current flowed out of a positive source into a negative source or an area that lacked an abundance of charge. The notation assigned to the electric charges was positive (+) for the abundance of charge and negative (–) for a lack of charge. It then seemed natural to visualize the flow of current as being from the positive (+) to the negative (–).

Later discoveries were made that proved just the opposite is true. Electron flow is what actually happens when an abundance of electrons flow out of the negative (–) source to an area that lacks electrons or the positive (+) source. Both conventional flow and electron flow are used in industry. Many textbooks use both electron flow and conventional flow methods.

Regardless of whether you are following electron flow or conventional current, two basic types of current flow exist: direct current (DC) and alternating current (AC).

Direct Current (DC)

In a DC circuit the electricity flows in one direction only. You could choose to follow the

rules that apply to conventional current or to electron flow, but the movement is always in a single direction. DC flows constantly in only one direction with a constant polarity. It changes magnitude only when the circuit is opened or closed, as shown in the DC waveform in Figure 3-1-7.

Alternating Current (AC)

In an AC circuit, the flow changes direction at regular intervals, increases in value at a definite rate from zero to a maximum positive strength, and decreases back to zero; then it flows in the opposite direction, similarly increasing to a maximum negative value, and again decreasing to zero. DC and AC waveforms are compared in Figure 3-1-7.

Section 2

Ohm's Law

So far, we have been introduced to the three basic values associated with electrical circuits (Table 3-2-1).

The relationship between these values remains constant, and they behave very predictably. In any electrical circuit, when voltage is applied to it, current flows. The resistance present in the circuit determines how much current flows under that voltage. In most cases, the greater the circuit resistance, the less the current. If the resistance is reduced,

Value	Measured in	Symbol
Electromotive force (emf)	Volts (V)	E
Current flow	Amps (I)	I
Resistance	Ohms (Ω)	R

Table 3-2-1. The three basic values at play in electrical circuits.

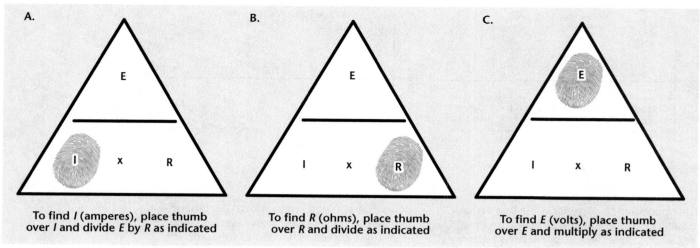

Figure 3-2-1. Ohm's Law chart.

the current increases. This relationship is linear and is known as Ohm's Law.

Ohm's Law can be expressed as the following equation:

Equation 1

$$I = E / R$$

where

I = current in amperes (A)

E = voltage (V)

R = resistance (Ω)

If any two of these circuit quantities are known, the third can be found by simple algebraic transposition. With this equation, we can calculate current in a circuit if we know the voltage and resistance. We can use this same formula to calculate voltage. By multiplying

both sides of Equation 1 by R, we get an equivalent form of Ohm's Law, which is

Equation 2

$$E = I \times R$$

Finally, if we divide Equation 2 by I, we solve for resistance. This relationship is true only if the resistance in the circuit remains constant. If the resistance changes, current also changes.

Equation 3

$$R = E / I$$

All three formulas presented in this section are equivalent to each other and are simply different ways of expressing Ohm's Law. The various equations, which can be derived by transposing the basic law, can be easily obtained by using the triangles as shown in Figure 3-2-1.

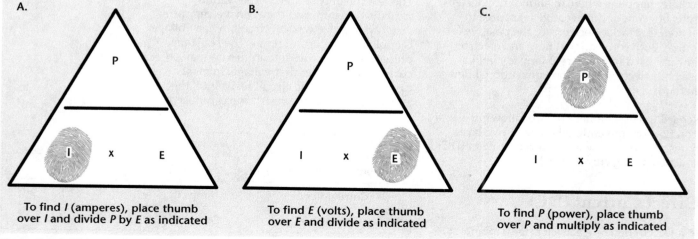

Figure 3-3-1. The power equation chart.

The triangles containing E, R, and I are divided into two parts, with E above the line and I × R below it. To determine an unknown circuit quantity when the other two are known, cover the unknown quantity with a thumb. The location of the remaining uncovered letters in the triangle indicate the mathematical operation to be performed. For example, to find I, see Figure 3-2-1 view A and cover I with the thumb. The uncovered letters indicate that E is to be divided by R, or I = E / R. To find R, see Figure 3-2-1 view B and cover R with the thumb. The result indicates that E is to be divided by I, or R = E / I. To find E, see Figure 3-2-1 view C and cover E with the thumb. The result indicates that I is multiplied by R, or E = I × R.

This chart is useful when learning to use Ohm's Law. It should be used to supplement the beginner's knowledge of the algebraic method.

Section 3

Power

The unit measurement for power is the watt (W). In a DC circuit, power is obtained by the equation, $P = E \times I$, (that is, watts equal volts times amperes). Thus, if 1 ampere of current flows in a circuit at a pressure of 200 volts, the power is 200 watts. The product of the volts and the amperes is the true power in the circuit.

For a simple DC electrical system, power dissipation can then be given by the equation $P = I \times E$ and illustrated in Figure 3-3-1.

For example, if a circuit has a voltage of 24 volts and a current of 2 amps, the power in the circuit becomes:

$P = 2\,A \times 24\,V$

$P = 48\,W$

The watt is named for James Watt, the inventor of the steam engine. Watt devised an experiment to measure the power of a horse to find a means of measuring the mechanical power of his steam engine. One horsepower is required to move 33,000 lbs. 1 ft. in 1 minute. Because power is the rate of doing work, it is equivalent to the work divided by time. Stated as a formula, this is

1 Horsepower = 33,000 ft-lbs / 60 second

1 horsepower = 550 ft-lbs / second

Electrical power can be rated in a similar manner. For example, an electric motor rated as a 1 horsepower motor requires 746 watts of electrical energy.

Section 4

Electrical Circuits

The essential components that make up an electrical circuit are

- A source of electrical power

- A load (any component that consumes electricity)

- The conductors that connect the units to each other

To understand circuit construction, you should be able to recognize a few standard graphical symbols used to depict each of these components. Figure 3-4-1 shows the most common symbols used.

The schematic depiction of a conductor is simple enough. This is generally shown as a solid line. Two methods are used to show wire crossovers and wire connections. Figure 3-4-2 shows the two ways of drawing wires that cross, versions A and B. Figure 3-4-3 shows the two ways of drawing wire that connect versions A and B. If version A in Figure 3-4-2 is used to show crossovers, version A for wire connections in Figure 3-4-3 is used. The same can then be said about using version B methods.

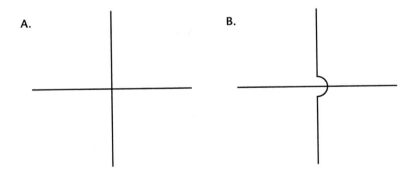

Figure 3-4-2. Unconnected crossover wires.

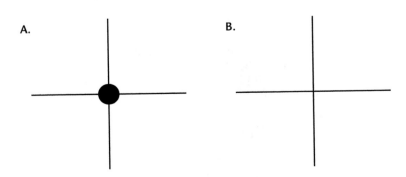

Figure 3-4-3. Connected wires.

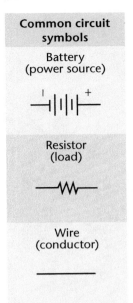

Common circuit symbols

Battery (power source)

Resistor (load)

Wire (conductor)

Figure 3-4-1. Basic circuit symbols.

Series Circuits

The series circuit is the most basic electrical circuit and provides a good introduction to basic circuit analysis. The series circuit represents the first building block for all the circuits to be studied and analyzed. Figure 3-4-4 shows this simple circuit with nothing more than a voltage source or battery, a conductor, and a resistor. This is classified as a series circuit because the components are connected end to end, so that the same current flows through each component equally. The current can take only one path, and the battery and resistor are in series with each other.

Parallel Circuits

A circuit in which two or more electrical resistances or loads are connected across the same voltage source is called a parallel circuit. The primary difference between the series circuit and the parallel circuit is that more than one path is provided for the current in the parallel circuit. Each of these parallel paths is called a branch. The minimum requirements for a parallel circuit are the following:

- A power source
- Conductors
- A resistance or load for each current path
- Two or more paths for current flow

Figure 3-4-5 shows the most basic parallel circuit. Current flowing out of the source divides at point A in the diagram and goes through R_1 and R_2. As more branches are added to the circuit, more paths for the source current are provided.

Series-Parallel Circuits

Most of the circuits that you encounter will not be a simple series or parallel circuit. Circuits are usually a combination of both, known as series-parallel circuits, which are groups consisting of resistors in parallel and in series. Figure 3-4-6 is an example of this type of circuit.

Although the series-parallel circuit can initially appear to be complex, the same relationships that have been used for the series and parallel circuits are applied to these circuits.

Conductors and Wire Size

Although wire of any size or resistance value can be used, *conductor* usually refers to materials that offer low resistance to current

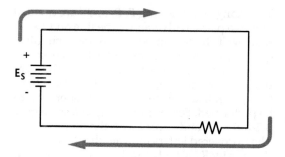

Figure 3-4-4. A series DC circuit.

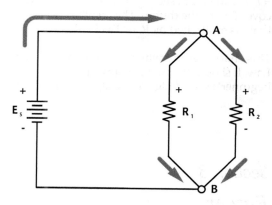

Figure 3-4-5. A parallel circuit.

flow, and *insulator* describes materials that offer high resistance to current. No distinct dividing line exists between conductors and insulators; under the proper conditions, all types of material conduct some current. Materials offering a resistance to current flow midway between the best conductors and the poorest conductors (insulators) are sometimes referred to as *semiconductors* and find their greatest application in the field of transistors.

The best conductors are materials, chiefly metals, that have many free electrons. Insulators are materials with few free electrons. The best conductors are silver, copper, gold, and aluminum; but some nonmetals, such as carbon and water, can be used as conductors. Materials such as rubber, glass, ceramics, and plastics are such poor conductors that they are usually used as insulators. The current flow in some of these materials is so low that it is usually considered zero.

As discussed earlier, resistance is measured in ohms (Ω). In mathematical formulas, the capital letter R refers to resistance. The resistance of a conductor and the voltage applied to it determine the number of amperes of current flowing through the conductor. Thus, 1 ohm of resistance limits the current flow to 1 ampere in a conductor to which a voltage of 1 volt is applied.

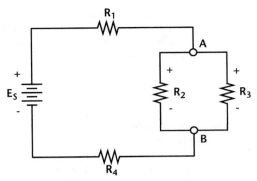

Figure 3-4-6. A series-parallel circuit.

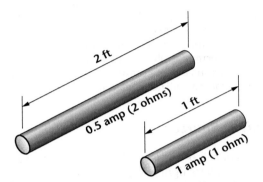

Figure 3-4-7. Resistance varies with the conductor's length.

A material's resistance is determined by four properties: material, length, area, and temperature. We take a look at each of these factors.

Material. The resistance of a metallic conductor is dependent on the type of conductor material. It has been pointed out that certain metals are commonly used as conductors because of the large number of free electrons in their outer orbits. Copper is usually considered the best available conductor material, because a copper wire offers less resistance to current flow than an aluminum wire of the same diameter. However, aluminum is much lighter than copper, and for this reason, and cost considerations, aluminum is often used when the weight factor is important.

Distance. The resistance of a metallic conductor is directly proportional to its length. The longer a wire is, the greater its resistance. Figure 3-4-7 shows two wire conductors of different lengths. If 1 volt of electrical pressure is applied across the two ends of the conductor that is 1 ft. long, and the resistance to the movement of free electrons is assumed to be 1 ohm, the current flow is limited to 1 ampere. If the same size conductor's length is doubled, the same electrons set in motion by the 1 volt applied now find twice the resistance; consequently, the current flow is reduced by one-half.

Area. The resistance of a metallic conductor is inversely proportional to the cross-sectional area. This area could be triangular or even square but is usually circular. If the cross-sectional area of a conductor is doubled, the resistance to current flow is reduced by half. This is true because of the increased area in which an electron can move without collision or capture by an atom. Thus, the resistance varies inversely with the cross-sectional area of a conductor.

Temperature. The fourth major factor influencing the resistance of a conductor is temperature. Although some substances, such as carbon, show a decrease in resistance as the ambient (surrounding) temperature increases, most materials used as conductors increase in resistance as temperature increases. Charts listing the temperature coefficient of resistance for different materials are available.

In the case of using copper conductors, we are spared the task of tedious calculations by using a table as shown in Table 3-4-1. Wire sizes are classified by an AWG Number (American Wire Gage) and are assigned numbers from AWG 0000 to AWG 30. AWG is a small diameter wire. The AWG diameters get smaller as the AWG number increases. For example an AWG 10 wire has a much larger diameter than an AWG 30 wire. Note that cross-sectional dimensions listed in the table are such that each decrease of one-gauge number equals a 25 percent increase

AWG number	Diameter (mils)	Ohms per 1,000 ft.
0000	460.0	0.04901
000	409.6	0.06180
00	364.8	0.07793
0	324.9	0.09827
1	289.3	0.1239
2	257.6	0.1563
3	229.4	0.1970
4	204.3	0.2485
5	181.9	0.3133
6	162.0	0.3951
8	128.5	0.6282
10	101.9	0.9989
12	80.81	1.588
14	64.08	2.525
18	40.30	6.385
20	31.96	10.15
22	25.35	16.14
24	20.10	25.67
26	15.94	40.81
28	12.64	64.9
30	10.03	103.2

Table 3-4-1. Conversion table of AWG numbers to mils or ohms in copper conductors

in the cross-sectional area. Because of this, a decrease of three-gauge numbers represents an increase in cross-sectional area of approximately 2:1. Likewise, change of 10 wire gauge numbers represents a 10:1 change in cross-sectional area—also, by doubling the cross-sectional area of the conductor, the resistance is cut in half. A decrease of three wire gauge numbers cuts the resistance of the conductor of a given length in half.

Sources of Electricity

Electrical energy can be produced in several methods. The most common sources are pressure, chemical, thermal, light and electromagnetic induction. Virtually all mechanical devices (generators and alternators) that produce electrical power use the process of electromagnetic induction.

Pressure Source

This form of electrical generation is commonly known as piezoelectric (piezo or piez taken from Greek: to press; pressure; to squeeze) and is a result of applying mechanical pressure on a dielectric or nonconducting crystal.

Applying a mechanical stress produces an electric polarization that is proportional to this stress. This polarization establishes a voltage across the crystal. If a circuit is connected across the crystal, a flow of current is observed when the crystal is loaded (pressure is applied). An opposite condition occurs, where applying a voltage between certain faces of the crystal produces a mechanical distortion. This effect is commonly referred to as the piezoelectric effect.

Piezoelectric materials are used extensively in transducers for converting a mechanical strain into an electrical signal. Such devices include microphones, phonograph pickups, and vibration-sensing elements. The opposite effect, in which a mechanical output is derived from an electrical signal input, is also widely used in headphones and loudspeakers.

Chemical Source

Chemical energy can be converted into electricity; the most common form of this is the battery. A battery produces electricity using two metals in a chemical solution like alkaline electrolyte, where a chemical reaction between the metals and the chemicals frees more electrons in one metal than in the other. One terminal of the battery is attached to one of the metals such as zinc; the other terminal is attached to the other metal such as manganese oxide. The end that frees more electrons develops a positive charge, and the other end develops a negative charge. If a wire is attached from one end of the battery to the other, electrons flow through the wire to balance the electrical charge.

Thermal Sources

The most common source of thermal electricity found in the aviation industry comes from thermocouples. Thermocouples are widely used as temperature sensors. They are cheap and interchangeable, have standard connectors, and can measure a wide range of temperatures. Thermocouples are pairs of dissimilar metal wires joined at least at one end and generate a voltage between the two wires that is proportional to the temperature at the junction. Thermocouples are often used to measure various engine temperatures (exhaust gas temperature, cylinder head temperature).

Light Sources

A solar cell or a photovoltaic cell is a device that converts light energy into electricity. Fundamentally, the device contains chemical elements that, when exposed to light energy, release electrons.

Photons in sunlight are taken in by the solar panel or cell, where they are then absorbed by semiconducting materials, such as silicon. Electrons in the cell are broken loose from their atoms, allowing them to flow through the material to produce electricity. The complementary positive charges that are also created are called holes (absence of electron) and flow in the direction opposite of the electrons in a silicon solar panel.

Solar cells have many applications.

Electromagnetic Induction

Electromagnetic induction is a process that produces a voltage (emf) by moving a magnetic field in relationship to a conductor. Aircraft use a generator or alternator to transform mechanical energy into electrical energy. Both devices produce electrical energy to power the aircraft's electrical loads and charge the aircraft's battery. Generators and alternators are mounted on the engine and driven by a v-belt or drive gear mechanism that is powered by the aircraft engine.

In general, alternators are lighter and more efficient than generators. Alternators are used for most modern, light, piston-driven aircraft. The next section provides more detail on electromagnetic induction.

Section 5

Electromagnetism and Electromagnetic Induction

In 1820 the Danish physicist, Hans Christian Oersted, discovered that a compass needle brought near a current-carrying conductor would deflect. When the current flow stopped, the compass needle returned to its original position. This important discovery demonstrated a relationship between electricity and magnetism that led to the electromagnet and to many of the inventions on which modern industry is based.

Theory

Oersted discovered that the magnetic field had no connection with the conductor in which the electrons were flowing, because the conductor was made of nonmagnetic copper. It was the electrons moving through the wire that created the magnetic field. Because a magnetic field accompanies a charged particle, the greater the current flow, the greater the magnetic field is. Figure 3-5-1 illustrates the magnetic field around a current-carrying wire. A series of concentric circles around the conductor represent the field, which if all the lines were shown would appear more as a continuous cylinder of such circles around the conductor.

As long as current flows in the conductor, the lines of force remain around it (Figure 3-5-2). If a small current flows through the conductor, a line of force extends out to circle A. If the current flow is increased, the line of force increases to circle B, and a further increase in current expands it to circle C. As the original line (circle) of force expands from circle A to B, a new line of force appears at circle A. As the current flow increases, the number of circles of force increases, expanding the outer circles farther from the surface of the current-carrying conductor.

If the current flow is a steady, nonvarying DC, the magnetic field remains the same size. When the current stops, the magnetic field collapses and the magnetism around the conductor disappears.

Figure 3-5-3 shows a method you can use to determine the direction of the lines of force when the direction of the current flow is known. If you grasp the conductor with your left hand with the thumb pointing in the direction of current flow, the fingers wrap around the conductor and are pointing in the

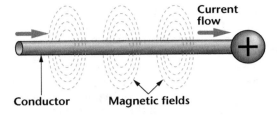

Figure 3-5-1. A magnetic field is formed around a conductor in which current is flowing.

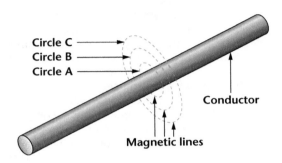

Figure 3-5-2. Expansion of magnetic field as current increases.

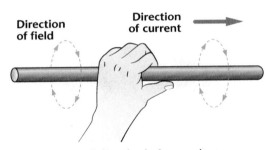

Figure 3-5-3. Left-hand rule for conductors.

same direction as the lines of the magnetic field. This is called the left-hand rule for conductors.

Although it has been stated that the lines of force have direction, this should not be construed to mean that the lines move in a circular direction around the conductor. Although the lines of force tend to act in a clockwise or counterclockwise direction, they are not revolving around the conductor.

In a coil made from loops of a conductor, many of the lines of force are dissipated between the loops of the coil. By placing a soft iron bar inside the coil, the lines of force are concentrated in the center of the coil. This combination of an iron core in a coil of wire loops, or turns, is called an electromagnet because the poles (ends) of the coil have the characteristics of a bar magnet.

Adding the soft iron core does two things for the current-carrying coil. First, the magnetic flux is increased. Second, the flux lines are more highly concentrated.

When DC flows through the coil, the core becomes magnetized with the same polarity (location of north and south poles) as the coil would have without the core. If the current is reversed, the polarity is also reversed.

The polarity of the electromagnet is determined by the left-hand rule just as the polarity of the coil without the core was determined. If you grasp the coil with your left hand so that the fingers curve around the coil in the direction of electron flow (minus to plus), the thumb points in the direction of the north pole (Figure 3-5-4).

Electromagnets are used in electrical instruments, motors, generators, relays, and other devices. Some electromagnetic devices operate on the principle that an iron core held away from the center of a coil is rapidly pulled into a center position when the coil is energized. This principle is used in the solenoid, also called solenoid switch or relay, in which the iron core is spring-loaded off center and moves to complete a circuit when the coil is energized.

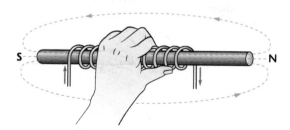

Figure 3-5-4. Left-hand rule applied to a coil.

Simple Generator

After the discovery that an electric current flowing through a conductor creates a magnetic field around the conductor, there was considerable scientific speculation about whether a magnetic field could create a current flow in a conductor. In 1831 Michael Faraday discovered that this could be done.

To show how an electric current is created by a magnetic field, we will use Figure 3-5-5. Several turns of a conductor are wrapped around a cylinder, and the ends of the conductor are connected to form a complete circuit that includes a galvanometer. A galvanometer is an instrument used for detecting small amounts of electrical current. If a simple bar magnet is plunged into the cylinder, the galvanometer deflects in one direction from its zero (center) position (Figure 3-5-5 view A).

When the magnet is at rest in the cylinder, the galvanometer shows a reading of zero, indicating that no current is flowing (Figure 3-5-5 view B).

In Figure 3-5-5 view C, the galvanometer indicates a current flow in the opposite direction when the magnet is pulled from the cylinder.

We obtain the same results by holding the magnet stationary and moving the cylinder over the magnet, indicating that current flows whenever there is relative motion between the wire coil and the magnetic field. Using the idea of a rotating loop of wire and a fixed magnet, we can construct a simple generator.

An electrical generator is a machine that converts mechanical energy into electrical energy by electromagnetic induction. Figure 3-5-6

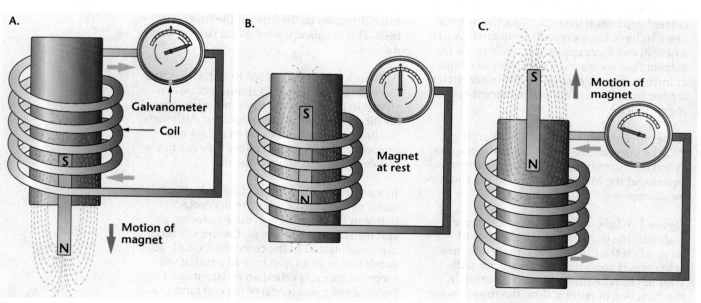

Figure 3-5-5. Inducing a current flow.

Position 1

Rotating conductors moving parallel to magnetic field, cutting minimum lines of force. Any electrical current generated is transferred to the slip rings C_1 and C_2 and registers as movement on the galvanometer.

Position 2
One-quarter turn completed

Conductors cutting directly across the magnetic field as conductor A passes across the north magnetic pole and B passes across the south pole.

Position 3
One-half turn completed

Conductors again moving parallel to magnetic field cutting minimum lines of force.

Position 4
Three-quarter turn completed

Conductors again moving directly across magnetic field A passes across south magnetic pole and B across north magnetic pole.

Position 5
Full turn completed

Conductor A has made one complete cycle and is in same position as position 1. The generator has generated one complete cycle of alternating voltage or current.

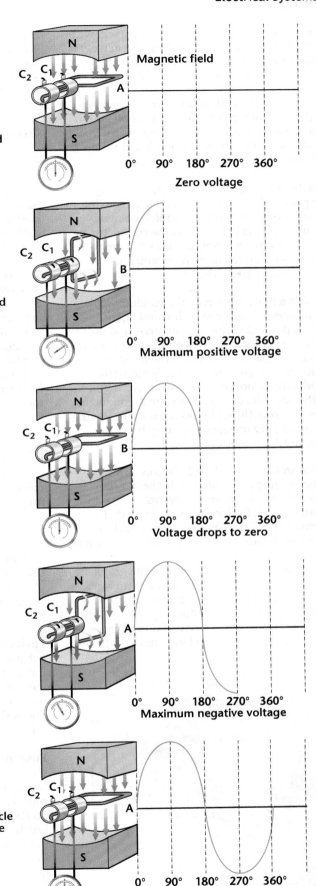

Figure 3-5-6. Generating a sine wave.

illustrates generating an electrical current with a simple loop conductor rotating in a magnetic field. As it rotates counterclockwise, varying values of voltages are induced in it.

Position 1. The conductor A moves parallel to the lines of force. Because it cuts no lines of force, the induced voltage is zero. As the conductor advances from position 1 to position 2, the voltage induced gradually increases.

Position 2. The conductor is now moving perpendicular to the flux and cuts a maximum number of lines of force; therefore, a maximum voltage is induced. As the conductor moves beyond position 2, it cuts a decreasing amount of flux at each instant, and the induced voltage decreases.

Position 3. At this point, the conductor has made one-half of a revolution and again moves parallel to the lines of force, and no voltage is induced in the conductor. As the A conductor passes position 3, the direction of induced voltage now reverses because the A conductor is moving downward, cutting flux in the opposite direction. As the A conductor moves across the south pole, the induced voltage gradually increases in a negative direction, until it reaches position 4.

Position 4. Like position 2, the conductor is again moving perpendicular to the flux and generates a maximum negative voltage. From position 4 to 5, the induced voltage gradually decreases until the voltage is zero, and the conductor and wave are ready to start another cycle.

Position 5. The curve shown on the graph at position 5 is called a sine wave. It represents the polarity and the magnitude of the instantaneous values of the voltages generated. The horizontal base line is divided into degrees, or time, and the vertical distance above or below

the base line represents the value of voltage at each point in the rotation of the loop. This is the basic waveform for AC. The output of this simple generator is AC. If we want to generate DC output, we must modify the design.

Simple DC Generator

By replacing the slip rings of the basic AC generator we saw earlier with two half cylinders (segments), called a commutator, we make a basic DC generator (Figure 3-5-7). In this illustration, the black side of the coil is connected to the black segment and the white side of the coil to the white segment.

The commutator segments are insulated from each other. The two stationary brushes are placed on opposite sides of the commutator and are mounted so that each brush contacts each segment of the commutator as the latter revolves simultaneously with the loop. The rotating parts of a DC generator (coil and commutator) are called an armature. Generating an emf by the loop rotating in the magnetic field is the same for both AC and DC generators, but the action of the commutator produces a DC voltage.

Figure 3-5-8 illustrates in an elementary, step-by-step manner, how a DC voltage is generated. This is done by showing a single-wire coil rotating through a series of positions in a magnetic field.

Position A. The coil starts in position A and is rotating clockwise. However, no lines of flux are cut by the coil sides, which means that no emf is generated. The black segment of the commutator is coming into contact with the black brush, and the white segment is just coming into contact with the white brush.

Position B. In position B, the flux is now being cut at a maximum rate, which means that the induced emf is maximum. Here the black segment is contacting the black brush, and the white segment is contacting the white brush. The deflection of the meter is to the right, indicating the polarity of the output voltage.

Position C. At position C, the coil has completed 180° of rotation. Like position A, no flux lines are being cut and the output voltage is zero. The important condition to observe at position C is the action of the segments and brushes. Here the black brush is contacted by both black and white segments on one side of the commutator, and the white brush is contacted by both segments on the other side of the commutator. After the coil rotates slightly past the 180° point, the white segment is contacting only the black brush, and the black segment is contacting only the white brush.

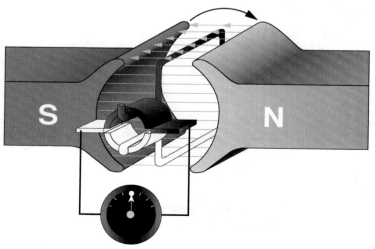

Figure 3-5-7. Basic DC generator.

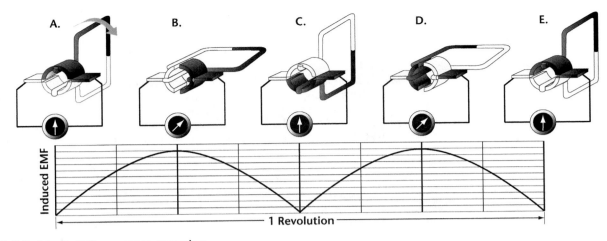

Figure 3-5-8. A basic DC generator operating.

Because of this switching of commutator elements, the black brush is always contacted by the coil segment moving downward, and the white brush is always contacted by the coil segment moving upward. Though the current reverses its direction in the coil in exactly the same way as in the AC generator, the commutator action causes the current to flow always in the same direction through the external circuit or meter.

Position D. At position D, commutator action reverses the current in the external circuit, and the second half cycle has the same waveform as the first half cycle. The process of commutation is sometimes called rectification, because rectification is the converting of AC voltage to DC voltage.

The Neutral Plane. At the instant that two segments on the commutator are contacting each brush (positions A, C, and E), a direct short circuit is produced. If an emf were generated in the coil at this time, a high current would flow in the circuit, causing an arc and damaging the commutator. For this reason, the brushes must be placed in the exact position where the short occurs when the generated emf is zero. This position is called the neutral plane. If the brushes are installed properly, no sparking occurs between the brushes and the commutator. Sparking is an indication of improper brush placement, which is the main cause of improper commutation.

The voltage generated by the basic DC generator in Figure 3-5-8 varies from zero to its maximum value twice for each revolution of the loop. This variation of DC voltage is called *ripple*, and can be reduced by using more coils. As the number of coils is increased, the variation between maximum and minimum values of voltage is reduced, and the output voltage of the generator approaches a steady DC value.

This type of DC generator has been used on aircraft for many years. The size and internal wiring configurations can vary somewhat and result in units designed for light-duty 12-volt systems to heavy-duty 24-volt systems used on larger aircraft. However, newer designs in alternators with built-in diode-type rectifiers have become the first choice for most light aircraft manufacturers and have largely replaced the DC generators.

Alternator

A generator that produces alternating current is referred to as an AC generator or *alternator*. This book treats the two terms synonymously and uses alternator to distinguish between AC and DC generators.

The major difference between an alternator (Figure 3-5-9) and a DC generator is how it is

Figure 3-5-9. A belt-driven alternator for small aircraft.

connected to the external circuit. The alternator is connected to the external circuit by slip rings; the DC generator is connected by a commutator.

Another method of classification is by the number of phases of output voltage. Alternators can be single phase, two phase, three phase, or even six phase and more. In aircraft electrical systems, the three-phase alternator is by far the most common.

A three-phase, or polyphase, circuit is used in most aircraft alternators instead of a single- or two-phase alternator. The three-phase alternator has three single-phase windings spaced so that the voltage induced in each coil (winding) is 120° out of phase with the voltages in the other two windings.

A schematic diagram of a three-phase alternator showing all the coils becomes complex and difficult to see what is actually happening. Figure 3-5-10 shows a simplified schematic diagram illustrating each of three phases. The rotor is omitted for simplicity. The waveforms of voltage are shown to the right of the schematic. The three voltages are 120° apart and are similar to the voltages that would be

generated by three single-phase alternators whose voltages are out of phase by angles of 120°. The three phases are independent of each other.

Many light aircraft use a type of alternator that has a diode rectifier built in to convert the AC output to DC. These can be called alternator-rectifier units, or simply alternators. These units in small aircraft are essentially the same as those used in automobiles.

Voltage Regulator

Electrical equipment in an aircraft operates efficiently only if the generator supplies constant voltage. Among the factors that determine the voltage output of a DC generator, only one, the strength of the magnetic field, is conveniently controlled. The magnetic field in the generator is created by an electrical current passing through wire wrapped around a laminated steel core. This is known as the field circuit, or simply the field. To illustrate this control, refer to Figure 3-5-11, showing a simple generator with a rheostat in the field circuit. A rheostat is a device that can be used to control current flow, by increasing or decreasing voltage. If the rheostat is set to increase the resistance in the field circuit, less current flows through the field winding and the strength of the magnetic field in which the armature rotates decreases. Consequently, the generator's voltage output decreases. If the resistance in the field circuit is decreased with the rheostat, more current flows through the field windings, the magnetic field becomes stronger, and the generator produces greater voltage.

Many light aircraft use a three-unit regulator for the generator system (Figure 3-5-12). This type of regulator includes a current limiter and a reverse current cutout in addition to a voltage regulator. The second of the three units is a current regulator to limit the generator's output current. The third unit is a reverse current cutout that disconnects the battery from the generator. If the battery is not disconnected, it discharges through the generator armature when the generator voltage falls below that of the battery, thus driving the generator as a motor. This action is called *motoring* the generator and, unless it is prevented, it discharges the battery in a short time.

A three-unit regulator's operation is described next, with the help of Figure 3-5-13.

The action of vibrating contact C1 in the voltage regulator unit causes an intermittent short circuit between points R1 and L2. When the

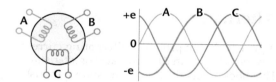

Figure 3-5-10. Simplified schematic of a three-phase alternator with output waveforms.

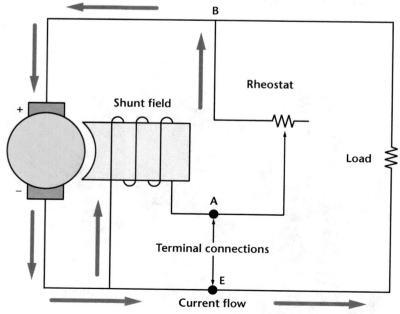

Figure 3-5-11. Regulating DC generator voltage by field rheostat.

generator is not operating, spring S1 holds C1 closed; C2 is also closed by S2. The shunt field is connected directly across the armature.

When the generator is started, its terminal voltage rises as the generator comes up to speed, and the armature supplies the field with current through closed contacts C2 and C1.

As the terminal voltage rises, the current flow through L1 increases and the iron core becomes more strongly magnetized. At a certain speed and voltage, when the magnetic attraction on the movable arm becomes strong enough to overcome the tension of spring S1, contact points C1 are separated. The field current now flows through R1 and L2. Because resistance is added to the field circuit, the field is momentarily weakened and the rise in terminal voltage is checked. Also, because the L2 winding is opposed to the L1 winding, the magnetic pull of L1 against S1 is partially neutralized, and spring S1 closes contact C1. Therefore, R1 and L2 are again shorted out of the circuit, and the field current again increases; the output voltage increases, and C1 is opened because of the action of L1. The cycle is rapid and occurs many times per second. The terminal voltage of the generator varies slightly, but rapidly, above and below an average value determined by the tension of spring S1, which can be adjusted.

The vibrator-type current limiter is made to limit the output current of the generator automatically to its maximum rated value to protect the generator. As shown in Figure 3-5-13, L3 is in series with the main line and load. Thus, the amount of current flowing in the line determines when C2 is opened and R2 placed in series with the generator field. By contrast, the voltage regulator is actuated by line voltage, whereas the current limiter is actuated by line current. Spring S2 holds contact C2 closed until the current through the main line and L3 exceeds a certain value, as determined by the tension of spring S2, and causes C2 to be opened. The increase in current is due to an increase in load. This action inserts R2 into the field circuit of the generator and decreases the field current and the generated voltage. When the generated voltage is decreased, the generator current is reduced. The core of L3 is partly demagnetized and the spring closes the contact points. This causes the generator voltage and current to rise until the current reaches a value sufficient to start the cycle again. A certain minimum value of load current is necessary to cause the current limiter to vibrate.

The reverse current cutout relay is used to automatically disconnect the battery from the generator when the generator voltage is less than the battery voltage. If this device were not used

Figure 3-5-12. A three-unit regulator.

in the generator circuit, the battery would discharge through the generator. This would tend to make the generator operate as a motor, but because the generator is coupled to the engine, it could not rotate such a heavy load. Under this condition, the generator windings could be severely damaged by excessive current.

Two windings, L4 and L5, are on the soft iron core. The current winding, L4, consisting of a few turns of heavy wire, is in series with the line and carries the entire line current. The voltage winding, L5, consisting of many turns of fine wire, is shunted across the generator terminals.

When the generator is not operating, the contacts, C3, are held open by spring S3. As the generator voltage builds up, L5 magnetizes the iron core. When the current (from the generated voltage) produces sufficient magnetism in the iron core, contact C3 is closed, as shown. The battery then receives a charging current. The coil spring, S3, is so adjusted that the voltage

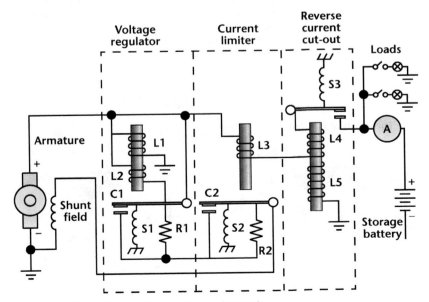

Figure 3-5-13. A three-unit regulator schematic.

Figure 3-5-14. A DC series starter motor.

winding does not close the contact points until the voltage of the generator exceeds the normal voltage of the battery. The charging current passing through L4 aids the current in L5 to hold the contacts tightly closed. Unlike C1 and C2, contact C3 does not vibrate. When the generator slows down or, for any other cause, the generator voltage decreases to a certain value below that of the battery, the current reverses through L4 and the ampere turns of L4 oppose those of L5. Thus, a momentary discharge current from the battery reduces the magnetism of the core and C3 opens, preventing the battery from discharging into the generator and motoring it. C3 does not close again until the generator terminal voltage exceeds that of the battery by a predetermined value.

The problem of voltage regulation in an AC system does not differ basically from that in a DC system. In each case, the regulator system's function is to control voltage, maintain a balance of circulating current throughout the system, and eliminate sudden changes in voltage (anti-hunting) when a load is applied to the system. Many aircraft alternator systems use a transistorized voltage regulator to control the alternator output.

Electric Motor

Most devices in an airplane, from the starter (Figure 3-5-14) to the automatic pilot, depend on mechanical energy furnished by DC motors. A DC motor is a rotating machine that transforms DC energy into mechanical energy. It consists of two principal parts—a field assembly and an armature assembly. The armature is the rotating part holding the current-carrying wires that a magnetic field acts on and drives.

If a coil in which current is flowing is placed in a magnetic field, a force is produced that causes the coil to rotate. In the coil shown in Figure 3-5-15, current flows inward on side A and outward on side B. The magnetic field about B is clockwise and the one about A, counterclockwise. A force develops that pushes side B downward.

At the same time, the field of the magnets and the field about A, in which the current is inward, adds at the bottom and subtracts at the top. Therefore, A moves upward. The coil rotates until its plane is perpendicular to the magnetic lines between the magnet's north and south poles.

The tendency of a force to produce rotation is called torque. When the steering wheel of a car is turned, torque is applied. The aircraft's engine gives torque to the propeller. Torque is also developed by the reacting magnetic fields about the current-carrying coil just described. This is the torque that turns the coil.

To determine the direction a current-carrying wire moves in a magnetic field, we can use the right-hand motor rule. As illustrated in Figure 3-5-16, if the index finger of the right hand is pointed in the direction of the magnetic field and the second finger in the direction of current flow, the thumb indicates the direction the current-carrying wire moves.

The amount of torque developed in a coil depends on several factors: the strength of the magnetic field, the number of turns in the coil, and the position of the coil in the field. Magnets are made of special steel that produces a strong field. Because torque is acting on each turn, the more turns on the coil, the greater the torque. In a coil carrying a steady current in a uniform magnetic field, the torque varies at successive positions of rotation. When the plane of the coil is parallel to the lines of force, the torque is zero. When its plane cuts the lines of force at right angles, the torque is 100 percent. At intermediate positions, the torque ranges between 0 and 100 percent.

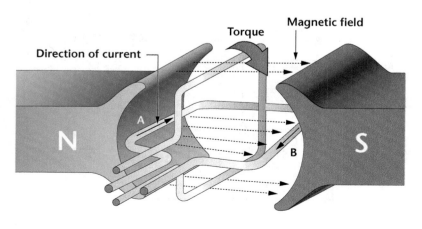

Figure 3-5-15. Developing torque.

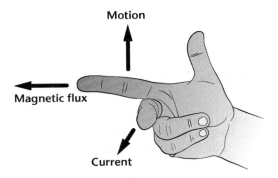

Figure 3-5-16. The right-hand motor rule.

A coil of wire through which the current flows rotates when placed in a magnetic field. This is the technical basis governing the construction of a DC motor (Figure 3-5-17). However, if the connecting wires from the battery were permanently fastened to the terminals of the coil and there was a flow of current, the coil would rotate only until it lined itself up with the magnetic field. Then, it would stop, because the torque at that point would be zero.

A motor, of course, must continue rotating. It is therefore necessary to design a device that reverses the current in the coil just at the time the coil becomes parallel to the lines of force. This creates torque again and causes the coil to rotate. If the current-reversing device is set up to reverse the current each time the coil is about to stop, the coil can be made to continue rotating.

One method of doing this is to connect the circuit so that as the coil rotates, each contact slides off the terminal to which it connects and slides onto the terminal of opposite polarity. In other words, the coil contacts switch terminals continuously as the coil rotates, preserving the torque and keeping the coil rotating.

In Figure 3-5-17, the coil terminal segments are labeled A and B. As the coil rotates, the segments slide onto and past the fixed terminals or brushes. With this arrangement, the direction of current in the side of the coil next to the north-seeking pole flows toward the reader, and the force acting on that side of the coil turns it downward. The part of the motor that changes the current from one wire to another is called the commutator.

Position A. When the coil is as shown in Figure 3-5-17 position A, current flows from the negative terminal of the battery to the negative (–) brush, to commutator segment B, through the coil to commutator segment A, to the positive (+) brush, and then back to the positive terminal of the battery. By using the right-hand motor rule, we see that the coil

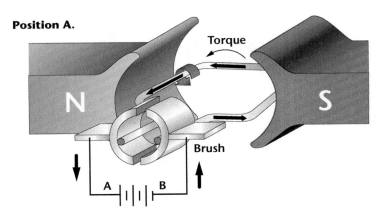

Position A.

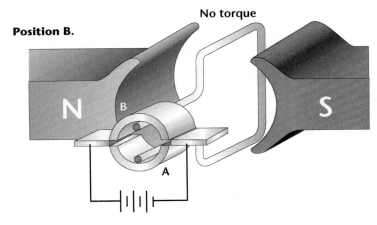

Position B.

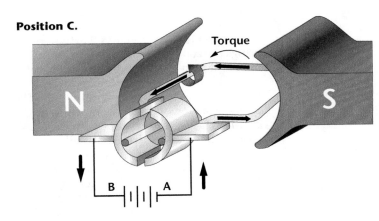

Position C.

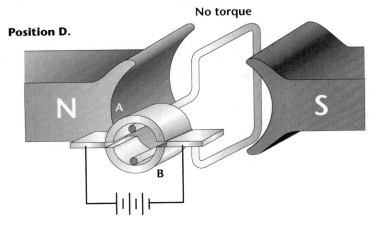

Position D.

Figure 3-5-17. Basic DC motor operation.

rotates counterclockwise. The torque at this position of the coil is maximum, because the greatest number of lines of force is being cut by the coil.

Position B. When the coil has rotated 90° as shown in Figure 3-5-17 position B, the commutator segments A and B no longer make contact with the battery circuit and no current can flow through the coil. At this position, the torque has reached a minimum value, because a minimum number of lines of force are being cut. However, the coil's momentum carries it beyond this position until the segments again make contact with the brushes, and current again enters the coil; this time, though, it enters through segment A and leaves through segment B. However, since the positions of segments A and B have also been reversed, the effect of the current is as before, the torque acts in the same direction, and the coil continues its counterclockwise rotation.

Position C. On passing through the field as shown in position C, the torque again reaches maximum.

Position D. Continued rotation carries the coil again to a position of minimum torque as in position D, the brushes no longer carry current, but again the momentum rotates the coil to the point where current enters through segment B and leaves through A. Further rotation brings the coil to the starting point and, thus, one revolution is completed. The coil terminals' switching from the positive to the negative brushes occurs twice per revolution. The torque in a motor with only one coil is neither continuous nor very effective because it has two positions where there is actually no torque at all. To overcome this, a practical DC motor contains many coils wound on the armature. These coils are spaced so that, for any position of the armature, coils exist near the poles of the magnet. This makes the torque both continuous and strong. The commutator, likewise, contains many segments instead of only two.

The armature in a practical motor is not placed between the poles of a permanent magnet but between those of an electromagnet, because a much stronger magnetic field can be furnished. The core is usually made of a mild or annealed steel, which can be magnetized strongly by induction. The current magnetizing the electromagnet is from the same source that supplies the current to the armature.

Three three basic types of DC motors are made: series motors, shunt motors, and compound motors. They differ largely in the method in which their field and armature coils are connected.

Series DC Motor

In the series motor, the field windings, consisting of a relatively few turns of heavy wire, are connected in series with the armature winding. A series DC motor's diagrammatic and schematic illustrations are shown in Figure 3-5-18. The same current flowing through the field winding also flows through the armature winding. Any increase in current, therefore, strengthens the magnetism of both the field and the armature.

Because of the low resistance in the windings, the series motor can draw a large current in starting. This starting current, in passing through both the field and armature windings, produces a high starting torque, which is the series motor's principal advantage.

The speed of a series motor varies according to the load on it. Any change in load is accompanied by a substantial change in speed. A series motor runs at high speed when it has a light load and at low speed with a heavy load. If the load is removed

Diagrammatic

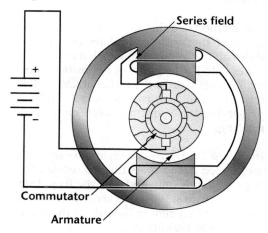

Schematic

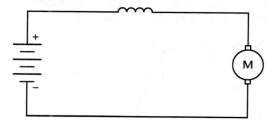

Figure 3-5-18. A series DC motor.

entirely, the motor can run so fast that the armature falls apart. If high starting torque is needed under heavy load conditions, series motors have many applications.

Series motors are often used in aircraft as engine starters and for raising and lowering landing gear, cowl flaps, and wing flaps.

Shunt DC Motor

In the shunt motor, the field winding is connected in parallel, or in shunt, with the armature winding (Figure 3-5-19). The resistance in the field winding is high. Because the field winding is connected directly across the power supply, the current through the field is constant. The field current does not vary with motor speed as in the series motor and, therefore, the torque of the shunt motor varies only with the current through the armature. The torque developed at starting is less than that developed by a series motor of equal size.

The shunt motor's speed varies very little with changes in load. When all load is removed, it assumes a speed slightly higher than the loaded speed. This motor is especially suitable for use where constant speed is desired and when high starting torque is not needed.

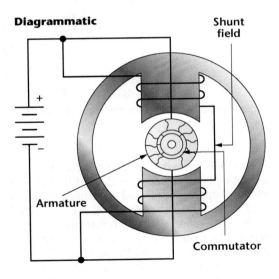

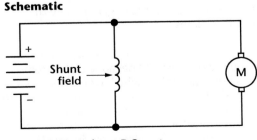

Figure 3-5-19. A shunt DC motor.

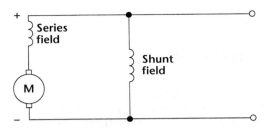

Figure 3-5-20. A compound DC motor schematic.

Compound DC Motor

The compound DC motor is a combination of the series and shunt motors. The motor has two windings in the field: a shunt winding and a series winding (Figure 3-5-20). The shunt winding is composed of many turns of fine wire and is connected in parallel with the armature winding. The series winding consists of a few turns of large wire and is connected in series with the armature winding. The starting torque is higher than in the shunt motor but lower than in the series motor. Variation of speed with load is less than in a series-wound motor but greater than in a shunt motor. The compound motor is used wherever the combined characteristics of the series and shunt motors are desired.

Electric motors are used to operate under various conditions. Some operate intermittently; others operate continuously. Motors built for intermittent duty can be operated for short periods only and then must be allowed to cool before being operated again. If such a motor is operated for long periods under full load, it becomes overheated. Motors built for continuous duty can be operated at rated power for long periods.

By reversing the direction of current flow in either the armature or the field windings, the direction of a motor's rotation can be reversed. This reverses the magnetism of either the armature or the magnetic field in which the armature rotates. If the wires connecting the motor to an external source are interchanged, the direction of rotation is not reversed because changing these wires reverses the magnetism of both field and armature and leaves the torque in the same direction as before.

One way of reversing the direction of rotation is to have two field windings wound in opposite directions on the same pole. This type of motor is called a split field motor.

Another way of reversing direction, called the switch method, uses a double-pole, double-throw switch that changes the direction of current flow in either the armature or the field.

Section 6

Batteries

One of the most popular ways to create a source of electrical energy is using a battery. This method produces electrical current using a chemical reaction. Many battery technologies are used today, and we will explore a few of the most common. Batteries can be classified as either a primary cell or a secondary cell, and then further identified by the chemistry involved.

Primary Cells

The dry cell is the most common type of primary-cell battery. This type of a battery is basically designed with a metal electrode or graphite rod acting as the cathode (+ or positive) terminal, immersed in an electrolytic paste. This electrode/electrolytic paste is then encased in a metal container, usually made of zinc, which itself acts as the anode (– or negative) terminal. When the battery is in a discharge condition, an electrochemical reaction takes place resulting in one of the metals being consumed. Because of this consumption, the charging process is not reversible. Attempting to reverse the chemical reaction in a primary cell by way of recharging is usually dangerous and can lead to a battery explosion.

Dry cell batteries (Figure 3-6-1) are commonly used to power items such as flashlights. The most common primary cells today are found in alkaline batteries, silver-oxide, and lithium batteries. The earlier carbon-zinc cells have been joined by zinc-chloride cells which exhibit somewhat better performance.

Secondary Cells

A secondary-cell battery is any kind of electrolytic cell in which the electrochemical reaction that releases energy is reversible. Such batteries can be recharged. A lead-acid car battery is a secondary-cell battery (Figure 3-6-2). Other commonly used secondary-cell chemistry types are nickel-cadmium (Ni-Cad), nickel metal hydride (NiMH), lithium-ion (Li-ion), and lithium-ion polymer (Li-ion polymer).

Lead-Acid Batteries

Lead-acid batteries used in aircraft are like automobile batteries. The lead-acid battery is made up of a series of identical cells each containing sets of positive and negative plates.

Figure 3-6-1. Common types of primary cell batteries.

Figure 3-6-2. A secondary cell lead-acid battery for aircraft.

Figure 3-6-3 shows that each cell contains positive plates of lead dioxide (PbO_2), negative plates of spongy lead, and electrolyte (sulfuric acid and water). A practical cell is constructed with many more plates than just two to get the required current output. All positive plates are connected, as are all the negative plates. Because each positive plate is positioned between two negative plates, these batteries always have one more negative plate than positive plates.

Between the plates are porous separators that keep the positive and negative plates from touching each other, which would short out the cell. The separators have vertical ribs on the side facing the positive plate. This construction permits the electrolyte to circulate freely around the plates. It also provides a path for sediment to settle to the bottom of the cell.

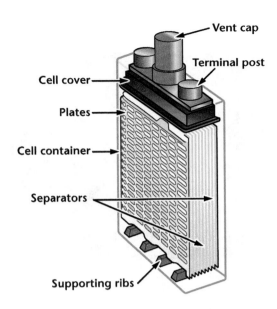

Figure 3-6-3. Lead-acid battery construction.

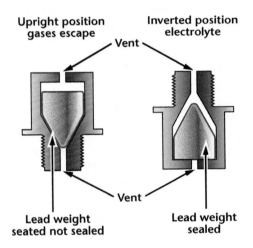

Figure 3-6-4. A nonspill battery vent plug.

Each cell is seated in a hard rubber casing. The top of the casing houses terminal posts and a hole in which a nonspill vent cap is screwed. The hole provides access for testing the strength of the electrolyte and adding water. The vent plug permits gases to escape from the cell with minimal electrolyte leakage, regardless of the position the airplane might assume (Figure 3-6-4). In level flight, the lead weight allows gas to vent through a small hole. In inverted flight, the lead weight covers this hole.

The individual cells of the battery are connected in series by means of cell straps. The complete assembly is enclosed in an acid-resisting metal container (battery box) that serves as electrical shielding and mechanical protection. The battery box has a removable top and a vent tube nipple at each end. When the battery is installed in an airplane, a vent tube is attached to each nipple. One tube is the intake tube and is exposed to the slipstream. The other is the exhaust vent tube and is attached to the battery drain sump, which is a glass jar containing a felt pad moistened with a concentrated solution of sodium bicarbonate (baking soda). With this arrangement, the airstream is directed through the battery case where battery gases are picked up, neutralized in the sump, and then expelled overboard without damage to the airplane.

The voltage of each lead acid cell is about 2 volts. These cells are connected to attain the voltage required for the application. Each cell is connected in series with heavy-gauge metal straps to form a battery. In a typical battery, such as that used in an aircraft for starting, the voltage required is 12 or 24 volts. This voltage is achieved by connecting 6 cells or 12 cells, respectively, together in series and enclosing them in one plastic box.

Each cell containing the plates is filled with an electrolyte made of sulfuric acid and distilled water with a specific gravity of 1.270 at 60°F. This solution contains positive hydrogen ions and negative sulfate (SO_4) ions that are free to combine with other ions and form a new chemical compound. When the cell is discharged, electrons leave the negative plate and flow to the positive plates where they cause the lead dioxide (PbO_2) to break down into negative oxygen ions and positive lead ions. The negative oxygen ions join with positive hydrogen ions from the sulfuric acid and form water (H_2O). The negative sulfate ions join with the lead ions in both plates and form lead sulfate ($PbSO_4$). After the discharge, the specific gravity changes to about 1.150.

Nickel-Cadmium Batteries

Active materials in Ni-Cad are nickel hydrate (NiOOH) in the charged positive plate and sponge cadmium (Cd) in the charged negative plate. The electrolyte is a potassium hydroxide (KOH) solution in a concentration of 20–34 percent by weight pure KOH in distilled water.

Sintered Ni-Cad cells have relatively thin, sintered nickel matrices forming a plate grid structure. The grid structure is highly porous and is impregnated with the active positive material (nickel-hydroxide) and the negative material (cadmium-hydroxide). The plates are then formed by sintering nickel powder to fine-mesh wire screen. In other variations of the process, the active material in the sintered matrix is converted chemically, or thermally, to an active state and then formed.

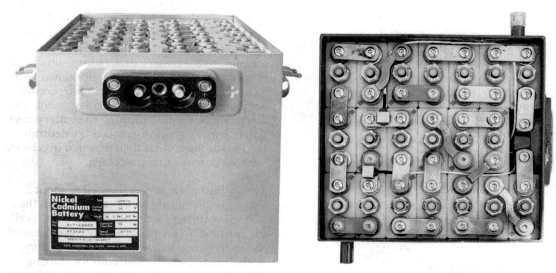

Figure 3-6-5. A Ni-Cad aircraft battery.

In general, these cycles of impregnation and formation involve many steps. Thin, sintered plate cells are ideally suited for very high rate charge and discharge service. Pocket plate Ni-Cad cells have the positive or negative active material, pressed into pockets of perforated nickel-plated steel plates or into tubes. The active material is trapped securely in contact with a metal current collector so active material shedding is largely eliminated. Plate designs vary in thickness depending on cycling service requirements.

The typical open-circuit cell voltage of a Ni-Cad battery is about 1.25 volts. Figure 3-6-5 shows a Ni-Cad aircraft battery. The Ni-Cad battery is usually interchangeable with the lead-acid type.

Sealed Lead Acid (SLA) Batteries

In many applications, sealed lead acid (SLA) batteries (Figure 3-6-6) are gaining in use over flooded lead acid and Ni-Cad batteries. One leading characteristic of Ni-Cad batteries is that they perform well in low voltage, full-discharge, high cycle applications. However, they do not perform as well in extended standby applications, such as auxiliary or as emergency battery packs used to power inertial reference units or stand-by equipment (attitude gyro).

Some SLA battery manufacturers have included in the battery packs a means to test the battery while it is still installed on the aircraft. Ni-Cad batteries must have a scheduled energy test performed on the bench because of the inability to measure their energy level on the aircraft and because of their notable *memory* shortcoming.

The SLA battery can be designed to alert personnel if a battery is failing. It might also be possible to test the failure detection circuits by activating a built-in test equipment (BITE) button. Such capability significantly reduces FAA paperwork and maintenance workload.

Lithium-Ion Batteries

Lithium-ion batteries are the primary type of battery for many types of consumer equipment, such as cell phones, battery-powered tools, and computers, but they are now also being used in commercial and military aircraft. The FAA has certified lithium-ion batteries to be used on aircraft, and one of the first aircraft to use them was the Boeing 787.

The three primary functional components of a lithium-ion battery are the positive and negative electrodes and electrolyte. Generally, the negative electrode of a conven-

Figure 3-6-6. A sealed lead acid (SLA) battery.

Figure 3-6-7. A lithium-ion battery.

tional lithium-ion cell is made from carbon. The positive electrode is a metal oxide, and the electrolyte is a lithium salt in an organic solvent. The electrochemical roles of the electrodes reverse between anode and cathode, depending on the direction of current flow through the cell.

Lithium-ion batteries can be dangerous under some conditions and can pose a safety hazard because they contain, unlike other rechargeable batteries, a flammable electrolyte and are kept pressurized. Under certain conditions, they can overheat and a fire can occur. The Boeing 787 aircraft uses two large 32 V, 8-cell, lithium-ion batteries (Figure 3-6-7). These batteries are much lighter and more powerful than Ni-Cad batteries used in similar-sized aircraft.

Battery Capacity

The most common battery rating is the amp-hour rating. This is a unit of measurement for battery capacity. It is determined by multiplying a current flow in amperes by the time in hours that the battery is being discharged.

A battery with a capacity of 1 amp-hour should be able to continuously supply a current of 1 amp to a load for exactly 1 hour, or 2 amps for 1/2 hour, or 1/3 amp for 3 hours, and so on, before becoming completely discharged. The amp-hour output of a battery depends on the rate at which it is discharged. Heavy discharge current heats the battery and decreases its efficiency and total amp-hour output.

For airplane batteries, 5 hours has been established as the discharge time in rating battery capacity. However, this time of 5 hours is only a basis for rating and does not necessarily mean how long the battery is expected to provide current. Under actual service conditions, the battery could be completely discharged in a few minutes, or it might never be discharged if the generator provides sufficient charge.

The battery's amp-hour capacity depends on its total effective plate area. Connecting batteries in parallel increases amp-hour capacity. Connecting batteries in series increases the total voltage but not the amp-hour capacity.

Section 7

Electrical Components

To help you better understand the information presented in aircraft manuals regarding electrical circuits, you should recognize the basic components of electrical circuits and the symbols used to represent them. The schematic is the most common place where you will find electrical components presented in symbol form. A schematic is a diagram that shows the interconnection and logic of an electrical circuit. This section briefly introduces some of the most common components, their functions, and the symbols used to represent them on a schematic.

Bus Bar

A bus bar is used as a terminal in the aircraft electrical system to connect the main electrical system to the equipment using electricity as a power source. This simplifies the wiring system and provides a common point from which voltage can be distributed throughout the system.

Multiple bus bars are typically used in an aircraft (Figure 3-7-1). For example, it is common to have a main bus bar that provides power to lights, flaps, starter, pitot heat, and other equipment. Additional bus bars are used to supply electrical power to the avionics equipment and other systems.

Switches

Switches control the current in most aircraft electrical circuits. A switch is used to start, to stop, or to change the direction of the current in the circuit. The switch in each circuit must be able to carry the normal current of the circuit and must be insulated heavily enough for the voltage of the circuit.

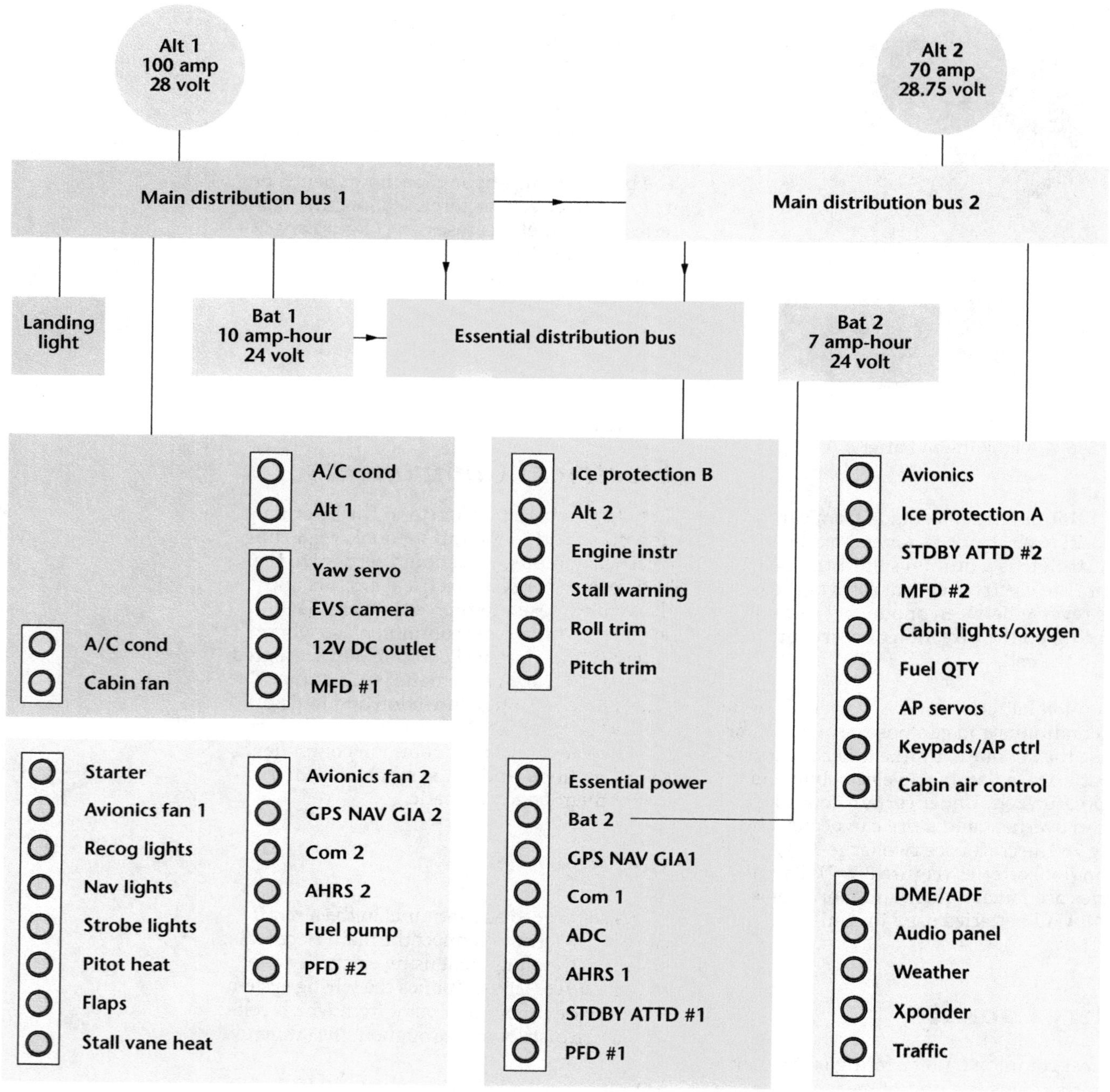

```
                  ( Alt 1          )                                    ( Alt 2          )
                  ( 100 amp        )                                    ( 70 amp         )
                  ( 28 volt        )                                    ( 28.75 volt     )
```

Main distribution bus 1	→	Main distribution bus 2

```
[ Landing ]      [ Bat 1       ] → [ Essential distribution bus ]   [ Bat 2       ]
[ light   ]      [ 10 amp-hour ]                                    [ 7 amp-hour  ]
                 [ 24 volt     ]                                    [ 24 volt     ]
```

○ A/C cond	○ Ice protection B	○ Avionics	
○ Alt 1	○ Alt 2	○ Ice protection A	
	○ Engine instr	○ STDBY ATTD #2	
○ Yaw servo	○ Stall warning	○ MFD #2	
○ EVS camera	○ Roll trim	○ Cabin lights/oxygen	
○ 12V DC outlet	○ Pitch trim	○ Fuel QTY	
○ MFD #1		○ AP servos	
		○ Keypads/AP ctrl	
○ A/C cond		○ Cabin air control	
○ Cabin fan			

○ Starter	○ Avionics fan 2	○ Essential power	○ Avionics
○ Avionics fan 1	○ GPS NAV GIA 2	○ Bat 2	
○ Recog lights	○ Com 2	○ GPS NAV GIA1	
○ Nav lights	○ AHRS 2	○ Com 1	
○ Strobe lights	○ Fuel pump	○ ADC	
○ Pitot heat	○ PFD #2	○ AHRS 1	
○ Flaps		○ STDBY ATTD #1	○ DME/ADF
○ Stall vane heat		○ PFD #1	○ Audio panel
			○ Weather
			○ Xponder
			○ Traffic

Figure 3-7-1. A typical small-aircraft electrical system with primary and avionics bus bars.

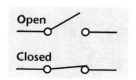

Figure 3-7-2. An example of a switch in the open and closed positions.

An understanding of some basic definitions of the switch is necessary before discussing any of the switch types. The number of poles, throws, and positions they have designates toggle switches and other types of switches.

Pole. The pole is the switch's movable blade or contactor. The number of poles is equal to the number of circuits, or paths for current flow, that can be completed through the switch at any one time.

Throw. The throw indicates the number of circuits, or paths for current, that it is possible to complete through the switch with each pole or contactor.

Position. The positions indicate the number of places at which the operating device (toggle, plunger, and so forth) comes to rest and at the same time open or close one or more circuits (Figure 3-7-2). When the switch is open, no current flows. Closing the switch completes the circuit.

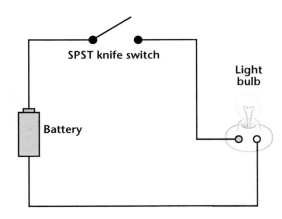

Figure 3-7-3. A switch in the open position, and the light is off.

Figure 3-7-3 shows a switch in a simple circuit. This switch is shown in the open position. With the switch in this position, the light is off. Moving the switch to the closed position turns on the light.

Throws and Poles

Single-Pole, Single-Throw (SPST). The SPST switch opens and closes a single circuit and allows a connection between two contacts. One of two conditions exist. The circuit is open in one position or closed in the other position.

Single-Pole, Double-Throw (SPDT). The SPDT switch routes circuit current to either of two paths. With this switch, contact between one contact can be made between one contact and the other.

Double-Pole, Single-Throw (DPST). The DPST switch turns two circuits on and off with one lever. The DPST connection can be made between one set of contacts and either of two other sets of contacts.

Double-Pole, Double-Throw (DPDT). The DPDT switch activates two separate circuits at the same time. It makes a connection from one set of contacts to either of two other sets of contacts.

Schematic symbols for these four types of switches are shown in Figure 3-7-4.

Toggle Switches

A toggle switch is an on/off switch that uses a toggle joint with a spring to open or close an electric circuit using an attached lever that is pushed through a small arc (Figure 3-7-5). A toggle switch that is spring-loaded to the OFF position and must be held in

the ON position to complete the circuit is a momentary contact two-position switch. One that comes to rest at either of two positions—opening the circuit in one position and closing it in another—is a two-position switch. A toggle switch that comes to rest at any one of three positions is a three-position switch.

Locking toggles require the operator to pull out on the toggle switch before moving it to another position. Once in the new position, the switch toggle is released back into a lock, which then prevents the switch from inadvertently being moved.

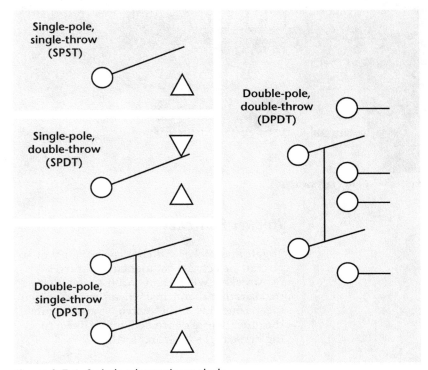

Figure 3-7-4. Switch schematic symbols.

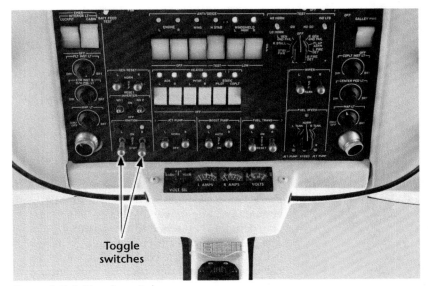

Figure 3-7-5. Toggle switches.

Figure 3-7-6. Rocker switches.

Rocker Switches

Toggle and rocker switches control most of an aircraft's electrical components (Figure 3-7-6). A rocker switch is an on/off switch that rocks (rather than trips) when pressed, which means one side of the switch is raised while the other side is depressed, much like a rocking horse rocks back and forth.

Spring-Loaded Switches

Spring-loaded switches are available in two types: normally open (NO) and normally closed (NC). A switch that stays open, except when it is held in the closed position, is an NO switch. One that stays closed, except when it is held in the open position is an NC switch. Both types are spring loaded to their normal position and return to that position as soon as they are released.

Pushbutton Switches

Pushbutton switches have one stationary contact and one movable contact. The movable contact is attached to the pushbutton. The pushbutton is either an insulator itself or is insulated from the contact. This switch is spring loaded and designed for momentary contact.

Microswitches

A microswitch opens or closes a circuit with a very small movement of the tripping device (1/16 in. or less). This is what gives the switch its name because micro means small. Microswitches are usually pushbutton switches. They are used primarily as limit switches to provide automatic control of landing gears, actuator motors, and the like.

Rotary Selector Switches

A rotary selector switch takes the place of several switches. When the knob of the switch is rotated, the switch opens one circuit and closes another. Ignition switches and voltmeter selector switches are typical examples of this kind of switch (Figure 3-7-7).

Fuses

Fuses are used to protect the circuit from over current conditions (Figure 3-7-8). The fuse is installed in the circuit so that all the current in the circuit passes through it. In most fuses, the strip of metal is made of an alloy of tin and bismuth that melts and opens the circuit when the current exceeds the rated capacity of the fuse. For example, if a 5-amp fuse is placed into a circuit, the fuse allows currents up to 5 amps to pass. Because the fuse is intended to protect the circuit, it is quite important that its capacity match the needs of the circuit in which it is used.

When replacing a fuse, consult the manufacturer's instructions to be sure to install a fuse of the correct type and capacity. Two types of fuses are installed in aircraft. *Plug-in holders* or in-line holders are used for small and low-capacity fuses. *Clip* type holders are used for heavy, high-capacity fuses and current limiters.

Circuit Breakers

The circuit breaker is commonly used in place of a fuse and is designed to break the circuit and stop the current flow when the current exceeds a predetermined value. Unlike the fuse, the circuit breaker can be reset; whereas the fuse or current limiter must be replaced (Figure 3-7-9).

Several types of circuit breakers are used in aircraft systems. One is a magnetic type. Where excessive current flows in the circuit, it makes an electromagnet strong enough to move a small armature that trips the breaker. Another type is the thermal overload switch or breaker. This consists of a bimetallic strip that, when it becomes overheated from excessive current, bends away from a catch on the switch lever and permits the switch to trip open.

Most circuit breakers must be reset by hand. If the overload condition still exists, the circuit breaker trips again to prevent damage to the circuit. At this point, you should not continue resetting the circuit breaker; instead, initiate troubleshooting to determine the cause. Resetting a circuit breaker repeatedly can lead to circuit or component damage or, worse, possibly starting a fire or causing an explosion. Automatic reset type circuit breakers are not allowed in aircraft. Circuit breakers are typically grouped on a circuit breaker panel that is accessible to the flight crew.

Load

The term *load* is a very generic and universal description for anything present in the circuit that consumes power. This could be as simple as a resistor or light bulb or could be describing a complex component operating with the circuit. A load could be represented by a simple box appearing on the schematic and labeled as such.

Resistors

A resistor in a circuit is primarily used to limit the amount of current flow. Several methods are used in constructing and sizing a resistor that control properties such as resistance value, the precision of the resistance value, and the ability to dissipate heat. In some applications, the resistive element is used to generate heat, such as in propeller anti-ice boots, but heat typically is the unwanted loss of energy.

Many types of resistors are designed to do a specific job. We will examine a few of the most common types. Resistors can be made with a fixed or a variable ohmic value (Figure 3-7-10).

Carbon Composition Resistors

The carbon composition resistor is probably the most common type of fixed resistance unit used in electrical circuits. It is made from a mixture of finely grouped carbon/graphite, an insulation material for filler, and a substance for binding the material together. The amount of graphite in relation to the insulation material determines the ohmic or resistive value of the resistor. This mixture is compressed into a rod that is fitted with axial leads or *pigtails*. The finished product is sealed in an insulating coating for isolation and physical protection.

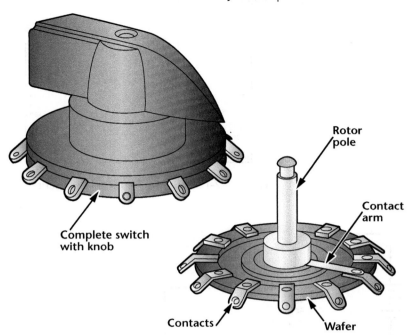

Figure 3-7-7. A rotary selector switch

Wire-Wound Resistors

Wire-wound resistors typically control large amounts of current and have high power ratings. Resistors of this type are constructed by winding a resistance wire around an insulating rod usually made of porcelain. The windings are coated with an insulation material for physical protection and to conduct heat. Both ends of the windings are connected to terminals that are used to connect the resistor to a circuit (Figure 3-7-11).

A wire-wound resistor with tap is a special type of fixed resistor that can be adjusted. These adjustments can be made by moving a slide bar tap or by moving the tap to a preset incremental position. Although the tap might be adjustable, the adjustments are usually set at the time of installation to a specific value and then operated in service as a fixed resistor.

Variable Resistors

Variable resistors are made so that the resistive value can be changed easily. This adjustment can be manual or automatic, and the adjustments can be made while the system to

Figure 3-7-8. The schematic symbol for a fuse.

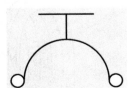

Figure 3-7-9. The schematic symbol for a circuit breaker.

Figure 3-7-10. Symbol for a fixed resistor.

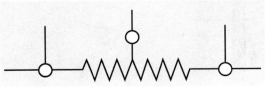

Figure 3-7-11. Schematic of a wire-wound resistor.

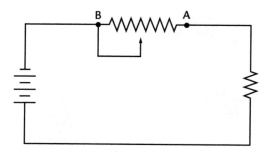

Figure 3-7-12. A rheostat connected in series.

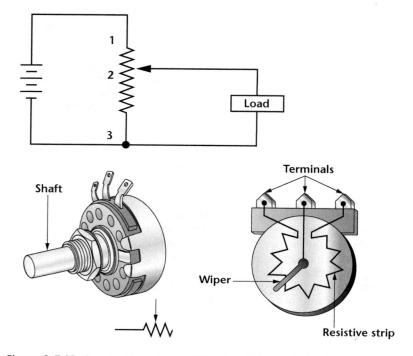

Figure 3-7-13. A potentiometer and its schematic symbol.

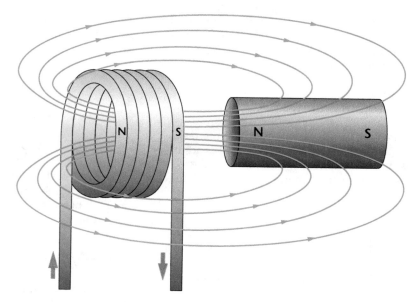

Figure 3-7-14. A solenoid with an iron core.

which it is connected is operating. Two basic types of manual adjustors are used: the rheostat and the potentiometer.

Rheostat. A rheostat is a variable resistor used to vary the amount of current flowing in a circuit. Figure 3-7-12 shows a rheostat connected in series with an ordinary resistor in a series circuit. As the slider arm moves from point A to B, the amount of rheostat resistance (AB) is increased. Because the rheostat resistance and the fixed resistance are in series, the total resistance in the circuit also increases, and the current in the circuit decreases. On the other hand, if the slider arm is moved toward point A, the total resistance decreases and the current in the circuit increases.

Potentiometer. The potentiometer is considered a three-terminal device. Figure 3-7-13 shows a potentiometer in a circuit diagram (top) and two illustrations and its schematic symbol (bottom). As illustrated, terminals 1 and 2 have the entire value of the potentiometer resistance between them. Terminal 3 is the wiper or moving contact. Through this wiper, the resistance between terminals 1 and 3 or terminals 2 and 3 can be varied. While the rheostat is used to vary the current in a circuit, the potentiometer is used to vary the voltage in a circuit. A typical use for this component is in the volume controls on an audio panel and input devices for flight data recorders, among many other applications.

The current flowing through the circuit of Figure 3-7-13 leaves the negative terminal electron flow of the battery and divides one part flowing through the lower portion of the potentiometer (points 3 to 2) and the other part through the load. Both parts combine at point 2 and flow through the upper portion of the potentiometer (points 2 to 1) back to the positive terminal of the battery.

Solenoid

A solenoid is a type of electromagnet whose purpose is to generate a controlled magnetic field. Some electromagnetic devices operate on the principle that an iron core held away from the center of a coil is rapidly pulled into a center position when the coil is energized. This principle is used in the solenoid, also called solenoid switch or relay, in which the iron core is spring-loaded off center and moves to complete a circuit when the coil is energized (Figure 3-7-14).

A soft iron bar is attracted to either pole of a permanent magnet and, likewise, is attracted by a current-carrying coil. The lines of force extend through the soft iron, magnetizing it by induction and pulling the iron bar toward the coil. If the bar is free to move, it is drawn into the coil to a position near the center where the field is strongest.

Relay

A relay is simply an electromechanical switch where a small amount of current can control a large amount of current (Figure 3-7-15). When a voltage is applied to the coil of the relay, the electromagnet is energized with the current. When energized, an electromagnetic field pulls the common (C) or arm of the relay down. When the arm or common is pulled down, the circuit between the arm and the normally closed (NC) contacts is opened, and the circuit between the arm and the normally open (NO) contacts is closed. When the energizing voltage is removed, the spring returns the arm contacts back to the NC contacts. The relay usually has two connections for the coil. The (+) side is designated as X_1, and the ground side of the coil is designated as X_2.

Transformers

A transformer changes electrical energy of a voltage into electrical energy at a different voltage level. It consists of two coils that are not electrically connected but are arranged so that the magnetic field surrounding one coil cuts through the other coil. When an alternating voltage is applied to (across) one coil, the varying magnetic field set up around that coil creates an alternating voltage in the other coil by mutual induction. A transformer can also be used with pulsating DC, but a pure DC voltage cannot be used because only a varying voltage creates the varying magnetic field that is the basis of the mutual induction process.

A transformer consists of three basic parts (Figure 3-7-16). These are an iron core, which provides a circuit of low reluctance for magnetic lines of force; a primary winding, which receives the electrical energy from the source of applied voltage; and a secondary winding, which receives electrical energy by induction from the primary coil. The primary and secondary of this closed core transformer are wound on a closed core to obtain maximum inductive effect between the two coils.

Transformers are used for stepping up or stepping down voltages in a circuit. In a voltage transformer, the primary coils are connected in parallel across the supply voltage. Many types of voltage transformers are made. Most of these are either step-up or step-down trans-

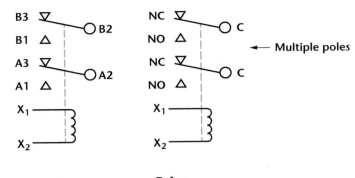

Schematic Symbol for a Relay

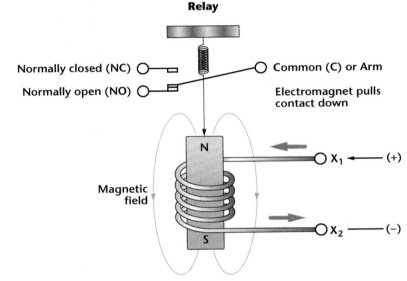

Figure 3-7-15. A basic relay.

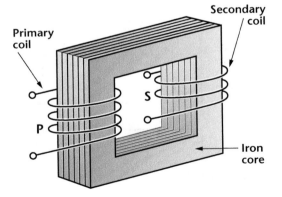

Figure 3-7-16. An iron-core transformer.

formers. The factor that determines whether a transformer is a step-up or step-down type is the *turns* ratio. The turns ratio is the ratio of the number of turns in the primary winding to the number of turns in the secondary winding. For example, the turns ratio of the step-down transformer is 5 to 1 because it has five times as many turns in the primary as in the

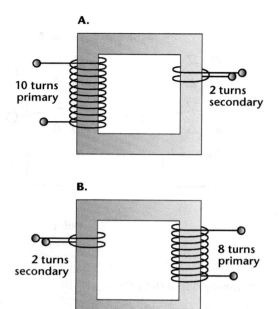

Figure 3-7-17. A step-down (A) and step-up (B) transformer.

secondary (Figure 3-7-17 view A). The step-up transformer has a 1 to 4 turns ratio (Figure 3-7-17 view B).

The ratio of the transformer input voltage to the output voltage is the same as the turns ratio if the transformer is 100 percent efficient. Thus, when 10 volts are applied to the primary winding of the step-down transformer, two volts are induced in the secondary winding (view A). If 10 volts are applied to the primary winding of the step-up transformer, the output voltage across the terminals of the secondary is 40 volts (view B).

Rectifiers

A rectifier is a device that transforms AC into DC by limiting or regulating the direction of current flow. The principal types of rectifiers are dry disk and solid state. Solid-state, or semiconductor, rectifiers have replaced virtually all other types, and because dry disk and motor generators are largely limited to older model aircraft, the major part of the study of rectifiers is devoted to solid-state devices used for rectification.

Rectification can be applied to either one or both halves of the sine wave produced by AC. A half-wave rectifier simply clips off half of the AC input and leaves only half of the waveform. This is known as pulsating DC.

Full-wave rectification inverts half of the wave form and results in an output signal that is much closer to pure DC. It still has some variation in peak value, but it is much closer to DC than the pulsating output of a half wave rectifier. The three wave forms are shown in Figure 3-7-18.

Inverters

An inverter is used in some aircraft systems to convert a portion of the aircraft's DC power

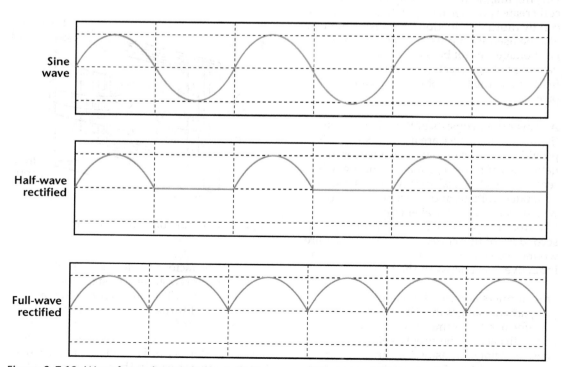

Figure 3-7-18. Wave forms for AC, half- and full-wave rectified current.

to AC. The AC is used mainly for instruments, radio, radar, lighting, and other accessories. These inverters are usually built to supply current at a frequency of 400 hertz, but some are designed to provide more than one voltage; for example, 26-volt AC in one winding and 115 volts in another.

Two basic types of inverters are made: the rotary and the static. Either type can be single phase or multiphase. The multiphase inverter is lighter for the same power rating than the single phase, but distributing multiphase power and keeping the loads balanced introduces complications.

In many applications where continuous DC voltage must be converted to alternating voltage, static inverters are used in place of rotary inverters or motor generator sets. The rapid progress made by the semiconductor industry is extending the range of applications of such equipment into voltage and power ranges that would have been impractical a few years ago. Such applications include power supplies for frequency sensitive military and commercial AC equipment, aircraft emergency AC systems, and converting wide frequency range power to precise frequency power (Figure 3-7-19).

Capacitor

In an electrical circuit, a capacitor serves as a reservoir or storehouse for electricity. In its most basic form, the capacitor is made of two parallel plates separated by a nonconductor called a dielectric. As described below, an electrical charge can be held on those plates.

When a capacitor is connected across a DC source, such as a storage battery in the circuit shown in Figure 3-7-20 view A, and the switch is then closed, the plate marked B becomes positively charged and plate A is negatively charged. Current flows in the external circuit when the electrons are moving from B to A.

The current flow in the circuit is at a maximum the instant the switch is closed, but it then continually decreases until it reaches zero. The current becomes zero as soon as the difference in voltage of A and B becomes the same as the voltage of the battery. If the switch is opened as shown in Figure 3-7-20 view B, the plates remain charged. Once the capacitor is shorted, it discharges quickly as shown Figure 3-7-20 view C.

It should be clear that when the capacitor is being charged or discharged, current exists in the circuit, even though the circuit is broken by the gap between the capacitor plates. Current is present only during the time of charge and discharge, and this time is usually short.

Figure 3-7-19. A static inverter.

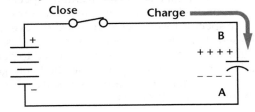

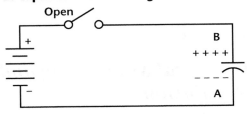

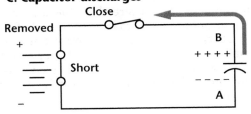
Figure 3-7-20. Capacitors in DC.

Diode

One type of semiconductor material by itself is not very useful. Useful applications are developed only when one component contains both P-type and N-type semiconductor materials.

The semiconductor diode is also known as a PN junction diode. This is a two-element semiconductor device that uses the rectifying properties of a PN junction to convert AC into DC by permitting current flow in one direction only.

When an external voltage is applied to a PN junction, it is called bias. In a forward biased PN junction or diode, the negative voltage source is connected to the N material and the positive voltage source is connected to the P material. In this configuration, the current can easily flow. When the battery is turned around, the diode is said to be reverse biased and current does not flow.

To summarize, the important thing to remember is that these PN junction diodes offer very little resistance to current when the diode is forward biased. Maximum resistance happens when the diode is reverse biased.

Diodes are a common component found in many electrical circuits today. Many specialty types of diodes are also available that produce specific results when forward or reverse biased. This includes photosensitive diodes, light emitting diodes, diodes designed to permit current to pass only at a specified voltage, and many more. These are best discussed individually as they come up in circuits.

Section 8

Electrical Monitoring and Regulation

Whether you are operating an aircraft on the ground to make certain that it is ready for flight or you are already in the air, it is important to be able to have some sort of feedback that all systems are operating normally. Depending on the aircraft size and the sophistication of the systems installed, several indicators could help you verify proper operation.

Ammeter. An ammeter is used to monitor the performance of the aircraft electrical system. The ammeter shows if the alternator/generator is producing an adequate supply of electrical power. It also indicates whether the battery is receiving an electrical charge.

Ammeters are designed with the zero point in the center of the face and a negative or positive indication on either side (Figure 3-8-1). When the pointer of the ammeter is on the plus side, it shows the charging rate of the battery. A minus indication means more current is being drawn from the battery than is being replaced. A full-scale minus deflection indicates the alternator/generator is malfunctioning. A full-scale positive deflection indicates the regulator is malfunctioning. In

either case, consult the aircraft flight manual (AFM) or pilot operating handbook (POH) for appropriate action to be taken.

Not all aircraft are equipped with an ammeter. Some have a warning light that, when lighted, indicates a discharge in the system as a generator/alternator malfunction. For the appropriate action to be taken, see the AFM/POH.

To test an ammeter, turn the alternator off. It should discharge. Then turn it back on, and it should charge (until it has replenished what you used; it will not take long).

Loadmeter. Another electrical monitoring indicator is a loadmeter. This type of gauge has a scale beginning with zero and shows the load being placed on the alternator/generator (Figure 3-8-1). The loadmeter reflects the total percentage of the load placed on the generating capacity of the electrical system by the electrical accessories and battery. When all electrical components are turned off, it reflects only the amount of charging current demanded by the battery.

To test a loadmeter, do something power intensive like lower the flaps (if electric) and you should see the needle go up.

Voltage regulator. The voltage regulator controls the rate of charge to the battery by stabilizing the generator or alternator electrical output. The generator/alternator voltage output should be higher than the battery voltage. For example, a 12-volt battery would be fed by a generator/alternator system of about 14 volts. The difference in voltage keeps the battery charged.

Ammeter

Loadmeter

Figure 3-8-1. An ammeter and a loadmeter.

Section 9
Problems

An electrical system can fail in many ways, and to cover all the possibilities is beyond the scope of this book. However, some common faults are encountered in the aircraft.

Often overlooked because it is *too obvious*, the best starting place in locating electrical problems is with the power source. Is the battery installed? Connected? Charged? Is the master switch on? Are all circuit breakers in the on position? Have you checked all fuses installed (if the aircraft still has fuses)? You would be surprised at how often one of these items is the source of an electrical failure.

When discussing basic circuits problems, you should understand the following definitions:

- Short circuit—an unintentional low resistance path between two components in a circuit or between a component/conductor and ground. It usually creates high current flow that burns out or causes damage to the circuit conductor or components.

- Open circuit—a circuit that is not a complete or continuous path. An open circuit represents an infinitely large resistance. Switches are common devices used to open and close a circuit. Sometimes a circuit opens because of a component failure, such as a light bulb or a burned-out resistor.

- Continuity—the state of being continuous, uninterrupted or connected together.

- Discontinuity—the opposite of continuity, indicating that a circuit is broken or not continuous.

One of the most common modes of failure is the *open* circuit. A component, such as a resistor, can overheat because of the power rating being exceeded. The circuit shown in Figure 3-9-1 is designed to cause current to flow through a lamp, but because of the open resistor, the lamp will not light.

An open fault can cause a component or system not to work. A shorting fault (Figure 3-9-2) can be more of a severe nature than the open type of fault. A short circuit, or *short*, causes the opposite effect. A short across a series circuit produces a greater than normal current flow. Faults of this type can develop slowly when a wire bundle is not properly secured and the wire insulation is damaged.

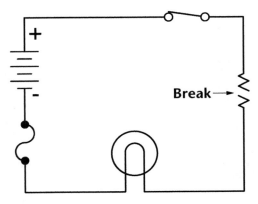

Figure 3-9-1. Example of an open circuit; the circuit is broken, and the lamp cannot light

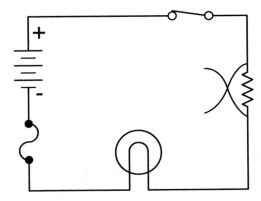

Figure 3-9-2. A shorted resistor.

Section 10
Putting it All Together

The ability to read simple schematics is probably the best test of your electrical system knowledge.

Schematic diagrams do not indicate the location of the individual components in the aircraft, nor do they show the actual size and shape of the components. Instead, they show the component's locations with respect to each other in the system. Schematics show the principles of operating an aircraft system and are often used for troubleshooting and training.

A schematic is the most common place where you will find electronic symbols. Schematics shows the interconnection and logic of an electronic or electrical circuit. Many symbols are used in schematic drawings, blueprints, and illustrations (Figure 3-10-1). Throughout this chapter we have introduced some of the more common symbols; now we will take a second look at those and introduce others.

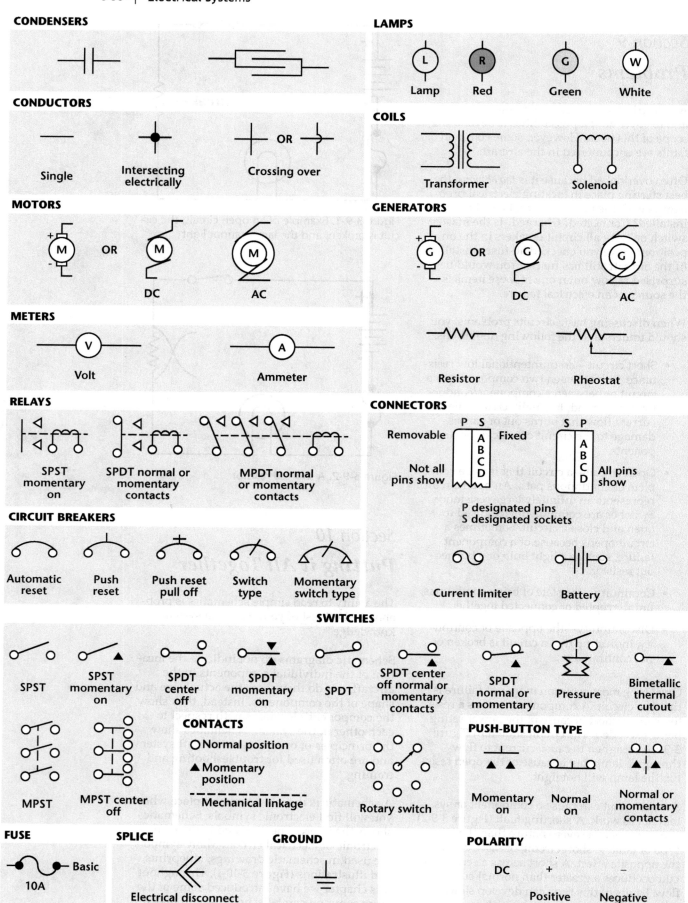

Figure 3-10-1. Electrical symbols.

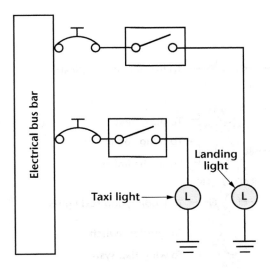

Figure 3-10-2. Example of a landing and taxi light circuit.

Figure 3-10-2 is an example of a landing and taxi light schematic. With the switches in the open position (as shown), the circuit is not completed because of the position of the switches. When either switch is closed, current flows from the bus bar, through the circuit breaker, through the light (illuminating the light), and back to the bus bar through the common ground.

Figure 3-10-3 is an example of a starter circuit. The main bus can get power either from the aircraft battery or an external power plug. With power to the main bus, turning the ignition switch to the start position (S) energizes the starter contactor (solenoid) and completes the circuit to the starter. When the ignition switch is released from the start position, the solenoid removes power from the starter motor.

> NOTE: Some aircraft have receptacles to which an external ground power unit (GPU) can be connected to provide electrical energy for starting. These are very useful, especially in cold-weather starting.

Many aircraft are equipped with a split master switch. An alternator switch is installed on the left side that permits the pilot to exclude the alternator from the electrical system if the alternator fails; the battery switch is on the right (Figure 3-10-4). With the alternator half of the switch OFF, the entire electrical load is placed on the battery. All nonessential electrical equipment should be turned off to conserve battery power.

Figure 3-10-5 shows an example of a small-aircraft electrical system.

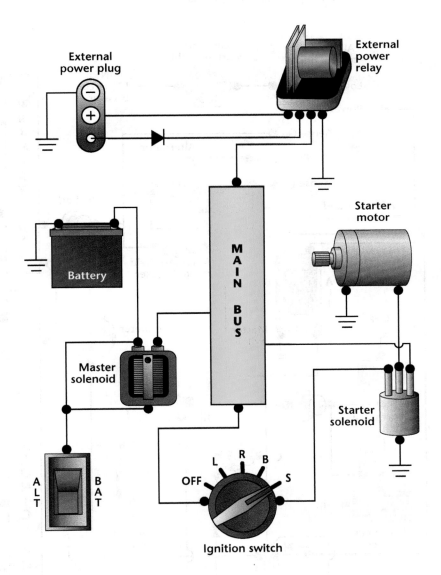

Figure 3-10-3. A typical starting circuit.

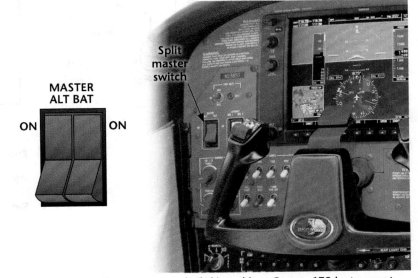

Figure 3-10-4. A split master switch (left) and in a Cessna 172 instrument panel (right)

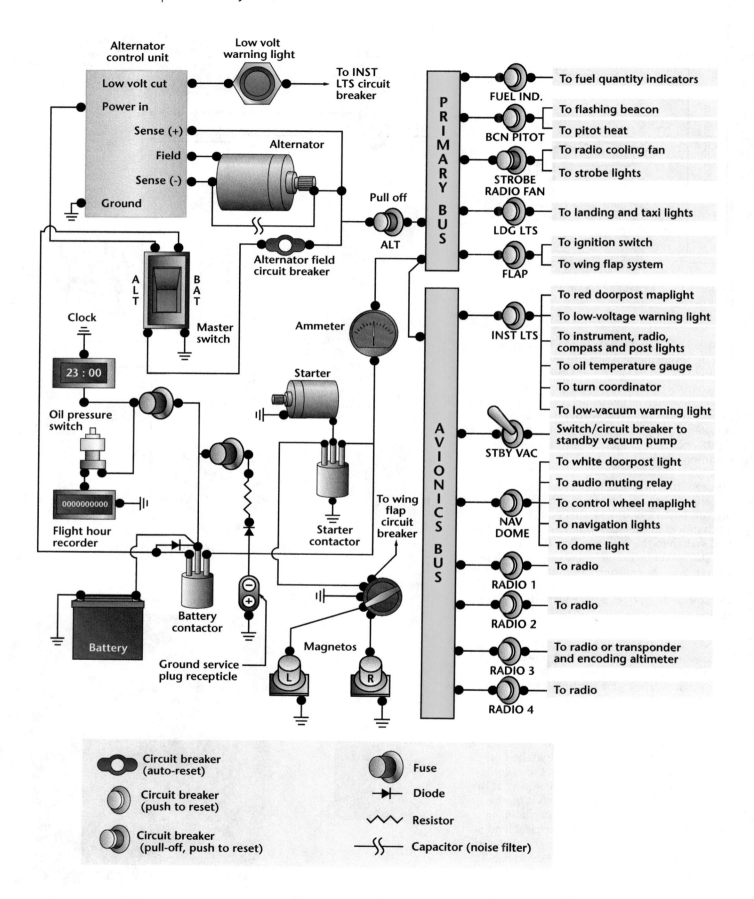

Figure 3-10-5. Example of a small-aircraft electrical system.

Figure 3-11-1. A Boeing 737 taking off.

Section 11

Large Aircraft Electrical Power Supply

Large, transport category aircraft use AC and DC power, just like small aircraft. Some of the equipment and components used to generate and manage the power are larger and specialized, however. The next sections provide an overview of how AC and DC power are generated and distributed in some Boeing aircraft models (Figure 3-11-1).

AC Electrical Power

Some Boeing aircraft electrical power systems consist of 28-volt DC, 28-volt AC, and 115-volt AC systems. Three isolated generators that supply 115/200-volt, three-phase, 400-Hz power are primary sources of power for the main AC buses and the entire electrical system. Each engine drives a generator and the auxiliary power unit (a small turbine engine in the aircraft's tail cone) drives the third generator. For ground operations, 115/200-volt, three-phase, 400-Hz external power can be connected to the aircraft. (Figure 3-11-2). Figure 3-11-3 shows the basic electrical distribution.

Figure 3-11-2. An external power port on a Boeing 737.

Transformers that reduce a 115-volt AC input down to 28-volt AC provide power to the 28-volt AC buses. Emergency power is obtained from a static inverter that converts 28-volt DC battery power to 115-volt AC power. Emergency power supplies critical flight loads on the AC standby bus when the primary power sources have either failed or shut down. The static inverter is on an electrical equipment shelf in the electronic compartment, or as it is also known, the E&E bay.

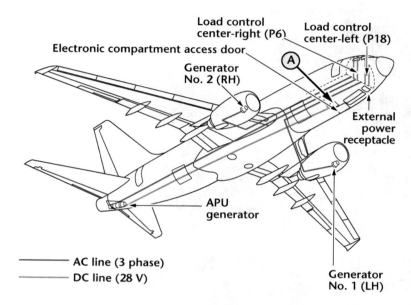

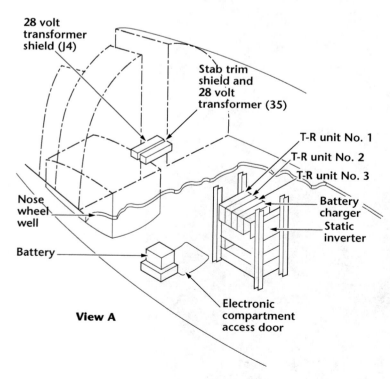

Figure 3-11-3. The basic power generation and conversion system for a Boeing 737.

DC Electrical Power

In some Boeing aircraft, three transformer-rectifier (T-R) units provide 28-volt DC power by converting 115-volt AC power to 28-volt DC power. T-R units are on electrical equipment shelves. A 36-amp hour Ni-Cad battery provides 28-volt DC power to start the auxiliary power unit. The battery provides power to loads connected to the battery bus when other power sources are de-energized. It is in the electronic compartment near the electrical equipment shelves.

Each engine-driven generator is driven by a constant-speed drive to obtain a generator speed of 6,000 r.p.m. The constant-speed drive is a mechanical, differential, hydraulically controlled unit attached to the engine accessory gearbox. The engine supplies torque to the input shaft at various engine speeds. This torque is transmitted to the input end of the planetary differential gear unit in the drive. Depending on the difference between the output speed and 6,000 r.p.m., the variable displacement hydraulic unit boosts or retards the speed of the planetary differential output gear to maintain an output speed of 6,000 r.p.m. as required by the governor.

Section 12

Static Buildup

The aircraft surface can become highly charged with static electricity while in flight. Measures are required to eliminate unwanted electrical charges from building up and radiating.

Bonding. One of the most important measures taken to eliminate unwanted electrical charges that can damage or interfere with avionics equipment is bonding. Charges flowing in paths of variable resistance produce electrical disturbances (noise) in avionics. Such charges are the result of intermittent contact from vibration or a control surface's movement. Bonding provides the necessary electric connection between metallic parts of an aircraft to prevent variable resistance in the airframe. It provides a low-resistance ground return that minimizes interference from static electricity charges.

All metal parts of the aircraft should be bonded to prevent electrical potential from building up. Bonding also provides the low-resistance return path for single-wire electrical systems. Bonding jumpers and clamps are examples of bonding connectors. Jumpers should be as short as possible. Be sure finishes are removed in the contact area of a bonding device so that metal-to-metal contact is made. Resistance should not exceed 0.003 ohm. When a jumper is used only to reduce radio frequency noise and is not used for carrying current, a resistance of 0.01 ohm is satisfactory.

Static dischargers. Static dischargers, or wicks, are installed on aircraft to reduce radio receiver interference. This interference is caused by corona discharge emitted from the aircraft as a result of precipitation static. Corona occurs in short pulses that produce noise at the radio frequency spectrum. Static dischargers are normally mounted on the trailing edges of the control surfaces, wing tips, and the vertical stabilizer. They discharge precipitation static at points a critical distance away from avionics antennas where there is little or no coupling of the static to cause interference or noise.

Flexible and semiflexible dischargers are attached to the aircraft structure by metal screws, rivets, or epoxy. The connections should be checked periodically for security.

A resistance measurement from the mount to the airframe should not exceed 0.1 ohm. Inspect the condition of all static dischargers in accordance with manufacturer's instructions. Figure 3-12-1 shows examples of static dischargers.

Although lightning strikes to aircraft are rare, they do occur. When lightning strikes an aircraft, the electrical current must be conducted through the structure and allowed to discharge or dissipate at controlled locations. These controlled locations are primarily the aircraft's static discharge wicks or, on more sophisticated aircraft, null field dischargers.

When surges of high-voltage electricity pass through good electrical conductors, such as aluminum or steel, damage is likely to be minimal or nonexistent. When surges of high-voltage electricity pass through nonmetallic structures, such as a fiberglass radome, engine cowl or fairing, glass or plastic window, or a composite structure that does not have built-in electrical bonding, burning and more serious damage to the structure can occur.

Figure 3-12-1. Static dischargers or wicks dissipate built up static energy in flight at points a safe distance from avionics antennas to prevent radio frequency interference.

Hydraulic Systems

Section 1

Introduction

The word *hydraulics* is based on the ancient Greek word for water and originally meant the study of the physical behavior of water at rest and in motion. Today, the meaning has been expanded to include the physical behavior of all liquids, including hydraulic fluid used for aircraft hydraulic systems. Early aircraft had hydraulic brake systems. As aircraft became more sophisticated, additional systems using hydraulic power were developed.

Hydraulic systems in aircraft provide a means for operating aircraft components. Operating landing gear, flaps, flight control surfaces, and brakes is largely done with hydraulic power systems. Hydraulic system complexity varies from small aircraft that require fluid only for manually operating the wheel brakes to transport category aircraft where the systems are large and complex. To achieve the necessary redundancy and reliability, the system can consist of several subsystems. Each subsystem has a power generating device (pump) reservoir, accumulator, heat exchanger, filtering system, and so on. System operating pressure can vary from a couple hundred pounds per square inch (p.s.i.) in small aircraft and rotorcraft to 5,000 p.s.i. in large transport aircraft.

Hydraulic systems have many advantages as power sources for operating various aircraft units; they combine the advantages of light weight, easy installation, simplified inspection, and minimum maintenance requirements. Hydraulic operations are also almost 100 percent efficient, with only negligible loss from fluid friction.

Learning Objectives

IDENTIFY
• Types of hydraulic fluid

EXPLAIN
• Functions of hydraulic system components

DISCUSS
• Basic hydraulic principles
• Types of hydraulic systems

Left: Hydraulic systems efficiently operate the nose landing gear on this transport aircraft.

Section 2

Hydraulic Principles

A fluid is any substance that can flow if it is not in some way confined or restricted. Liquids and gases are both classified as fluids and often act in a very similar way. One significant difference comes into play when a force is applied to these fluids. Liquids tend to be incompressible and gases are highly compressible. Many of the principles on which aviation is based, such as the theory of lift on a wing and the force generated by a hydraulic system, can be explained and quantified by using the laws of fluid mechanics.

Fluid Properties

The pressure exerted on the bottom of a container by a liquid is determined by the height of the liquid and not by the shape of the container. This can be seen in Figure 4-2-1, where three different shapes and sizes of con-

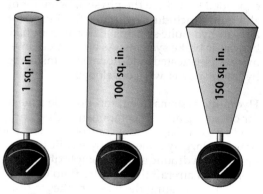

Each container is filled with colored water to a height of 231 in.

Each pressure gauge reads 8.34 p.s.i.

Figure 4-2-1. Fluid pressure is determined by column height.

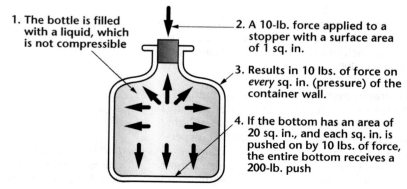

1. The bottle is filled with a liquid, which is not compressible

2. A 10-lb. force applied to a stopper with a surface area of 1 sq. in.

3. Results in 10 lbs. of force on *every* sq. in. (pressure) of the container wall.

4. If the bottom has an area of 20 sq. in., and each sq. in. is pushed on by 10 lbs. of force, the entire bottom receives a 200-lb. push

Figure 4-2-2. A demonstration of Pascal's law.

tainers are full of colored water. Even though they are different shapes and have different volumes of liquid, each one has a height of 231 inches (in.). Each one would exert a pressure on the bottom of 8.34 p.s.i. because of this height. The container on the left, with a surface area of 1 square in. (sq. in.), contains a volume of 231 cubic inches (cu. in.) or 1 gallon. One gallon of water weighs 8.34 pounds (lbs.), which is why the pressure on the bottom is 8.34 p.s.i.

Still thinking about Figure 4-2-1, if the pressure was measured half way down, it would be half of 8.34, or 4.17 p.s.i. In other words, the pressure is adjustable by varying the height of the column. Pressure determined by the column height of a fluid is known as static pressure. With liquids it is sometimes referred to as a head of pressure. For example, if a carburetor needs to have 2 p.s.i. supplied to its inlet, or head of pressure, this could be done by having the fuel tank positioned the appropriate number of inches higher than the carburetor.

Pascal's Law

The foundations of modern hydraulics and pneumatics were established in 1653 when Blaise Pascal discovered that if pressure is applied to a fluid inside a container, the pressure is exerted equally in all directions. This pressure acts at right angles to container surfaces. When the pressure in the fluid is caused solely by the fluid's height, the pressure against the walls of the container is equal at any given level, but it is not equal if the pressure at the bottom is compared to the pressure half way down. The concept of the pressure set up in a fluid, and how it relates to the force acting on the fluid and the surface area through which it acts, is Pascal's law. This is illustrated in Figure 4-2-2.

Pascal's law, when dealing with the variables of force, pressure, and area, is expressed with the following formula.

$$Force = Pressure \times Area$$

In this formula, the force is in units of pounds, the pressure is in p.s.i., and the area is in square inches. By transposing the original formula, we have two additional formulas:

$$Pressure = Force \div Area$$

and

$$Area = Force \div Pressure$$

An easy and convenient way to remember the formulas for Pascal's law, and the relation-

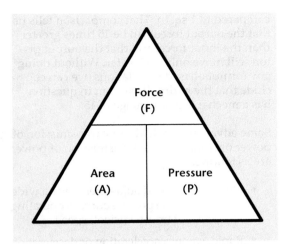

Figure 4-2-3. Force, area, pressure relationship.

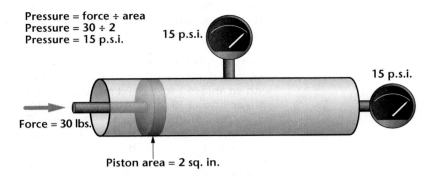

Figure 4-2-4. Pressure created in a hydraulic system.

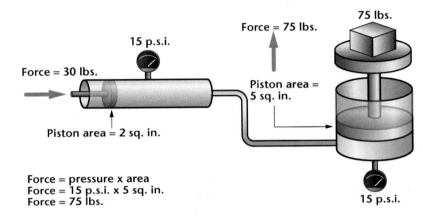

Figure 4-2-5. Output force created in a hydraulic system.

ship among the variables, is with the triangle shown in Figure 4-2-3. If the variable we want to solve for is covered up, the position of the remaining two variables shows the proper math relationship. For example, if the A, or area, is covered up, what remains is the F on the top and the P on the bottom, meaning force divided by pressure.

The simple hydraulic system in Figure 4-2-4 has 30 lbs. of force acting on a piston with a 2-sq.-in. surface area. Using Pascal's law, the pressure in the system is equal to the force applied divided by the area of the piston, or 15 p.s.i. As shown in Figure 4-2-4, the pressure of 15 p.s.i. is present everywhere in the fluid.

The hydraulic system shown in Figure 4-2-5 is a little more complex than the one shown in Figure 4-2-4. In Figure 4-2-5, the input force of 30 lbs. is acting on a 2-sq.-in. piston, creating a pressure of 15 p.s.i. The input cylinder and piston are connected to a second cylinder, which contains a 5-sq.-in. piston. The pressure of 15 p.s.i. created by the input piston pushes on the piston in the second cylinder, creating an output force of 75 lbs.

Often, the purpose of a hydraulic system is to generate a large output force with a small input force. In Figure 4-2-5, the input force is 30 lbs. and the output force is 75 lbs., or 2.5 times greater. The relationship between the output force and the input force, as discussed earlier in this chapter, is known as mechanical advantage. The mechanical advantage in Figure 4-2-5 would be 75 divided by 30, or 2.5. The following formulas can be used to calculate mechanical advantage:

Mechanical advantage = Force out ÷ Force in

or

Mechanical advantage = Distance out ÷ Distance in

No machine allows us to gain work; we get no more work out of a hydraulic system than we put in. Because work is equal to force times distance, if we gain force with a hydraulic system, we must lose distance. We only get the same work out, if the system is 100 percent efficient.

To think about the distance that the output piston moves in response to the input piston's movement, we must consider the volume of fluid displaced. In studying geometry, one learns that the volume of a cylinder is equal to the cylinder's surface area multiplied by its height. So, when a piston of 2 sq. in. moves down in a cylinder a distance of 10 in., it displaces a volume of fluid equal to 20 cu. in. (2 sq. in. × 10 in.). The 20 cu. in. displaced by the first piston is what moves over to the second cylinder and causes its piston to move. In a simple two-piston hydraulic system, the relationship between the piston area and the distance moved is shown by the following formula:

Input piston area × (Distance moved) = Output piston area × (Distance moved)

The formula shows that the volume in is equal to the volume out. This concept is shown in

Figure 4-2-6, where a small input piston moves a distance of 30 in., and the larger output piston moves a distance of only 2 in.

Example: A two-piston hydraulic system, like that shown in Figure 4-2-6, has an input piston with an area of 1 sq. in. and an output piston with an area of 15 sq. in. An input force of 50 lbs. is applied, and the input piston moves 30 in. What is the pressure in the system, how much force is generated by the output piston, how far would the output piston move, and what is the mechanical advantage?

Pressure = Force ÷ Area

= 50 ÷ 1

= 50 p.s.i.

Force = Pressure × Area

= 50 × 15

= 750 lbs.

Mechanical advantage = Force out ÷ Force in

= 750 ÷ 50

= 15

Input piston area (distance moved) = Output piston area (distance moved)

1 (30) = 15 (Distance moved)

1 (30) ÷ 15 = Distance moved

Distance moved = 2 in.

Part of understanding Pascal's law and hydraulics involves using formulas and recognizing the relationship between the individual variables. Before the numbers are plugged into the formulas, it is often possible to analyze the variables in the system and realize what is happening.

For example, look at the variables in Figure 4-2-6 and notice that the output piston is 15 times larger than the input piston, 15 sq. in.

compared to 1 sq. in. That comparison tells us that the output force will be 15 times greater than the input force, and that the output piston will move only 1/15 as far. Without doing any formula-based calculations, we can conclude that the hydraulic system in question has a mechanical advantage of 15.

Some advantages of hydraulic transmission of power over mechanical transmission of power are as follows:

- Quick, easy speed adjustment over a wide range while the power source is operating at a constant (most efficient) speed

- Rapid, smooth acceleration or deceleration

- Control over maximum torque and power

- Cushioning effect to reduce shock loads

- Smoother reversal of motion

Although the items above indicate the positive aspects of hydraulic power, that is not the whole story. Some disadvantages of hydraulic systems include the following:

- The weight of the fluid in the system. This must include the fluid in the reservoir, the fluid in all the lines (both to and from actuators), and the fluid in the actuators and accumulators.

- The likelihood of leaks developing over time.

- The negative effects of some hydraulic fluids, such as corrosion, on other components and structures.

Improvements in hydraulic system design, using self-contained units to supply local power, and other innovations indicate that the aviation industry will not be abandoning hydraulic systems in the near future.

Section 3

Hydraulic Fluid

If incompressibility and fluidity were the only qualities required, any liquid that is not too thick could be used in a hydraulic system. But a satisfactory liquid for an installation must have several other properties. Manufacturers of hydraulic devices usually specify the type of liquid best suited for use with their equipment in view of the working conditions, the service required, temperatures expected inside and outside the systems, pressures

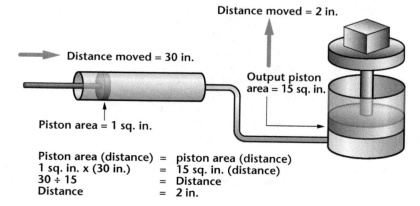

Distance moved = 2 in.

Distance moved = 30 in.

Output piston area = 15 sq. in.

Piston area = 1 sq. in.

Piston area (distance) = piston area (distance)
1 sq. in. x (30 in.) = 15 sq. in. (distance)
30 ÷ 15 = Distance
Distance = 2 in.

Figure 4-2-6. Piston movement in a hydraulic system.

the liquid must withstand, the possibilities of corrosion, and other conditions that must be considered. Some of the properties and characteristics that must be considered when selecting a satisfactory liquid for a system are discussed next.

One of the most important properties of any hydraulic fluid is its viscosity. Viscosity is internal resistance to flow. A liquid such as gasoline has a low viscosity and flows easily, whereas a liquid such as tar that has a high viscosity flows slowly. Viscosity increases as temperature decreases. A satisfactory liquid for a hydraulic system must be viscous enough to give a good seal at pumps, valves, and pistons, but it must not be so thick that it offers excess resistance to flow, leading to power loss and higher operating temperatures. These factors add to the load and to excessive wear of parts. A fluid that is too thin also leads to rapid wear of moving parts or of parts that have heavy loads.

Chemical stability is another property that is exceedingly important in selecting a hydraulic liquid. It is the liquid's ability to resist oxidation and deterioration for long periods. All liquids tend to undergo unfavorable chemical changes under severe operating conditions. This is the case, for example, when a system operates for a considerable time at high temperatures.

Liquids can break down if exposed to air, water, salt, or other impurities, especially if they are in constant motion or subject to heat. Some metals, such as zinc, lead, brass, and copper, have an undesirable chemical reaction on certain liquids. These chemical processes result in forming sludge, gums, and carbon or other deposits that clog openings, cause valves and pistons to stick or leak, and give poor lubrication to moving parts. As soon as small amounts of sludge or other deposits are formed, the rate of formation generally increases more rapidly. As they are formed, certain changes in the physical and chemical properties of the liquid take place. The liquid usually becomes darker, higher in viscosity, and acids are formed.

A high flash point is desirable for hydraulic liquids because it indicates good resistance to combustion. Flash point is the temperature at which a liquid gives off vapor in sufficient quantity to ignite momentarily or flash when a flame is applied.

Like flash point, a high fire point is required of desirable hydraulic liquids. Fire point is the temperature at which a substance gives off vapor in sufficient quantity to ignite and continue to burn when exposed to a spark or flame.

To ensure proper system operation and to avoid damage to nonmetallic components of the hydraulic system, the correct fluid must be used. When adding fluid to a system, use the type specified in the aircraft manufacturer's maintenance manual or on the instruction plate affixed to the reservoir or unit being serviced.

The three principal categories of hydraulic fluids are mineral, polyalphaolefin (synthetic), and phosphate ester (synthetic). When servicing a hydraulic system, the technician must be certain to use the correct category of replacement fluid. Hydraulic fluids are not necessarily compatible.

Mineral-Based Fluids

Mineral oil-based hydraulic fluid (MIL-H-5606) is the oldest, dating back to the 1940s. It is used in many systems, especially where the fire hazard is comparatively low. Mineral-based hydraulic fluid is processed from petroleum. This type of hydraulic fluid is commonly used for general aviation hydraulic systems and is dyed red (Figure 4-3-1).

Polyalphaolefin-Based Fluids

MIL-H-83282 is a fire-resistant hydrogenated polyalphaolefin based fluid developed in the 1960s to overcome the flammability characteristics of MIL-H-5606. MIL-H-83282 is significantly more flame resistant than MIL-H-5606, but a disadvantage is the high viscosity at low temperature. It is generally limited to –40°F. However, it can be used in the same system and with the same seals, gaskets, and hoses as MIL-H-5606. Small aircraft predominantly use MIL-H-5606, but some have been switched to MIL-H-83282 if they can accommodate the high viscosity at low temperature.

Figure 4-3-1. This common petroleum-based hydraulic fluid is red.

Phosphate Ester-Based Fluid (Skydrol®)

Phosphate ester-based fluids (Figure 4-3-2) are used in most commercial transport category aircraft and are extremely fire-resistant. However, they are not fireproof and under certain conditions, they burn. The earliest generation of these fluids was developed after World War II as a result of the growing number of aircraft hydraulic brake fires that drew the collective concern of the commercial aviation industry. Progressive development of these fluids occurred because of the performance requirements of newer aircraft designs.

The airframe manufacturers dubbed these new generations of hydraulic fluid as types based on their performance. Today, type IV and V fluids are used.

Intermixing Fluids

Because of the difference in composition, petroleum-based and phosphate ester-based fluids will not mix; neither are the seals for any one fluid usable with or tolerant of any of the other fluids.

Figure 4-3-2. Skydrol is purple for identification.

Section 4

Aircraft Pneumatic Systems

Some aircraft are equipped with a pneumatic system. Such systems operate a great deal like hydraulic systems, except they employ air instead of a liquid for transmitting power. Pneumatic systems are sometimes used for the following:

- Operating brakes
- Opening and closing doors
- Driving hydraulic pumps, alternators, starters, water injection pumps, and so on
- Operating emergency devices

Both pneumatic and hydraulic systems are similar units and use contained fluids. The word *contained* means trapped or completely enclosed. As mentioned earlier, *fluid* implies such liquids as water, oil, or anything that flows. Because both liquids and gases flow, they are considered as fluids; however, their characteristics are very different. Liquids are

practically incompressible; a quart of water still occupies about a quart of space regardless of how hard it is compressed. But gases are highly compressible; a quart of air can be compressed into a thimbleful of space. In spite of this difference, gases and liquids are both fluids and can be made to transmit power. The type of unit used to provide pressurized air for pneumatic systems is determined by the system's air pressure requirements.

Pneumatic systems are often compared to hydraulic systems, but such comparisons can hold true only in general terms. Pneumatic systems do not use reservoirs, hand pumps, accumulators, regulators, or engine-driven or electrically driven power pumps for building normal pressure. But many similarities do exist.

The scope of this text is limited to the study of hydraulic systems.

Section 5

Hydraulic System Components

Regardless of its function and design, every hydraulic system has a minimum number of basic components in addition to a means through which the fluid is moved through the system. A basic system consists of a pump, reservoir, check valve, pressure relief valve, pressure regulator, selector valve, actuator, and filter (Figure 4-5-1).

Reservoirs

The reservoir is a tank that stores a supply of fluid for the hydraulic system. Fluid flows from the reservoir to the pump, where it is forced through the system and eventually returned to the reservoir. The reservoir supplies the operating needs of the system, and it replenishes fluid lost through leakage. Additionally, the reservoir serves as an overflow basin for excess fluid forced out of the system by thermal expansion (the increase of fluid volume caused by temperature changes), and displacement of the fluid as components are actuated. A typical reservoir design is shown in Figure 4-5-2.

The reservoir also provides a place for the fluid to purge itself of air bubbles that can enter the system. Foreign matter picked up in the system can also be separated from the fluid in the reservoir or as it flows through line filters. Reservoirs can be pressurized or nonpressurized depending on the operation profile of the aircraft.

Baffles and fins are incorporated in most reservoirs to keep the fluid in the reservoir from having random movement, such as vortexing (swirling) and surging. These conditions can cause fluid to foam and air to enter the pump along with the fluid. Many reservoirs incorporate strainers in the filler neck to prevent foreign matter from entering during servicing. These strainers are made of fine mesh screening and are usually referred to as finger strainers because of their shape.

Most aircraft have emergency hydraulic systems that take over if main systems fail. In many such systems, the pumps of both systems obtain fluid from the same reservoir. Under such circumstances, a supply of fluid for the emergency pump is ensured by drawing the hydraulic fluid from the bottom of the reservoir. The main system draws its fluid through a standpipe at a higher level. With this arrangement, if the main system's fluid supply becomes depleted, adequate fluid is left for operating the emergency system.

Reservoirs on aircraft designed for high-altitude flight are usually pressurized. Pressurizing ensures a positive flow of fluid to the pump at high altitudes where atmospheric pressure is low. On some aircraft, the reservoir is pressurized by bleed air taken from the compressor section of the engine. On others, the reservoir can be pressurized by hydraulic system pressure.

Pumps

Aircraft today generally use power-driven pumps to supply hydraulic pressure for most applications. Power-driven pumps can be engine driven, electric motor driven, or air driven. They are further classified as constant-displacement (or volume) pumps and variable-displacement pumps. The constant-displacement pumps are positive-displacement pumps, which means that for each rotation of the pump, a fixed amount of fluid is forced through the outlet port. The variable-displacement pump changes the amount of fluid discharge to meet the requirements of the system.

Constant-Displacement Pumps and Variable-Displacement Pumps

A constant-displacement pump, regardless of pump rotations per minute, forces a fixed or unvarying quantity of fluid through the outlet port for each revolution of the pump. Constant-

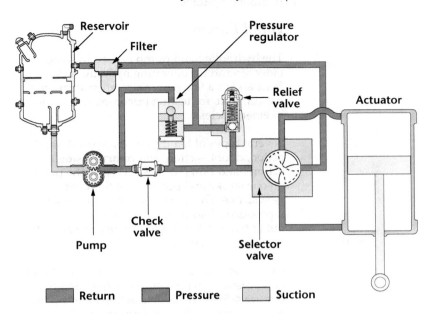

Return **Pressure** **Suction**

Figure 4-5-1. A basic hydraulic system.

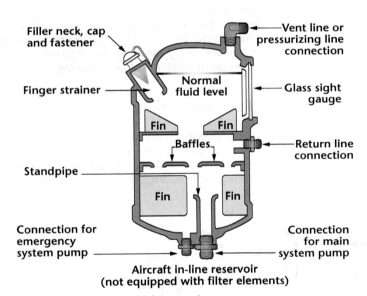

Figure 4-5-2. A nonpressurized reservoir.

displacement pumps are sometimes called constant-volume pumps. They deliver a fixed quantity of fluid per revolution, regardless of the pressure demands. Because the constant-displacement pump provides a fixed quantity of fluid during each revolution of the pump, the quantity of fluid delivered per minute depends upon pump rotations per minute. When a constant-displacement pump is used in a hydraulic system in which the pressure must be kept at a constant value, a way to regulate pressure is required.

Variable-displacement pumps can vary the quantity of fluid delivered for each revolution of the pump. The pump can, therefore, regulate pressure as pump speed changes.

Hand Pumps

The hydraulic hand pump is used in some older aircraft for operating hydraulic systems and in a few newer aircraft systems as a backup unit, for testing purposes and for use in emergencies.

Several types of hand pumps are used: single-action, double-action, and rotary. A single-action hand pump draws fluid into the pump on one stroke and pumps that fluid out on the next stroke. This pump is inefficient because it produces fluid flow and pressure on one out of two strokes. It is rarely used in aircraft because of this inefficiency.

Double-action hand pumps produce fluid flow and pressure on each stroke of the handle (Figure 4-5-3). The double-action hand pump consists essentially of a housing that has a cylinder bore and two ports, a piston, two spring-loaded check valves, and an operating handle. An O-ring on the piston seals against leakage between the two chambers of the piston cylinder bore. An O-ring in a groove in the end of the pump housing seals against leakage between the piston rod and housing.

Gear Power Pumps

A gear power pump is a constant-displacement pump. It consists of two meshed gears that revolve in a housing (Figure 4-5-4). The driving gear is turned by the aircraft engine

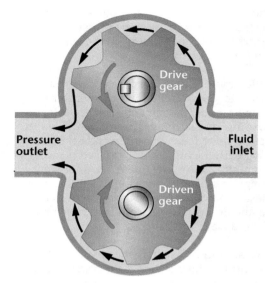

Figure 4-5-4. Fluid flow in a gear power pump.

or some other power unit. The driven gear meshes with, and is driven by, the driving gear. The clearance between the teeth as they mesh and between the teeth and the housing is very small. The inlet port of the pump is connected to the reservoir, and the outlet port is connected to the pressure outlet line.

When the driving gear turns, as shown in Figure 4-5-4, it turns the driven gear. Fluid is captured by the teeth as they pass the inlet, and it travels around the housing and exits at the outlet.

Gerotor Pumps

Another type of constant-displacement pump is a gerotor pump. A gerotor power pump consists, essentially, of a housing containing an eccentric-shaped stationary liner, an internal gear rotor with seven wide and short teeth, a spur-driving gear with six narrow teeth, and a pump cover that contains two crescent-shaped openings (Figure 4-5-5). One opening extends into an inlet port and the other extends into an outlet port.

When the pump turns, the gears turn clockwise together. As the pockets between the gears on the left side of the pump move from the lowest position toward a top position, the pockets get larger, resulting in a partial vacuum being created in these pockets. Because the pockets enlarge while over the inlet port crescent, fluid is drawn into them. As these same pockets (now full of fluid) rotate over to the right side of the pump, moving from the top position toward the lowest position, they become smaller. This results in the fluid being expelled from the pockets through the outlet port crescent.

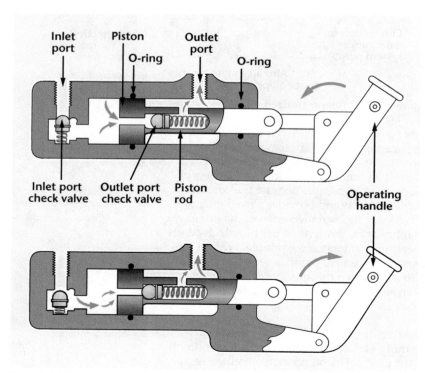

Figure 4-5-3. A double-action hand pump.

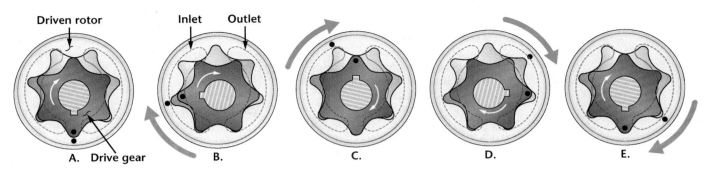

Figure 4-5-5. Gerotor pump.

Vane Pumps

The vane-type power pump is also a constant-displacement pump. It consists of a housing with four vanes (blades), a hollow steel rotor with slots for the vanes, and a coupling to turn the rotor (Figure 4-5-6). The rotor is positioned off center in the sleeve. The vanes, which are mounted in the slots in the rotor, together with the rotor, divide the bore of the sleeve into four sections.

As the rotor turns, each section passes one point where its volume is at a minimum and another point where its volume is at a maximum. The volume gradually increases from minimum to maximum in the first half of a revolution and gradually decreases from maximum to minimum in the second half. As the volume of a section increases, that section is connected to the pump inlet port through a slot in the sleeve. Because a partial vacuum is produced by the increase in volume of the section, fluid is drawn into the section through the pump inlet port and the slot in the sleeve.

As the rotor turns through the second half of the revolution and the volume of the section is decreasing, fluid is displaced out of the section, through the slot in the sleeve aligned with the outlet port, and out of the pump.

Piston Pumps

Hydraulic piston pumps can be constant-displacement or variable-displacement pumps.

Several designs of piston pumps are made. A typical constant-displacement pump is shown in Figure 4-5-7. The angular housing of the pump causes a corresponding angle to exist between the cylinder block and the drive shaft plate to which the pistons are attached. The pump's angular configuration causes the pistons to stroke as the pump shaft turns.

When the pump operates, all parts in the pump turn together as a rotating group. At

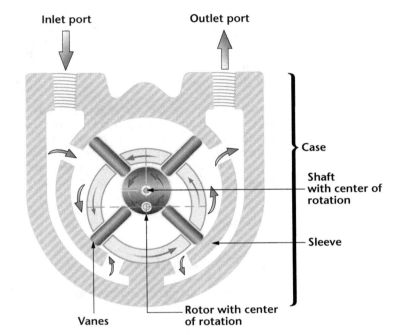

Figure 4-5-6. A vane pump.

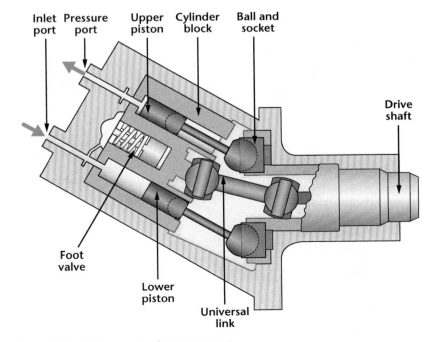

Figure 4-5-7. A bent axis piston pump.

one point of rotation, a minimum distance exists between the top of the cylinder block and the upper face of the drive shaft plate. Because of the angled housing at a point of rotation 180° away, the distance between the top of the cylinder block and the upper face of the drive shaft plate is at a maximum.

At any moment, three of the pistons are moving away from the top face of the cylinder block, producing a partial vacuum in the bores in which these pistons operate. This occurs over the inlet port, so fluid is drawn into these bores. At the same moment, on the opposite side of the cylinder block, the three other pistons are moving toward the top face of the block. This occurs while the rotating group is passing over the outlet port, causing fluid to be expelled from the pump by these pistons.

A variable-displacement piston pump has a fluid output that is varied to meet the pressure demands of the system. The pump output is changed automatically by a pump compensator inside the pump. The stroke of the pistons are variable, which varies the volume of fluid flow.

Valves

Flow Control Valves

Flow control valves are used to control the fluid flow's speed or direction, or both, in the hydraulic system. They cause various components to operate when desired and at the speed the component operates. Examples of flow control valves include selector valves, check valves, sequence valves, priority valves, shuttle valves, quick disconnect valves, and hydraulic fuses.

Pressure Control Valves

Pressure control valves ensure that hydraulic systems operate safely and efficiently. The fluid power systems, system components, and related equipment all require a means of controlling pressure. Many types of automatic pressure control valves are made. Some are an escape for pressure that exceeds a set pressure; some only reduce the pressure to a lower pressure system or subsystem; and some keep the pressure in a system within a required range. Examples of pressure control valves include relief valves, pressure regulators, and pressure reducers.

Selector Valves

A selector valve is used to control the direction of fluid flow for actuating a component, such as moving the landing gear to the gear up or gear down position.

Two main types of selector valves are used: open-center and closed-center. An open-center valve allows a continuous flow of system hydraulic fluid through the valve. A closed-center selector valve blocks the flow of fluid through the valve when it is in the neutral or off position (Figure 4-5-8 view A).

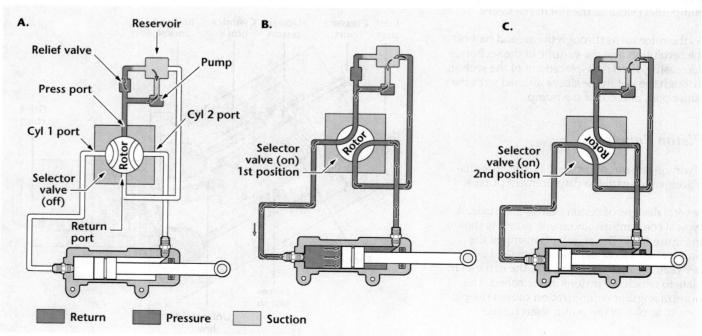

Figure 4-5-8. Operating a closed-center four-way selector valve that controls an actuator.

Figure 4-5-8 illustrates how a selector valve connects to the pressure and return lines of the hydraulic system and to the two ports on a common actuator. Most selector valves are mechanically controlled by a lever or electrically controlled.

Four ports are shown on the selector valve. One port receives pressurized fluid from the system hydraulic pump. A second port always returns fluid to the reservoir. The third and fourth ports are used to connect the selector valve to the actuating unit. The actuating unit has two ports. When the selector valve is positioned to connect pressure to one port on the actuator, the other actuator port is simultaneously connected to the reservoir return line through the selector valve (Figure 4-5-8 view B). Thus, the unit operates in a certain direction. When the selector valve is positioned to connect pressure to the other port on the actuating unit, the original port is simultaneously connected to the return line through the selector valve and the unit operates in the opposite direction (Figure 4-5-8 view C).

Check Valves

In hydraulic systems, check valves control the flow of fluid under pressure in the system. Check valves allow fluid to flow in one direction and not the other. The two common types of check valves are the inline cone and the inline ball (Figure 4-5-9). The valve has a marker to indicate the direction of free flow (Figure 4-5-10 view C). Fluid pressure into the inlet port forces the ball or cone off its seat against the spring's holding pressure. When pressure decreases or when fluid attempts to flow in the opposite direction, the spring (and any developed pressure) forces the ball or cone back on its seat, blocking reverse flow.

Orifice Check Valves

Some check valves allow full fluid flow in one direction and restricted flow in the opposite direction. These are known as orifice-type check valves, or damping valves. The valve contains the same spring, ball, and seat combination as a normal check valve, but the seat area has a calibrated orifice machined into it. Thus fluid flow is unrestricted in the designed direction while the ball is pushed off of its seat. The downstream actuator operates at full speed. When fluid backflows into the valve, the spring forces the ball against the seat, which limits fluid flow to the amount that can pass through the orifice. The reduced flow in this opposite direction slows the motion, or dampens, the actuator associated with the check valve (Figure 4-5-10 views B and D).

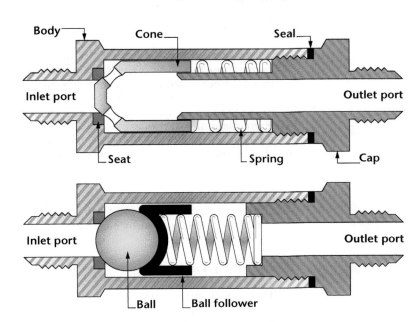

Figure 4-5-9. Cone (top) and ball (bottom) check valves.

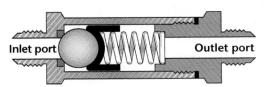

A. Simple-type in-line check valve (ball-type)

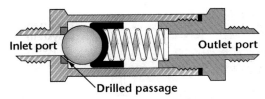

B. Orifice-type in-line check valve (ball-type)

C. Flow direction marking on simple-type in-line check valve

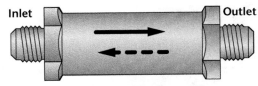

D. Flow direction marking on orifice-type in-line check valve

Figure 4-5-10. An in-line check valve and orifice check valve.

Sequence Valves

A sequence valve is used in a hydraulic system to cause one hydraulic action to follow another in a set order or sequence. For example, the landing gear should retract only after the landing gear compartment doors are completely open (assuming the doors close when the landing gear is extended). A sequence valve actuated by the fully open door allows the pressure to enter the landing gear cylinder.

Several types of sequence valves are made and are controlled differently: by pressure, by mechanical means, and by electric switches.

Priority Valve

The priority valve is used in hydraulic systems to ensure that if pressure becomes low, the priority hydraulic units receive fluid before noncritical ones. The valve is installed in the line between a nonessential actuating unit and the fluid pressure source. It permits free, unrestrained flow of fluid to nonessential units as long as system pressure is normal.

Shuttle Valves

Emergency systems are not completely separate from the normal system. The emergency system can use a separate reservoir, pump, and such, but only one set of actuators is used to transmit power from either system. To do this, the normal system must be separated from the emergency system at the actuator and allow either system to operate when needed. The shuttle valve (Figure 4-5-11) is the unit that serves this purpose.

Quick-Disconnect Couplings

Quick-disconnect couplings are installed in hydraulic lines to prevent loss of fluid when removing hydraulic units such as power pumps and brake assemblies. They are also installed in the system's pressure and suction lines just before and after the power pump to provide a place for a hydraulic test stand to be attached. These couplings consist of two interconnecting sections that are held together by a nut when installed in a system.

Each section has a piston and poppet assembly that is spring loaded. When the unit is disconnected, the springs press the assemblies to the closed position (Figure 4-5-12, top) and fluid cannot escape either section. When the unit is being connected, and the coupling nut draws the two sections together (Figure 4-5-12, bottom), the protrusion on the piston forces the opposite piston back against the spring. This unseats the poppet, and fluid can flow through that end of the coupling. As the nut is drawn tighter, one piston hits a stop so that now the other piston must move back against its spring and, in turn, unseat its poppet. Fluid can now flow through the coupling unrestricted and on through the system.

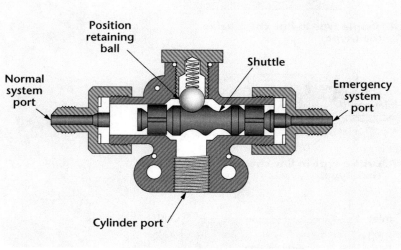

Figure 4-5-11. A shuttle valve.

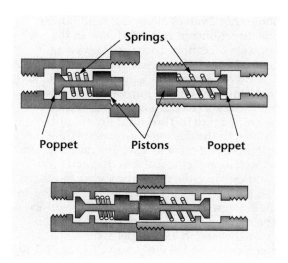

Figure 4-5-12. A quick disconnect coupling.

Hydraulic Fuse

In aircraft that use hydraulic systems to operate the flight control surfaces, it is necessary to protect the system from complete failure. In a system with no protective devices, a leak in any line or a blown seal in any unit might allow all the fluid to leak out of the system. To divide the system into sections so that a leak does not allow total fluid loss from the system, a hydraulic fuse is used.

As its name implies, this unit is similar to an electrical fuse. When too much current flows, the electrical fuse *blows* and opens the circuit, stopping the flow of current. The hydraulic fuse stops the flow when too much fluid has passed through it. Hydraulic fuses are used in brake lines that are connected to the main hydraulic system. If one of the lines breaks, most of the main system fluid could be lost. The fuse prevents this from happening by shutting down the flow when it becomes excessive.

Relief Valves

Hydraulic pressure must be regulated to use it to perform the desired tasks. A pressure relief valve is used to limit the amount of pressure being exerted on a confined liquid. This is necessary to prevent failure of components

or rupture of hydraulic lines under excessive pressures. The pressure relief valve is, in effect, a system safety valve.

Pressure relief valves are typically adjustable and spring-loaded. They discharge fluid from the pressure line into a reservoir return line when the pressure exceeds the predetermined maximum for which the valve is adjusted. Various makes and designs of pressure relief valves are used, but they all use a spring-loaded valving device operated by hydraulic pressure and spring tension (Figure 4-5-13). Pressure relief valves are adjusted by increasing or decreasing the tension on the spring to determine the pressure required to open the valve.

Pressure Regulators

The term *pressure regulator* is applied to a device used in hydraulic systems that are pressurized by constant-displacement pumps. One purpose of the pressure regulator is to manage the output of the pump to maintain system operating pressure within a predetermined range. The other purpose is to permit the pump to turn without resistance (called unloading the pump) at times when pressure in the system is within normal operating range (Figure 4-5-14).

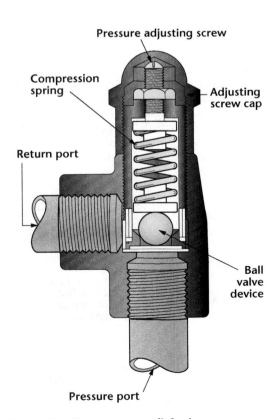

Figure 4-5-13. A pressure relief valve.

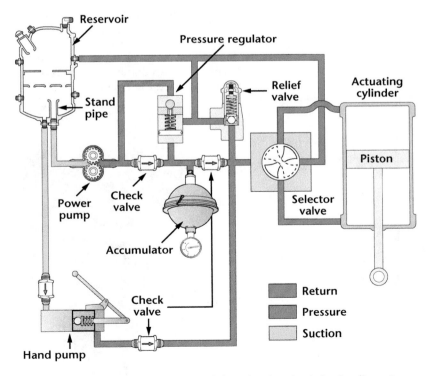

Figure 4-5-14. The pressure regulator's location in a basic hydraulic system. The regulator unloads the constant-displacement pump by bypassing fluid to the return line when the predetermined system pressure is reached.

Pressure Reducers

Pressure-reducing valves are used in hydraulic systems where it is necessary to lower the normal system operating pressure by a specified amount. Pressure reducers provide a steady pressure into a system that operates at a lower pressure than the supply system. A reducing valve can normally be set for any desired downstream pressure within the design limits of the valve. Once the valve is set, the reduced pressure is maintained regardless of changes in supply pressure (as long as the supply pressure is at least as high as the reduced pressure desired) and regardless of the system load, if the load does not exceed the designed capacity of the reducer.

Filters

In the normal wear of hydraulic system selector valves, pumps, and other components, hydraulic fluid receives small particles of metal. Hydraulic system parts are machined so finely that even a tiny particle lodged in a unit can prevent it from functioning properly. A filter is a screening or straining device that cleans the fluid, preventing foreign particles and contaminating substances from remaining in the system. If such objectionable material were not removed, the entire hydraulic system of the aircraft could fail if a single unit fails.

The hydraulic fluid holds in suspension tiny particles of metal that are deposited during the normal wear of selector valves, pumps, and other system components. Such minute particles of metal can damage the units and parts through which they pass if they are not removed by a filter. Because tolerances in the hydraulic system components are quite small, the system's reliability and efficiency depends on adequate filtering.

Filters can be in the reservoir, in the pressure line, in the return line, or in any other location the system designer decides that they are needed to safeguard the hydraulic system against impurities. Modern designs often use a filter module that contains several filters and other components (Figure 4-5-15). Many models and styles of filters are available. Their position in the aircraft and design requirements determine their shape and size.

Most filters used in modern aircraft are of the inline type. The inline filter assembly is made up of three basic units: head assembly, bowl, and filter. The head assembly is secured to the aircraft structure and connecting lines. In the head, a bypass valve routes the hydraulic fluid directly from the inlet to the outlet port if the filter element becomes clogged with foreign matter. The bowl is the housing that holds the filter to the head assembly and is removed when filter removal is required.

The filter element can be a micron, porous metal, or magnetic type. The micron element is made of paper and is normally thrown away when removed. The porous metal and magnetic filter elements can be cleaned by various methods and replaced in the system.

A typical micron filter assembly uses an element made of specially treated paper that is formed in vertical convolutions (wrinkles). An internal spring holds the elements in shape. The micron element is designed to prevent solids larger than 10 microns (0.000394 in.) from passing through (Figure 4-5-16). If the filter element becomes clogged, the spring-loaded relief valve in the filter head bypasses the fluid after a differential pressure of 50 p.s.i. has been built

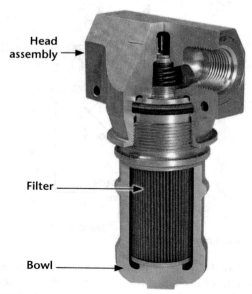

Figure 4-5-15. Filter module components.

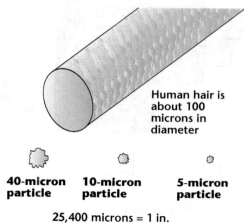

Human hair is about 100 microns in diameter

40-micron particle   10-micron particle   5-micron particle

25,400 microns = 1 in.

Figure 4-5-16. Size comparison in microns.

up. Hydraulic fluid enters the filter through the inlet port in the filter body and flows around the element inside the bowl. Filtering takes place as the fluid passes through the element into the hollow core, leaving the foreign material on the outside of the element.

Accumulators

Many aircraft have several accumulators in the hydraulic system. Some have a main system accumulator and an emergency system accumulator. Auxiliary accumulators can also be used in various subsystems.

An accumulator has several functions:

- Dampens pressure surges in the hydraulic system caused by a unit's actuation and the effort of the pump to maintain pressure at a preset level.

- Aids or supplements the power pump when several units are operating at once by supplying extra power from its accumulated, or stored, power.

- Stores power for the limited hydraulic unit operation when the pump is not running.

- Supplies pressurized fluid to compensate for small internal or external (not desired) leaks that would cause the system to cycle continuously by the pressure switches continually kicking in.

The typical accumulator is a steel sphere divided into two chambers by a synthetic rubber diaphragm. The upper chamber contains fluid at system pressure, and the lower chamber is charged with nitrogen or air. Cylindrical types are also used in high-pressure hydraulic systems. A common, spherical design is shown in Figure 4-5-17.

Actuators

A hydraulic actuator transforms fluid pressure (energy) into mechanical force, or action, to perform work. It imparts powered or rotary motion to some movable object or mechanism.

Linear actuators. A typical actuating cylinder consists of a cylinder housing, one or more pistons and piston rods, and some seals. The cylinder housing contains a polished bore in which the piston operates, and one or more ports through which fluid enters and leaves the bore. The piston and rod form an assembly. The piston moves forward and backward in the cylinder bore, and an attached piston rod moves into and out of the cylinder housing through an opening in one end of the cylinder housing.

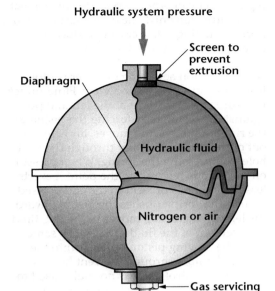

Figure 4-5-17. A spherical accumulator with diaphragm.

Seals prevent leakage between the piston and the cylinder bore and between the piston rod and the end of the cylinder. Both the cylinder housing and the piston rod have provisions for mounting and for attachment to an object or mechanism that is to be moved by the actuating cylinder.

Two main types of actuating cylinders are made: single-action and double-action (Figure 4-5-18). The single-action (single port) actuat-

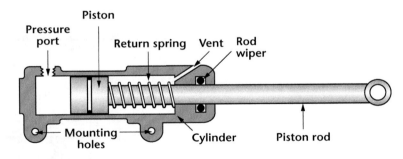

Single-action actuating cylinder

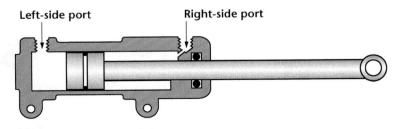

Double-action actuating cylinder

Figure 4-5-18. A linear actuator.

ing cylinder can produce powered movement in one direction only. The double-action (two ports) actuating cylinder can produce powered movement in two directions.

A single-action actuating cylinder is illustrated in Figure 4-5-18, top view. Fluid under pressure enters the port at the left and pushes against the piston face, forcing the piston to the right. As the piston moves, air is forced out of the spring chamber through the vent hole, compressing the spring. When pressure on the fluid is released to the point it exerts less force than is present in the compressed spring, the spring pushes the piston toward the left. As the piston moves to the left, fluid is forced out of the fluid port. At the same time, the moving piston pulls air into the spring chamber through the vent hole. A three-way control valve is normally used to control a single-action actuating cylinder.

A double-action (two ports) actuating cylinder is illustrated in the bottom view of Figure 4-5-18. A four-way selector valve usually controls the double-action actuating cylinder's operation. Besides being able to move a load into position, a double-acting cylinder can also hold a load in position. This is because when the selector valve is in the off position, fluid is trapped in the chambers on both sides of the actuating cylinder piston. Internal

locking actuators also are used in some applications.

Rotary actuators. Another type of actuator that is used is a rotary actuator. Rotary actuators can mount right at the part without taking up the long stroke lengths required of linear actuators. Rotary actuators can achieve arc lengths of 180°, 360°, or even 720° or more, depending on the configuration. One type of rotary actuator is the rack and pinion actuator, often used for many nose wheel steering mechanisms. In a rack-and-pinion actuator, a long piston with one side machined into a rack engages a pinion to turn the output shaft (Figure 4-5-19). One side of the piston receives fluid pressure while the other side is connected to the return. When the piston moves, it rotates the pinion.

Hoses and Lines

Hydraulic fluid lines deliver the fluid between the components in a system. They are usually made of metal tubing or flexible hose. Metal tubing (also called rigid fluid line) is used in stationary applications and where long, relatively straight runs are possible.

Tubing made of aluminum alloy is often used in general purpose systems of low and

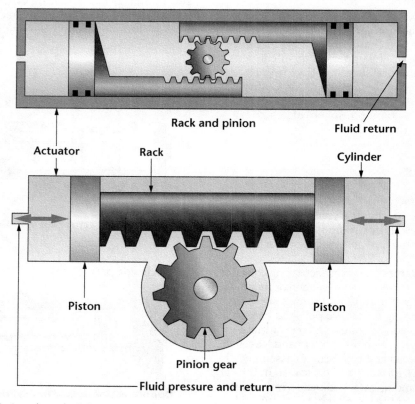

Figure 4-5-19. A rack-and-pinion gear actuator.

medium pressure. This includes hydraulic systems operating up to 1,500 p.s.i. Above that, operating pressure you might find stainless steel or titanium tubing used. This is generally on transport category and military aircraft.

Flexible hose is used in aircraft fluid systems to connect moving parts with stationary parts in locations subject to vibration or where much flexibility is needed. It can also serve as a connector in metal tubing systems.

Flexible rubber hose consists of a seamless synthetic-rubber inner tube covered with layers of cotton braid, wire braid, and an outer layer of rubber-impregnated cotton braid. The types of hose are normally classified by the amount of pressure they are designed to withstand under normal operating conditions: low, medium, and high.

Flexible hoses used for brake systems sometimes have a stainless-steel wire braid installed over the hose to protect the hose from damage (Figure 4-5-20).

Figure 4-5-20. The stainless steel braid protects the flexible hose.

Section 6

System Types

When designing a hydraulic system for an aircraft, the designers usually try to use the simplest design that meets the operational criteria of the systems it operates. Several common system designs are used: open-center and closed-center systems, and power packs. These are briefly discussed next.

Open-Center Hydraulic System

An open-center system is one that, when the actuating mechanisms are idle, has fluid flow but no pressure in the system. The pump circulates the fluid from the reservoir, through the selector valves, and back to the reservoir (Figure 4-6-1 view A). The open-center system can use any number of subsystems, with a selector valve for each subsystem. Unlike the closed-center system, the selector valves of the open-center system are always connected in series with each other. In this arrangement, the system pressure line goes through each selector valve. Fluid is always allowed free passage through each selector valve and back to the reservoir until one of the selector valves is positioned to operate a mechanism.

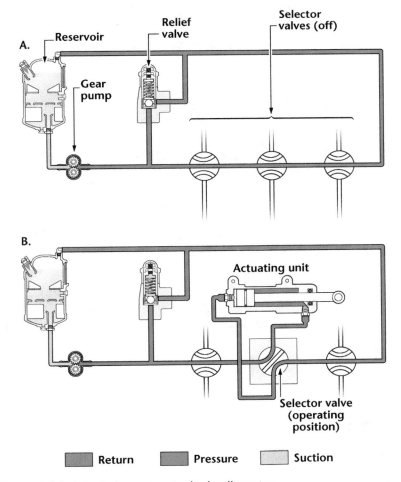

Figure 4-6-1. A typical open-center hydraulic system.

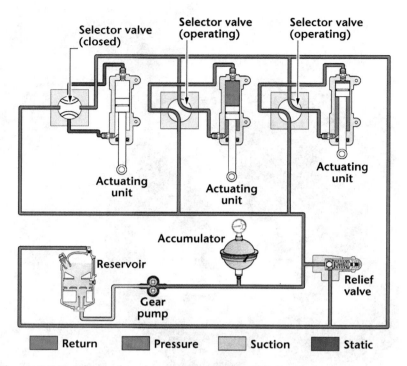

Figure 4-6-2. A basic closed-center hydraulic system.

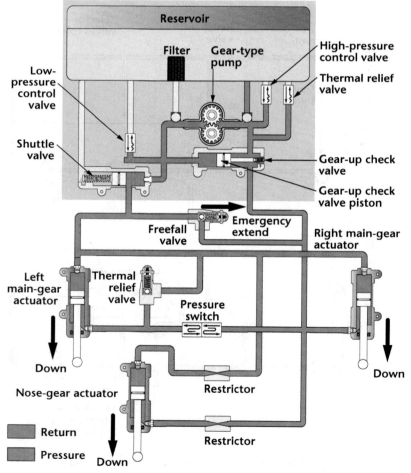

Figure 4-6-3. An aircraft gear retraction system that uses a hydraulic power pack in the gear-down position.

When one of the selector valves is positioned to operate an actuating device, it directs fluid from the pump through one of the working lines to the actuator (Figure 4-6-1 view B). With the selector valve in this position, the flow of fluid through the valve to the reservoir is blocked. The pressure builds up in the system to overcome the resistance and moves the piston of the actuating cylinder; fluid from the opposite end of the actuator returns to the selector valve and flows back to the reservoir.

After the component actuation ends, the system operation varies depending on the type of selector valve. Several types of selector valves are used in conjunction with the open-center system. One type is both manually engaged and manually disengaged; the other is manually engaged and pressure disengaged.

Manually engaged and disengaged. First, the valve is manually moved to an operating position. Then, the actuating mechanism reaches the end of its operating cycle, and the pump output continues until the system relief valve relieves the pressure. The relief valve unseats and allows the fluid to flow back to the reservoir. The system pressure remains at the relief valve set pressure until the selector valve is manually returned to the neutral position. This action reopens the open-center flow and allows the system pressure to drop to line resistance pressure.

Manually engaged, pressure disengaged. The manually engaged and pressure disengaged type of selector valve is similar to the valve previously discussed. When the actuating mechanism reaches the end of its cycle, the pressure continues to rise to a predetermined pressure. The valve automatically returns to the neutral position and to open-center flow.

Closed-Center Hydraulic System

In the closed-center system, the fluid is under pressure whenever the power pump is operating. In Figure 4-6-2, the three actuators are arranged in parallel. This allows several actuators to operate at the same time. The center and right side actuators are operating at the same time, and the actuator on the left is not operating. This system differs from the open-center system in that the selector or directional control valves are arranged in parallel and not in series. The means of controlling pump pressure varies in the closed-center system. If a constant-displacement pump is used, a pressure regulator keeps the system pressure within limits. A relief valve acts as a backup safety device in case the regulator fails.

If a variable-displacement pump is used, the pump's integral pressure mechanism compensator keeps the system pressure within limits. The compensator automatically varies the volume output. When pressure approaches normal system pressure, the compensator begins to reduce the flow output of the pump.

When normal system pressure is attained, the pump is fully compensated (near zero flow). In such a condition, its internal bypass mechanism provides fluid circulation through the pump for cooling and lubrication. A relief valve is installed in the system as a safety backup.

An advantage of the open-center system over the closed-center system is that the continuous pressurization of the system is eliminated. Because the pressure is built up gradually after the selector valve is moved to an operating position, there is very little shock from pressure surges. This action provides a smoother operation of the actuating mechanisms. However, the operation is slower than the closed-center system, in which the pressure is available the moment the selector valve is positioned. Because most aircraft applications require instantaneous operation, closed-center systems are the most widely used.

Power Pack

A common electric/hydraulic system found in many Cessna and Piper aircraft is known as a power pack system. A hydraulic power pack is a small unit that consists of an electric pump, filters, reservoir, valves, and pressure relief valve.

In this system, when the gear selector handle is put in the gear-down position, a switch turns on the electric motor in the power pack. The motor turns in the direction to rotate the hydraulic gear pump so that it pumps fluid to the gear-down side of the actuating cylinders (Figure 4-6-3). Pump pressure moves the spring-loaded shuttle valve to the left to allow fluid to reach all three actuators. Restrictors are used in the nose wheel actuator inlet and outlet ports to slow down the motion of this lighter gear.

When hydraulic fluid is pumped to extend the gear, fluid from the upside of the actuators returns to the reservoir through the gear-up check valve. When the gear reaches the down and locked position, pressure builds in the gear-down line from the pump and the low-pressure control valve unseats to

return the fluid to the reservoir. Electric limit switches turn off the pump when all three gear are down and locked.

To raise the gear, the gear handle is moved to the gear-up position. This sends current to the electric motor, which drives the hydraulic gear pump in the opposite direction, causing fluid to be pumped to the gear-up side of the actuators (Figure 4-6-4). In this direction, pump inlet fluid flows through the filter. Fluid from the pump flows through the gear-up check valve to the gear-up sides of the actuating cylinder. As the cylinders begin to move, the pistons release the mechanical down locks that hold the gear rigid for ground operations. Fluid from the gear-down side of the actuators returns to the reservoir through the shuttle valve. When the three gear are fully retracted, pressure builds in the system, and a pressure switch is opened that cuts power to the electric pump motor. The gear are held in the retracted position with hydraulic pressure. If pressure declines, the pressure switch closes to run the pump and raise the pressure until the pressure switch opens again.

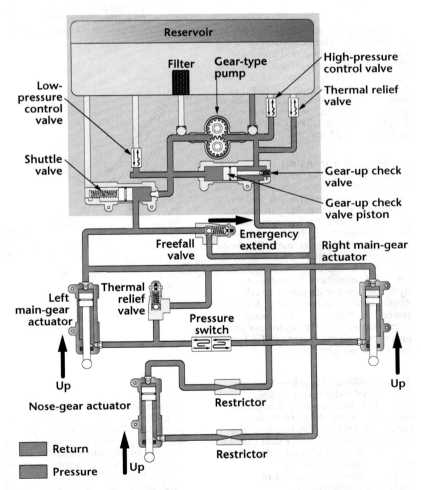

Figure 4-6-4. A hydraulic power pack gear retraction system in the gear up condition.

Section 7

Large Aircraft Hydraulic Systems

Transport category aircraft have special requirements in hydraulic systems that are being met in innovative ways in modern designs. The size of these aircraft and the weight of the equipment needed for hydraulic systems have forced designers to look for ways to provide the mechanical advantage of a hydraulic system but reduce weight wherever possible. Figure 4-7-1 provides an overview of hydraulic components in large aircraft.

The system shown in Figure 4-7-2 is one example of those that have been in place for many years. This aircraft has three 3,000-p.s.i. hydraulic systems: system A, system B, and standby. The standby system is used if systems A or B, or both, lose pressure. The hydraulic systems power the following aircraft systems:

- Flight controls
- Leading edge flaps and slats
- Trailing edge flaps
- Landing gear
- Wheel brakes
- Nose wheel steering

1. AC Motor Pump
Auxiliary power is provided by a 3,110-p.s.i., 12-gpm, 8,000-r.p.m. fluid-cooled motor pump. Some AC motor pumps feature a ceramic feed-through design. This protects the electrical wiring from being exposed to the caustic hydraulic fluid environment.

2. Leading Edge Slat Drive Motor
Leading edge slat actuation on the aircraft provided by one constant displacement, nine-piston, bent-axis, hydraulic motor. The motor produces 544.3 in.-lbs torque at 2,250 p.s.i.d. with a rated speed of 3,170 r.p.m. and an intermittent speed of 4,755 r.p.m. Displacement is 1.52 sq. in. per rev; weight is 13.21 lbs.

3. Power Transfer Unit
A nonreversible power transfer unit (PTU) transfers hydraulic power (but not fluid) between the left and right independent hydraulic systems. It provides an alternate power source for the leading and trailing edge flaps and the landing gear, including nose gear steering, which are normally driven by the left hydraulic system. The PTU consists of a bent-axis hydraulic motor driving a fixed displacement, in-line pump. Rated speed is 3,900 r.p.m. The pump displacement is 1.39 sq. in. per rev and motor displacement is 1.52 sq. in. per rev. It weighs 35 lbs.

4. Nose Wheel Steering System
Consists of a digital electronic controller, hydromechanical power unit, mounting collar, tiller, and rudder pedal position sensors. The hydromechanical power unit (an integrated assembly) includes all the hydraulic valving, power amplification, actuation, and damping components.

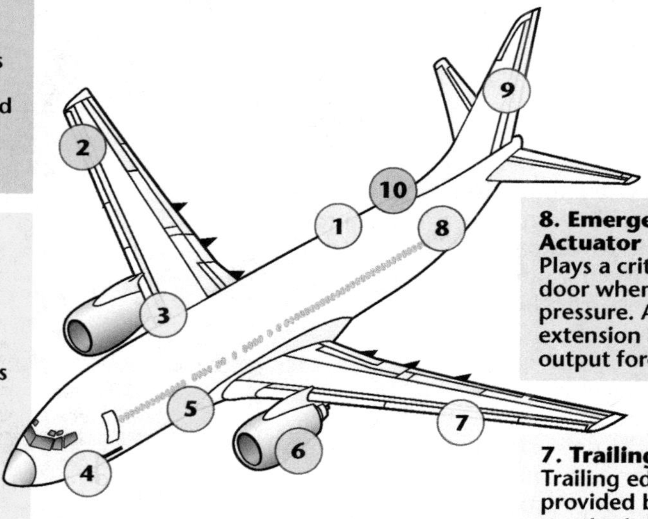

5. Ram Air Turbine Pump
A 3,025 p.s.i. in-line piston pump provides 20 gpm at 3,920 r.p.m., delivering hydraulic power for the priority flight control surfaces if both engines are lost or a total electrical power failure occurs. Displacement is 1.25 sq. in. per rev; weight is 15 lbs.

10. Hydraulic Motor-Driven Generator - The hydraulic motor-driven generator (HMDG) is a servo-controlled, variable displacement, inline axis-piston hydraulic motor integrated with a three-stage, brushless generator. The HMDG is designed to maintain a steady state generator output frequency of 400 ±2V (at the point of regulation) over a rated electrical output range of 10kVA.

9. Stabilizer Trim Motor
Stabilizer trim actuation on the aircraft is provided by two 3,000-p.s.i., constant-displacement, nine-piston, bent-axis hydraulic motors. Each motor produces 77.3 in.-lbs torque at 2,250 p.s.i.d. with a rated speed of 2,700 r.p.m. and an intermittent speed of 4,050 r.p.m. Displacement is 0.216 sq in. per rev; weight is 3.9 lbs.

8. Emergency Passenger Door Actuator
Plays a critical role in safety; extends door when actuated by nitrogen gas pressure. Assembly reaches full extension in 2.75 to 4.16 seconds with output force of 2,507 to 2,830 lbs.

7. Trailing Edge Flap Drive Motor
Trailing edge flap actuation is provided by one 3,000-p.s.i., constant-displacement, nine-piston, bent-axis, hydraulic motor. The motor produces 21.4 in.-lbs of torque at 2,250 p.s.i.d. with a rated speed of 3,750 r.p.m. and an intermittent speed of 5,660 r.p.m.. Displacement is 0.596 sq. in. per rev; weight 6.5 lbs.

6. Engine-Driven Pump
Hydraulic power for the left and right systems is supplied by two 48-gpm variable-displacement, 3,000-p.s.i. pressure-compensated in-line pumps. Displacement is 3.0 sq. in. per rev; weight 40.1 lbs.

Figure 4-7-1. The hydraulic components in a transport category aircraft.

- Thrust reversers
- Autopilots

Newer aircraft continue to use hydraulic power for most of these same systems. Some manufacturers have opted for even higher-pressure systems that can go up to 5,000 p.s.i. However, some manufacturers have realized that the combined weight of the necessary components, plumbing, and fluid used in traditional hydraulic systems have a negative effect on fuel efficiency. To combat this, they have sought lighter alternatives. Traditional hydraulics are sometimes being replaced with smaller independent systems where the pump, reservoir, actuators, and entire fluid system are mounted next to the component that had been operated by the main hydraulic system.

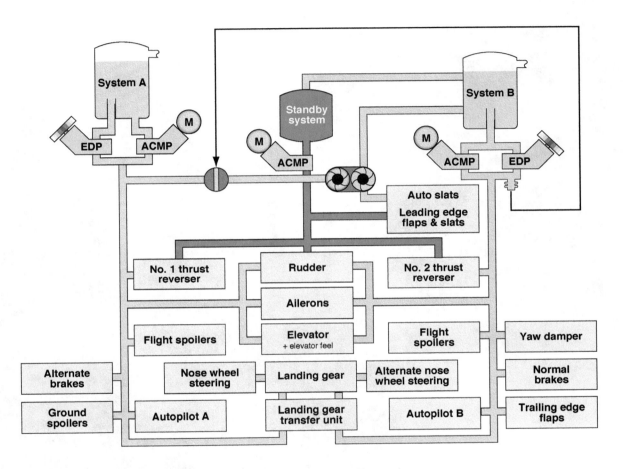

Figure 4-7-2. A simplified diagram of large-aircraft hydraulic systems.

5

Landing Gear, Wheels, Tires, and Brakes

The aircraft's landing gear supports the entire weight of an aircraft during landing and ground operations. The gear are attached to primary structural members of the aircraft. The type of gear depends on the aircraft design and its intended use. Most landing gear use wheels to facilitate ground operation to and from hard surfaces, such as airport runways. Other aircraft such as helicopters typically feature skids for this purpose. Aircraft that operate to and from frozen lakes and snowy areas can be equipped with landing gear that have skis. Aircraft that operate to and from the surface of water have pontoon-type landing gear.

Regardless of the type of landing gear used, shock absorbing equipment, brakes, retraction mechanisms, controls, warning devices, cowling, fairings, and structural members necessary to attach the gear to the aircraft are considered parts of the landing gear system.

Learning Objectives

IDENTIFY
- Types of landing gear

DESCRIBE
- Retractable landing gear indications

DISCUSS
- Aircraft wheel and tire construction
- Tire tread inspection

Section 1

Design Requirements

Landing gear design criteria are governed by the Federal Aviation Administration (FAA). Manufacturers must determine the applicable structural design loads resulting from likely externally or internally applied pressures, forces, or moments that could occur in flight, ground and water operations, ground and water handling, and while the airplane is parked or moored. Additional governed gear design criteria include emergency operation, gear locks, position indicator and warnings.

Left: This business jet's landing gear, tires, and brakes do the job well for ground operations.

Figure 5-2-1. A steerable tailwheel.

Figure 5-2-2. Tandem landing gear along the longitudinal axis of the aircraft permits using flexible wings on sailplanes (top) and select military aircraft like the B-52 (center). The VTOL Harrier (bottom) has tandem gear with outrigger gear.

The landing gear must be designed to meet both of the following requirements:

1. Provide stable support and control to the airplane during surface operation

2. Account for likely system failures and likely operation environments (including anticipated limitation exceedances and emergency procedures)

Additional requirements in the regulations regarding braking include the following:

- All airplanes must have a reliable means of stopping the airplane.

- Airplanes that are required to demonstrate aborted takeoff capability must account for this additional kinetic energy.

Section 2

Landing Gear Types

Three basic arrangements of landing gear are used: tailwheel landing gear (also known as conventional gear), tandem landing gear, and tricycle landing gear.

Conventional Landing Gear

Tailwheel landing gear is also known as conventional gear because many early aircraft use this type of arrangement. The main gear are forward of the center of gravity (CG), causing the tail to require support from a third wheel assembly. A few early aircraft designs use a skid rather than a tailwheel. This helped slow the aircraft on landing and provide directional stability.

Because most runways today are hard surfaced, the tail skid has been rendered obsolete in favor of the tailwheel. Directional control is maintained through differential braking until the aircraft speed enables control with the rudder. A steerable tailwheel, connected by cables to the rudder or rudder pedals, is also a common design (Figure 5-2-1).

The angle of the aircraft fuselage on aircraft fitted with conventional gear allows for using a longer propeller that can compensate for older, underpowered engines. The increased clearance of the forward fuselage offered by tailwheel landing gear is also advantageous when operating in and out of unpaved runways. Today, aircraft are still manufactured with conventional gear for this reason, and for the weight savings accompanying the relatively light tailwheel assembly.

With the CG behind the main landing gear, directional control using this type of landing gear is more difficult while on the ground. This is the main disadvantage of the tailwheel landing gear. For example, if the pilot allows the aircraft to swerve while rolling on the ground at a low speed, he or she might not have sufficient rudder control and the CG can get ahead of the main gear, which could cause the airplane to make a rapid uncontrolled turn (ground loop).

Diminished forward visibility when the tailwheel is on or near the ground is a second disadvantage of tailwheel landing gear airplanes. Because of these disadvantages, specific training is required to operate tailwheel airplanes.

Tandem Landing Gear

Few aircraft are designed with the tandem landing gear design. As the name implies, this type of landing gear has the main gear and tail gear aligned on the longitudinal axis of the aircraft. Sailplanes commonly use tandem gear, although many only have one actual gear forward on the fuselage with a skid under the tail. A few military bombers, such as the B-47 and the B-52, have tandem landing gear, as does the U2 spy plane. The VTOL Harrier has tandem gear but uses small outrigger gear under the wings for support. Generally, plac-

ing the gear under only the fuselage facilitates using flexible wings (Figure 5-2-2).

Tricycle Landing Gear

The most commonly used landing gear arrangement today is the tricycle landing gear. It is composed of main gear and nose gear (Figure 5-2-3).

Tricycle landing gear is used on large and small aircraft with the following benefits:

1. Allows more forceful application of the brakes without nosing over when braking, which enables higher landing speeds.

2. Provides better visibility from the flight deck, especially during landing and ground maneuvering.

3. Prevents ground-looping of the aircraft. Because the aircraft CG is forward of the main gear, forces acting on the CG tend to keep the aircraft moving forward rather than looping, such as with a tailwheel landing gear.

The nose gear of a few aircraft with tricycle landing gear is not controllable. It simply casters as steering is done with differential braking during taxi. One such aircraft today is the popular Cirrus SR series as seen in Figure 5-2-3. Steering is performed by applying the main gear brakes at different rates, called differential braking.

Figure 5-2-3. Cirrus aircraft incorporate a castering nosewheel.

With the exception of those using castering nosewheels, nearly all aircraft have a steerable nose wheel. On light aircraft, the nose gear is directed through mechanical linkage to the rudder pedals. Figure 5-2-4 is an example of the mechanical linkage between the rudder pedals and nose gear.

Heavy aircraft typically use hydraulic power to steer the nose gear. The flight crew controls it through an independent tiller in the flight deck. An example of this tiller control is shown in Figure 5-2-5.

Figure 5-2-4. Linkage between the rudder pedals and nose gear.

Figure 5-2-5. A nose wheel steering tiller in the flight deck is used for ground movements.

The main landing gear on a tricycle configuration is attached to reinforced wing structure or fuselage structure. The number and location of wheels on the main gear vary. Main gear on larger aircraft can have two or more wheels. Multiple wheels spread the weight of the aircraft over a larger area. They also provide a safety margin if one tire fails.

Some heavy aircraft can have four or more wheel assemblies on each main gear. When more than two wheels are attached to a landing gear strut, the attaching mechanism is known as a bogie. The number of wheels included in the bogie is a function of the aircraft's gross design weight and the surface type on which the loaded aircraft is required to land. Figure 5-2-6 shows the triple bogie main gear of a large airliner.

The tricycle landing gear arrangement can consist of many additional parts and assemblies. These include air/oil shock struts, gear alignment units, support units, retraction and safety devices, steering systems, wheel and brake assemblies, and so on. We discuss many of these later in this chapter.

Fixed and Retractable Landing Gear

Further classification of aircraft landing gear can be made into two categories: fixed and retractable. Many small, single-engine, light aircraft have fixed landing gear, as do a few light twins. This means the gear is attached to the airframe and remains exposed to the slipstream as the aircraft flies. As the speed of an aircraft increases, so does parasite drag.

Mechanisms to retract and stow the landing gear to eliminate parasite drag add weight to the aircraft. On slow aircraft, the penalty of this added weight is not overcome by the reduction of drag, so fixed gear is used. As the aircraft's design speed increases, the drag caused by the landing gear becomes greater, and a means to retract the gear to eliminate parasite drag is required, despite the weight of the mechanism.

Fixed Landing Gear

A great deal of the parasitic drag caused by light aircraft landing gear can be reduced by building the landing gear as aerodynamically clean as possible. Additional reduction in drag can come by adding fairings or *wheel pants* to streamline the airflow past the protruding assemblies. A small, smooth profile to the oncoming wind greatly reduces landing gear drag. Figure 5-2-7 shows a spring steel aircraft

Figure 5-2-6. Triple bogie main landing gear assembly on an airliner.

landing gear used on many light planes. The thin cross section of the spring steel struts combines with the fairings over the wheel and brake assemblies to raise performance of the fixed landing gear by minimizing parasite drag.

Retractable Landing Gear

As the design speed of an aircraft increases, the designer reaches a point where the parasite drag created by the landing gear in the slipstream is greater than the induced drag caused by the added weight of a retractable landing gear system. At this point the manufacturer decides to install retractable landing gear.

Aircraft landing gear are attached to the wing spars or other structural members that are designed for supporting the landing gear. Retractable gear must be engineered to provide strong attachment to the aircraft and still be able to move into a recess or wheel well when stowed.

Retractable landing gear stow in fuselage or wing compartments while in flight. Once in these wheel wells, the landing gear are out of the slipstream and do not cause parasite drag. Most retractable gear have a close-fitting panel attached to them that fairs with the aircraft skin when the gear is fully retracted. Other aircraft have separate doors that open, allowing the gear to enter or leave, and then close again. The flight crew can use the parasite drag caused by extended landing gear to slow

Figure 5-2-7. Wheel fairings and low-profile struts can reduce the drag on fixed landing gear.

the aircraft. Extending and retracting landing gear is usually done with electric motors or hydraulic cylinders.

Electric and Electric/Hydraulic

Electrically operated landing gear systems are often found on light aircraft. An all-electric system uses an electric motor and gear reduction to power the system. The rotary motion of the electric motor is converted to linear motion to actuate the gear. This is possible only with the relatively lightweight gear found on smaller aircraft.

A more common use of electricity in gear retraction systems is that of an electric/hydraulic system found in many Cessna and Piper aircraft. This is also known as a power pack system. A small, lightweight hydraulic power pack contains several components required in a hydraulic system (Figure 5-2-8). These include the reservoir, a reversible electric motor-driven hydraulic pump, a filter, high- and low-pressure control valves, a thermal relief valve, and a shuttle valve. Some power packs incorporate an emergency hand pump. A hydraulic actuator for each gear is driven to extend or retract the gear by fluid from the power pack.

Hydraulic power packs that perform one function have proven to be a viable alternative to installing a full engine-driven hydraulic system on an aircraft. Initially used for convenience on smaller aircraft, they have now become a part of the effort to obtain significant weight savings and the corre-

sponding reduction in fuel burn of transport category aircraft. The integrated essential filters, sensors, and transducers are lighter, practically eliminate external leakage, and make troubleshooting easier.

With these components in one unit, the power pack is capable of controlling items such as the stabilizer trim, landing gear, or flight control surfaces without a centralized hydraulic system and its long supply lines. This reduces weight.

Hydraulic

Large-aircraft retraction systems are nearly always powered by hydraulics. Typically, the hydraulic pump is driven off the engine accessory drive. Auxiliary electric hydraulic pumps are also common. Other devices used in a hydraulically operated retraction system include actuating cylinders, selector valves, uplocks, downlocks, sequence valves, priority valves, tubing, and other conventional hydraulic system components. These units are interconnected so that they permit properly sequenced retraction and extension of the landing gear and the landing gear doors.

The correct operation of any aircraft landing gear retraction system is extremely important. Figure 5-2-9 illustrates an example of a simple, large-aircraft hydraulic landing gear system. The aircraft has doors that open before the gear is extended and close after the gear is retracted. The nose gear doors operate via mechanical linkage and do not require hydraulic power. Many gear and gear door arrangements are used on aircraft. Some aircraft have gear doors that close to fair the wheel well after the gear is extended. Others have doors mechanically attached to the outside of the gear so that when it stows inward, the door stows with the gear and fairs with the fuselage skin.

Raising Gear

In the system shown in Figure 5-2-9, when the gear selector is moved to the gear-up position, it positions a selector valve to allow pump pressure from the hydraulic system manifold to pressurize eight different components. The three downlocks are pressurized and unlocked so the gear can retract. At the same time, the actuator cylinder on each gear also receives pressurized fluid to the gear-up side of the piston through an unrestricted orifice check valve. This drives the gear into the wheel well. Two sequence valves (C and D) also receive fluid pressure.

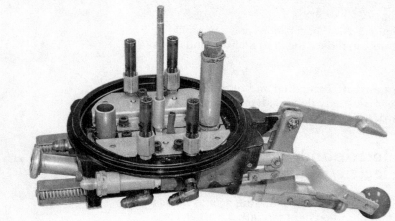
Figure 5-2-8. A hydraulic power pack.

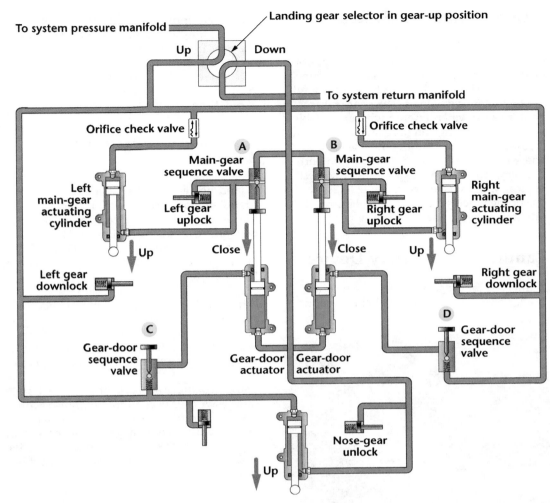

Figure 5-2-9. A simple, large-aircraft hydraulic gear retraction system.

Gear door operation must be controlled so that it occurs after the gear is stowed. The sequence valves are closed and delay flow to the door actuators. When the gear cylinders are fully retracted, they mechanically contact the sequence valve plungers that open the valves and allow fluid to flow into the close side of the door actuator cylinders. This closes the doors. Sequence valves A and B act as check valves during retraction. They allow fluid to flow one way from the gear-down side of the main gear cylinders back into the hydraulic system return manifold through the selector valve.

Lowering Gear

To lower the gear, the selector is put in the gear-down position. Pressurized hydraulic fluid flows from the hydraulic manifold to the nose gear uplock, which unlocks the nose gear. Fluid flows to the gear-down side of the nose gear actuator and extends it. Fluid also flows to the open side of the main gear door

actuators. As the doors open, sequence valves A and B block fluid from unlocking the main gear uplocks and prevent fluid from reaching the down side of the main gear actuators.

When the doors are fully open, the door actuator engages the plungers of both sequence valves to open the valves. The main gear uplocks, then receives fluid pressure and unlock. The main gear cylinder actuators receive fluid on the down side through the open sequence valves to extend the gear. Fluid from each main gear cylinder up-side flows to the hydraulic system return manifold through restrictors in the orifice check valves. The restrictors slow the extension of the gear to prevent impact damage.

Numerous hydraulic landing gear retraction system designs exist. Priority valves are sometimes used instead of mechanically operated sequence valves. This controls some gear component activation timing via hydraulic pressure. Specific information about any gear system is in the aircraft manufacturer's manuals.

Other Retraction Systems

To extend the flexibility of operations for some aircraft, combinations of two types of landing gear can be used. Amphibious aircraft are designed with gear that allow landing on water or dry land. The gear features pontoons for water landing with extendable wheels for landings on hard surfaces. A similar system is used to allow the use of skis and wheels on aircraft that operate on both slippery, frozen surfaces and dry runways. Typically, the skis are retractable to allow use of the wheels when needed. Figure 5-2-10 illustrates these types of landing gear.

Landing Gear Safety Devices

Numerous landing gear safety devices are used. These include squat switches, ground

Figure 5-2-10. An amphibious aircraft with retractable wheels (top) and an aircraft with retractable skis (bottom).

locks, gear indicators and nose wheel centering. The most common are those that prevent the gear from retracting or collapsing while on the ground. Gear indicators are another safety device. They communicate to the flight crew the position status of each landing gear at any time.

Squat Switch (Weight on Wheels Switch)

A landing gear squat switch is a safety switch found on most aircraft with retractable gear. This is a switch positioned to open and close depending on the extension or compression of the main landing gear strut (Figure 5-2-11). They are also called weight-on-wheels or WOW switches.

When the landing gear is compressed, the squat switch is compressed, deactivating the retraction system. At takeoff, the landing gear strut extends. The safety switch closes and allows the retraction system to operate.

Using proximity sensors for gear position safety switches is common in high-performance aircraft. An electromagnetic sensor returns a different voltage to a gear logic unit depending on the proximity of a conductive target to the switch. No physical contact is made.

Ground Locks

Ground locks are commonly used on aircraft landing gear as extra insurance that the landing gear remains down and locked while the aircraft is on the ground. They are external devices that are placed in the retraction mechanism to prevent its movement. A ground lock can be as simple as a pin placed in the predrilled holes of gear components that keep the gear from collapsing. Another commonly used ground lock clamps onto the exposed piston of the gear retraction cylinder and prevents it from retracting.

All ground locks should have a red streamers attached to them so they are visible and removed before flight. Ground locks are typically carried in the aircraft and put into place by the flight crew in the post-landing walk-around (Figure 5-2-12).

Landing Gear Position Indicators

Landing gear position indicators are on the instrument panel next to the gear selector handle. They inform the flight crew of gear position status. Many arrangements for gear

Figure 5-2-11. A typical landing gear squat switch.

Figure 5-2-12. Gear pin ground lock devices.

indication can be used, usually with a dedicated light for each gear. The most common display for the landing gear being down and locked is an illuminated green light. Three green lights means it is safe to land. All lights out typically indicates that the gear is up and locked, or there can be gear-up indicator lights. Gear-in-transit lights are used on some aircraft when a gear is not up or down and locked. Figure 5-2-13 is an example of landing gear position indicators.

Nose Wheel Centering

Because most aircraft have steerable nose wheel gear assemblies for taxiing, a means is needed for aligning the nose gear before retraction. Centering cams built into the shock strut structure do this. An upper cam is free to mate into a lower cam recess when the gear is fully extended. This aligns the gear for retraction. When weight returns to the wheels after landing, the shock strut is compressed, and the centering cams separate allowing the lower shock strut (piston) to rotate in the upper strut cylinder. This rotation is controlled to steer the aircraft.

Figure 5-2-13. Landing gear position indicators and landing gear selector switch.

Section 3

Shock Absorbers

In addition to supporting the aircraft for taxi, the forces of impact on an aircraft when landing must be controlled by the landing gear. This is done in two ways:

- The shock energy is altered and transferred throughout the airframe at a different rate and time than the single strong pulse of impact.

- The shock is absorbed by converting the motion energy into heat energy.

Before curved spring steel landing struts were developed, many early aircraft were designed with rigid, welded, steel landing gear struts. Shock load transfer to the airframe is direct with this design. Using pneumatic tires helps soften the impact loads. Other common designs or devices for absorbing shock are described next.

Bungee

Some small aircraft use bungee cords on non-shock absorbing landing gear. The gear geometry allows the strut assembly to flex on landing impact. Bungee cords are positioned between the rigid airframe structure and the flexing gear assembly (Figure 5-3-1) to take up the loads and return them to the airframe at a non-damaging rate. The bungees are made of many individual small strands of elastic rubber.

Rubber

Solid, donut-type rubber cushions are also used on some aircraft landing gear. A landing gear using this type of shock absorbing system is seen in Figure 5-3-2.

Spring

Many light aircraft use flexible spring steel, aluminum, or composite struts that receive the impact of landing and return it to the airframe to dissipate at a rate that is not harmful (Figure 5-3-3). The gear flexes initially, and forces are transferred as it returns to its original position.

The most common example that use this type of non-shock absorbing landing gear are the thousands of single-engine Cessna aircraft. Cessna has used both flat spring steel gear legs and tapered tubular steel gear legs. The tubular design is lighter but requires aerodynamic fairings to maintain the same speed and climb performance as the flat steel design.

Other manufacturers make landing gear struts of this type from composite materials. These are lighter, more flexible, and do not corrode.

Air/Oil Oleo

True shock absorption occurs when the shock energy of landing impact is converted into heat energy, as in a shock strut landing gear. This common method of dissipating shock is

Figure 5-3-1. Bungee cord landing gear system.

Figure 5-3-2. Solid rubber donuts are used on some landing gear for shock absorption.

Figure 5-3-3. Cessna aircraft have used spring steel landing gear for many years.

used on aircraft of all sizes. Shock struts are self-contained hydraulic units that support an aircraft while on the ground and protect the structure during landing. Many designs of shock struts are used, but most operate similarly.

A typical pneumatic/hydraulic shock strut uses compressed air or nitrogen combined with hydraulic fluid to absorb and dissipate shock loads. It is sometimes referred to as an air/oil or oleo strut. A typical shock strut is shown in Figure 5-3-4. The shock strut is made with two telescoping cylinders or tubes that are closed on the external ends. The upper cylinder is fixed to the aircraft and does not move. The lower cylinder is called the piston and is free to slide in and out of the upper cylinder. Two chambers are formed. The lower chamber is always filled with hydraulic fluid, and the upper chamber is filled with compressed air or nitrogen. An orifice between the two cylinders provides a passage for the fluid from the bottom chamber to enter the top cylinder chamber when the strut is compressed.

Shock struts are usually equipped with an axle as part of the lower cylinder, and aircraft wheels are installed on the axles. Struts without an integral axle have provisions on the end of the lower cylinder for installing the axle assembly. All shock strut upper cylinders have suitable connections to attach the strut to the airframe.

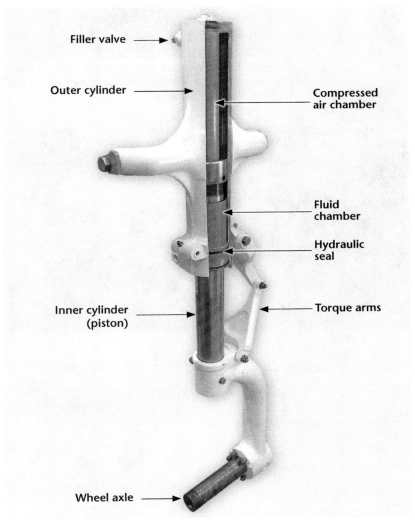

Figure 5-3-4. A landing gear shock strut controls the flow of hydraulic fluid from the lower chamber to the upper chamber during compression.

Figure 5-4-1. Torque links align the landing gear and retain the piston in the upper cylinder when the strut is extended.

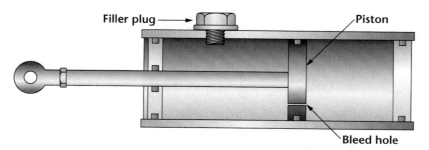

Figure 5-4-2. A shimmy damper on the nose strut of a small aircraft. The diagram shows the basic internal arrangement of most shimmy dampers.

Section 4

Torque Links and Shimmy Dampers

Torque Links

To keep the piston in the shock strut and wheels aligned, most shock struts are equipped with torque links or torque arms. One link is attached to the fixed upper cylinder. A second link is attached to the lower cylinder (piston) so it cannot rotate. This keeps the wheels aligned. The links also retain the piston in the upper cylinder when the strut is extended, such as after takeoff (Figure 5-4-1).

Nose gear struts are often equipped with a locking or disconnect pin to enable quick turning of the aircraft while towing or positioning the aircraft when on the ramp or in a hangar. Disengaging this pin allows the wheel fork spindle on some aircraft to rotate 360°, thus enabling the aircraft to be turned in a tight radius. The nose wheel of any aircraft should not ever be rotated beyond the limit lines marked on the airframe.

Shimmy Dampers

Torque links attached from the stationary upper cylinder of a nose wheel strut to the bottom moveable cylinder or piston of the strut are not sufficient to prevent most nose gear from the tendency to oscillate rapidly, or shimmy, at certain speeds. This vibration must be controlled using a shimmy damper. A shimmy damper controls nose wheel shimmy. The damper can be built integrally within the nose gear, but it is most often an external unit attached between the upper and lower shock struts. It is active during all phases of ground operation while permitting the nose gear steering system to function normally.

Aircraft not equipped with hydraulic nose wheel steering use an additional external shimmy damper unit. The case is attached firmly to the upper shock strut cylinder. The shaft is attached to the lower shock strut cylinder and to a piston inside the shimmy damper. As the lower strut cylinder tries to shimmy, hydraulic fluid is forced through a bleed hole in the piston. The restricted flow through the bleed hole dampens the oscillation (Figure 5-4-2).

Non-hydraulic shimmy dampers are certified for many aircraft. They look and fit like piston shimmy dampers but contain no fluid (Figure

5-4-3). In place of the metal piston, a rubber piston presses out against the inner diameter of the damper housing when the shimmy motion is received through the shaft. The rubber piston rides on a very thin film of grease and the rubbing action between the piston and the housing provides the damping. This is known as surface-effect damping. The materials used to construct this type of shimmy damper provide a long service life without the need to ever add fluid to the unit.

Figure 5-4-3. A non-hydraulic shimmy damper.

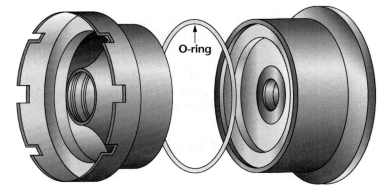

Figure 5-5-1. Two-piece aircraft wheels are found on modern, light aircraft.

Section 5

Wheels

Aircraft wheels are an important component of the landing gear system. With tires mounted on them, they support the aircraft's entire weight during taxi, takeoff, and landing. The typical aircraft wheel is lightweight, strong, and made from aluminum alloy. Some magnesium alloy wheels are also made.

Early aircraft wheels were of single-piece construction, much the same as the modern automobile wheel. As aircraft tires were improved for the purpose they serve, they were made stiffer to better absorb the forces of landing without blowing out or separating from the rim. Stretching such a tire over a single piece wheel rim was not possible.

A two-piece wheel was developed. Early two-piece aircraft wheels were essentially one-piece wheels with a removable rim to allow mounting access for the tire. Later, wheels with two nearly symmetrical halves were developed. A typical modern aircraft wheel is shown in Figure 5-5-1. Nearly all modern aircraft wheels are of this two-piece construction.

Construction

The typical modern two-piece aircraft wheel is cast or forged from aluminum or magnesium alloy. The halves are bolted together and contain a groove at the mating surface for an O-ring, which seals the rim because most modern aircraft use tubeless tires. The bead seat area of a wheel is where the tire contacts the wheel. It is the critical area that accepts the significant tensile loads from the tire during landing.

Wheel halves are not identical. The primary reason for this is that the inboard wheel half must have a means for accepting and driving the rotors of the aircraft brakes that are

mounted on both main wheels. Tangs on the rotor are fitted into steel reinforced keyways on many wheels. Other wheels have steel keys bolted to the inner wheel halves. These are made to fit slots in the perimeter of the brake rotor. Some small aircraft wheels have provisions for bolting the brake rotor to the inner wheel half. Regardless, the inner wheel half is distinguishable from the outer wheel half by its brake mounting feature.

The outboard wheel half bolts to the inboard wheel half to make up the wheel assembly on which the tire is mounted. The center boss is constructed to receive a bearing cup and bearing assembly as it does on the inboard wheel half. The outer bearing and end of the axle is capped to prevent contaminants from entering this area. Aircraft with antiskid brake systems typically mount the wheel-spin transducer here. It is sealed and can also serve as a hub cap.

The outboard wheel half also provides a convenient location of the valve stem used to inflate and deflate tubeless tires. Alternately, it can contain a hole through which a valve stem extension passes from the inner wheel half or the valve stem itself might fit through such a hole if a tube-type tire is used.

The landing gear area is such a hostile environment that frequent inspections are required of the landing gear including the wheels, tires, and brakes. The general condition of wheel assemblies should be inspected at every preflight and in scheduled maintenance.

Section 6

Tires

Aircraft tires can be tube-type or tubeless. They support the aircraft's weight while it is on the ground and provide the necessary traction for braking and stopping. The tires also help absorb the shock of landing and cushion the roughness of takeoff, rollout, and taxi operations. Aircraft tires must be carefully maintained to perform as required. They accept a variety of static and dynamic stresses and must do so dependably in a wide range of operating conditions.

Tire Classifications

Aircraft tires are classified in various ways:

- Type
- Whether they have tubes or are tubeless
- Ply rating
- Bias ply tires or radials
- Dimensions

Type

A common classification of aircraft tires is by type as classified by the United States Tire and Rim Association. Although nine types of tires are made, only Types I, III, VII, and VIII, also known as a Three-Part Nomenclature tires, are still in production.

Type I. Type I tires are manufactured, but their design is no longer active. They are used on fixed-gear aircraft and are designated only by their nominal overall diameter in inches. These are smooth profile tires that are obsolete for use in the modern aviation fleet. They can be found on older aircraft.

Type III. Type III tires are common general aviation tires. They are typically used on light aircraft with landing speeds of 160 miles per hour (mph) or less. Type III tires are relatively low-pressure tires that have small rim diameters, compared to the overall width of the tire.

Type VII. Type VII tires are high-performance tires used on jet aircraft. They are inflated to high pressure and have exceptional high load-carrying capability.

Type VIII. Type VIII aircraft tires are used on high-performance jet aircraft. The typical Type VIII tire has relatively low profile and can operate at very high speeds and with very high loads. It is the most modern design of all tire types.

Tube or Tubeless

Aircraft tires can have tubes or be tubeless. This is often used as a means of tire classification. Tires that are made to be used without a tube inside have an inner liner designed to hold air. Tube tires do not contain this inner liner because the tube holds the air from leaking out of the tire. Tires that are to be used without a tube have the word *tubeless* on the sidewall. If this designation is absent, the tire requires a tube.

Bias Plies or Radial

Another means of classifying an aircraft tire is by the direction of the plies used in constructing the tire, either bias or radial.

Tire plies are reinforcing layers of fabric encased in rubber that are laid into the tire to provide strength. In early tires, the number of plies used was directly related to the load the tire could carry. Today, refinements to tire construction techniques and using modern materials to build up aircraft tires makes the exact number of plies somewhat irrelevant when determining the tire's strength. More details about bias and radial ply tires are given in the Tire Construction section.

Tire Construction

An aircraft tire is constructed for the purpose it serves. Unlike an automobile or truck tire, it does not have to carry a load for a long period of continuous operation. However, an aircraft tire must absorb the high-impact loads of landing and be able to operate at high speeds even if only for a short time. The deflection built into an aircraft tire is more than twice that of an automobile tire. This enables it to handle the forces during landings without being damaged. Use only tires designed for an aircraft as specified by the manufacturer.

To help you understand tire construction, the next discussions identify the many tire components and how they affect a tire's characteristics and performance. Figure 5-6-1 introduces the tire nomenclature used.

Carcass Plies

Carcass plies, sometimes called casing plies, are used to form the tire. Each ply consists of

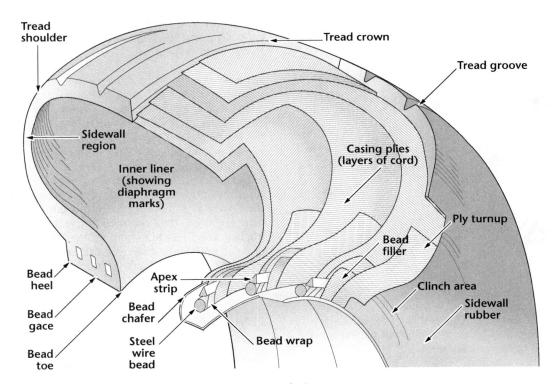

Figure 5-6-1. Construction nomenclature of an aircraft tire.

fabric, usually nylon, sandwiched between two layers of rubber. The plies are applied in layers to give the tire strength and form the tire's carcass body. The ends of each ply are anchored by wrapping them around the bead on both sides of the tire to form the ply turn-ups. The angle of the fiber in the ply is manipulated to create a bias tire or radial tire as desired. Typically, radial tires require fewer plies than bias tires.

Once the plies are in place, bias tires and radial tires each have their own type of protective layers on top of the plies but under the tread of the running surface of the tire. On bias tires, these single or multiple layers of nylon and rubbers are called tread reinforcing plies. On radial tires, an undertread and a protector ply do the same job. These additional plies stabilize and strengthen the tire's crown area. They reduce tread distortion under load and increase stability of the tire at high speeds. The reinforcing plies and protector plies also help resist puncture and cutting while protecting the tire's carcass body.

Bias plies. Traditional aircraft tires are bias ply tires. The plies are wrapped to form the tire and give it strength. The angle of the plies in relation to the direction of rotation of the tire varies between 30° and 60°. In this manner, the plies have the bias of the fabric from which they are constructed facing the direction of rotation and across the tire. Therefore, they are called bias tires. The result is flex-

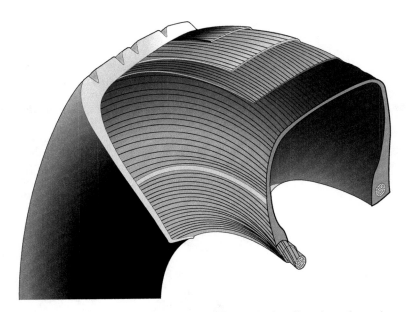

Figure 5-6-2. A bias ply tire's fabric is oriented with the direction of rotation and the sidewall. Because fabric can stretch on the bias, the tire is flexible and can absorb loads. Adding plies increases strength.

ibility because the sidewall can flex with the fabric plies laid on the bias (Figure 5-6-2).

Radial plies. Some modern aircraft tires are radial tires. The plies in radial tires are laid at a 90° angle to the direction of rotation of the tire. This configuration puts the nonstretchable fiber of the plies perpendicular to the sidewall and direction of rotation. This creates

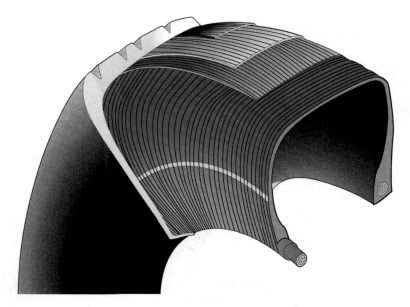

Figure 5-6-3. A radial tire's fabric fiber is oriented with and at 90° to the direction of rotation and the sidewall. This restricts sidewall flexibility but strengthens the tire, allowing it to carry heavy loads.

strength in the tire allowing it to carry high loads with less deformation (Figure 5-6-3).

Bead

The tire bead is an important part of an aircraft tire. It anchors the tire carcass and provides a dimensioned, firm mounting surface for the tire on the wheel rim. Tire beads are strong. They are typically made from high-strength carbon steel wire bundles encased in rubber. One, two, or three bead bundles are used on each side of the tire depending on its size and the load it is designed to handle. Radial tires have a single bead bundle on each side of the tire. The bead transfers the impact loads and deflection forces to the

wheel rim. The bead toe is closest to the tire centerline and the bead heel fits against the flange of the wheel rim.

An apex strip is additional rubber formed around the bead to give a contour for anchoring the ply turn-ups. Layers of fabric and rubber called flippers are placed around the beads to insulate the carcass from the beads and improve tire durability. Chafers are also used in this area. Chafer strips made of fabric or rubber are laid over the outer carcass plies after the plies are wrapped around the beads. The chafers protect the carcass from damage when mounting and demounting the tire. They also help reduce the effects of wear and chafing between the wheel rim and the tire bead especially during dynamic operations.

Tread

The tread is the crown area of the tire designed to come into contact with the ground. It is a rubber compound formulated to resist wear, abrasion, cutting, and cracking. It is also made to resist heat buildup. Most modern aircraft tire tread is formed with circumferential grooves that create tire ribs. The grooves provide cooling and help channel water from under the tire in wet conditions to help the tire adhere to the ground.

As illustrated in Figure 5-6-4 aircraft tire treads are designed for different uses. View A shows a rib tread designed for use on paved surfaces. It is the most common aircraft tire tread design. View B shows a diamond tread designed for unpaved runways. View C shows an all-weather tread that combines a ribbed center tread with a diamond tread pattern of the edges. View D shows a smooth tread tire found on older, slow aircraft.

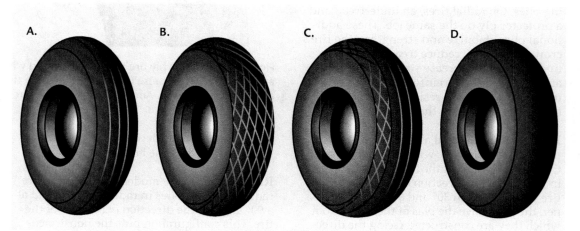

Figure 5-6-4. Aircraft tire treads are designed for different uses.

The tread is designed to stabilize the aircraft on the operating surface and wears with use. Many aircraft tires are designed with protective undertread layers. Extra tread reinforcement is sometimes done with breakers. These are layers of nylon cord fabric under the tread that strengthen the tread while protecting the carcass plies. Tires with reinforced tread are often designed to be retreaded and used again once the tread has worn beyond limits.

Sidewall

The sidewall of an aircraft tire is a layer of rubber designed to protect the carcass plies. It can contain compounds designed to resist the negative effects of ozone on the tire. It is also where the manufacturer places information about the tire. The tire sidewall imparts little strength to the cord body. Its main function is protection. (Figure 5-6-5)

The inner sidewall of a tire is covered by the tire inner liner. A tube tire has a thin rubber liner adhered to the inner surface to prevent the tube from chafing on the carcass plies. Tubeless tires are lined with a thicker, less permeable rubber. This replaces the tube and contains the nitrogen or inflation air in the tire and keeps it from seeping through the carcass plies.

Chine

Some tire sidewalls are mounded to form a chine. A chine is a built-in deflector used on nose wheels of certain aircraft, usually those with fuselage-mounted engines. The chine diverts runway water to the side and away from the engine intake. Tires with a chine on both sidewalls are produced for aircraft with a single nose wheel. A chine is shown in Figure 5-6-6.

Tube Tires

Many aircraft tires use a tube inside to contain air. Aircraft tire tubes are made of a natural rubber compound. They contain the air with minimal leakage. Unreinforced and special reinforced heavy-duty tubes are made. The heavy-duty tubes have nylon reinforcing fabric layered into the rubber to provide strength to resist chafing and to protect against heat such as during braking.

Tubes come in a wide range of sizes. Only the tube specified for the applicable tire size must be used.

Figure 5-6-5. A sidewall's main function is protection, but manufacturers also place tire information on it.

Figure 5-6-6. A chine diverts runway water away from the engine's intake.

Tire Inspection

Crews regularly inspect condition of tires that are mounted on the aircraft. To ensure proper tire performance, they continuously monitor inflation pressure, tread wear and condition, and sidewall condition.

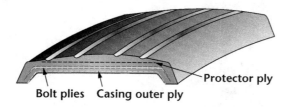

Figure 5-6-7. Normal tread wear on a tire.

Figure 5-6-8. Landing with the brake on causes a flat spot, exposing the underlying plies. The tire must be replaced.

Tread Condition

A tire's tread condition can be determined while the tire is inflated and mounted on the aircraft. Here, we discuss some of the tread conditions and damage that you might encounter while inspecting tires.

Evenly worn tread is a sign of proper tire maintenance. Uneven tread wear has a cause that should be investigated and corrected. Figure 5-6-7 shows normal tire wear.

Asymmetrical tread wear can be caused by the wheels being out of alignment. Occasionally, asymmetrical tire wear is a result of landing gear geometry that cannot be, or is not required to be, corrected. It can also be caused by regular taxiing with a single engine or high-speed cornering while taxiing.

A flat spot on a tire is the result of the tire skidding (not rotating) on the runway surface. This occurs when the brakes lock while the aircraft is moving (Figure 5-6-8).

In addition to tread wear, an aircraft tire should be inspected for damage. Cuts, bruises, bulges, imbedded foreign objects, chipping, and other damage must be within limits to continue the tire in service.

Inflation

To perform as designed, an aircraft tire must be properly inflated.

Underinflated aircraft tires wear unevenly, which leads to premature tire replacement. Operating with underinflated tires leads to wear on the outside edge of the tire. Underinflated tires can also creep or slip on the wheel rim when under stress or when the brakes are applied. Severely underinflated tires can pinch the sidewall between the rim and the runway causing sidewall and rim damage. Damage to the bead and lower sidewall area are also likely. This type of abuse like any over flexing damages the integrity of the tire, and it must be replaced.

Tire overinflation is another undesirable condition. Although overinflation does not cause carcass damage, it does reduce traction. Over a long time, overinflation leads to premature tread wear in the center of the tread. Therefore, overinflation reduces the number of landings before the tire must be replaced. It makes the tire more susceptible to bruises, cutting, shock damage, and blowout (Figure 5-6-9).

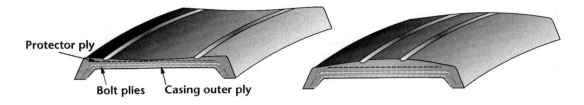

Protector ply

Bolt plies   Casing outer ply

Tread wear on an overinflated tire   **Tread wear on an underinflated tire**

Figure 5-6-9. Overinflated tires lack adherence to the runway and develop excess tread wear in the center of the tread. Underinflated tires develop excess tread wear on the tire shoulders.

Section 7

Brakes

Very early aircraft had no brake system to slow and stop the aircraft. Instead, they relied on slow speeds, soft airfield surfaces, and the friction developed by the tail skid to reduce speed during ground operation. Brake systems designed for aircraft became common after World War I as the speed and complexity of aircraft increased, and the use of smooth, paved runway surfaces became common.

Purpose

All modern aircraft are equipped with brakes. To safely operate an aircraft on the ground, the brakes must function properly. The brakes slow the aircraft and stop it in a reasonable time. They hold the aircraft stationary during engine run-up and, in many cases, steer the aircraft during taxi. On most aircraft, each of the main wheels is equipped with a brake unit. The nose wheel or tailwheel does not have a brake.

In the typical brake system, mechanical or hydraulic linkages (or both) to the rudder pedals allow the pilot to control the brakes. Pushing on the top of the right rudder pedal activates the brake on the right main wheel and pushing on the top of the left rudder pedal operates the brake on the left main wheel. Brake operation involves creating friction, which converts the kinetic energy of motion into heat energy. Much heat is developed, and forces on the brake system components are demanding. For effective operation, the brakes must be properly adjusted, inspected, and maintained.

Brake Types

Modern aircraft typically use disc brakes. The disc rotates with the turning wheel assembly, and when the brakes are applied, a stationary caliper resists the rotation by causing friction against the disc. The aircraft's size, weight, and landing speed influence the design and complexity of the disc brake system. Single, dual, and multiple disc brakes are common types of brakes. Segmented rotor brakes are used on large aircraft. Expander tube brakes are found on older, large aircraft. Carbon discs are increasingly being used in the modern aviation fleet.

Single Disc Brakes

Small, light aircraft typically achieve effective braking using a single disc that is keyed or bolted to each wheel. As the wheel turns, so does the disc. Braking occurs when friction is applied to both sides of the disc from a non-rotating caliper that is bolted to the landing gear axle flange. When the brakes are applied, hydraulic pressure on pistons in the caliper housing force wearable brake pads or linings against the disc. When the upper halves of the rudder pedals are pressed, hydraulic master cylinders connected to the rudder pedals supply the pressure. Figure 5-7-1 shows a single disc brake.

Figure 5-7-1. A single disc brake used on light aircraft.

Floating-Disc Brakes

A common brake with a single disc, a floating disc, and fixed caliper is called a floating-disc brake. The caliper straddles the disc. It has three cylinders bored through the housing, but on other brakes this number might vary. Each cylinder accepts an actuating piston assembly composed mainly of a piston, a return spring, and an automatic adjusting pin. Each brake assembly has six brake linings or pucks. Three are on the ends of the pistons, which are in the outboard side of the caliper. They are designed to move in and out with the pistons and apply pressure to the outboard side of the disc. Three more linings are opposite of these pucks on the inboard side of the caliper. These linings are stationary.

The brake disc is keyed to the wheel. It is free to move laterally in the key slots. This is known as a floating disc. When the brakes are applied, the pistons move out from the outboard cylinders and their pucks contact the disc. The disc slides slightly in the key slots until the inboard stationary pucks also contact the disc. The result is a fairly even amount of friction applied to each side of the disc and thus, the rotating motion is slowed.

When brake pressure is released, the return spring in each piston assembly forces the piston back away from the disc. The spring provides a preset clearance between each puck and the disc. The self-adjusting feature of the brake maintains the same clearance, regardless of the amount of wear on the brake pucks.

Fixed-Disc Brakes

Even pressure must be applied to both sides of the brake disc to generate the required friction and obtain consistent wear from the brake linings. The floating disc does this. It can also be done by bolting the disc rigidly to the wheel and allowing the brake caliper and linings to float laterally when pressure is applied. This is the design of a common fixed-disc brake used on light aircraft (Figure 5-7-2).

The fixed-disc, floating-caliper design allows the brake caliper and linings to adjust position in relationship to the disc. Linings are riveted to the pressure plate and backplate. Two anchor bolts that pass through the pressure plate are secured to the cylinder assembly. The other ends of the bolts are free to slide in and out of bushings in the torque plate, which is bolted to the axle flange. The cylinder assembly is bolted to the backplate to secure the assembly around the disc. When pressure is applied, the caliper and linings center on the disc via the sliding action of the anchor bolts in the torque plate bushings (Figure 5-7-3). This provides equal pressure to both sides of the disc to slow its rotation.

Multiple-Disc Brakes

Dual-disc brakes are used on aircraft where a single disc on each wheel does not supply sufficient braking friction. Two discs are keyed to the wheel instead of one. A center carrier is mounted between the two discs. It has linings on each side that contact each of the discs when the brakes are applied. The caliper mounting bolts are long and mount through the center carrier and the backplate, which bolts to the housing assembly.

Large, heavy aircraft require the use of multiple-disc brakes—heavy-duty brakes designed for use with power brake control valves or power boost master cylinders (discussed later

Brake lining

Fixed disc

Figure 5-7-2. A brake on a light aircraft is a fixed-disc brake. It allows the brake caliper to move laterally on anchor bolts to deliver even pressure to each side of the disc.

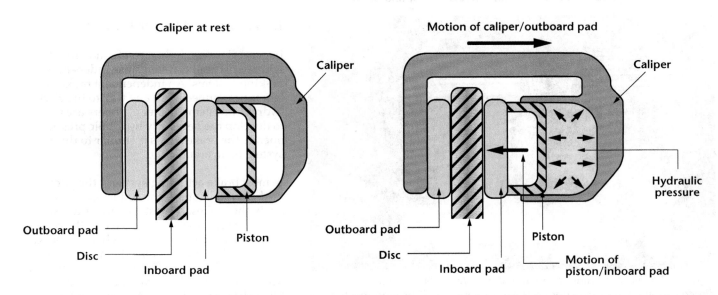

Figure 5-7-3. The caliper assembly at rest (left) and with hydraulic pressure applied (right), which forces the pads against the disc.

in this chapter). The brake assembly consists of an extended bearing carrier like a torque tube type unit that bolts to the axle flange. It supports the various brake parts, including an annular cylinder and piston, a series of steel discs alternating with copper or bronze-plated discs, a backplate, and a backplate retainer. The steel stators are keyed to the bearing carrier, and the copper or bronze plated rotors are keyed to the rotating wheel. Hydraulic pressure applied to the piston causes the entire stack of stators and rotors to be compressed. This creates enormous friction and heat and slows the wheel's rotation.

The great heat generated while slowing the wheel rotation on large and high-performance aircraft is problematic. To better dissipate this heat, segmented rotor-disc brakes have been developed. Segmented rotor-disc brakes are multiple-disc brakes but of more modern design than the type discussed earlier. Many variations are made. Most feature numerous elements that help control and dissipate heat. Segmented rotor-disc brakes are heavy-duty brakes especially adapted for use with the high-pressure hydraulic systems of power brake systems. Braking is performed with several sets of stationary, high-friction brake linings that make contact with rotating segments. The rotors are constructed with slots or in sections with space between them, which helps dissipate heat and give the brake its name. Segmented rotor multiple-disc brakes are the standard brake used on high-performance aircraft.

The segmented multiple-disc brake has given many years of reliable service to the aviation industry. It has evolved through time to make it lightweight and to quickly and safely dis-

sipate the frictional heat of braking. The latest iteration of the multiple-disc brake is the carbon-disc brake. These are found on high performance and air carrier aircraft.

Carbon brakes are so named because carbon fiber materials are used to construct the brake rotors (Figure 5-7-4). Carbon brakes are about 40 percent lighter than conventional brakes. On a large, transport categoryt aircraft, this alone can save several hundred pounds in weight. The carbon fiber discs are noticeably thicker than sintered steel rotors but are extremely light.

Figure 5-7-4. A carbon brake from an Airbus A320.

Figure 5-7-5. Master cylinders on an independent brake system are directly connected to the rudder pedals or connected through mechanical linkage.

Carbon brakes can withstand temperatures 50 percent higher than steel component brakes. The maximum designed operating temperature is limited by the ability of adjacent components to withstand the high temperature. They have been shown to withstand two to three times the heat of a steel brake in non-aircraft applications. Carbon rotors also dissipate heat faster than steel rotors. A carbon rotor maintains its strength and dimensions at high temperatures. Moreover, carbon brakes last 20 to 50 percent longer than steel brakes, which results in reduced maintenance.

Brake Actuating Systems

The various brake assemblies, described in the previous section, all use hydraulic power to operate. Different means of delivering the required hydraulic fluid pressure to brake assemblies and one electric brake system are discussed in this section.

- An independent system not part of the aircraft main hydraulic system

- A booster system that uses the aircraft hydraulic system intermittently when needed

- A power brake system that uses the aircraft main hydraulic system or systems as a source of pressure

- Electric brakes that are not hydraulic at all

Systems on different aircraft vary, but the general operation is similar to those described.

Independent Master Cylinders

In general, small, light aircraft and aircraft without hydraulic systems use independent braking systems. An independent brake system is not connected in any way to the aircraft hydraulic system. Master cylinders are used to develop the necessary hydraulic pressure to operate the brakes. This is similar to the brake system of an automobile.

In most brake actuating systems, the pilot pushes on the tops of the rudder pedals to apply the brakes. A master cylinder for each brake is mechanically connected to the corresponding rudder pedal (i.e., right main brake to the right rudder pedal, left main brake to the left rudder pedal) (Figure 5-7-5). When the pedal is depressed, a piston in a sealed fluid-filled chamber in the master cylinder forces hydraulic fluid through a line to the pistons in the brake assembly. The brake pistons push the brake linings against the brake rotor to create the friction that slows the wheel rotation (Figure 5-7-6). As the pedal is pushed harder, pressure increases throughout the entire brake systems and against the rotor.

Many master cylinders have built-in reservoirs for the brake hydraulic fluid. Others have one remote reservoir that services both of the aircraft's two master cylinders (Figure 5-7-7). A few light aircraft with nose wheel steering have only one master cylinder that actuates both main wheel brakes. This is possible because steering the aircraft during taxi does not require differential braking. Regardless of the setup, the master cylinder builds up the pressure required for braking.

A parking brake for this remote reservoir master cylinder brake system is a ratcheting mechanical device between the master cylinder and the rudder pedals. With the brakes applied, engage the ratchet by pulling the parking brake handle. To release the brakes, press the rudder further, which allows the ratchet to disengage.

Boosted Brakes

In an independent braking system, the pressure applied to the brakes is only as great as the foot pressure applied to the top of the rudder pedal. Boosted brake actuating systems augment the force developed by the pilot with hydraulic system pressure when needed. The boost is applied only in heavy braking and results in greater pressure applied to the brakes than the pilot alone can provide. Boosted brakes are used on medium and larger aircraft that do not require a full-power brake actuating system.

Power Brakes

Large and high-performance aircraft are equipped with power brakes to slow, stop, and hold the aircraft. Power brake actuating systems use the aircraft hydraulic system as the source of power to apply the brakes. The flight crew presses on the top of the rudder pedal for braking as with the other actuating systems. The volume and pressure of hydraulic fluid required cannot be produced by a master cylinder. Instead, a power brake control valve or brake metering valve receives the brake pedal input either directly or through linkages. The valve meters hydraulic fluid to the corresponding brake assembly in direct relation to the pressure applied to the pedal.

Many power brake system designs are used. Most are similar to the simplified system illustrated in Figure 5-7-8 view A. Power brake systems are made to facilitate graduated brake pressure control, brake pedal feel, and the necessary redundancy required in case of hydraulic system failure. Large-aircraft brake systems integrate antiskid detection and correction devices, which are needed because wheel skid is difficult to detect on the flight deck without sensors. However, a skid can be quickly controlled automatically by controlling the hydraulic fluid pressure that is applied to the brakes.

Hydraulic fuses are also commonly found in power brake systems. The hostile environment around the landing gear increases the potential for a line to break or sever, a fitting to fail, or other hydraulic system malfunctions to occur where hydraulic fluid is lost en route to the brake assemblies. A fuse stops any excessive flow of fluid when detected by closing to retain the remaining fluid in the hydraulic system. Shuttle valves are used to direct flow from optional sources of fluid, such as in redundant systems or when using an emergency brake power source. An airliner power brake system is illustrated in Figure 5-7-8 view B.

Electric Brakes

With the dawn of the 21st century, electric brakes for aircraft were introduced, which improved braking power and greatly reduced weight. For example, depending on the model, some modern airliners can be from 141 and 244 lbs. lighter by changing to electric brakes. This improves the aircraft's overall efficiency and a corresponding fuel savings.

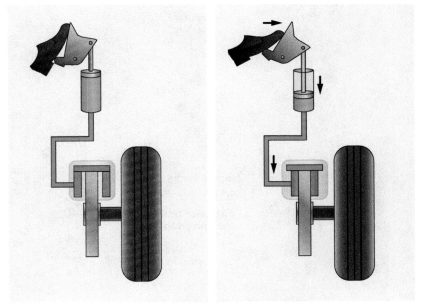

Figure 5-7-6. Pressing the rudder pedal creates hydraulic pressure that forces the brake pads against the brake rotor.

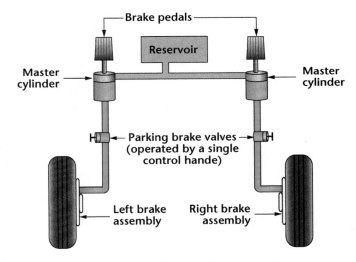

Figure 5-7-7. A remote reservoir services both master cylinders on some independent braking systems.

With electric brake systems, electronic control units and electrical wire replace the hydraulic lines and equipment, and electromechanical actuators replace the hydraulic pistons. When the pilot applies the brake pedal, a computer sends a signal to the control unit, which translates these electrical signals into an electromechanical command. The actuators on the brake ring (replacing the hydraulic pistons) are energized and press the carbon discs against each other, much the same as you see in any multiple-disc brake system. These actuators use small electric motors that drive a ball screw and nut assembly. The screw is linked to the piston that presses the carbon discs together just like a hydraulic piston does.

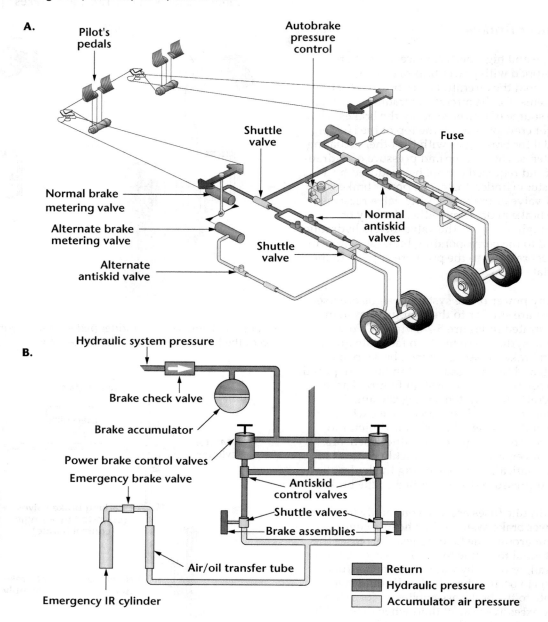

Figure 5-7-8. The orientation of components in a basic power brake system is shown in A. The general layout of an airliner power brake system is shown in B.

Antiskid and Auto Brakes

Large aircraft with power brakes require antiskid systems. In the flight deck, it is not possible to immediately tell when a wheel stops rotating and begins to skid, especially in aircraft with multiple-wheel main landing gear assemblies. If a skid is not corrected, it can quickly lead to a tire blowout, possibly damaging the aircraft, and causing the flight crew to lose control.

The antiskid system detects wheel skid, and it detects when wheel skid is imminent. It automatically relieves pressure to the brake piston or pistons of the wheel by momentarily connecting the pressurized brake fluid area to the hydraulic system return line. This allows the wheel to rotate and avoid a skid. Lower pressure is then maintained to the brake at a level that slows the wheel without skidding.

Aircraft equipped with automatic (auto) brakes typically bypass the brake control valves or brake metering valves and use a separate auto brake control valve to provide this function. In addition to the redundancy provided, auto brakes rely on the antiskid system to adjust pressure to the brakes if required because of an impending skid. Figure 5-7-9 shows a simplified diagram of a large aircraft brake system with the auto brake valve in relation to the main metering valve and antiskid valves in this eight-main wheel system.

Hydroplaning

Skidding on a wet, icy, or dry runway brings the threat of tire failure because of heat buildup and rapid tire wear damage. Hydroplaning on a wet runway can be overlooked as a damaging condition for a tire. Water building up in front of the tire provides a surface for the tire to run on and contact with the runway surface is lost. This is known as dynamic hydroplaning. Steering ability and braking action is also lost. A skid results if the brakes are applied and held.

Viscous hydroplaning occurs on runways with a thin film of water that mixes with contaminants to cause an extremely slick condition. This can also happen on a smooth runway surface. A tire with a locked brake during viscous hydroplaning can form an area of reverted rubber or skid burn in the tread. Although the tire can continue in service if the damage is not too severe, it can be cause for removal if the reinforcing tread or protector ply is penetrated. The same damage can occur while skidding on ice.

Modern runways are designed to drain water rapidly and provide good traction for tires in wet conditions. A compromise exists in that crosscut runways and textured runway surfaces cause tires to wear at a greater rate than a smooth runway.

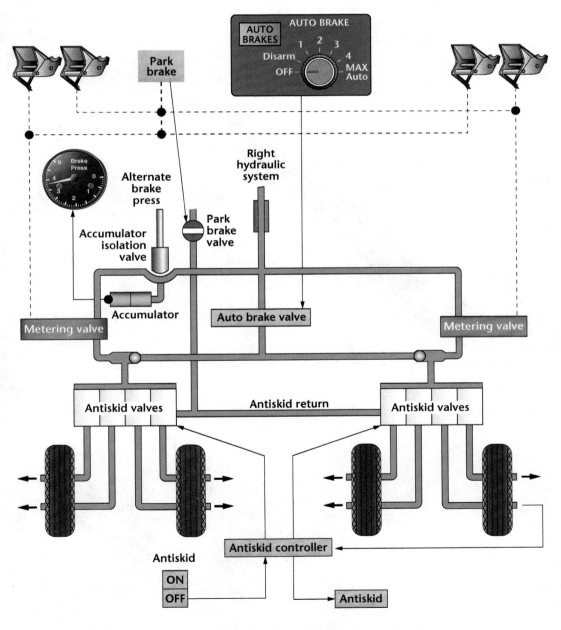

Figure 5-7-9. An airliner brake system with auto brake and antiskid.

6

Fuel Systems

Section 1

Fuel System Purpose

All powered aircraft require fuel on board to operate the engine or engines. A fuel system consisting of storage tanks, pumps, filters, valves, fuel lines, metering devices, and monitoring devices is designed and certified under strict guidelines of Title 14 of the *Code of Federal Regulations* (14 CFR). Each system must provide an uninterrupted flow of contaminant-free fuel regardless of the aircraft's attitude. Because the fuel load can be a significant portion of the aircraft's weight, a sufficiently strong airframe must be designed. Varying fuel loads and shifts in weight during maneuvers must not negatively affect control of the aircraft in flight.

Design Criteria

Each fuel system must be constructed and arranged to ensure fuel flow at a rate and pressure established for proper engine function under each likely operating condition. This includes any maneuver for which certification is requested and during which the engine could be operating (Figure 6-1-1). Each fuel system must be arranged so that no fuel pump can draw fuel from more than one tank at a time. A means is also required to prevent air from entering the system.

Each fuel system for a multiengine airplane must be arranged so that, in at least one system configuration, if any one component (other than a fuel tank) fails, it does not result in the loss of power of more than one engine or require the pilot or flight crew's immediate

Left: Over-the-wing refueling an aircraft is similar to refueling an automobile.

Figure 6-1-1. Aircraft fuel systems must deliver fuel during any maneuver for which the aircraft is certified.

action to prevent the loss of power of more than one engine.

The filler caps must be designed to minimize the probability of incorrect installation or in-flight loss.

Fuel Flow

It is vital that the aircraft's fuel system can provide fuel at a rate of flow and pressure sufficient for proper engine operation. Moreover, it must deliver the fuel at the aircraft attitude that is most critical in relation to fuel feed and quantity of unusable fuel. For gravity-flow fuel systems, the fuel flow rate must be 150 percent of the takeoff fuel consumption of the engine. For fuel pump systems, the fuel flow rate for each pump system (main and reserve supply) for each reciprocating engine must be 125 percent of the fuel flow required at the maximum takeoff power. However, the fuel pressure, with main and emergency pumps operating simultaneously, must not exceed the fuel inlet pressure limits of the engine. Auxiliary fuel systems and fuel transfer systems may operate under slightly different parameters. Turbine engine fuel systems must provide at least 100 percent required by the engine under each intended operating condition and maneuver.

Flow between Interconnected Tanks

In a gravity feed fuel system with interconnected tank outlets, it must be impossible for enough fuel to flow between the tanks to cause an overflow of fuel from any tank vent under the conditions specified in the regulations at 14 CFR 23.959. If fuel can be pumped from one tank to another in flight, the fuel tank vents and the fuel transfer system must be designed so that no structural damage to any airplane component can occur because of overfilling of any tank.

Unusable Fuel Supply

In any fuel tank arrangement, there is some fuel that cannot get to the engine. This could be because of internal baffles in the tank, or because the outlet does not drain the tank fully. The unusable fuel supply for each tank must be established. It cannot be less than the quantity at which the first evidence of malfunctioning appears under the most adverse fuel-feed condition occurring under each intended operation and flight maneuver involving that tank. The effect on the usable fuel quantity because of a failure of any pump is also determined.

Fuel System Hot-Weather Operation

Each fuel system must be free from vapor lock when using fuel at its critical temperature, with respect to vapor formation, when operating the airplane in all critical operating and environmental conditions for which approval is requested.

Section 2

Fuel Tanks

Each fuel tank must be able to withstand, without failing, the vibration, inertia, fluid, and structural loads to which it could be subjected in operation. The total usable capacity of any tank must be enough for at least 30 minutes of operation at maximum continuous power. Also, each fuel quantity indicator must be adjusted to account for the unusable fuel supply.

Three basic types of aircraft fuel tanks are used: rigid tanks, bladder tanks, and integral tanks. The type of aircraft, its design and intended use, and the aircraft age determine which fuel tank is installed in an aircraft.

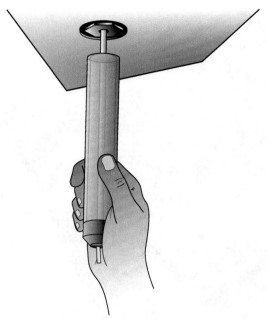

Figure 6-2-1. Sumping a fuel tank with a device that collects the fuel sample in a clear cylinder so that you can examine it for contaminants.

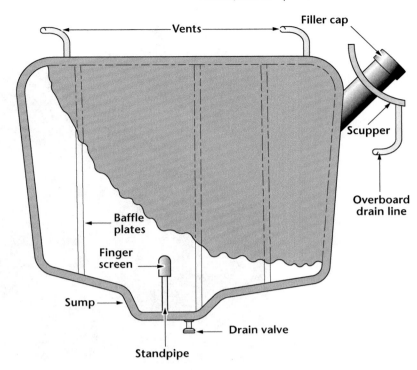

Figure 6-2-2. A typical rigid fuel tank and its parts.

Most tanks are constructed of noncorrosive materials. They are typically made to be vented either through a vent cap or a vent line. Aircraft fuel tanks have a low area called a sump where contaminants and water can settle. The sump has a drain valve used to remove the impurities in preflight walk-around inspection (Figure 6-2-1).

Most aircraft fuel tanks contain some sort of baffling to subdue the fuel from shifting rapidly in flight maneuvers. Using a scupper constructed around the fuel fill opening to drain away any spilled fuel is also common.

Rigid Fuel Tanks

Many aircraft, especially older ones, use an obvious choice for fuel tank construction. A rigid tank is made from various materials, and it is strapped into the airframe structure. They typically are made from aluminum alloy or stainless steel and are riveted and seam welded to prevent leaks. Figure 6-2-2 shows the parts of a typical rigid fuel tank.

Regardless of the actual construction of rigid metal tanks, they must be supported by the airframe and held in place with some sort of padded strap to resist shifting in flight. The wings are the most popular location for fuel tanks. Figure 6-2-3 shows a fuel tank bay in a wing root with the tank straps. Some tanks are formed to be part of the leading edge of the wing. These are assembled using electric

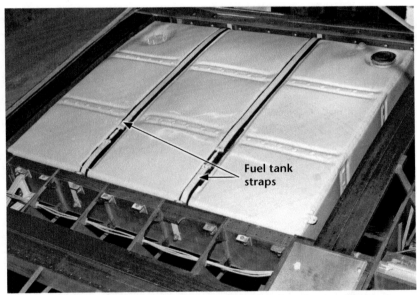

Figure 6-2-3. A fuel tank bay in the root of a light aircraft wing. Padded straps hold the fuel tank securely in the structure.

resistance welding and are sealed with a compound that is poured into the tank and allowed to cure. Many fuselage tanks also exist. In all cases, the structural integrity of the airframe does not rely on the fuselage tank or tanks being installed, so the tanks are not considered integral.

Being able to remove and repair or replace a fuel tank can be a great convenience if the tank leaks or malfunctions.

Figure 6-2-4. A typical bladder fuel tank for a light aircraft.

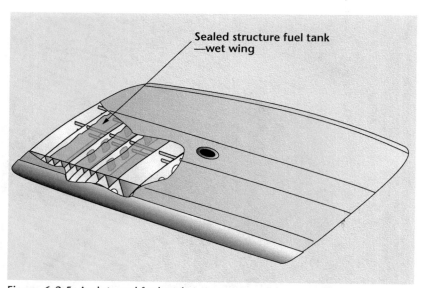

Figure 6-2-5. An integral fuel tank.

Bladder Fuel Tanks

A fuel tank made from a reinforced flexible material is called a bladder tank. This can be used instead of a rigid tank. A bladder tank contains most of the features and components of a rigid tank but does not require as large of an opening in the aircraft skin to install. The tank, or fuel cell as it is sometimes called, can be rolled up and put into a specially prepared structural bay or cavity through a small opening, such as an inspection opening.

Once inside, it can be unfurled to its full size. Bladder tanks must be attached to the structure with clips or other fastening devices. They should lie smooth and unwrinkled in the bay. It is especially important that no wrinkles exist on the bottom surface so that fuel contaminants are not blocked from settling into the tank sump (Figure 6-2-4).

Bladder fuel tanks are used on aircraft of all sizes. They are strong and have a long service life. When a bladder tank develops a leak, a technician can patch it following manufacturer's instructions. The tank can also be removed and sent to a repair station to perform repairs.

Integral Fuel Tanks

On many aircraft, especially transport category and high-performance aircraft, part of the structure of the wings or fuselage is sealed with a fuel-resistant sealant to form a fuel tank. The sealed skin and structural members provide the highest volume of space available with the lowest weight. This type of tank is called an integral fuel tank because it forms a tank as a unit in the airframe structure.

Integral fuel tanks in the otherwise unused space in the wings are most common. Aircraft with integral fuel tanks in the wings are said to have wet wings. For fuel management purposes, sometimes a wing is sealed into separate tanks and can include a surge tank or an overflow tank, which is normally empty but sealed to hold fuel when needed.

Baffling is used to keep the fuel from sloshing when an aircraft maneuvers, especially in long, horizontal integral wing tanks. Baffle check valves are commonly used. These valves allow fuel to move to the low, inboard sections of the tank but prevent it from moving outboard. They ensure that the fuel boost pumps in the bottom of the tanks at the lowest points above the sumps always have fuel to pump regardless of aircraft attitude. Figure 6-2-5 is an example of a wet wing integral fuel tank.

Header Tank

Although, technically, it is not another type of tank, some aircraft have a small tank, called a header tank, to meet specific needs. On some older aircraft with fuel tanks in the wings, a small header tank can be installed to help maintain constant fuel flow to the engine regardless of the attitude of the aircraft.

In some aerobatic aircraft, a header tank supplies fuel to the engine when the aircraft is in unusual positions. In such a plane, the main fuel tanks are in the wings, which are higher than the engine. In normal flight attitudes, the fuel has a gravity feed to the suction of the engine-driven fuel pump. For inverted flight, a small header tank near the pilot's feet is used. It is connected to the main tanks in the wings; in upright flight, fuel from the wing tanks flows by gravity into the header tank until it is full. The header tank is connected to the suction side of the fuel pump.

When the plane is rolled to an inverted position, the header tank is above the engine, and the fuel gravity flows from the header tank to the fuel pump. A check valve in the line that connects the main tank to the header tank prevents fuel from the header tank from draining back into the main tank when the plane is inverted. In a typical system (Figure 6-2-6), the header tank holds enough fuel for a few minutes of inverted flight.

Header tanks are also used with engines that have a carburetor that requires fuel under pressure. Any fuel not used by the carburetor must be returned to either the tank it was drawn from or to a header tank until it is

Figure 6-2-6. An aerobatic plane in inverted flight.

recycled back to the fuel pump. With multiple tanks, such an aircraft requires a device to ensure that fuel returns to the tank being used and does not overflow the wrong tank. This can be met with a header tank with enough capacity to contain the returned fuel or a selector valve capable of switching the return line.

Section 3

Components

Any system is only as reliable as its weakest link. To understand the importance of each major component in the fuel system, you need at least a basic knowledge of their purpose and operation.

Fuel Caps

Except on large aircraft that are fueled from one underwing attach point, most aircraft fuel tanks are filled by gravity through an opening on the top of the wing. This critical location means that the design, maintenance, and proper use of the fuel caps is important. Because the top of the wing is a low-pressure area, the lack of a good seal at the fuel cap could result in fuel loss.

Figure 6-2-7. A vented cap (left) like that used on the Piper Super Cub, a popular bush aircraft, and a nonvented type cap (right).

Many fuel cap designs are used. They all have the same objectives: keep the fuel in and keep water out. Some designs incorporate a vent system, and this can involve being certain that the vent tube is pointing the right direction in flight. Most are completely sealed, and the integrity of their gaskets and seals is important to maintain. Both of these types are shown in Figure 6-2-7. Both flight and ground personnel must be aware of the condition and installation of fuel caps after fueling and before flight.

Valves

Valves perform two important actions in the fuel system. They are to shut off the fuel in an emergency, and they allow the flight crew to select the tank from which the fuel is drawn.

Fuel Shutoff Valve

Aircraft must have a means to allow flight crew members to quickly shut off the fuel to each engine in flight. No shutoff valve may be on the engine side of any firewall. Also, a means is required to guard against each shutoff valve from inadvertently operating and to reopen quickly after it has been closed. Each valve and fuel system control must be supported so that loads resulting from its operation, or from accelerated flight conditions, are not transmitted to the lines connected to the valve. Gravity and vibration should not affect the selected position of any valve.

Selector Valve

With multiple fuel tanks, the flight crew needs a way to select the appropriate fuel

tank to manage the fuel supply. The simplest selection is simply ON or OFF. Fuel tank selector valves require a separate and distinct action to place the selector in the OFF position. The tank selector must be positioned so that it is impossible for the selector to pass through the OFF position when changing from one tank to another when multiple tanks are installed (Figure 6-2-8).

To help the flight crew know when the valve is in a specific position, hand-operated valves have a detent that gives a distinct feel when the valve is in the correct location. A detent is a device used to mechanically resist or arrest the rotation of a wheel, axle, or spindle (in this case a valve). Such a device is often a ball and spring arrangement with a hole to indicate position. If crewmembers do not feel the detent, they know that the valve is between operating positions.

Fuel Pumps

Fuel pumps are part of most aircraft fuel systems. Standards exist for main pumps and emergency pumps. Operating any fuel pump may not affect engine operation by creating a hazard, regardless of the engine power or thrust setting or the functional status of any other fuel pump. Any pump required for operation is considered a main fuel pump. Emergency pumps must be immediately available to supply fuel to the engine if any main pump fails.

Boost Pump

Boost pumps are used to ensure a positive supply of fuel to the inlet of the engine-

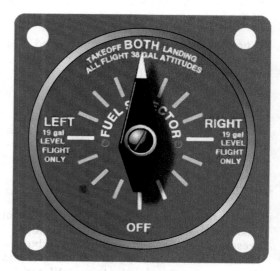

Figure 6-2-8. A fuel selector valve for a single-engine aircraft.

driven fuel pump. This prevents cavitation at the engine-driven pump. Cavitation is the rapid formation and collapse of vapor pockets (bubbles) in a flowing liquid in areas of very low pressure, like the inlet of the pump. Cavitation can damage the pump or interrupt fuel flow.

Boost pumps can also be used to back up the engine-driven pump and to transfer fuel from tank to tank if the aircraft is so designed. During startup, boost pumps can be used to provide fuel to the engine-driven pump, and they can be used during takeoff as a backup. They can also be used at high altitudes to prevent vapor lock.

You can find fuel boost pumps anywhere between the fuel tanks and the inlet of the engine-driven pump. Some systems use submersible pumps in the fuel tank; others use pumps in the line at some distance from the tank.

Engine-Driven Pump

The engine-driven fuel pump's main function is to supply the fuel metering system with adequate fuel at the proper pressure. This can be as simple as a diaphragm pump supplying low-pressure fuel to a float carburetor, or as sophisticated as an engine-driven pump that is an integral part of fuel metering in a fuel-injection system.

Vane-Type Fuel Pump

Vane-type fuel pumps are the most common fuel pumps found on reciprocating-engine aircraft. They are used as both engine-driven primary fuel pumps and as boost pumps. Regardless, the vane pump is a constant displacement pump—one that moves a fixed volume of fuel with each revolution of the pump. When used as an auxiliary pump, an electric motor rotates the pump shaft. On engine-driven applications, the vane pump is typically mounted on the engine accessory case and works when the engine is running. Figure 6-2-9 is an example of a vane fuel pump.

Fuel Strainers and Filters

Every effort must be made to ensure that the fuel supply is free of any contaminants— mainly water, dust, or other solid particles. Each aircraft has several points at which the fuel is strained or filtered to remove contaminants.

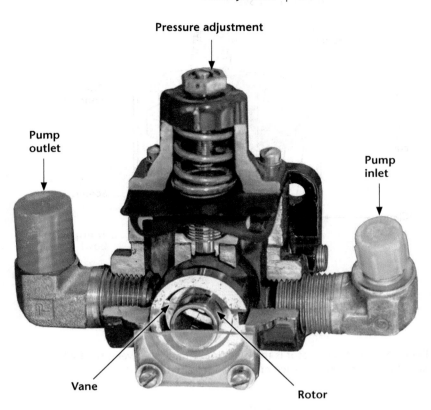

Figure 6-2-9. The basic parts of a vane fuel pump.

Figure 6-2-10. Fuel tank outlet finger screens are often used on light aircraft.

A strainer is needed for the fuel tank outlet or for the booster pump. It must be accessible for inspection and cleaning.

Finger screens are common on light aircraft. They effectively increase the area of the fuel tank outlet, allowing much debris to be trapped while still permitting fuel to flow. Figure 6-2-10 shows a finger screen that can be screwed into a fitting welded in the tank outlet.

In addition to the fuel tank strainer, a fuel strainer or filter is required between the fuel tank outlet and the inlet of the fuel metering device. This fuel strainer or filter must be accessible for draining and cleaning, and it must incorporate a screen or element that is easily removable. It should have a sediment trap and drain, but a drain is not needed if the strainer or filter is easily removable for draining.

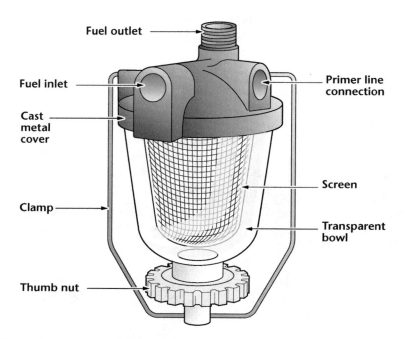

Fuel outlet
Fuel inlet
Primer line connection
Cast metal cover
Clamp
Screen
Transparent bowl
Thumb nut

Figure 6-2-11. A gascolator is the main fuel strainer between the fuel tanks and the fuel metering device on many light aircraft.

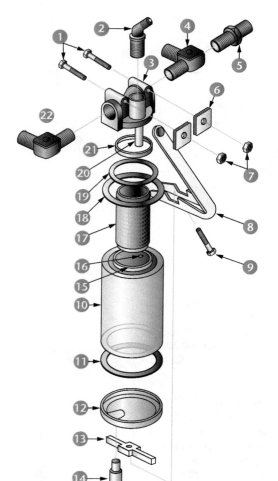

1. Bolt
2. Elbow
3. Body assembly
4. Fitting for left engine installation
5. Fitting for right engine installation
6. Mounting bracket nut
7. Nut
8. Arm assembly
9. Bolt
10. Glass bowl
11. Lower gasket
12. Cap
13. Stiffener
14. Drain valve
15. Lid assembly
16. Retainer spring
17. Filter
18. Upper gasket
19. Flat screen
20. Standpipe
21. Filter ring
22. Elbow

Figure 6-2-12. A filter assembly on a light twin reciprocating engine aircraft.

A gascolator is a fuel strainer or filter that incorporates a sediment collection bowl. The bowl is traditionally glass to allow quick visual checks for contaminants; however, many gascolators also have opaque bowls. A gascolator has a drain, or the bowl can be removed to inspect and discard trapped debris and water (Figure 6-2-11).

The main fuel strainer is commonly mounted at a low point on the engine firewall. The drain is accessible through an easy-access panel, or it extends through the bottom engine cowling. As with most filters or strainers, fuel can enter the unit but must travel up through the filtering element to exit. Water, which is heavier than fuel, becomes trapped and collects in the bottom of the bowl. Other debris too large to pass through the element also settles in the strainer bowl.

On some higher performance aircraft, this gascolator could be replaced by a main filter/strainer (Figure 6-2-12). On twin-engine aircraft, each engine has a main strainer. As with single-engine aircraft, a strainer is often mounted low on the engine firewall in each nacelle.

Fuel Drain/Sump

Aircraft fuel systems must have at least one drain to allow safe drainage of the entire fuel system with the airplane in its normal ground attitude. This is called the low-point drain. It must discharge the fuel clear of all parts of the aircraft. A readily accessible drain valve that can easily be opened and closed is required. It must have a manual or automatic means for locking in the closed position, and it must be observable that it is closed. The valve should be placed so that fuel does not spill if a gear-up landing is made.

In addition, each tank must have a drainable sump. Each fuel tank must allow drainage of any hazardous quantity of water from any part of the tank to its sump with the airplane in the normal ground attitude.

Fuel should be collectible from the system drain valve so it can be examined for water and other contaminants. This is normally done at each preflight inspection. When performing this test and draining the fuel tank sumps, it is important to properly dispose of the fuel that has been drained for testing.

Lines and Fittings

Aircraft fuel system fluid lines and fittings are designed to strict standards to ensure proper fuel system operation. Fuel lines can be rigid or flexible depending on location and application. Rigid lines are often made of aluminum alloy and are connected with Army/Navy (AN) or military standard (MS) fittings. However, in the engine compartment, wheel wells, and other areas, subject to damage from debris, abrasion, and heat, stainless steel lines are commonly used.

Flexible fuel hose has a synthetic rubber interior with a reinforcing fiber braid wrap, covered by a synthetic exterior (Figure 6-2-13). The hose is approved for fuel, and no other hose should be substituted. Some flexible fuel hose has a braided stainless-steel exterior. The diameters of all fuel hoses and lines are determined by the fuel flow requirements of the fuel system. Flexible hoses are used in areas where vibration exists between components, such as between the engine and the aircraft structure. Sometimes manufacturers wrap either flexible or rigid fuel lines to provide even further protection from abrasion and especially from fire. A fire sleeve cover can be installed and held over the line with steel clamps at the end fittings.

Metal fuel lines and all aircraft fuel system components must be electrically bonded and grounded to the aircraft structure. This is important because fuel flowing through the fuel system generates static electricity that must have a path to flow to ground rather than build up. Special bonded cushion clamps are used to secure rigid fuel lines in place. All fuel lines should be supported so that there is no strain on the fittings.

Section 4

Primer System

Because most fuel metering systems depend on air flowing through them to generate the pressures necessary to provide a metered supply of fuel, some help might be needed when starting. This is where the primer system is useful.

Airflow through a carburetor when the engine is being cranked over for starting is not enough to draw fuel from the main or idle jets. A primer is a hand-operated fuel pump that squirts fuel into the intake system to help start the engine. A typical primer used on light aircraft is shown in Figure 6-2-14. Follow the engine manufacturer's instructions for primer use during startup.

The term *primer* can also be applied to systems designed to introduce fuel for starting a pres-

sure carburetor or fuel-injection system. The idea is the same. Raw fuel is introduced into the intake system to facilitate starting. These are generally operated by electrically operated fuel pumps, and the flow can be directed by an electrically operated valve from a switch in the flight deck.

Figure 6-2-13. A typical flexible aircraft fuel line with braided reinforcement.

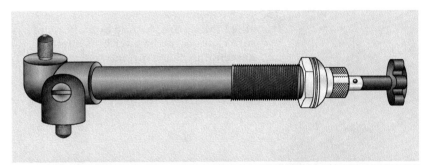

Figure 6-2-14. This engine primer is a hand-operated piston pump. It is usually mounted in the instrument panel.

Section 5
Fuel Venting

To allow proper fuel flow, each fuel tank must be vented. Venting allows quick relief of pressure differences between the inside and outside the tank. As fuel is drawn out of the tank, it must be replaced by air to prevent a partial vacuum from forming in the tank. If a fuel vent is plugged, a partial vacuum forms where the fuel was. When this happens, fuel flow is reduced because of the lower pressure in the tank. If allowed to continue, it starves the engine of fuel, causing the engine to run rough and eventually shut down.

The vent system also allows air to escape from the tank during fueling and allows for pressure changes as the aircraft is climbing and descending. Some aircraft use an individual vent for each tank (Figure 6-5-1, top). Many high-wing aircraft vent one tank, and vent the second tank using a crossover vent tube, as shown in Figure 6-5-1, bottom.

Section 6
Aircraft Fuel Systems

Each manufacturer designs its own fuel system, but the basic requirements referenced at the beginning of this chapter yield fuel systems of similar design and function in the field. The next sections provide representative of aircraft discussed. Other systems made are similar but not identical. Each aircraft fuel system must store and deliver clean fuel to the engines at a pressure and flow rate that can sustain operations regardless of the operating conditions of the aircraft.

Aircraft fuel systems vary depending on factors, such as tank location and method of metering fuel to the engine. A high-wing aircraft fuel system can be designed differently from one on a low-wing aircraft. An aircraft engine with a carburetor has a different fuel system than one with fuel injection. Gravity-feed systems are covered here. Transport category aircraft fuel systems are briefly described later in this chapter.

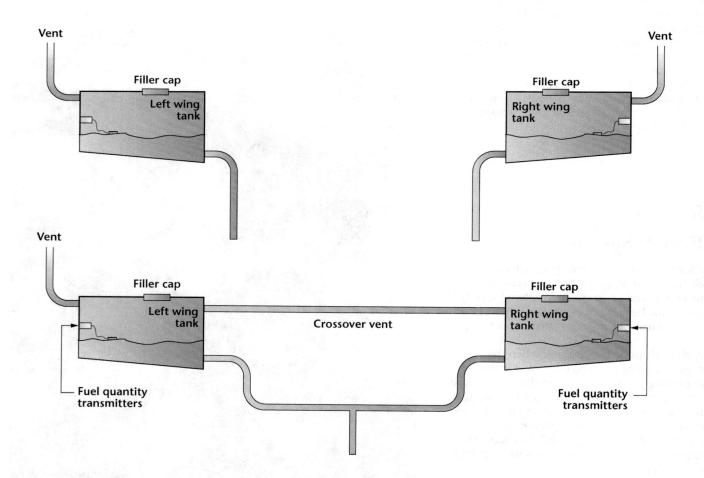

Figure 6-5-1. Fuel tank vents can be on each tank (top), or one vent on a tank with a crossover vent connecting the other tank (bottom).

Gravity-Feed Systems

High-wing aircraft with a fuel tank in each wing are common. In an aircraft equipped with a carbureted engine and tanks above the engine, gravity delivers the fuel. A simple gravity-feed fuel system is shown in Figure 6-6-1.

The space above the fuel is vented through the vent in the cap to maintain atmospheric pressure on the fuel as the tank empties. The two tanks are also vented to each other to ensure equal pressure when both tanks feed the engine. A screened outlet on each tank feeds lines that connect to either a fuel shutoff valve or multi-position selector valve. The shutoff valve has two positions: fuel ON and fuel OFF. If installed, the selector valve provides four options: fuel shutoff to the engine; fuel feed from the right wing tank only; fuel feed from the left fuel tank only; and fuel feed to the engine from both tanks simultaneously.

Downstream of the shutoff valve or selector valve, the fuel passes through a main system strainer. This often has a drain function to remove sediment and water. From there, it flows to the carburetor or to the primer pump for engine starting. Because it has no fuel pump, the gravity feed system is the simplest aircraft fuel system.

Low-Wing, Single Engine

Low-wing, single-engine aircraft cannot use gravity-feed fuel systems because the fuel tanks are not above the engine. Instead, one or more pumps are used to move the fuel from the tanks to the engine. A common fuel system of this type is shown in Figure 6-6-2.

Each tank has a line from the screened outlet to a selector valve. However, fuel cannot be drawn from both tanks simultaneously; if the fuel is depleted in one tank, the pump draws air from that tank instead of fuel from the full tank. Because fuel is not drawn from both tanks at the same time, there is no need to connect the tank vent spaces together. From the selector valve (LEFT, RIGHT, or OFF), fuel flows through the main strainer where it can supply the engine primer. Then, it flows downstream to the fuel pumps.

Typically, one electric and one engine-driven fuel pump are arranged in parallel. They draw the fuel from the tanks and deliver it to the carburetor. The two pumps provide redundancy. The engine-driven fuel pump acts as the primary pump. The electric pump can supply fuel if the other pump fails. The electric pump also supplies fuel pressure when start-

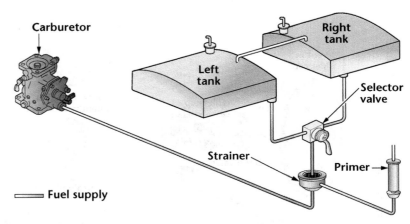

Figure 6-6-1. The gravity-feed fuel system in a single-engine, high-wing aircraft is the simplest fuel system.

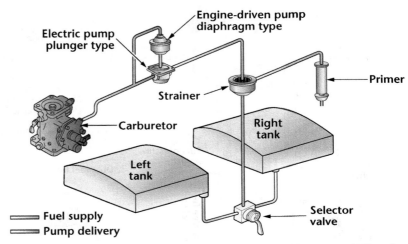

Figure 6-6-2. A single-engine aircraft with fuel tanks in the wing below the engine uses pumps to draw fuel from the tanks and deliver it to the engine.

ing and is used to prevent vapor lock during flight at high altitude.

Low-Wing, Twin Engine

The fuel system on a small, multiengine aircraft is more complicated than a single-engine aircraft but contains many of the same elements. An example system used on a low-wing aircraft is illustrated in Figure 6-6-3. It features the main fuel tanks in the wingtips and auxiliary tanks in the wing structure. A boost pump is at the outlet of each main tank. This pressurizes the entire fuel system from the tank to the injectors.

An engine can operate with just its boost pump running if the engine-driven injection pump fails. Typically, the boost pumps are used to prime and start the engine. Two selector valves are required on twin-engine aircraft—one for each engine. The right selector valve receives fuel from a main tank on either

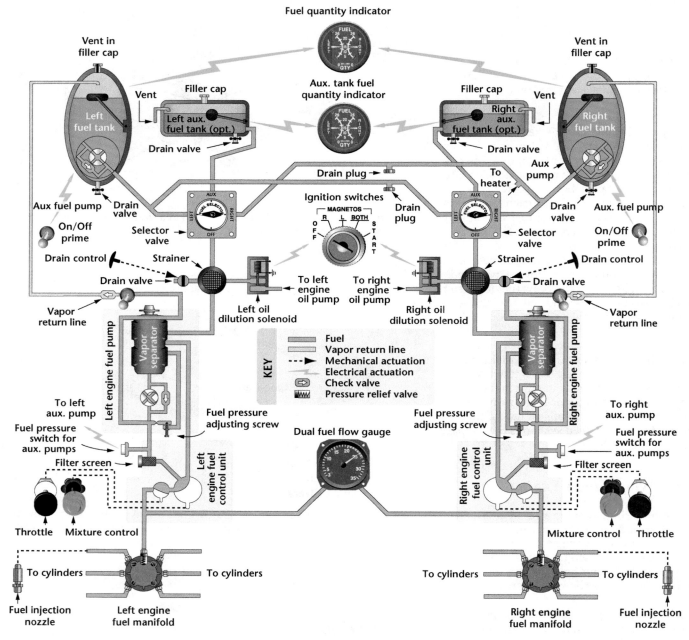

Figure 6-6-3. A low-wing, twin-engine, light aircraft fuel system.

side of the aircraft and directs it to the right engine. The left selector valve also receives fuel from either main tank and directs it to the left engine. This allows fuel to crossfeed from one side of the aircraft to the opposite engine if desired. The selector valves can also direct fuel from the auxiliary tank to the engine on the same side. Crossfeed of fuel from auxiliary tanks is not possible. From the outlet of the selector valve, fuel flows to the strainer. On some aircraft, the strainer is built into the selector valve unit. From the strainer, fuel flows to the engine-driven fuel pump.

The engine-driven fuel pump is an assembly that also contains a vapor separator and a pressure-regulating valve with an adjustment screw. The vapor separator helps eliminate air from the fuel. It returns a small amount of fuel and any vapor present back to the main fuel tank. The pump supplies pressurized fuel to the fuel control. The fuel control, one for each engine, responds to throttle and mixture control settings from the flight deck and supplies the proper amount of fuel to the fuel manifold. The manifold divides the fuel and sends it to an injector in each cylinder. A fuel pressure gauge is placed between the fuel control unit outlet and the manifold to monitor the injector-applied pressure that indicates engine power.

Section 7

Instrumentation

Aircraft fuel systems use various indicators. All systems are required to have some sort of fuel quantity indicator. Fuel flow, pressure, and temperature are also monitored on many aircraft. Valve position indicators and various warning lights and annunciations can be used on larger aircraft.

Quantity

All aircraft fuel systems must have some form of fuel quantity indicator. These devices vary widely depending on the fuel system and the aircraft complexity. Simple indicators requiring no electrical power were the earliest type of quantity indicators and are still in use today. These direct reading indicators are used only on light aircraft in which the fuel tanks are near the flight deck. Other aircraft require electric indicators or electronic capacitance-type indicators.

Mechanical. A sight glass is a clear glass or plastic tube open to the fuel tank that fills with fuel to the same level as the fuel in the tank. It can be calibrated in gallons or fractions of a full tank. Another type of sight gauge uses a float with an indicating rod attached to it. As the float moves up and down with the fuel level, the portion of the rod that extends through the fuel cap indicates the quantity of fuel in the tank (Figure 6-7-1). These two mechanisms are combined in yet another simple fuel quantity indicator in which the float is attached to a rod that moves up or down in a calibrated cylinder.

Figure 6-7-1. The fuel quantity indicator on this Piper Cub is a float attached to a rod that protrudes through the fuel cap.

More sophisticated mechanical fuel quantity gauges are common. A float that follows the fuel level remains the primary sensing element, but a mechanical linkage is connected to move a pointer across the instrument's dial face. This can be implemented with a crank and pinion arrangement that drives the pointer with gears, or with a magnetic coupling, to the pointer (Figure 6-7-2).

Electric. Electric fuel quantity indicators are more common than mechanical indicators in modern aircraft. Most of these units operate with direct current (DC) and use variable resistance in a circuit to drive a ratiometer-type indicator. The float's movement in the tank moves a connecting arm to the wiper on a variable resistor in the tank unit. This resistor is wired in series with one of the coils of the ratiometer fuel gauge in the instrument

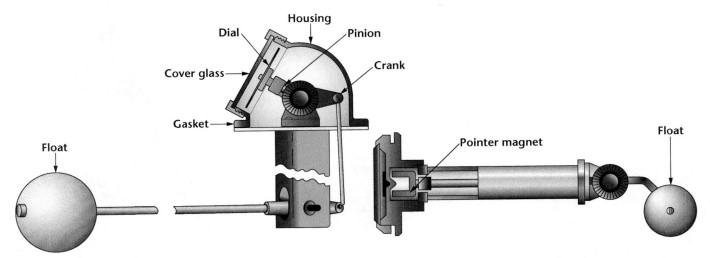

Figure 6-7-2. Simple mechanical fuel indicators used on light aircraft with fuel tanks that are close to the pilot.

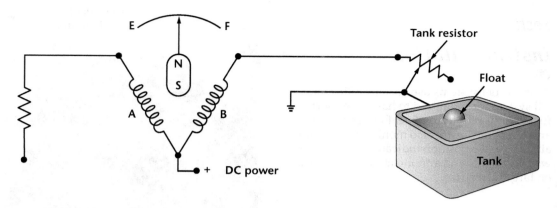

Figure 6-7-3. A DC electric fuel quantity indicator uses a variable resistor in the tank that is moved by a float arm.

panel. Changes to the current flowing through the tank unit resistor change the current flowing through one of the coils in the indicator. This alters the magnetic field in which the indicating pointer pivots. The calibrated dial indicates the corresponding fuel quantity (Figure 6-7-3).

Digital display with variable resistance. Digital indicators are available that work with the same variable resistance signal from the tank unit. They convert the variable resistance into a digital display in the flight deck instrument head. Fully digital instrumentation systems, such as those found in a *glass cockpit* aircraft, convert the variable resistance into a digital signal to be processed in a computer and displayed on a flat screen panel.

Electronic fuel quantity systems. Large and high-performance aircraft typically use electronic fuel quantity systems. These systems have the advantage of having no moving parts in the tank sending units. Variable capacitance transmitters are installed in the fuel tanks extending from the top to the bottom of each tank in the usable fuel (Figure 6-7-4). Several of these tank units, or fuel probes as they are sometimes called, can be installed in a large tank. They are wired in parallel.

As the level of the fuel changes, the capacitance of each unit changes. The capacitance

transmitted by all the probes in a tank is totaled and compared in a bridge circuit by a microchip computer in the digital fuel quantity indicator in the flight deck. As the aircraft maneuvers, some probes are in more fuel than others because of the aircraft's attitude. The indication remains steady, however, because the total capacitance transmitted by all the probes remains the same.

A capacitor is a device that stores electricity. The amount it can store depends on three factors: the area of its plates, the distance between the plates, and the dielectric constant of the material separating the plates. A fuel tank variable capacitance probe houses two concentric plates that are a fixed distance apart. Therefore, the capacitance of a unit changes if the dielectric constant of the material separating the plates changes. The

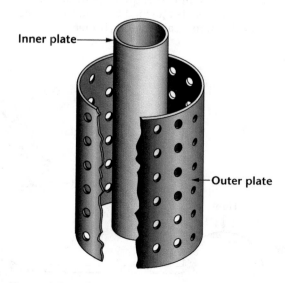

Figure 6-7-5. The capacitance of tank probes varies as the space between the inner and outer plates is filled with changing quantities of fuel and air.

Figure 6-7-4. A fuel tank transmitter for a capacitance-type fuel quantity indicating system.

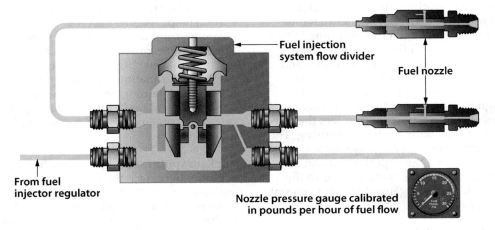

Figure 6-7-6. Fuel pressure is used to represent fuel flow in some light, reciprocating-engine aircraft.

units are open at the top and bottom, so they can assume the same level of fuel as is in the tanks. Therefore, the material between the plates is either fuel (if the tank is full), air (if the tank is empty), or some combination of fuel and air depending on how much fuel remains in the tank. Figure 6-7-5 shows a simplified illustration of this construction.

The bridge circuit that measures the capacitance of the tank units uses a reference capacitor for comparison. When voltage is induced into the bridge, the capacitive reactance of the tank probes and the reference capacitor can be equal or different. The magnitude of the difference is translated into an indication of the fuel quantity in the tank calibrated in pounds. Because this system measures fuel quantity in pounds, it provides the flight crew a more accurate report of fuel quantity than systems that measure liquid levels, which temperature can affect.

Fuel Flow Meter

A fuel flow meter indicates an engine's fuel use in realtime. This can help the flight crew determine engine performance and make flight planning calculations. The types of fuel flow meter used on an aircraft depends primarily on the powerplant being used and the fuel system.

Measuring fuel flow accurately is complicated because fuel mass changes with temperature or with the type of fuel used in turbine engines. In light aircraft with reciprocating engines, systems have been devised to measure fuel volume. The actual mass of fuel flowing to the engine is based on an assumption of the average weight of the fuel per unit volume.

The simplest fuel flow sensing device is used with fuel injection systems installed on horizontally opposed reciprocating engines. A pressure gauge is used, but it is calibrated

in gallons per hour or pounds per hour. The amount of fuel flowing through the fuel injectors has a direct relationship to the fuel pressure. Therefore, monitoring fuel pressure closely approximates fuel flow and provides useful flow information for mixture control and flight planning (Figure 6-7-6).

A major limitation to using fuel pressure as a flow indicator is that if an injector becomes clogged, fuel flow is reduced. However, the pressure gauge indicates a higher fuel pressure (and greater fuel flow) because of the restriction.

Another fuel-flow sensor used mainly on light aircraft detects the spinning velocity of a turbine in the fuel path. It, too, has a failsafe design if the turbine malfunctions. In this unit, notches in the rotor interrupt an infrared light beam between a light-emitting diode (LED) and phototransistor that creates a signal proportional to the amount fuel flow (Figure 6-7-7). This type of sensor can be coupled with an electronic indicator.

Figure 6-7-7. A turbine flow transducer in this fuel flow sensor produces a current pulse signal from an opto-electronic pickup with a preamplifier.

Larger, reciprocating-engine fuel systems might use a vane fuel flow meter that measures the volume of the fuel consumed by the engine. The fuel flow unit is typically between the engine-driven fuel pump and the carburetor. The entire volume of fuel delivered to the engine is made to pass through the flowmeter. Inside, the fuel pushes against a vane that counters the force of the fuel flow with a calibrated spring. The vane shaft rotates varying degrees to match the fuel flow rate through the unit. An auto-syn transmitter deflects the pointer in the flight deck fuel flow gauge the same amount as the vane deflects.

The indicator's dial face is calibrated in gallons per hour or pounds per hour according to an average weight of fuel. Because fuel fed to the engine must pass through the flow meter, a relief valve is incorporated to bypass the fuel around the vane if it malfunctions and restricts normal fuel flow. The vane chamber is eccentric. As more fuel pushes against the vane, it rotates further around in the chamber. The volume of the chamber gradually increases to allow more fuel flow without restriction or pressure buildup (Figure 6-7-8).

Other Fuel Management Instrumentation

Modern aircraft can have a variety of sensors including solid-state and those with digital output signals or signals that are converted to digital output. These can be processed in the instrument gauge microprocessor, if so equipped, or in a computer and sent to the display unit.

Fuel totalizer. Accurate fuel flow information helps the flight crew's situational awareness and improves flight planning. Most high-performance aircraft have a fuel totalizer that electronically calculates and displays information, such as total fuel used, total fuel remaining onboard the aircraft, total range and flight time remaining at the present airspeed, rate of fuel consumption, and so on.

Fuel computers. On light aircraft, it is common to replace the original analog fuel indicators with electronic gauges containing similar capabilities and built-in logic. Some of these fuel computers, as they are called, integrate global positioning satellite (GPS) location information (Figure 6-7-9). Aircraft with fully digital flight decks process fuel flow data in computers and display a wide array of fuel flow-related information on demand.

Increasing use of microprocessors and computers on aircraft enable integrating fuel temperature and other compensating factors to produce highly accurate fuel-flow information. Fuel-flow sensing with digital output facilitates this with a high degree of reliability.

Fuel pressure. Monitoring fuel pressure can give the pilot early warning of a fuel system-related malfunction. Verification that the fuel system is delivering fuel to the fuel metering device can be critical. Simple light, reciprocating-engine aircraft typically use a direct reading Bourdon tube pressure gauge. It is connected into the fuel inlet of the fuel metering device with a line extending to the

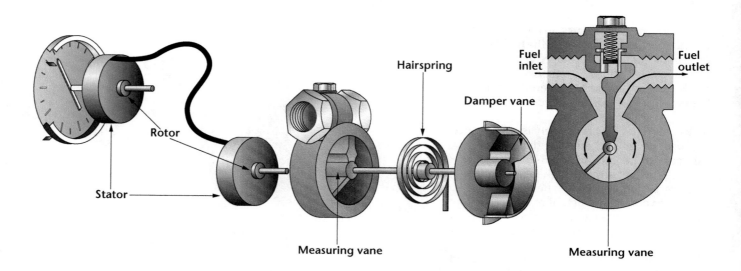

Figure 6-7-8. A vane-type fuel flow meter.

Figure 6-7-9. A modern fuel management gauge uses a microprocessor to display fuel flow and numerous other fuel consumption-related figures.

back of the gauge in the flight deck instrument panel.

A more complex aircraft can have a sensor with a transducer at the fuel inlet to the metering device that sends electrical signals to a flight deck gauge (Figure 6-7-10). The use of fuel-filled Bourdon tube type indicators has become less popular because of safety issues. In aircraft equipped with an auxiliary pump for starting and to backup the engine-driven pump, the fuel pressure gauge indicates the auxiliary pump pressure until the engine is started. When the auxiliary pump is switched off, the gauge indicates the pressure developed by the engine-driven pump.

Section 8
Fuel Contamination

Continuous vigilance is required when checking aircraft fuel systems for contaminants. Daily draining of strainers and sumps is combined with periodic filter changes and inspections to ensure that fuel is contaminant free.

Keeping a fuel system clean begins with an awareness of the common types of contamination. Water is the most common. Solid particles, surfactants, and microorganisms are also common. However, fuel contaminated with another fuel that is not intended for use on an aircraft is possibly the worst type of contamination.

Water

Water can be dissolved into fuel or entrained. Entrained water can be detected by a cloudy appearance to the fuel. Close examination is required. Air in the fuel tends to cause a similar cloudy condition but is near the top of the tank. The cloudiness caused by water in the fuel tends to be more toward the bottom of the tank as the water slowly settles out. An example of water in fuel is shown in Figure 6-8-1; the water has collected at the bottom of the cup and fuel is floating on top of it.

Water can enter a fuel system via condensation. The water vapor in the space above the liquid fuel in a fuel tank condenses when the

Figure 6-7-10. A typical fuel pressure gauge that uses a signal from a sensing transducer to display fuel inlet pressure at the metering device.

Figure 6-8-1. Water in fuel settles to the bottom of a cup.

temperature changes. It normally sinks to the bottom of the fuel tank into the sump where it can be drained off before flight (Figure 6-8-2). However, time is required for this to happen.

Figure 6-8-2. A sump drain tool is used to open and collect fuel and contaminants from the fuel system sumps.

Figure 6-8-3. Caution should be taken when fueling an aircraft to keep the area clean and prevent damage to the wing.

Solid Particles

Solid particles that do not dissolve in fuel are common contaminants. Dirt, rust, dust, metal particles, and just about anything that can find its way into an open fuel tank is of concern. Filter elements are designed to trap these contaminants, and some fall into the sump to be drained out. Pieces of debris from inside the fuel system can also accumulate, such as broken off sealant, or pieces of filter elements, corrosion, and the like.

Preventing solid contaminants from entering the fuel system is critical. Whenever the fuel system is open, be sure to keep out foreign matter. Cap lines immediately. Do not leave fuel tank caps open any longer than required to refuel the tanks. Clean the area next to any system opening before opening it (Figure 6-8-3).

Coarse sediments are those visible to the naked eye. If they pass beyond system filters, they can clog in fuel-metering device orifices, sliding valves, and fuel nozzles. Fine sediments cannot actually be seen as individual particles. They can be detected as a haze in the fuel or they can refract light when examining the fuel. Their presence in fuel controls and metering devices is indicated by dark shellac-like marks on sliding surfaces.

Foreign Fuel

Aircraft engines operate effectively only with the proper fuel. If an aircraft's fuel is contaminated with fuel not intended for use in that aircraft, it can have disastrous consequences. All aviators must put forth a continuous effort to ensure that only the fuel

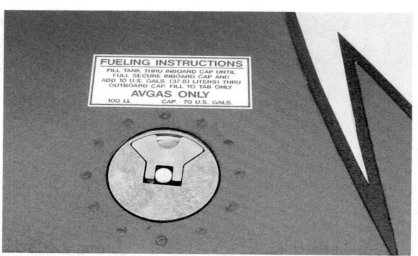

Figure 6-8-4. All fuel filling points are marked with the type of fuel to be used. Never introduce any other type of fuel into the aircraft other than that which is specified.

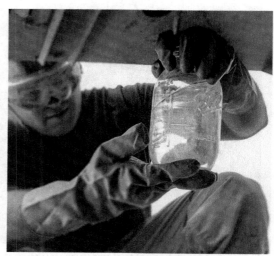

Figure 6-8-5. A clear fuel sampling container allows you to look for contamination and verify the color of the fuel.
Courtesy of USAF

designed for operating the aircraft's engine or engines is put into the fuel tanks. Each fuel tank receptacle or fuel cap area is clearly marked to indicate which fuel is required (Figure 6-8-4).

Detecting Contaminants

Visually inspecting fuel should always reveal a clean, bright liquid (Figure 6-8-5). Fuel should not be opaque, which could be a sign of contamination and demands further investigation. As mentioned, you must always be aware of the fuel's appearance and when and from what sources refueling was performed. Investigate any suspicion of contamination.

In addition to the detection methods mentioned for each type of contamination above, various field and laboratory tests can be performed on aircraft fuel to detect contamination. A common field test for water contamination is performed by adding a dye to a test sample drawn from the fuel tank. The dye dissolves in water but not in fuel. The more water is in the fuel, the greater the dye disperses and colors the sample.

Another common test kit that is commercially available contains a grey chemical powder that changes to pink or purple when a fuel sample contains more than 30 parts per million (ppm) of water. A 15-ppm test is available for turbine engine fuel. These levels of water are considered generally unacceptable and are not safe for operating the aircraft. If levels are discovered above these amounts, give time for the water to settle out of the fuel and then drain from the sump, or defuel and refuel the aircraft with acceptable fuel.

Section 9
Filling Point

Generally, two fueling processes are used: over-the-wing refueling and pressure refueling.

Over-the-Wing Refueling

Over-the-wing refueling is done by opening the fuel tank cap on the upper wing surface (or fuselage, if equipped with fuselage tanks), then the fueling nozzle is carefully inserted into the fill opening, and fuel is pumped into the tank. This process is like the process for refueling an automobile gas tank. Aviation fuel nozzles are equipped with static bonding wires that must be attached to the aircraft before the fuel cap is opened (Figure 6-9-1). When finished, the cap is secured, and subsequent tanks are opened and refilled until the aircraft has the desired fuel load onboard (Figure 6-9-2).

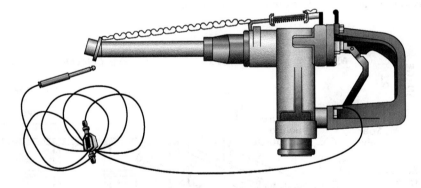

Figure 6-9-1. An AVGAS fueling nozzle with a static bonding wire.

Figure 6-9-2. Over-the-wing refueling is used on this turboprop aircraft.

Pressure Refueling

Pressure refueling occurs at the bottom, front, or rear of the fuel tank. A pressure refueling nozzle is locked onto the fueling port at the aircraft fueling station. Fuel is then pumped into the aircraft through this secured and sealed connection. Gauges are monitored to ascertain when the tanks are properly loaded. An automatic shutoff system can be part of the aircraft system. It closes the fueling valve when the tanks are full.

Single-point pressure fueling systems are used on many large, high-performance, and transport category aircraft. When pressure refueling, the aircraft receptacle is part of a fueling valve assembly. It allows all aircraft fuel tanks to be filled with one connection of the fuel hose. Leading and trailing edge wing locations are common for these stations. Figure 6-9-3 shows an airliner fueling station with the fueling rig attached.

When the fueling nozzle is properly connected and locked, a plunger unlocks the aircraft valve so fuel can be pumped through it. Normally, all tanks can be fueled from one point. Valves in the aircraft fuel system are controlled at the fueling station to direct the fuel into the proper tank. Before pumping fuel, ensure that the pressure developed by the refueling pump is correct for the aircraft.

Figure 6-9-3. A central refueling station on a transport category aircraft is used to fill all fuel tanks from one connection.

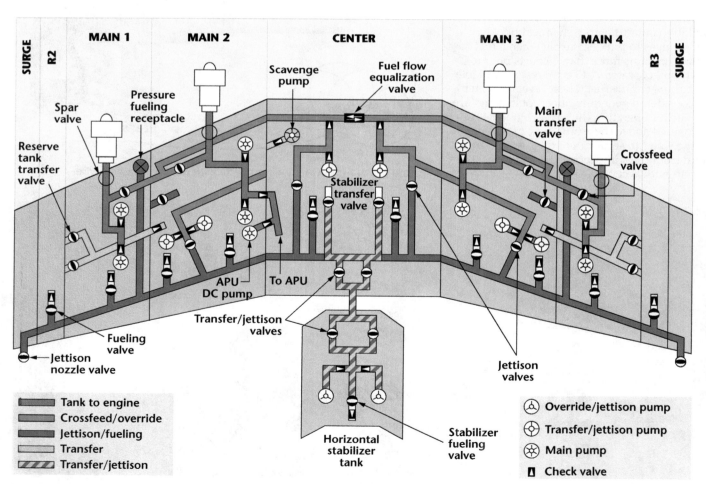

Figure 6-10-1. Like other transport category aircraft, this large aircraft's fuel system has features for fuel crossfeed and transfer.

Section 10

Transport Category Fuel Systems

Fuel systems on large, transport category jet aircraft are complex, with some features and components not found in reciprocating-engine aircraft fuel systems. They typically contain more redundancy and facilitate numerous options from which the crew can choose while managing the aircraft's fuel load (Figure 6-10-1).

Transport category aircraft fuel systems can be thought of as a handful of fuel subsystems:

- Storage
- Vent
- Distribution
- Feed
- Indicating

Most transport category aircraft fuel systems are very much alike. Integral fuel tanks are the norm, with much of each wing's structure sealed to enable its use as a fuel tank. Center wing section or fuselage tanks are also common. Figure 6-10-2 is an example of fuel tank locations and quantities.

If an aircraft's design landing weight is less than that of the maximum takeoff weight, a situation could occur in which a landing is desired before sufficient fuel has burned off to

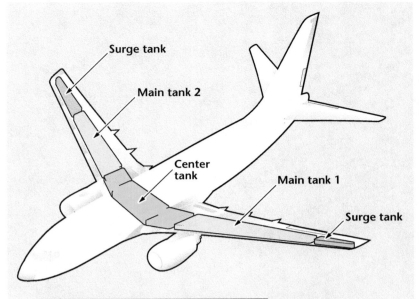

Tank	Gallons	Pounds*
Left main tank	9,560	64,000
Right main tank	9,560	64,000
Center tank	26,100	174,900
Total	45,220	302,900

*Usable fuel at level attitude

Fuel density = 6.7 pounds per U.S. gallon.

Figure 6-10-2. A large Boeing aircraft's fuel tank locations and capacities.

lighten the aircraft. Fuel jettisoning systems are required on these aircraft so that fuel can be jettisoned in flight to avoid structural damage caused by landing the aircraft when it is too heavy. Fuel jettisoning systems are also referred to as fuel dump systems.

7

Cabin Atmosphere

Section 1

Oxygen and Pressurization

Aircraft are flown at high altitudes for several reasons. First, an aircraft flown at high altitude consumes less fuel than it does at the same speed at a lower altitude because the aircraft is more efficient at a high altitude. Second, bad weather and turbulence can be avoided by flying in relatively smooth air above the storms. Many modern aircraft are designed to operate at high altitudes, taking advantage of that environment. To fly at higher altitudes, the aircraft must be pressurized or suitable supplemental oxygen must be provided for the occupants.

Earth's atmosphere is made up of about 21 percent oxygen, 78 percent nitrogen, and 1 percent other gases by volume (Figure 7-1-1). Of these gases, oxygen is the most important. As altitude increases, the air thins out and air pressure decreases. As a result, the amount of oxygen available to support life functions decreases. Aircraft oxygen systems are provided to supply the required amount of oxygen to keep a sufficient concentration of oxygen in the lungs to permit normal activity up to indicated altitudes of about 40,000 feet (ft.) mean sea level (MSL). (All altitudes in this chapter are in feet MSL.)

Modern transport aircraft cruise at altitudes where cabin pressurization is needed to maintain the cabin pressure altitude between 8,000 ft. and 15,000 ft. regardless of the aircraft's actual altitude. Under such conditions, supplemental oxygen is not needed; however, as a precaution, oxygen equipment is provided in case cabin pressurization

Left: Pressurized cabins are kept at an altitude of 8,000 ft. for passenger safety and comfort.

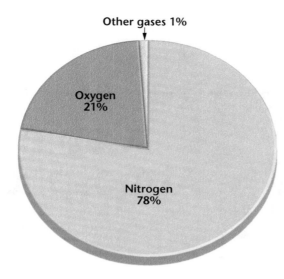

Figure 7-1-1. The percentage of the various gases that make up the atmosphere.

fails. Portable oxygen equipment can also be aboard for first-aid purposes. In smaller and medium-size aircraft designed without cabin pressurization, oxygen equipment could be permanently installed for when the aircraft is flown at high altitudes. In aircraft where no installed oxygen system is installed, passengers and crew depend on portable oxygen equipment.

14 CFR Legal Requirements for Oxygen and Pressurization

Requirements for Supplemental Oxygen

Regulations require, at a minimum, flight crews have and use supplemental oxygen after 30 minutes exposure to cabin pressure altitudes between 12,500 ft. and 14,000 ft. Supplemental oxygen must be used immediately upon exposure to cabin pressure altitudes above 14,000 ft. Every aircraft occupant, above 15,000 ft. cabin pressure altitude, must have supplemental oxygen. However, depending on a person's physical characteristics and condition, he or she might feel the effects of oxygen deprivation at much lower altitudes.

Requirements for Pressurization

The FAA does not require aircraft to have pressurized cabins. If, for the comfort of the passengers and crew, the aircraft manufacturer chooses to design an aircraft with a pressurized cabin, the FAA has very rigid regulations to ensure the safe design of this structure and operation of the system.

The regulations at 14 CFR 25.841 Pressurized Cabins provide this information:

Pressurized cabins and compartments to be occupied must be equipped to provide a cabin pressure altitude of not more than 8,000 ft. at the maximum operating altitude of the airplane under normal operating conditions.

(1) If certification for operation above 25,000 ft. is requested, the airplane must be designed so that occupants will not be exposed to cabin pressure altitudes in excess of 15,000 ft. after any probable failure condition in the pressurization system.

(2) The airplane must be designed so that occupants will not be exposed to a cabin pressure altitude that exceeds the following after decompression from any failure condition not shown to be extremely improbable:

(i) Twenty-five thousand (25,000) ft. for more than 2 minutes; or

(ii) Forty thousand (40,000) ft. for any duration.

(3) Fuselage structure, engine and system failures are to be considered in evaluating the cabin decompression.

Pressurized cabins must have at least the following valves, controls, and indicators for controlling cabin pressure:

Two pressure relief valves to automatically limit the positive pressure differential to a predetermined value at the maximum rate of flow delivered by the pressure source. The combined capacity of the relief valves must be large enough so that the failure of any one valve would not cause an appreciable rise in the pressure differential. The pressure differential is positive when the internal pressure is greater than the external.

Two reverse pressure differential relief valves (or their equivalents) to automatically prevent a negative pressure differential that would damage the structure. One valve is enough, however, if it is of a design that reasonably precludes its malfunctioning.

A means by which the pressure differential can be rapidly equalized.

An automatic or manual regulator for controlling the intake or exhaust airflow, or both, for maintaining the required internal pressures and airflow rates.

Instruments at the pilot or flight engineer station to show the pressure differential, the cabin pressure altitude, and the rate of change of the cabin pressure altitude.

Warning indication at the pilot or flight engineer station to indicate when the safe or preset pressure differential and cabin pressure altitude limits are exceeded. Appropriate warning markings on the cabin pressure differential indicator meet the warning requirement for pressure differential limits and an aural or visual signal (in addition to cabin altitude indicating means) meets the warning requirement for cabin pressure altitude limits if it warns the flight crew when the cabin pressure altitude exceeds 10,000 ft.

Hypoxia

The second-most prevalent substance in the atmosphere, oxygen, is essential for most living processes. Without oxygen, humans and animals die very quickly. Hypoxia means *reduced oxygen* or *not enough oxygen*. A reduction in the normal oxygen supply alters the human condition. It causes important changes in body functions, thought processes, and the maintainable degree of consciousness. The resultant sluggish condition of mind and body produced by insufficient oxygen is called hypoxia.

Several scenarios can result in hypoxia. In aircraft operations, it is brought about by a decrease in the pressure of oxygen in the lungs at high altitudes. The air contains the typical 21 percent of oxygen, but the rate at which oxygen can be absorbed into the blood depends on the oxygen pressure. Greater pressure pushes the oxygen from the lung alveoli into the bloodstream. As the pressure is reduced, less oxygen is forced into and absorbed by the blood. As altitude is increased, this pressure decreases.

- At sea level, oxygen pressure in the lungs is about 3 pounds per square inch (p.s.i.). This is sufficient to saturate the blood with oxygen and permit the mind and body to function normally.

- Below 7,000 ft. above sea level, the available oxygen quantity and pressure remain sufficient for saturation of the blood with oxygen. Above 7,000 ft., however, the oxygen pressure becomes increasingly insufficient to saturate the blood.

- At 10,000 ft., saturation of the blood with oxygen is only about 90 percent of normal. Long durations at this altitude can result in headache and fatigue, both symptoms of hypoxia.

- At 15,000 ft., oxygen transfer to the bloodstream drops to 81 percent of saturation. This typically results in sleepiness, headache, blue lips and fingernails, and increased pulse and respiration. Worse yet, vision and judgment become impaired and safe operation of an aircraft becomes compromised.

- At 22,000 ft., oxygen transfer to the bloodstream is only 68 percent oxygen saturation.

- Remaining at 25,000 ft. for 5 minutes, where oxygen transfer to the blood is reduced to about 50 percent saturation, causes unconsciousness.

For changes in pressure at various altitudes, see Table 7-1-1.

The most common causes of hypoxia in aviation are flying nonpressurized aircraft above 10,000 ft. without supplemental oxygen, rapid decompression during flight, pressurization system malfunction, or an oxygen system malfunction. One factor that makes hypoxia dangerous is its insidious onset; the signs and symptoms can develop so gradually that they are well established before a person recognizes them. Hypoxia is painless, and the signs and symptoms vary from person to person.

Hypoxia is divided into four types: hypoxic, hypemic, stagnant, and histotoxic.

Hypoxic Hypoxia

This is the most common form of hypoxia encountered in aviation and is commonly called altitude hypoxia. With increasing altitude, the molecules of oxygen in ambient air get farther apart and exert less pressure per square inch. The percentage of oxygen does not change as altitude increases; however, the partial pressure of oxygen in ambient air decreases as altitude increases. In other words, with increasing altitude, the partial pressure of oxygen gets lower and the lungs cannot effectively transfer oxygen from the ambient air to the blood.

Hypemic Hypoxia

Hypemic hypoxia occurs when the blood cannot take up and transport a sufficient amount of oxygen to the cells in the body. This type of hypoxia is caused by the reduced ability of the blood to carry oxygen. Even though there is an adequate supply of oxygen to breathe, the blood's capacity to carry the oxygen to the cells has been impaired. This can occur because of reduced blood volume (from donating blood) or from certain blood diseases, such as anemia, and carbon mon-

Altitude (ft. MSL)	Oxygen pressure (p.s.i.)
0	3.08
5,000	2.57
10,000	2.12
15,000	1.74
20,000	1.42
25,000	1.15
30,000	0.92
35,000	0.76
40,000	0.57

Table 7-1-1. Oxygen pressure in the atmosphere at various altitudes.

oxide interfere with the ability of the blood to carry oxygen. The most common cause for hypemic hypoxia in aviation is when carbon monoxide is inhaled because of aircraft heater malfunctions, engine manifold leaks, or contamination with exhaust from other aircraft.

Stagnant Hypoxia

Stagnant means *not flowing*, and stagnant hypoxia or ischemia results when the oxygen-rich blood in the lungs is not moving, for one reason or another, to the tissues that need it. If the blood flow is compromised for any reason, sufficient oxygen cannot get to the body tissues. Decreased blood flow can result from the heart failing to pump effectively, or a constricted artery. Stagnant hypoxia also occurs when the body is exposed to cold temperatures because the blood flow is decreased to the extremities. This can happen after a rapid decompression in flight or while operating an aircraft in cold conditions without cabin heating.

Histotoxic Hypoxia

The inability of the cells to effectively use oxygen is defined as histotoxic hypoxia (also called histoxic hypoxia). Even though there is an adequate supply of oxygen to breathe and that oxygen is being circulated by the blood, the cells are unable to accept or use the oxygen. Alcohol, narcotics, and cyanide are three primary factors that can cause histoxic hypoxia. Cyanide is a by-product of plastic combustion.

A pulse oximeter is a noninvasive device that measures heart rate and the amount of oxygen in a person's blood. It measures the color changes that red blood cells undergo when they become saturated with oxygen. By transmitting a special light beam through a fingertip to evaluate the color of the red cells, a pulse oximeter calculates the degree of oxygen saturation within 1 percent of directly measured blood oxygen. Because of their low cost, portability, and speed, pulse oximeters have become very useful for pilots operating in nonpressurized aircraft above 12,500 ft. where supplemental oxygen is required. A pulse oximeter permits crewmembers and passengers to evaluate their actual need for supplemental oxygen (Figure 7-1-2).

The negative effects of reduced atmospheric pressure at flight altitudes, forcing less oxygen into the blood, can be overcome. This is commonly done in two ways: by pressurizing the aircraft and by using supplemental oxygen.

Figure 7-1-2. A pulse oximeter tells you the degree of oxygen saturation in the blood.
Courtesy of Sporty's Pilot Shop

Supplemental Oxygen: Sources of Oxygen and Components

Aircraft oxygen systems can be fixed or portable, depending on the expected operating envelope and aircraft design. Systems are often characterized by the type of regulator used to dispense the oxygen: continuous-flow and demand flow.

- Fixed oxygen installation. Most high-altitude aircraft come equipped with some type of fixed oxygen installation. That is, the oxygen system is permanently installed in the aircraft

- Portable oxygen equipment. If the aircraft does not have a fixed installation, portable oxygen equipment must be readily accessible during high altitude flight.

These systems have significant differences in the equipment used, but both oxygen systems have some common elements: a source of oxygen, a delivery system (plumbing, regulating devices, and instruments), and a mask or other device that a person wears.

Stored Gas/Oxygen Cylinders

Pure or nearly pure gaseous oxygen is stored and transported in cylinders. Most oxygen storage cylinders are painted green, but yellow and other colors might also be used (Figure 7-1-3). Traditionally, these have been heavy steel tanks rated for pressure of 1,800–1,850 p.s.i. and capable of maintaining pressure up to 2,400 p.s.i. While these performed adequately, lighter tanks were sought. Some newer cylinders are made of a lightweight aluminum shell wrapped by Kevlar®. These can carry the same amount of oxygen at the same pressure as steel tanks but weigh much less. Also available are heavy-walled all-aluminum cylinders. These units are common as carry-on portable oxygen used in light aircraft.

Not all stored oxygen in cylinders is the same. Aviator's breathing oxygen (ABO) is tested for the presence of water. This is to prevent it from freezing in the small passageways of the oxygen system, which can prevent the oxygen from flowing when needed. Aircraft often operate in subzero temperatures, increasing the possibility of icing. The water level should be a maximum of 0.02 mililiter per liter of oxygen. The words "Aviator's Breathing Oxygen" should be marked clearly on any cylinders containing oxygen for aviation use.

Chemical or Solid Oxygen/Oxygen Generators

Sodium chlorate has a unique characteristic—when ignited, it produces oxygen as it burns. Solid oxygen candles, as they are called, are formed chunks of sodium chlorate wrapped in insulated stainless steel housings to control the heat produced when activated. Once lit, a sodium chlorate oxygen generator cannot be extinguished. It produces a steady flow of breathable oxygen until it burns out, typically generating 10–20 minutes of oxygen.

Chemical oxygen generators are primarily used as backup oxygen devices on pressurized aircraft. They are one-third as heavy as gaseous oxygen systems, which use heavy storage tanks for the same quantity of oxygen available. Such generators also have a long shelf life, making them a good choice as a standby form of oxygen.

The chemical oxygen supply is often ignited by a spring-loaded ring pin that, when pulled, releases a hammer that smashes a cap creating a spark to light the candle. Electric ignition via a current-induced hot wire is also used.

Oxygen Masks and Cannulas

Numerous types and designs of oxygen masks are used. The most important factor in oxygen mask use is to ensure that the masks and oxygen system are compatible.

Continuous-flow oxygen masks.
Continuous-flow oxygen masks are simple devices made to direct oxygen flow to the nose and mouth. They fit snugly but are typically not air tight. These masks are often a simple, cup-shaped rubber molding sufficiently flexible with an elastic head strap or the user can hold it to his or her face. Some continuous-flow masks might fit the face more tightly.

Often these masks have a reservoir bag that collects oxygen from the continuous-flow oxygen system when the mask user is exhaling. They

are called rebreather masks. This conserves oxygen because the oxygen in the rebreather bag can be inhaled in the next breath (Figure 7-1-4).

Cannula. A cannula is an ergonomic piece of plastic tubing that runs under the nose to supply oxygen to the user (Figure 7-1-5). Cannulas are typically more comfortable than masks but

Figure 7-1-3. "Aviator's breathing oxygen" is marked on all oxygen cylinders designed for this purpose.

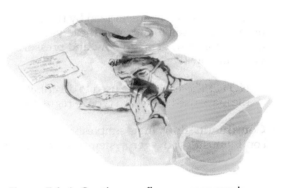

Figure 7-1-4. Continuous-flow oxygen mask.

Figure 7-1-5. An aviation cannula.

Courtesy of Sporty's Pilot Shop

might not provide an adequate flow of oxygen as reliably as masks when operating at higher altitudes.

Diluter demand/pressure demand oxygen masks. Demand masks provide a tight seal over the face to prevent dilution with outside air (Figure 7-1-6). These masks often have a built-in microphone to allow communication while the mask is in use. The masks are usually provided with a way to hang them inside the aircraft, by the straps attached to the masks, and are easy for the user to access. These are often referred to as *quick-donning* masks.

Smoke masks. Smoke masks cover the user's eyes, nose, and mouth. They are used when the situation in the flight deck demands more protection (Figure 7-1-7).

Regulators/Flow Rate Adjusters

Systems are often characterized by the type of regulator used to dispense the oxygen: continuous flow, demand flow, and pressure-demand flow (Figure 7-1-8).

> NOTE: These terms are used to describe the mask used with each type of regulator.

Continuous-flow. In its simplest form, a continuous-flow oxygen system allows oxygen to exit the storage tank through a valve and passes it through a regulator/reducer attached to the top of the tank. The flow of high-pressure oxygen passes through a section of the regulator that reduces the pressure of the oxygen, which is then fed into a hose attached to a mask worn by the user.

More sophisticated continuous-flow oxygen systems use a regulator that is adjustable to provide varying amounts of oxygen flow to match increasing need as altitude increases. These regulators can be manual or automatic.

In this type of system, the flow of oxygen is continuous, even when the user is exhaling. This can be wasteful. The lowest sufficient flow rates can be achieved by using a rebreather mask.

Diluter-demand flow. Demand-flow oxygen regulators differ significantly from continuous-flow oxygen regulators. They work in conjunction with close-fitting, demand-type masks to control the flow of oxygen. The diluter-demand type regulator holds back the flow of oxygen until the user inhales with a demand-type oxygen mask. In other words, diluter-demand oxygen systems supply oxygen only when the user inhales through the mask, and no oxygen flows when the user exhales. Thus, oxygen supply lasts longer because none is wasted while the user exhales. Demand-flow systems are used most frequently by the crew on high-performance and transport category aircraft.

The regulator dilutes the pure oxygen supply with cabin air each time a breath is drawn. An automix lever allows the regulators to automatically mix cabin air and oxygen or supply 100 percent oxygen, depending on the altitude. The demand mask provides a tight seal over the face to prevent dilution with outside air and can be used safely up to 40,000 ft.

Pressure-demand flow. Pressure-demand oxygen systems operate similarly to diluter-demand systems, except that oxygen is delivered under higher pressure than with a diluter-demand regulator. When used with an airtight mask, it provides a positive pressure application of oxygen, allowing the user's lungs to be pressurized with oxygen. Pressure-demand regulators are used on aircraft that regularly fly at 40,000 ft. and above. They are also found on many airliners and high-performance aircraft that might not typically fly that high. Forcing oxygen into the lungs under pressure ensures saturation of the blood, regardless of altitude or cabin altitude. Dilution with cabin air also occurs at lower altitudes.

Figure 7-1-6. A demand flow, quick-don mask.

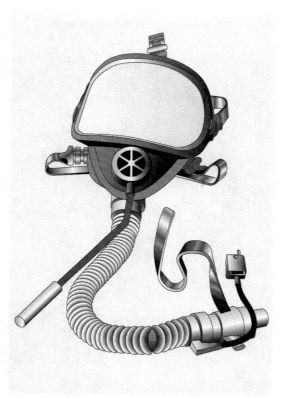

Figure 7-1-7. A smoke mask.

Oxygen Plumbing

Valves, tubing and fittings make up most of the oxygen system plumbing and connect the various components. Most lines are metal in permanent installations. High-pressure lines are usually stainless steel. Tubing in the low-pressure parts of the oxygen system is typically aluminum. Flexible plastic hosing is used deliver oxygen to the masks; its use is increasing in permanent installations to save weight. Plastic tubing is also used for portable oxygen systems.

Five types of valves are commonly found in high-pressure gaseous oxygen systems: filler, check, shutoff, pressure reducer, and pressure relief.

Instruments

Flow indicators, or flow meters, are common in all oxygen systems. Many flow meters in continuous-flow oxygen regulators also double as flow rate adjusters. Demand-flow oxygen systems usually have flow indicators built into the regulators at each user station. Flow indicators provide a quick verification that an oxygen system is functioning.

Pressure gauges are used to monitor system and cylinder pressures.

How Supplemental Oxygen is Provided

Portable Oxygen Equipment

If the aircraft does not have a fixed installation, portable oxygen equipment must be readily accessible for high-altitude flight. The portable equipment usually consists of an oxygen cylinder, regulator, mask outlet, and pressure gauge. A portable oxygen setup for a light aircraft exemplifies this type of continuous-flow system and is shown in Figure 7-1-9.

Fixed Oxygen Installation

Most high-altitude aircraft come equipped with some type of fixed oxygen installation. In some aircraft, a continuous-flow oxygen system is installed for both passengers and crew. The pressure demand system is widely used as a crew system, especially on the larger transport aircraft. Many aircraft have a combination of both systems that can be augmented by portable equipment.

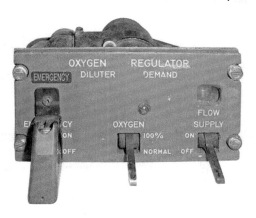
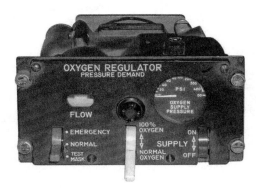

Figure 7-1-8. Examples of panel-mounted regulators: diluter demand (top) and pressure demand (bottom).

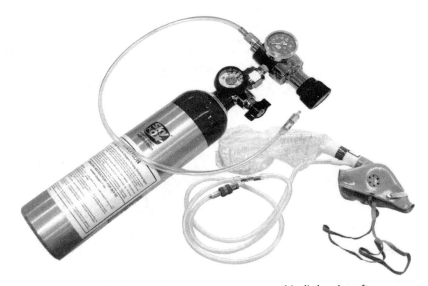

Figure 7-1-9. A typical portable oxygen system used in light aircraft.

Continuous–flow system. Many continuous-flow systems include a fixed location for the oxygen cylinders with permanent delivery plumbing installed to all passenger and crew stations in the cabin. In large aircraft, separate storage cylinders for crew and passengers are typical. Fully integrated oxygen systems usually have separate, remotely mounted compo-

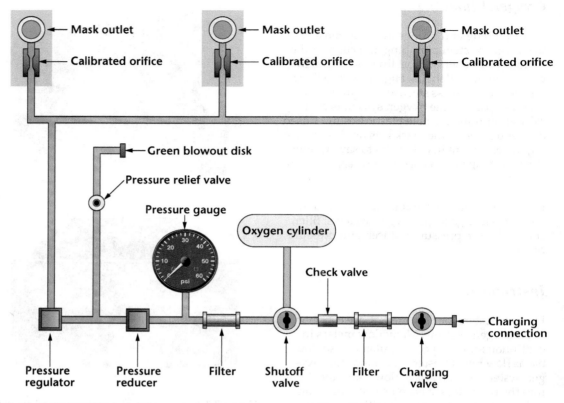

Figure 7-1-10. Continuous-flow oxygen system found on small- to medium-size aircraft.

nents to reduce pressure and regulate flow. A pressure relief valve is also typically installed in the system, as is some sort of filter and a gauge to indicate the amount of oxygen pressure remaining in the storage cylinders. Figure 7-1-10 diagrams the type of continuous-flow system that is used on small to medium-sized aircraft.

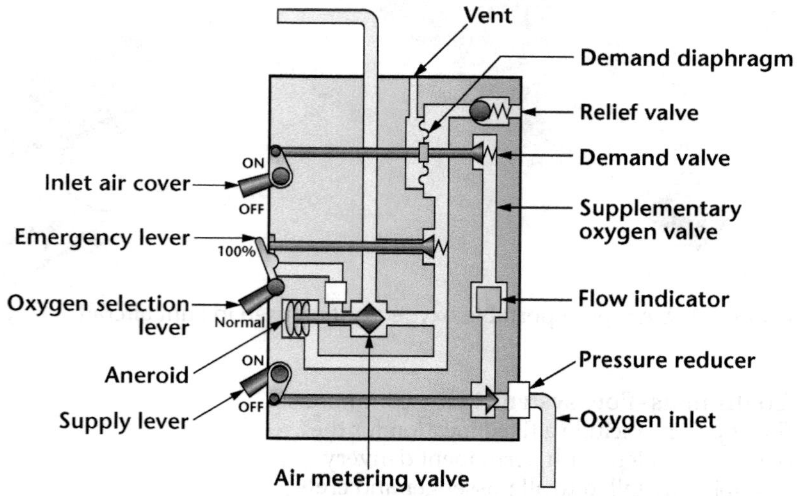

Built-in continuous-flow oxygen systems achieve a final flow rate to individual user stations using a calibrated orifice in each mask. Larger diameter orifices are usually used in crew masks to provide greater flow than that for passengers.

The passenger section of a continuous-flow oxygen system can consist of a series of plug-in supply sockets fitted to the cabin walls adjacent to the passenger seats to which oxygen masks can be connected. Flow is inhibited until a passenger manually plugs in.

Diluter-demand and pressure-demand.
In a demand-flow oxygen system, the system pressure-reducing valve is sometimes called a pressure regulator. This device lowers the oxygen pressure from the storage cylinders and delivers it to individual regulators dedicated for each user. A pressure reduction also occurs at the inlet of the individual regulator by limiting the size of the inlet orifice. Two types of individual regulators are made: the diluter-demand type and the pressure-demand type.

Both types of regulators hold back the flow of oxygen until the user inhales. A diluter-demand regulator dilutes the pure oxygen supply with cabin air each time a breath is drawn. With its control toggle switch set to normal, the amount of dilution depends on the cabin altitude. As altitude increases, an

Figure 7-1-11. A diluter-demand regulator operates when low pressure caused by inhalation moves the demand diaphragm. A demand valve connected to the diaphragm opens, letting oxygen flow through the metering valve. The metering valve adjusts the mixture of cabin air and pure oxygen via a connecting link to an aneroid that responds to cabin altitude.

aneroid allows more oxygen and less cabin air to be delivered to the user by adjusting flows through a metering valve. At about 34,000 ft., the diluter-demand regulator meters 100 percent oxygen. This should not be needed unless cabin pressurization fails. The user can also select 100 percent oxygen delivery at any time by positioning the oxygen selection lever on the regulator. A built-in emergency switch also delivers 100 percent oxygen, but in a continuous flow as the demand function is bypassed (Figure 7-1-11).

Pressure-demand oxygen systems. Pressure-demand oxygen systems operate similarly to diluter-demand systems, except that oxygen is delivered through the individual pressure regulators under higher pressure. When the demand valve is unseated, oxygen under pressure forces its way into the user's lungs. The demand function still operates, extending the overall supply of oxygen beyond that of a continuous-flow system. Dilution with cabin air also occurs if cabin altitude is less than 34,000 ft. An example of a demand-flow oxygen system is shown in Figure 7-1-12.

Many larger aircraft use a combination of continuous-flow system for passengers and demand-flow system for the crew.

Chemical Oxygen Systems

The two primary types of chemical oxygen systems are the portable type, much like a portable carry-on gaseous oxygen cylinder, and the fully integrated supplementary oxygen system used

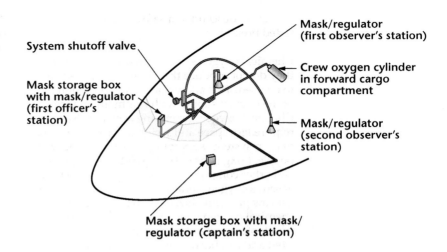

Figure 7-1-12. Location of demand-flow oxygen components on a transport category aircraft.

as backup on pressurized aircraft in case of pressurization failure (Figure 7-1-13). This latter use of solid chemical oxygen generators is most common on airliners. The generators are stored in the overhead passenger service unit (PSU) attached to hoses and masks for every passenger on board the aircraft. When a depressurization occurs, or the flight crew activates a switch, a compartment door opens, and the masks and hoses fall out in front of the passengers. The action of pulling the mask down to a usable position actuates an electric current or ignition hammer that ignites the oxygen candle and initiates the flow of oxygen. Typically, 10 to 20 minutes of oxygen is available for each person. This is calculated to be enough time for the

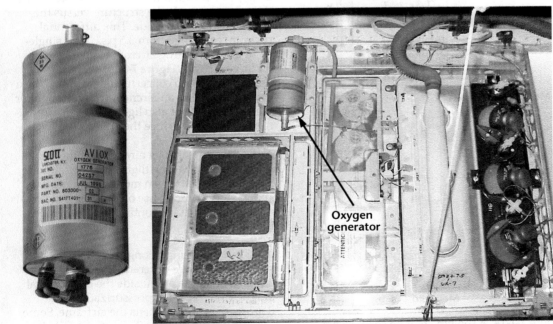

Figure 7-1-13. An oxygen generator mounted in place in an overhead passenger service unit of a transport category aircraft.

aircraft to descend to a safe altitude for unassisted breathing.

Chemical oxygen systems are unique in that they do not produce the oxygen until it is time to be used. This allows safer transportation of the oxygen supply with less maintenance. Chemical oxygen-generating systems also require less space and weigh less than gaseous oxygen systems supplying the same number of people. Long runs of tubing, fittings, regulators, and other components are avoided, as are heavy gaseous oxygen storage cylinders. Each passenger row grouping has its own fully independent chemical oxygen generator. The generators, which often weigh less than a pound, are insulated and can burn completely without getting hot. The size of the orifice opening in the hose-attach nipples regulates the continuous flow of oxygen to the users. A cross section of one of these generators is shown in Figure 7-1-14.

Cabin Pressurization

Pressurizing an aircraft cabin makes flight possible in the hostile environment of the upper atmosphere. The degree of pressurization and the operating altitude of any aircraft are limited by critical design factors.

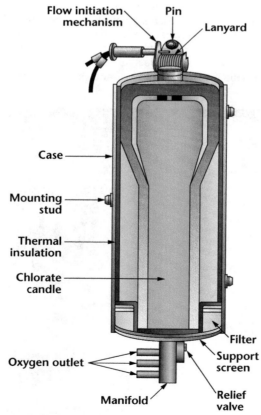

Figure 7-1-14. A sodium chlorate solid oxygen candle is at the core of a chemical oxygen generator.

A cabin pressurization system must perform several functions if it is to ensure adequate passenger comfort and safety.

- Maintain a cabin pressure altitude of about 8,000 ft. or lower regardless of the cruising altitude of the aircraft. This is to ensure that passengers and crew have enough oxygen at sufficient pressure to facilitate full blood saturation.

- Prevent rapid changes of cabin pressure, which can be uncomfortable or can injure passengers and crew.

- Circulate air from inside the cabin to the outside at a rate that quickly eliminates odors and removes stale air.

- Incorporate cabin air heating or cooling systems.

To be pressurized, the portion of the aircraft that will contain air at a higher pressure than outside must be sealed. A wide variety of materials facilitate this. Compressible seals around doors combine with various other seals, grommets, and sealants to essentially establish an airtight pressure vessel. This usually includes the cabin, flight deck, and the baggage compartments. Air is then pumped into this area at a constant rate sufficient to raise the pressure slightly above that which is needed. Control is maintained by adjusting the rate at which the air is allowed to flow out of the aircraft through a valve called an outflow valve (Figure 7-1-15).

A key factor in pressurization is the fuselage's ability to withstand the forces associated with the pressure inside the structure versus the ambient pressure outside. This differential pressure can range from 3.5 p.s.i. for a single-engine reciprocating aircraft, to about 9 p.s.i. for large aircraft (Figure 7-1-16). If aircraft weight were of no concern, this would not be a problem. Making an aircraft strong enough for pressurization, yet also light, has been an engineering challenge since the 1930s.

The development of jet aircraft and their ability to exploit low-drag flight at higher altitude made the problem even more pronounced. Today, the expanded use of composite materials in aircraft structures continues this engineering challenge.

In addition to being strong enough to withstand the pressure differential between the air inside and the air outside the cabin, metal fatigue from repeated pressurization and depressurization weakens the airframe. Some early pressurized aircraft structures failed because of this and resulted in fatal accidents. The FAA's aging aircraft program was cre-

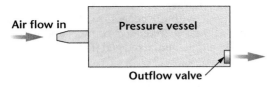

Figure 7-1-15. The outflow valve controls how much pressure is in the aircraft.

ated to increase inspection scrutiny of older airframes that can fatigue because of the pressurization cycle.

Aircraft of any size can be pressurized. Weight considerations when making the fuselage strong enough to endure pressurization usually limit pressurization to high-performance light aircraft and larger aircraft. A few pressurized single-engine reciprocating aircraft exist, as do many pressurized single-engine turboprop aircraft.

Sources of Air and Components

The source of air to pressurize an aircraft varies mainly with engine type. Reciprocating-engine aircraft have pressurization sources different from those of turbine-powered aircraft. Note that compressing air raises its temperature. A means for keeping pressurization air cool enough is built into most pressurization systems. It could be in the form of a heat exchanger, using cold ambient air to modify the temperature of the air from the pressurization source. A full air cycle air conditioning system with expansion turbine can also be used. The latter has the advantage of temperature control on the ground and at low altitudes where ambient air temperature can be higher than comfortable for the passengers and crew.

Reciprocating engine systems. Three typical sources of air are used to pressurize reciprocating aircraft: supercharger, turbocharger, and engine-driven compressor.

Superchargers and turbochargers are installed on reciprocating engines to permit better performance at high altitude by increasing the quantity and pressure of the air in the engine induction system. Some of the air produced by each of these can be routed into the cabin to pressurize it.

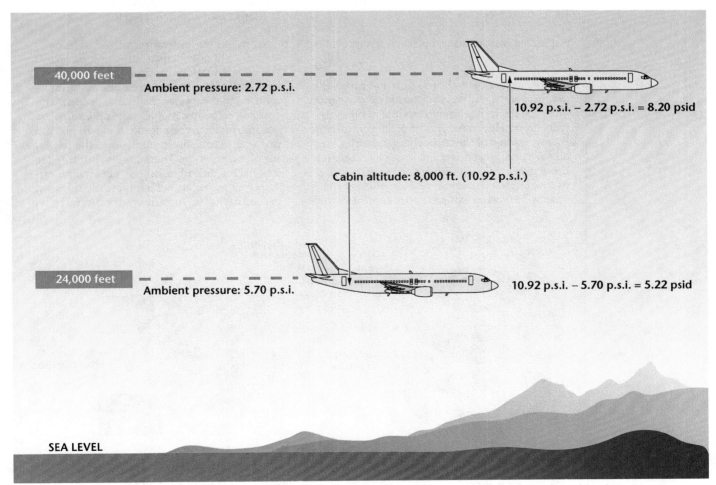

Figure 7-1-16. Differential pressure (psid) is calculated by subtracting the ambient air pressure from the cabin air pressure.

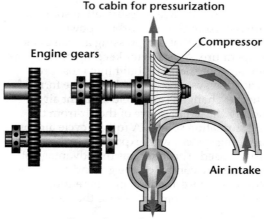

To cabin for pressurization

Compressor

Engine gears

Air intake

To engine carburetor and intake

Figure 7-1-17. A reciprocating engine supercharger can be used as a source of pressurization if it is upstream of carburetion.

A supercharger is mechanically driven by the engine. Despite engine performance increases from higher induction system pressure, some of the engine output is used by the supercharger. Furthermore, superchargers have limited capability to increase engine performance. If supplying both the intake and the cabin with air, the engine performance ceiling is lower than if the aircraft were not pressurized.

Superchargers are found on older reciprocating engine aircraft (Figure 7-1-17).

Turbochargers, sometimes known as turbosuperchargers, are driven by engine exhaust gases. They are the most common source of pressurization on modern reciprocating engine aircraft. By using some of the turbocharger compressed air for cabin pressurization, less is available for the engine intake charge, resulting in lower overall engine performance. Nonetheless, the otherwise wasted exhaust gases are put to work

in the turbocharger compressor, enabling high-altitude flight with the benefits of low drag and weather avoidance in relative comfort and without using supplemental oxygen (Figure 7-1-18).

Both superchargers and turbochargers are oil lubricated. The supercharger is part of the fuel intake system, and the turbocharger is part of the exhaust system. As such, there is a risk of contamination of cabin air from oil, fuel, or exhaust fumes if a malfunction occurs—a shortcoming of these pressurization sources.

A third source of air for pressurizing the cabin in reciprocating aircraft is an engine-driven compressor. Either belt driven, or gear driven by the accessory drive, an independent, dedicated compressor for pressurization avoids some of the potential contamination issues of superchargers and turbochargers. The compressor device does, however, add significant weight. It also consumes engine output because it is engine driven.

The roots blower is an engine-driven compressor (Figure 7-1-19) commonly used on older, large, reciprocating-engine aircraft for pressurization. The two lobes in this compressor do not touch each other or the compressor housing. As they rotate, air enters the space between the lobes and is compressed and delivered to the cabin.

Near maximum operating altitude, the performance of any reciprocating engine and the pressurization compressor suffers. This is because of the reduced pressure of the air at altitude that supplies the intake of each. The result is difficulty in maintaining a sufficient volume of air to the engine intake to produce power and to allow enough air to the fuselage for pressurization. These are the limiting factors for the design ceiling of most reciprocating-engine aircraft, which typically does not exceed 25,000 ft. Turbine engine aircraft over-

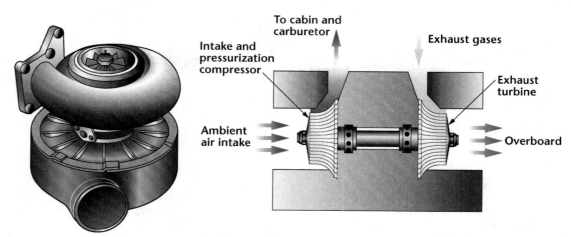

To cabin and carburetor

Exhaust gases

Intake and pressurization compressor

Exhaust turbine

Ambient air intake

Overboard

Figure 7-1-18. A turbocharger can be used for pressurizing cabin air and engine intake air on a reciprocating engine aircraft.

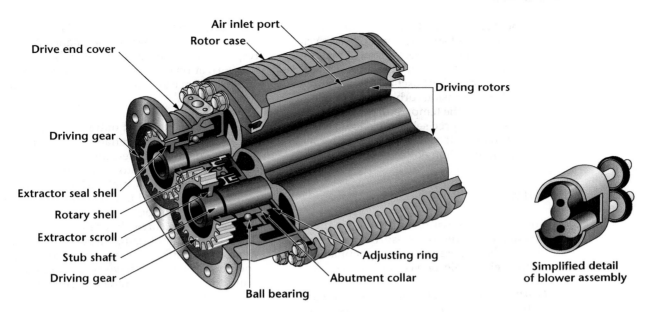

Figure 7-1-19. A roots blower is gear driven by the engine and is used on some older aircraft.

come these shortcomings, permitting them to fly at much higher altitudes.

Turbine engine systems. The main principle of operation of a turbine engine involves compressing large amounts of air to be mixed with fuel and burned. Bleed air from the engine's compressor section is relatively free of contaminants. That makes it a great source of air for cabin pressurization. However, the volume of air for engine power production is reduced. The amount of air bled off for pressurization compared to the overall amount of air compressed for combustion is relatively small but should be minimized.

Hot, high-pressure bleed air can be exploited in many ways. Smaller turbine aircraft, or sections of a large aircraft, use a jet pump flow multiplier (Figure 7-1-20). With this device, bleed air is tapped off the turbine engine's compressor section. It is ejected into a venturi jet pump mounted in air ducting that has one end open to the ambient air and the other end directed into the compartment to be pressurized. Because of the low pressure established in the venturi by the bleed air flow, air is drawn in from outside the aircraft. It mixes with the bleed air and is delivered to the pressure vessel to pressurize it. An advantage of this type of pressurization is the lack of moving parts. A disadvantage is only a relatively small volume of space can be pressurized in this manner.

Another method of pressurizing an aircraft using turbine engine compressor bleed air is to have the bleed air drive a separate compressor that has an ambient air intake. A turbine turned by bleed air rotates a compressor impellor mounted on the same shaft. Outside air is

drawn in and compressed. It is mixed with the bleed air outflow from the turbine and is sent to the pressure vessel. Turboprop aircraft often use this device, known as a turbo-compressor. A simplified drawing of this arrangement is in Figure 7-1-21.

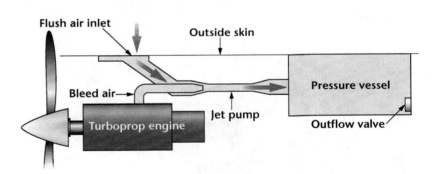

Figure 7-1-20. A jet pump ejects bleed air into a venturi that draws air for pressurization from outside the aircraft.

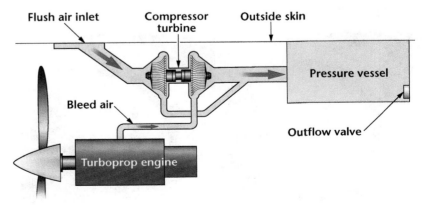

Figure 7-1-21. A turbo-compressor used to pressurize cabins mostly in turboprop aircraft.

The most common method of pressurizing turbine-powered aircraft is with an air cycle air conditioning and pressurization system. Bleed air is used, and through an elaborate system including heat exchangers, a compressor, and an expansion turbine, cabin pressurization and the temperature of the pressurizing air are precisely controlled. This air cycle system is discussed in detail in the air conditioning section of this chapter.

Valves

Control of air pressure in the cabin is the function of a series of pressure sensors and valves. Their operation can be pneumatic, electric, electronic, or a combination of those.

Outflow valve. Controlling cabin pressurization is done by regulating the amount of air that flows out of the cabin. The principal control of the pressurization system is the outflow valve. The cabin outflow valve opens, closes, or modulates to establish the amount of air pressure maintained in the cabin. Some outflow valves contain the pressure regulat-

ing mechanism and the valve mechanism in one unit. They operate pneumatically in response to the settings on the flight deck pressurization panel that influence the balance between cabin and ambient air pressure (Figure 7-1-22).

Pneumatic operation of outflow valves is common. It is simple, reliable, and eliminates the need to convert air pressure operating variables into some other form. Diaphragms, springs, metered orifices, jet pumps, bellows, and poppet valves are used to sense and manipulate cabin and ambient air pressures to correctly position the outflow valve without using electricity. Outflow valves that combine using electricity with pneumatic operation have all-pneumatic standby and manual modes, as shown in Figure 7-1-23.

Outflow valves are typically installed at the rear of the aircraft as shown in Figure 7-1-24.

Cabin air pressure safety valve. Aircraft pressurization systems incorporate various features to limit human and structural damage if the system malfunctions or becomes inoperative. A means for preventing over-pressurization is incorporated to ensure the structural integrity of the aircraft if control of the pressurization system is lost. A cabin air safety valve is a pressure relief valve set to open at a predetermined pressure differential. It allows air to flow from the cabin to prevent internal pressure from exceeding design limitations. On most aircraft, safety valves are set to open between 8 psid and 10 psid.

Pressurization safety valves are used to prevent the overpressurization of the cabin. They open at a preset differential pressure and allow air to flow out of the cabin. Widebody transport category aircraft cabins can have more than one cabin pressurization safety valve.

Some outflow valves incorporate the safety valve function into their design. This is common on some corporate jets when two outflow valves are used. One outflow valve operates as the primary and the other as a secondary. Both contain a pilot valve that opens when the pressure differential increases to a preset value. This, in turn, opens the outflow valves to prevent further pressurization. The outflow valves shown in Figure 7-1-24 operate in this manner.

Negative pressure relief valve. A negative pressure relief valve is also included on pressurized aircraft to ensure that air pressure outside the aircraft does not exceed cabin

Pressurization panel

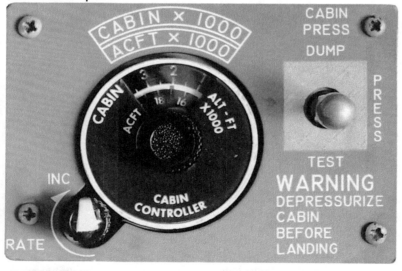

Figure 7-1-22. The pressurization panel in the flight deck (top) and the outflow valve, shown fully closed (left), and partially open (right).

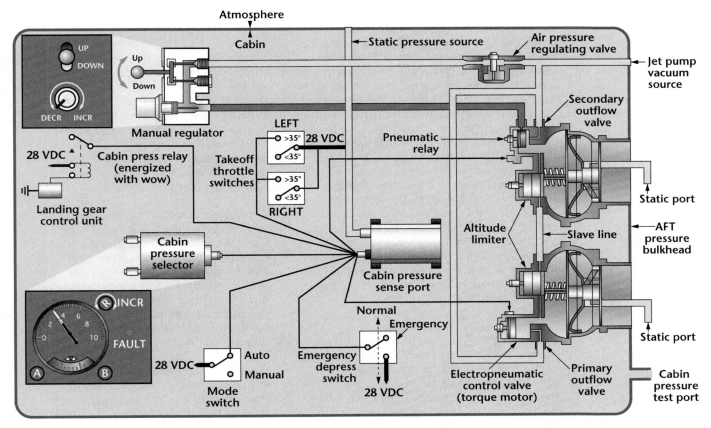

Figure 7-1-23. The pressurization control system on many small transport and business jets uses a combination of electronic, electric, and pneumatic control elements.

air pressure. In such a case, the valve opens to allow ambient air to enter the cabin. Too much negative pressure can cause difficulty when opening the cabin door. If high enough, it could cause structural damage because the pressure vessel is designed for cabin pressure to be greater than ambient pressure.

Pressurization dump valve. Some aircraft are equipped with pressurization dump valves. These essentially are safety valves that are operated automatically or manually by a switch in the flight deck. They are used to quickly remove air and air pressure from the cabin, usually in abnormal, maintenance, or emergency situations.

Pressurization Modes of Operation

When operating at lower altitudes, all aircraft can be operated in unpressurized mode. The option of selecting pressurization is entirely optional, and the mode of operation is dependent on the system design.

Aircraft cabin pressurization can be controlled via two modes of operation. The first is the isobaric mode, which works to maintain cabin altitude at one pressure despite the

changing altitude of the aircraft. The other is constant differential mode.

Constant differential mode. The constant differential mode controls cabin pressure to maintain a constant pressure difference between the air pressure inside the cabin and the ambient air pressure, regardless of aircraft altitude changes. The constant differential mode pressure differential is lower than the maximum differential pressure for which the airframe is designed, keeping the integrity of the pressure vessel intact.

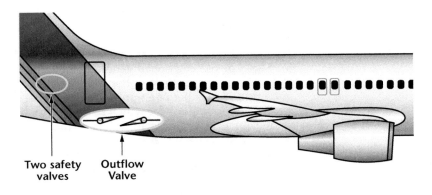

Figure 7-1-24. Outflow valves are at the rear of the aircraft.

Isobaric mode. In isobaric mode, the pressurization system maintains the cabin altitude selected by the crew. For example, the flight crew selects to maintain a cabin altitude of 8,000 ft. (10.92 p.s.i.). In the isobaric mode, the cabin pressure is established at the 8,000-ft. level and remains at this level, even as the altitude of the aircraft fluctuates.

This is the condition for normal operations. But when the aircraft climbs beyond a certain altitude, maintaining the selected cabin altitude can result in a differential pressure above that for which the airframe was designed. In this case, the mode of pressurization automatically switches from isobaric to constant differential mode. This occurs before the cabin's max differential pressure limit is reached. A constant differential pressure is then maintained, regardless of the selected cabin altitude.

In addition to the modes of operation described above, the rate of change of the cabin pressure, also known as the cabin rate of climb or descent, is also controlled. This can be done automatically or manually by the flight crew. Typical rates of change for cabin pressure are 300 to 500 feet per minute. Also, note that modes of pressurization can also refer to automatic versus standby versus manual operation of the pressurization system.

Section 2

Heating Systems

For aircraft that are not equipped with an environmental system that provides pressurization, heating, and air conditioning, they are equipped with separate systems to maintain passenger and crew comfort. These systems take several forms depending on the size and sophistication of the aircraft design. They all are designed to supply ventilating air, heated air, and usually air to defog the windshield.

Several types of heaters are used on aircraft. The type of heater used generally depends on the size and speed of the aircraft, the type and number of engines used, and the type of operations for which the aircraft was designed. A business aircraft is certainly likely to have a better heater system than an agricultural spray plane. Here, we discuss the two systems most commonly used on aircraft with reciprocating engines—an exhaust shroud heat exchanger and a fuel-fired (combustion) heater.

Exhaust Shroud Heat Exchanger

Most single-engine, light aircraft use exhaust shroud heating systems to heat the cabin air. Ambient air is directed into a metal shroud, or jacket, that encases part of the engine's exhaust system. The air is warmed by the exhaust and directed through a firewall heater valve into the cabin. This simple solution requires no electrical or engine power, and it uses heat that would otherwise be wasted (Figures 7-2-1 and 7-2-2).

A major concern of exhaust shroud heat systems is that exhaust gases could contaminate the cabin air. Even the slightest crack in an exhaust manifold can send enough carbon monoxide into the cabin to be fatal. Strict inspection procedures are in place to minimize this threat. Regardless of age or condition, aircraft with exhaust shroud heating systems should contain a carbon monoxide detection device in the cabin.

Figure 7-2-3 shows an exhaust manifold with its shroud removed. You can see many small studs welded on the unit to increase the heat transfer from the exhaust to the ambient air going to the cabin. This makes the heat exchanger much more efficient. You can also see how important the inspection program discussed above is to ensure that no leaks are present that would permit carbon monoxide to enter the cabin.

Combustion Heaters

An aircraft combustion heater is used on many small- to medium-sized aircraft. It is a heat source independent of the aircraft's engines, although it does use fuel from the aircraft's main fuel system. Combustion heaters are manufactured by several companies that supply the aviation industry. Most are built much like the one described here and look similar to the one in Figure 7-2-4. The most up to date units have electronic ignition and temperature control switches.

Combustion heaters are similar to exhaust shroud heaters in that ambient air is heated and sent to the cabin. The source of heat in this case is an independent combustion chamber inside the cylindrical outer shroud of the heater unit. The correct amount of fuel and air is ignited in the airtight inner chamber. The exhaust from combustion is funneled overboard. Ambient air is directed between the combustion chamber and the outer shroud. It absorbs the combustion heat by convection and is channeled into the cabin. For the following discussions of the

Figures 7-2-1 through 7-2-4

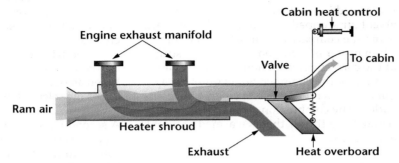

Figure 7-2-1. The basic arrangement of an aircraft exhaust shroud heater.

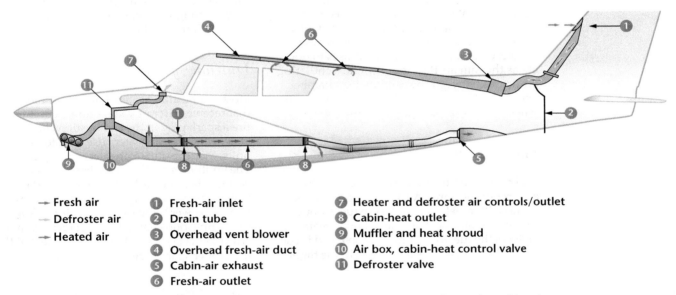

→ Fresh air
→ Defroster air
→ Heated air

1 Fresh-air inlet
2 Drain tube
3 Overhead vent blower
4 Overhead fresh-air duct
5 Cabin-air exhaust
6 Fresh-air outlet

7 Heater and defroster air controls/outlet
8 Cabin-heat outlet
9 Muffler and heat shroud
10 Air box, cabin-heat control valve
11 Defroster valve

Figure 7-2-2. The environmental system of a single-engine Piper aircraft using an exhaust shroud heating system.

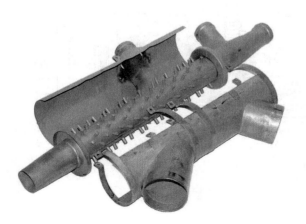

Figure 7-2-3. An exhaust manifold with the shroud removed.

Figure 7-2-4. A combustion heater.

combustion heater subsystems and heater operation, refer to Figure 7-2-5.

Combustion Air System

The air used in the combustion process is ambient air scooped from outside the aircraft, or from the compartment in which the combustion heater is mounted. A blower ensures that the correct quantity and pressure of air are sent into the chamber. Some units have regulators or a relief valve to control the combination. The combustion air is completely separate from the air that is warmed and sent into the cabin.

Ventilating Air System

Ventilating air is the name given to the air that is warmed and sent into the cabin. Typically, it comes into the combustion heater through a ram air intake. When the aircraft is on the ground, a ventilating air fan controlled by a landing gear squat switch operates to draw in the air. Once airborne, that fan ceases to operate as the ram air flow is sufficient. Ventilating air passes between the combustion chamber and the outer shroud of the combustion heater where it is warmed and sent to the cabin.

Fuel System

Fuel for the combustion heater is drawn from an aircraft fuel tank. A constant pressure fuel pump with relief valve pulls the fuel through a filter. A main solenoid valve downstream delivers the fuel to the unit. The solenoid is controlled by the cabin heater switch in the flight deck and three safety switches on the combustion heater. The first safety switch is a duct limit switch that keeps the valve closed if the unit does not have enough ventilating airflow to keep it in the correct operating temperature range. The second is a pressure switch that must sense pressure from the combustion air fan to allow the solenoid to open. Fuel is delivered to the combustion chamber only if air can be mixed with it. Finally, an overheat switch also controls the main fuel supply solenoid. When an over temperature condition occurs, it closes the solenoid to stop the supply of fuel.

A secondary solenoid is downstream of the main fuel supply solenoid. It is part of a fuel control unit that also houses a pressure regulator and an additional fuel filter. The valve opens and closes on command from the combustion heater thermostat. In normal operation, the heater cycles on and off by opening and closing this solenoid at the entrance to the combustion chamber. When opened, fuel flows through a nozzle that sprays it into the combustion chamber.

Ignition System

Most combustion heaters have an ignition unit that receives aircraft voltage and steps it up to fire a spark plug in the combustion chamber. Older combustion heaters use vibrator ignition units. Modern units have electronic ignition. The ignition is continuous when activated. This occurs when the heater switch is placed in the ON position in the flight deck and the combustion air blower builds sufficient air pressure in the combustion chamber. Both older and modern systems use a spark plug. It is essential that the proper spark plug is used for the heater.

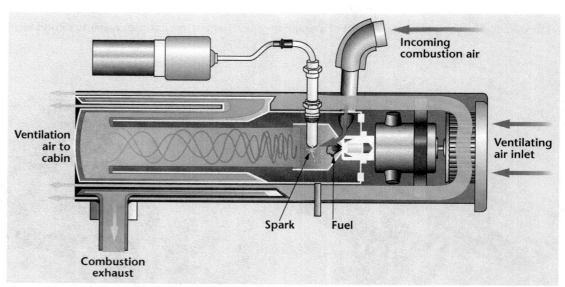

Figure 7-2-5. Combustion heater operation.

Controls

The combustion heater controls consist of a cabin heat switch and a thermostat. The cabin heat switch starts the fuel pump, opens the main fuel supply solenoid, and turns on the combustion air fan and the ventilating air fan if the aircraft is on the ground. When the combustion air fan builds pressure, it allows the ignition unit to start. The thermostat sends power to open the fuel control solenoid when heat is needed. This triggers combustion in the unit and heat is delivered to the cabin. When the selected temperature is reached, the thermostat cuts power to the fuel control solenoid and combustion stops. Ventilating air continues to circulate and carry heat away. When the temperature falls below the thermostat setting, the combustion heater cycles on again.

While they do increase the aircraft's fuel consumption by a little, these heaters offer the advantage of a relatively high output and both a combustion air blower and a ventilating air blower they can provide a reasonable amount of heat while the aircraft is on the ground. This is a feature that the exhaust shroud heating system cannot provide.

Section 3

Cooling Systems

Whether on the ground or in the air, extremely high temperatures can be just as uncomfortable to flight crews and passengers as cold ones. Air conditioning systems might not be an option on some small aircraft because of their weight and power requirements, but advancements in technology have been making it possible to extend this welcome addition to aircraft that, in the past, could not accommodate it.

The type of system used to provide air for cabin cooling varies with the size, age, and mostly with the type of engine installed on the aircraft. Aircraft with reciprocating engines use a vapor cycle system, much like the one installed on an automobile or in a home. Turbine-powered aircraft can use a vapor cycle system but are more likely to use an air cycle machine that takes advantage of the supply of high-pressure air available at the engine compressor's outlet. We look at both the vapor cycle and air cycle system components and how the systems operate.

Vapor Cycle System

Energy can be neither created nor destroyed; however, it can be transformed and moved. This is what occurs in vapor cycle air conditioning. Vapor cycle air conditioning is a closed system in which a refrigerant is circulated through tubing and a variety of components. The purpose is to remove heat from the aircraft cabin. While circulating, the refrigerant changes state. By manipulating the latent heat required to do so, hot air is replaced with cool air in the aircraft cabin. Figure 7-3-1 illustrates a vapor cycle system and is the primary reference for the components discussion.

The vapor cycle air conditioning system has two sides. One accepts heat and is known as the low side. The other gives up heat and is known as the high side. The low and high refer to the temperature and pressure of the refrigerant. As such, the compressor and the expansion valve are the two components that separate the low side from the high side of the cycle. Refrigerant on the low side has low pressure and temperature. Refrigerant on the high side has high pressure and temperature.

Vapor Cycle System Components

By examining each component in the vapor cycle air conditioning system, we gain greater insight into its function.

Refrigerant. For many years, dichlorodifluoromethane (R12) was the standard refrigerant used in aircraft vapor cycle systems. Some of these systems remain in use today. R12 has a negative effect on the environment. It degrades the earth's protective ozone layer. In most cases, it has been replaced by tetrafluoroethane (R134a), which is safer for the environment.

Receiver dryer. The receiver dryer acts as the reservoir of the vapor cycle system. It is downstream of the condenser and upstream of the expansion valve. When it is very hot, more refrigerant is used by the system than when temperatures are moderate. Extra refrigerant is stored in the receiver dryer for this purpose.

Liquid refrigerant from the condenser flows into the receiver dryer. Inside, it passes through filters and a desiccant material. The filters remove any foreign particles that might be in the system. The desiccant captures any water in the refrigerant. Water in the refrigerant causes two major problems. First, the refrigerant and water combine to form an acid. If left in contact with the inside of the components and tubing, the acid deteriorates the materials from which these are made. The second problem with water is that it could form ice and block the flow of refrigerant around the system, rendering it inoperative. Ice is especially a problem if it forms at the orifice in the expansion valve, which is the coldest point in the cycle.

Expansion valve. Refrigerant exits the receiver dryer and flows to the expansion valve. The thermal expansion valve has an adjustable orifice through which the correct amount of refrigerant is metered to obtain optimal cooling. This is done by monitoring the temperature and pressure of the refrigerant at the outlet of the next component in the cycle, the evaporator.

Ideally, the expansion valve should let only the amount of refrigerant spray into the evaporator that can be completely converted to a vapor.

Evaporator. Most evaporators are constructed of copper or aluminum tubing coiled into a compact unit. Fins are attached to increase surface area, facilitating rapid heat transfer between the cabin air blown over the outside of the evaporator with a fan and the refrigerant inside. The expansion valve at the evaporator inlet releases high-pressure, high-temperature liquid refrigerant into the evaporator. As the

refrigerant absorbs heat from the cabin air, it changes into a low-pressure vapor. This is discharged from the evaporator outlet to the next component in the vapor cycle system, the compressor.

The temperature and pressure pickups that regulate the expansion valve are at the evaporator outlet. The evaporator is placed such that cabin air is pulled to it by a fan. The fan blows the air over the evaporator and discharges the cooled air back into the cabin.

When cabin air is cooled by flowing over the evaporator, it can no longer retain the water that it could at a higher temperature. As a result, it condenses on the outside of the evaporator and must be collected and drained overboard.

Pressurized aircraft can contain a valve in the evaporator drain line that opens periodically to discharge the water to maintain pressurization. Fins on the evaporator must be protected; if damaged, they could inhibit airflow. The continuous movement of warm cabin air around the fins keeps condensed water from freezing. Ice on the evaporator reduces the efficiency of the heat exchange to the refrigerant.

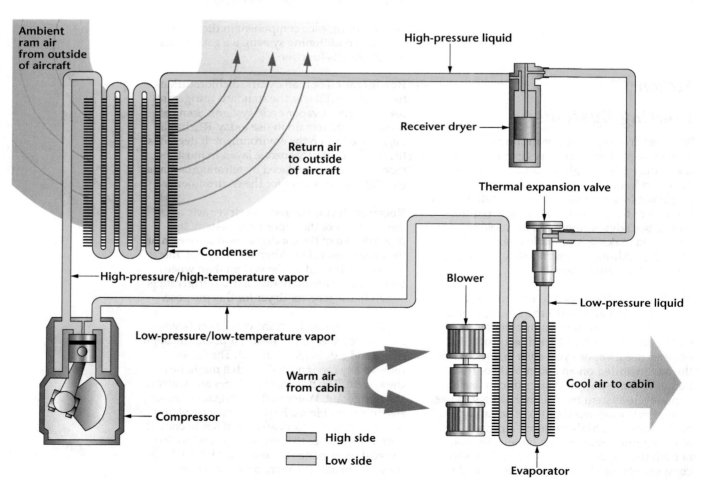

Figure 7-3-1. A basic vapor cycle air conditioning system.

Compressor. The compressor is the heart of the vapor cycle air conditioning system. It circulates the refrigerant around the vapor cycle system. It receives low-pressure, low-temperature refrigerant vapor from the outlet of the evaporator and compresses it. As the pressure is increased, the temperature also increases. The refrigerant temperature is raised above that of the outside air temperature. The refrigerant then flows out of the compressor to the condenser where it gives off the heat to the outside air.

The compressor is the dividing point between the low side and the high side of the vapor cycle system. Often it is incorporated with fittings or has fittings in the connecting lines to it that are designed to service the system with refrigerant. Access to the low and high sides of the system are required for servicing—this is provided by using fittings upstream and downstream of the compressor.

Modern compressors are either engine driven or driven by an electric motor. Occasionally, a hydraulically driven compressor is used. A typical engine-driven compressor, like that used in an automobile, is in the engine nacelle and operated by a drive belt off of the engine crankshaft. An electromagnetic clutch engages when cooling is required, which causes the compressor to operate. When cooling is sufficient, power to the clutch is cut, and the drive pulley rotates but the compressor does not. Dedicated electric motor-driven compressors are also used on aircraft. Using an electric motor allows the compressor to be nearly anywhere on the aircraft because wires can be run from the appropriate bus to the control panel and to the compressor. Hydraulically driven compressors can also be remotely located. Hydraulic lines from the hydraulic manifold are run through a switch-activated solenoid to the compressor. The solenoid allows fluid to the compressor or bypasses it. This controls the operation of the hydraulically driven compressor.

Regardless of how the vapor cycle air conditioning compressor is driven, it is usually a piston pump. It requires using a lightweight oil to lubricate and seal the unit. The oil is entrained by the refrigerant and circulates with it around the system. The compressor's crankcase retains a supply of the oil, and technicians can check the oil level and adjust it. Some compressor installations have valves that can be closed to isolate the compressor from the remainder of the vapor cycle system when oil servicing is done.

Condenser. The condenser is the final component in the vapor cycle system. It is a radiator-like heat exchanger over which outside air flows and absorbs heat from the high-pressure, high-temperature refrigerant received from the compressor. A fan is usually included to draw the air through the condenser during ground operation. On some aircraft, outside air is ducted to the condenser. On others, the condenser is lowered into the airstream from the fuselage via a hinged panel. Often, the panel is controlled by a switch on the throttle levers. It is set to retract the condenser and streamline the fuselage when full power is required.

The outside air absorbs heat from the refrigerant flowing through the condenser. The heat loss causes the refrigerant to change state back into a liquid. The high-pressure liquid refrigerant then leaves the condenser and flows to the receiver dryer. A properly engineered system that is functioning normally fully condenses all the refrigerant flowing through the condenser.

Vapor Cycle System Operation

To begin, the refrigerant is filtered and stored under pressure in the receiver dryer reservoir. The refrigerant at this point is in liquid form. It flows from the receiver dryer through tubing to an expansion valve. This is sometimes called the thermal expansion valve (TXV). Inside this valve, a restriction in the form of a small orifice blocks most of the refrigerant. Because it is under pressure, some of the refrigerant is forced through the orifice. It emerges as a spray of tiny droplets in the tubing downstream of the valve. The tubing is coiled into the evaporator, which is a radiator type assembly. A fan is positioned to blow cabin air over the surface of the evaporator. As it does, the refrigerant absorbs the heat in the cabin air and changes state from a liquid to a vapor. So much heat is absorbed that the cabin air blown by the fan across the evaporator cools significantly. This is the vapor cycle conditioned air that lowers the temperature in the cabin.

The gaseous refrigerant exiting the evaporator is drawn into the compressor. There, the refrigerant's pressure and the temperature are increased. The high-pressure, high-temperature gaseous refrigerant flows through tubing to the condenser. The condenser is like a radiator made of long tubing with fins attached to promote heat transfer. Outside air is directed over the condenser. The refrigerant temperature inside is higher than the ambient air temperature, so heat is transferred from the refrigerant to the outside air.

The amount of heat given off is enough to cool the refrigerant and to condense it back to a high-pressure liquid. It flows through tubing and back into the receiver dryer, completing the vapor cycle.

Air Cycle System

Air cycle air conditioning prepares engine bleed air to pressurize the aircraft cabin. The temperature and quantity of the air must be controlled to maintain a comfortable cabin environment at all altitudes and on the ground. The air cycle system is often called the air conditioning package or pack. It is usually in the lower half of the fuselage or in the tail section of turbine-powered aircraft.

By examining the operation of each component in the air cycle process, you will better understand how bleed air is conditioned for cabin use. Figure 7-3-2 illustrates the air cycle air conditioning system of a large aircraft.

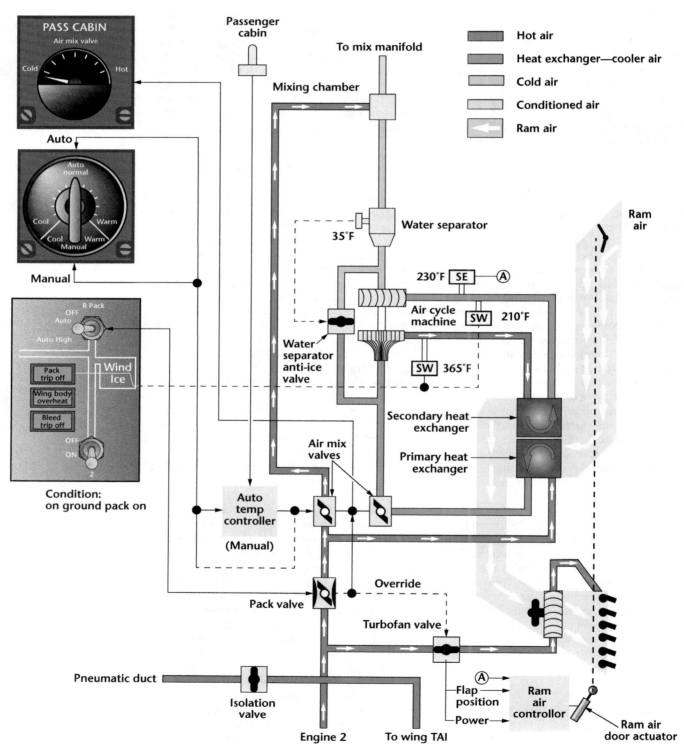

Figure 7-3-2. The air cycle air conditioning system in a large aircraft.

Pneumatic System Supply

The air cycle air conditioning system is supplied with air by the aircraft pneumatic system. In turn, the pneumatic system is supplied by bleed air tap-offs on each engine compressor section or from the auxiliary power unit pneumatic supply. An external pneumatic air supply source can also be connected while the aircraft is on the ground and parked. In normal flight operations, a pneumatic manifold is supplied by the engine bleed air using valves, regulators, and ducting. The air conditioning packs are supplied by this manifold as are other critical airframe systems, such as the anti-ice and hydraulic pressurization system.

Air Cycle System Operation

Even with the frigid temperatures at high altitudes, bleed air is too hot to be used in the cabin without being cooled. It is let into the air cycle system and routed through a heat exchanger where ram air cools the bleed air. This cooled bleed air is directed into the air cycle machine. There, it is compressed before flowing through a secondary heat exchanger that cools the air again with ram air. The bleed air then flows back into the air cycle machine where it drives an expansion turbine and cools even more. Water is then removed, and the air is mixed with bypassed bleed air for final temperature adjustment. It is sent to the cabin through the air distribution system.

Section 4

Large Aircraft Environmental Control System

The environmental control system (ECS) of a transport category aircraft is a multipurpose system. It provides heating, ventilating, air-conditioning air supply, thermal control, and cabin pressurization for the crew and passengers. Avionics cooling, smoke detection, and fire suppression can also be part of an aircraft's ECS.

Transport category aircraft use all the components and subsystems along with all the monitoring and controls discussed in this chapter. However, on some modern aircraft equipped with digital aircraft monitoring systems with LCDs, such as engine indicating and crew alerting system (EICAS) or electronic centralized aircraft monitor (ECAM), many of these systems might have no gauges (Figure 7-3-3). The ECS page of the monitoring system must be selected to display similar information. Increased use of automatic redundancy and advanced operating logic simplifies pressurization system operation to the point that it is almost completely automatic. It is probably fair to expect that as new sensors and electronic circuitry are developed, additional development will occur for both large and small aircraft.

MAN ALT
Controls pressurization in manual mode

UP/DOWN—commands cabin altitude to climb/descend

MAN RATE
Controls the rate of change of the cabin altitude in manual mode

PRESS CONT
When pressed, selects manual pressurization

FAULT—indicates both controllers failed
MAN—indicates manual mode selected

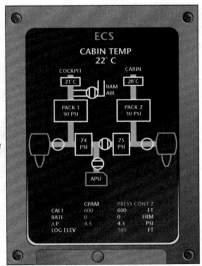

Figure 7-3-3. The pressurization panel and ECS pages on a regional jet have no gauges. Traditional data is presented in digital format at the bottom of the page.

8

Instrument Systems

Since the beginning of manned flight, it has been recognized that supplying the pilot with information about the aircraft and its operation could be useful and lead to safer flight. The Wright Brothers had very few instruments on their Wright Flyer, but they did have an engine tachometer, an anemometer (wind meter), and a stop watch. They were obviously concerned about the aircraft's engine and the progress of their flight. From that simple beginning, a wide variety of instruments have been developed to inform flight crews of different parameters. Instrument systems now exist to provide information on the condition of the aircraft, engine, components, the aircraft's attitude in the sky, weather, cabin environment, navigation, and communication.

As the range of desired information has grown, so too have the size and complexity of modern aircraft, thus expanding even further the need to inform the flight crew without sensory overload or over cluttering the flight deck. As a result, the old instrument panel in the front of the flight deck with various individual instruments attached to it has evolved into a sophisticated computer-controlled digital interface with flat-panel display screens and prioritized messaging.

Any instrument or instrument system usually has two parts. One part senses the situation, and the other part displays it. Some instruments are known as direct-sensing instruments. In direct-sensing instruments, both functions (sensing and display) often take place in a single unit or instrument (case). Remote-sensing requires the information to be sensed, or captured, and then sent to a separate display unit in the flight deck.

Important information can be relayed in various ways. Electricity is often used by way of

Learning Objectives

IDENTIFY
- Flight instruments, engine instruments, and auxiliary instruments

EXPLAIN
- Standard instrument markings

DISCUSS
- Types of aircraft and engine instruments
- Instrument operating principles
- Communication and navigation equipment

Left: This flight deck uses both mechanical gauges and electronic displays to inform the crew of the aircraft's status and position.

wires that carry sensor information into the flight deck. Sometimes hydraulic or pneumatic lines are used.

In complex, modern aircraft, this can lead to an enormous amount of tubing and wiring terminating behind the instrument display panel. More efficient information transfer has been achieved by using digital data buses. Essentially, these are wires that share message carrying for many instruments by digitally encoding the signal for each. This reduces the number of wires and weight required to transfer remotely sensed information for the pilot's use. Flat-panel computer display screens that can be controlled to show only the information desired are also lighter than the numerous individual gauges it would take to display the same information simultaneously. An added bonus is the increased reliability inherent in these solid-state systems.

Section 1

Instrument Classifications

Traditionally, three basic kinds of instruments were made and classified by the job they perform: flight instruments, engine instruments, and navigation instruments. However, on today's aircraft, both large and small, the integration of electronic systems has blurred the lines between navigation and instrumentation so much that it is very difficult to sort out in which classification a system belongs. For that reason, we look at flight instruments, engine instruments, and leave all the other systems to a rather ambiguous category of auxiliary instruments. Navigation instruments have gone so far beyond the days of magnetic compasses, clocks, and an airspeed indicator (ASI) that we will not include that as a category of instruments here. However, we have included a section at the end of this chapter that covers basic navigation and communication equipment and how it interfaces with the modern instrument systems to which you will be introduced.

Flight Instruments

The instruments used in controlling the aircraft's flight attitude are known as the flight instruments. Basic flight instruments are made, such as the altimeter that displays aircraft altitude; the ASI; and the magnetic direction indicator, a form of compass. Additionally, an artificial horizon, turn coordinator, and vertical speed indicator (VSI) are flight instruments present in most aircraft. Much variation exists for these instruments, which is explained throughout this chapter. Over the years, flight instruments have come

Figure 8-1-1. The basic T arrangement of analog flight instruments.

to be situated similarly on the instrument panels in most aircraft. This basic T arrangement for flight instruments is shown in Figure 8-1-1. The top center position directly in front of the pilot and copilot is the basic display position for the artificial horizon even in modern glass cockpits (those with solid-state, flat-panel screen indicating systems).

Original analog flight instruments are operated by vacuum or air pressure and using gyroscopes. This avoids using electricity, which could put the pilot in a dangerous situation if the aircraft lost electrical power. Development of sensing and display techniques, combined with advanced aircraft electrical systems, has made it possible for reliable primary and secondary instrument systems that are electrically operated. Often a pneumatic altimeter, a gyro artificial horizon, and a magnetic direction indicator are retained somewhere in the instrument panel for redundancy (Figure 8-1-2).

Engine Instruments

Engine instruments are those designed to measure operating parameters of the aircraft's engine or engines. These are usually quantity, pressure, and temperature indications. They also include measuring engine speed. The most common engine instruments are the fuel and oil quantity and pressure gauges, tachometers, and temperature gauges. Table 8-1-1 contains various engine instruments found on reciprocating and turbine-powered aircraft.

Engine instrumentation is often displayed in the center of the flight deck where it is easily visible to the pilot and copilot. This arrange-

Reciprocating engines	Turbine engines
Oil pressure	Oil pressure
Oil temperature	Exhaust gas temperature (EGT)
Cylinder head temperature (CHT)	Turbine inlet temperature (TIT) or Turbine gas temperature (TGT)
Manifold pressure	Engine pressure ratio (EPR)
Fuel quantity	Fuel quantity
Fuel pressure	Fuel pressure Fuel flow
Tachometer	Tachometer (percent calibrated) N_1 and N_2 compressor speeds
Carburetor temperature	Torquemeter (on turboprop and turboshaft engines)

Table 8-1-1. Common engine instruments for different types of aircraft.

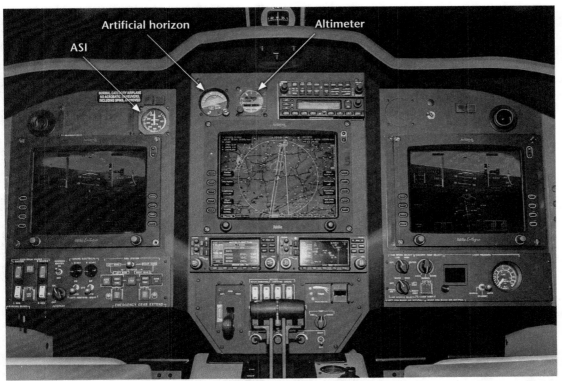

Figure 8-1-2. This flat screen display panel, or glass cockpit, retains an analog ASI, gyro-driven artificial horizon and analog altimeter as a backup.

ment can be seen in Figure 8-1-3. However, on light aircraft requiring only one flight crewmember, this might not be the case. Multiengine aircraft often use a single gauge for an engine parameter, such as manifold pressure, but it displays information for all engines by using multiple pointers on the same dial face.

Auxiliary Instruments

The category of auxiliary instruments includes everything that does not fit into the flight, engine, or navigation categories. This varies from aircraft to aircraft depending on the equipment installed. Some light aircraft might have no instruments in this category.

Auxiliary instruments can probably be sorted into three basic categories. Those that measure pressure, those that measure quantity, and those that measure position. Each of these can provide valuable information to the flight crew that contributes to safely completing the flight mission.

Pressure measuring instruments can include those recording cabin air pressure, oxygen supply pressure, and vacuum pressure for the instrument systems. Quantity measuring instruments can include deicing fluid, or oxygen supply. Position indicating system can include landing gear position indicators (other than lights) and flap position indicators.

Section 2
Display Types and Inputs

With the introduction of electronic flight instruments, some new terms have come into use and some rather backhanded terms have been assigned to the older technologies. The newer, flat-panel units that can be programmed to display a variety of flight instruments, engine instruments, navigation displays, and other aircraft information systems have taken on the general name of *glass cockpits*. The older, individual gauges with needles and colored range markings have become known as *steam gauges*. Some aircraft might incorporate a combination of the technologies because the industry is somewhat reluctant to give up on what they have known to be reliable for many years.

We will take a brief look at some of the types of displays that you might encounter in an aircraft today. They are found in various combinations as aircraft have been updated over the years and newer systems added to older aircraft.

Analog

The traditional round dial instrument is an example of an analog display. Probably the most recognizable analog display is the tra-

Figure 8-1-3. Engine instrumentation in the middle of the panel can be seen by the pilot and the copilot.

ditional clock face with its hands indicating hours, minutes and seconds. On the aircraft instrument panel, the traditional (or legacy) analog instruments are the ones now referred to as *steam gauges*. A typical analog instrument is shown in Figure 8-2-1.

Vertical Tape

As a standalone instrument display, the vertical tape display was not used as widely as the dial type indicator but has been in use for many years. It appears more in jet aircraft. When used to display engine operating parameters on a multiengine aircraft and arranged side by side, this display forms a neat horizontal line when all engines are operating at the same level. This can provide an excellent safety check at a glance. An example of this type of display is shown in Figure 8-2-2.

This design is seeing a comeback. The rectangular, vertical orientation lends itself very well to multifunction displays because it can be placed almost anywhere. It has proven to be very popular on the new glass cockpit equipment.

Electronic/Digital

In their simplest form, electronic instruments use an electrical circuit in both the sensor and display units to provide data for the flight crew. These systems generally offer an advantage of reduced weight and increased reliability. In the earliest days, it was a matter of replacing one mechanical instrument with an electric instrument for the same function, and usually designed to fit the same hole in the instrument panel. However, as we replace more and more of the legacy instruments with

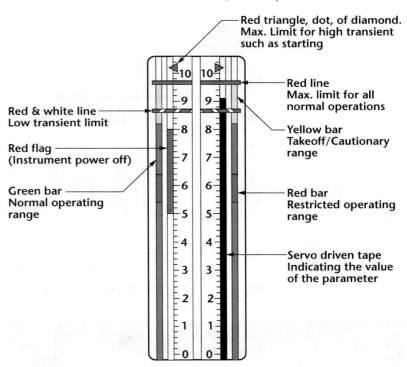

Figure 8-2-2. Vertical tape instrument with explanation of colors used.

electronic equivalents, we can see the possibility of going one step further and integrating several instrument readouts onto one display. Figure 8-2-3 shows an electronic engine and system analyzer that can replace 15 engine instruments.

Inputs

Two types of signals are analog and digital (not to be confused with display types). A signal transmits information between devices, in many cases a sender (sensor) and an instrument. An analog signal, whether

Figure 8-2-1. An analog display.

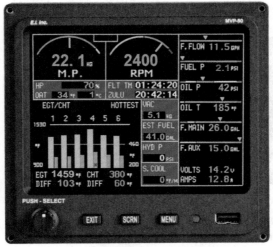

Figure 8-2-3. An electronic engine and system analyzer. *Courtesy of Electronics International, Inc.*

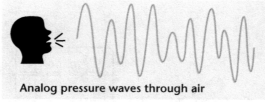
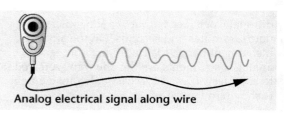

Figure 8-2-4. Examples of an analog signal.

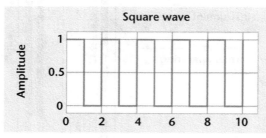

Figure 8-2-5. Example of a square wave.

mechanical or electrical, registers continuous change and is represented as a sine wave (Figure 8-2-4).

Analog signals are defined by continuous change, and digital signals are noncontinuous. Digital signals are identified by defined levels and have two distinct values. In an analog signal, changes are measured, as opposed to a digital signal where changes are counted. Digital signals are represented with a square wave (Figure 8-2-5).

Modern digital circuitry and the many display options available give us a variety of digital displays for aircraft instrumentation. This technology makes it possible to provide real-time analog data depiction and digital value display. One of the more popular systems is shown in Figure 8-2-6.

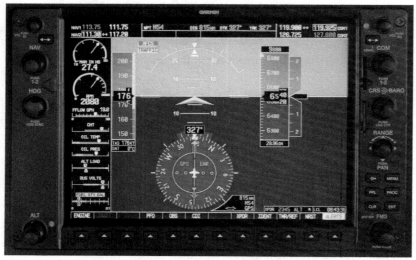

Figure 8-2-6. A popular flight display unit.

Section 3

Standard Instrument Markings

Instrument markings, ranges of operation, minimum and maximum limits, and the interpretation of these markings are general to all the instruments. Generally, the instrument marking system consists of three colors: red, yellow, and green. A red radial line, or mark, indicates a point beyond which a dangerous operating condition exists. Red radials can represent both maximum and minimum limits. A red arc on the tachometer indicates a dangerous operating range—generally an engine propeller vibration range. This arc can be passed through, but the engine cannot be operated in this area. A yellow arc covers a given range of operation and is an indication of caution. A green arc shows the normal and safe range of operation. White arcs are used on ASIs and represent the safe flap operating range of the aircraft.

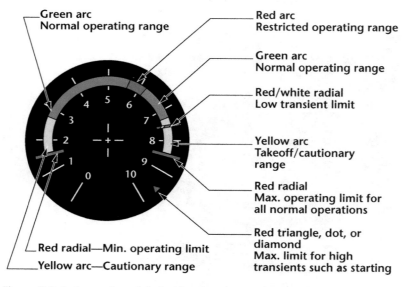

Figure 8-3-1. Examples of typical instrument marking schemes.

Figure 8-3-1 shows a hypothetical instrument dial with illustrative range markings. This dial face is intended only as a guide. Most instruments have only a few of these markings.

Section 4

Pressure-Sensing Instruments

Several instruments inform the pilot of the aircraft's condition and flight situations by measuring pressure. Pressure-sensing instruments can be found in both the flight group and the engine group. They can be either direct reading or remote sensing. These are some of the most critical instruments on the aircraft and must accurately inform the pilot to maintain safe operations.

Methods of Pressure Sensing

Pressure measurement involves some sort of mechanism that can sense changes in pressure. A technique for calibration and displaying the information is then added to inform the pilot. The type of pressure needed to be measured often makes one sensing mechanism more suited for use in each situation. The three basic types of pressure-sensing mechanisms used in aircraft instrument systems are the Bourdon tube, the diaphragm or bellows, and the solid-state sensing device.

Bourdon tube. A Bourdon tube is illustrated in Figure 8-4-1. The open end of this coiled tube is fixed in place, and the other end is sealed and free to move. When a fluid that needs to be measured is directed into the open end of the tube, the unfixed portion of the coiled tube tends to straighten out. The higher the pressure of the fluid, the more the tube straightens. When the pres-

sure is reduced, the tube recoils. A pointer is attached to this moving end of the tube, usually through a linkage of small shafts and gears. By calibrating this motion of the straightening tube, a face or dial of the instrument can be created. Thus, by observing the pointer movement along the scale of the instrument face positioned behind it, pressure increases and decreases are communicated to the pilot.

The Bourdon tube is the internal mechanism for many pressure gauges used on aircraft. When high pressures need to be measured, the tube is designed to be stiff. Gauges used to indicate lower pressures use a more flexible tube that uncoils and coils more readily. Most Bourdon tubes are made from brass, bronze, or copper. Alloys of these metals can be made to coil and uncoil the tube consistently numerous times.

Diaphragm. The diaphragm or bellows is another basic sensing mechanism used in aircraft instruments for measuring pressure. The diaphragm is a hollow, thin-walled, metal disk, usually corrugated (Figure 8-4-2). When pressure is introduced through an opening on one side of the disk, the entire disk expands. By placing a linkage in contact against the other side of the disk, the movement of the pressurized diaphragm can be transferred to a pointer that registers the movement against the scale on the instrument face.

Diaphragms can also be sealed. The diaphragm can be evacuated before sealing. When this is done, it is called an aneroid. Aneroids are used in many flight instruments. A diaphragm can also be filled with

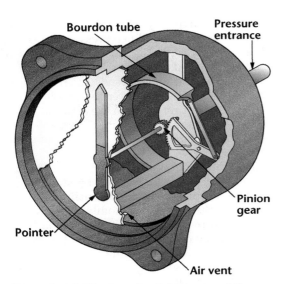

Figure 8-4-1. The Bourdon tube is one of the basic mechanisms for sensing pressure changes.

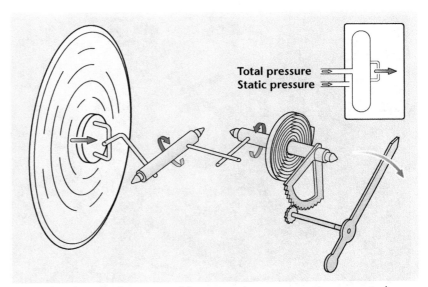

Figure 8-4-2. A diaphragm used for measuring pressure. An evacuated, sealed diaphragm is called an aneroid.

a gas to standard atmospheric pressure and then sealed. Each of these diaphragms has its uses; they are described in the next section. The common factor in all is that the expansion and contraction of the diaphragm's side wall is the movement that correlates to increasing and decreasing pressure.

When several diaphragm chambers are connected together, the device is called a bellows (Figure 8-4-3). This accordionlike assembly of diaphragms can be very useful when measuring the difference in pressure between two gases, called differential pressure. Just as with a single diaphragm, it is the movement of the

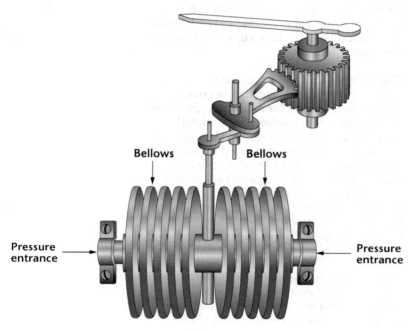

Figure 8-4-3. Using bellows to measure differential pressure.

Figure 8-4-4. Most solid-state pressure sensors vary their electronic output signals according to the pressure changes.

side walls of the bellows assembly that correlates with changes in pressure and to which a pointer linkage and gearing is attached to inform the pilot.

Diaphragms and bellows are often inside the single instrument housing that contains the pointer and instrument dial read by the pilot on the instrument panel. Thus, many instruments that make use of these sensitive and reliable mechanisms are direct reading gauges. But many remote-sensing instrument systems also make use of the diaphragm and bellows. In such a cases, the sensing device containing the pressure sensitive diaphragm or bellows is located remotely on the engine or airframe. It is part of a transducer that converts the pressure into an electrical signal. The transducer, or transmitter, sends the signal to the gauge in the flight deck, or to a computer, for processing and subsequent display of the sensed condition.

Solid-state sensor. Solid-state sensing devices are used in modern aircraft to determine the critical pressures needed for safe operation. Many of these have digital output ready for processing by electronic flight instrument computers and other onboard computers. Some sensors send microelectric signals that are converted to digital format for use by computers. As with the analog sensors described above, the key to the function of solid-state sensors is their consistent property changes as pressure changes (Figure 8-4-4).

The solid-state sensors used in most aviation applications exhibit varying electrical output or resistance changes when pressure changes occur. Crystalline piezoelectric, piezoresistor, and semiconductor chip sensors are most common. In the typical sensor, tiny wires are embedded in the crystal or pressure-sensitive semiconductor chip. When pressure deflects the crystal or crystals, a small amount of electricity is created or, in the case of a semiconductor chip and some crystals, the resistance changes. Because the current and resistance changes vary directly with the amount of deflection, outputs can be calibrated and used to display pressure values.

Nearly all the pressure information needed for engine, airframe, and flight instruments can be captured or calculated using solid-state pressure sensors in combination with temperature sensors. But it is worth noting that aneroid devices are still used for comparisons involving absolute pressure. Solid-state pressure-sensing systems are remote-sensing systems. The sensors are mounted on the aircraft at convenient and effective locations.

Pitot-Static System

Some of the most important flight instruments derive their indications from measuring air pressure. Gathering and distributing various air pressures for flight instrumentation is the function of the pitot-static system. The altimeter, ASI, and VSI are the three most common pitot-static instruments.

A pitot tube is shown in Figure 8-4-5 (top). It is open and faces into the airstream to receive the full force of the impact air pressure as the aircraft moves forward. This air passes through a baffled plate designed to protect the system from moisture and dirt entering the tube. Below the baffle, a drain hole is provided, allowing moisture to escape. An upright tube, or riser, leads this pressurized air out of the pitot assembly to the ASI.

The small holes in the static port (Figure 8-4-5, bottom) are designed to collect air pressure that is at atmospheric pressure in a static, or still, condition. The static port is also connected to the altimeter, the ASI, and the VSI. Generally, an alternate static source is provided in case the primary source becomes blocked. The flight crew can select this source by using a valve.

Figure 8-4-6 shows an example of a typical pitot-static system. Note that the ASI uses both pitot and static pressures, whereas the VSI and the altimeter use only static pressure.

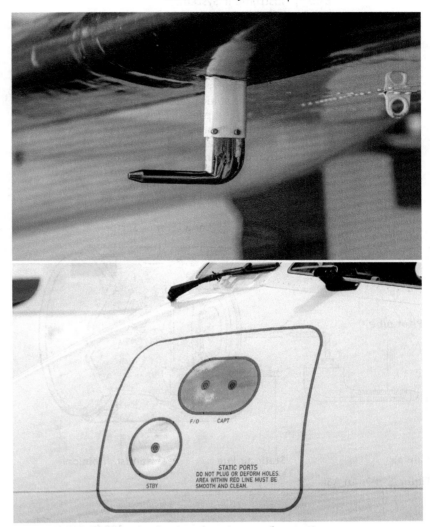

Figure 8-4-5. A pitot tube (top) and static port (bottom).

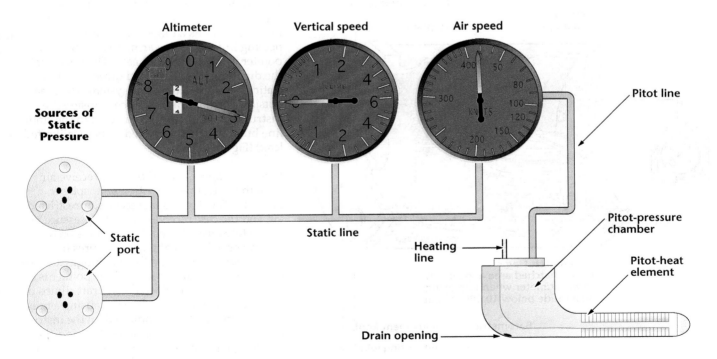

Figure 8-4-6. A typical pitot-static static system for use by the flight instruments.

Airspeed Indicator (ASI)

The ASI is a differential pressure measuring instrument that uses both the pitot and the static systems (Figure 8-4-7). The ASI introduces the static pressure into the airspeed case, and the pitot pressure (dynamic) is introduced into the diaphragm. These two pressures are equal when the aircraft is parked on the ground in calm air. When the aircraft moves through the air, the pressure on the pitot line becomes greater than the pressure in the static

lines. As described in the diaphragm discussion earlier, the differential pressure expands or contracts the diaphragm, which is attached to an indicating system. The system drives the mechanical linkage and the airspeed needle.

Altimeter

The altimeter is an instrument that measures the height of an aircraft above a given pressure level. The main component of the altimeter is a stack of sealed aneroid diaphragms. An aneroid is a sealed diaphragm that is evacuated to an internal pressure of 29.92 inches of mercury ("Hg). These diaphragms are free to expand and contract with changes to the static pressure. A higher static pressure presses down on the diaphragms and causes them to collapse. A lower static pressure (less than 29.92 "Hg) allows the diaphragms to expand. A mechanical linkage connects the diaphragm movement to the needles on the indicator face, which translates compression of the diaphragms into a decrease in altitude and translates an expansion of the diaphragms into an increase in altitude (Figure 8-4-8).

Notice how the static pressure is introduced into the rear of the sealed altimeter case. The altimeter's outer chamber is sealed, which allows the static pressure to surround the aneroid diaphragms.

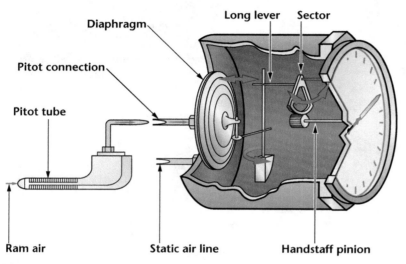

Figure 8-4-7. An ASI.

Vertical Speed Indicator (VSI)

Although the VSI operates solely from static pressure, it is a differential pressure instrument. It contains a diaphragm with connecting linkage and gearing to the indicator pointer inside an airtight case. The inside of the diaphragm is connected directly to the static line of the pitot-static system. The area outside the diaphragm, which is inside the instrument case, is also connected to the static line but through a restricted orifice (calibrated leak) (Figure 8-4-9).

Both the diaphragm and the case receive air from the static line at existing atmospheric pressure. The diaphragm receives unrestricted air, and the case receives the static pressure via the metered leak. When the aircraft is on the ground or in level flight, the pressures inside the instrument case and the diaphragm and the instrument case are equal, and the pointer is at the zero indication. When the aircraft climbs or descends, the pressures change, causing a pressure differential that is indicated on the instrument needle as a climb or descent. Inside, the diaphragm pressure changes immediately, but because of the metering action of the restricted passage, the case pressure remains higher or

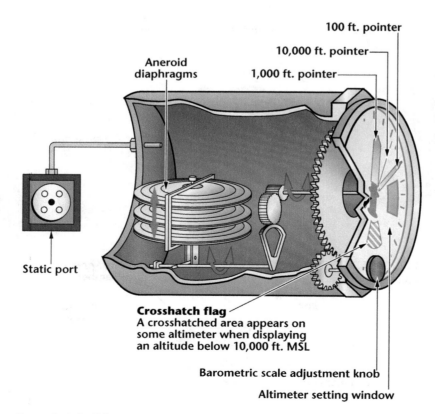

Figure 8-4-8. Altimeter.

lower for a short time. The initial change in the rate of climb causes the indication to lag. During the lag period, the VSI indicates *trend* information. When the pressure differential stabilizes at a definite ratio, the needle indicates the *rate* of altitude change.

Pitot-Static System Blockages

Many pitot-static tube heads contain heating elements to prevent icing during flight. The pilot can send electric current to the element with a switch in the flight deck when ice-forming conditions exist. Often, this switch is wired through the ignition switch so that when the aircraft is shut down, a pitot tube heater inadvertently left on does not continue to draw current and drain the battery.

> **CAUTION:** When near the pitot tube, be careful; these heating elements make the tube too hot to be touched without receiving a burn.

Errors almost always indicate that the pitot tube, the static port, or both, are blocked. This can be caused by moisture (including ice), dirt, or even insects.

The pitot system can become blocked completely or only partially if the pitot tube drain hole remains open. If the pitot tube becomes blocked and its associated drain hole remains clear, ram air is no longer able to enter the pitot system. Air already in the system vents through the drain hole, and the remaining pressure drops to ambient (outside) air pressure. Under these circumstances, the ASI reading decreases to zero because the ASI senses no difference between ram and static air pressure.

If both the pitot tube opening and the drain hole become clogged simultaneously, the pressure in the pitot tube is trapped. No change is noted on the airspeed indication if the airspeed increases or decreases. If the static port is unblocked and the aircraft changes altitude, a change is noted on the ASI. The change is not related to a change in airspeed but a change in static pressure.

If the static system becomes blocked but the pitot tube remains clear, the ASI continues to operate; however, it is inaccurate. The airspeed indicates lower than the actual airspeed when the aircraft is operated above the altitude where the static ports became blocked because the trapped static pressure is higher than normal for that altitude. When operating at a lower altitude, a faster than actual airspeed is displayed because of the relatively low static pressure trapped in the system. A blocked static system also affects the altimeter and VSI.

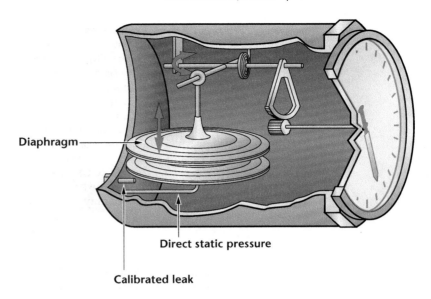

Figure 8-4-9. A VSI.

Trapped static pressure causes the altimeter to freeze at the altitude where the blockage occurred. In the case of the VSI, a blocked static system produces a continuous zero indication.

Some aircraft are equipped with an alternate static source in the flight deck. In the case of a blocked static source, opening the alternate static source introduces static pressure from the flight deck into the system.

Oil Pressure

The most important instrument used by the pilot to perceive the health of an engine is the engine oil pressure gauge. A typical direct reading oil pressure gauge is shown in Figure 8-4-10. Oil pressure is usually indicated in pounds per square inch (p.s.i.). The normal operating range is typically represented by a green arc on the circular gauge.

Figure 8-4-10. A direct reading analog oil pressure gauge.

Aircraft using analog instruments often use direct reading oil pressure gauges. Many direct reading oil pressure indicators use a Bourdon tube (shown earlier). Digital instrument systems use an analog or digital remote oil pressure-sensing unit that sends output to the computer, driving the display of oil pressure values on the aircraft's flight deck display screens. Oil pressure can be displayed in a circular or linear gauge fashion and can even include a numerical value on the screen. Often, oil pressure is grouped with other engine parameter displays on the same page or portion of a page on the display.

Fuel Pressure

Fuel pressure gauges also provide critical information to the pilot. Typically, fuel is pumped out of various fuel tanks on the aircraft for use by the engines. A malfunctioning fuel pump, or a tank that has been emptied beyond the point at which there is enough fuel entering the pump to maintain desired output pressure, is a condition that requires the pilot's immediate attention. While direct-sensing fuel pressure gauges using Bourdon tubes, diaphragms, and bellows sensing arrangements exist, it is especially undesirable to run a fuel line into the flight deck because of the potential for fire if a leak develops. Therefore, the preferred arrangement is to have the sensing mechanism be part of a transmitter device that uses electricity to send a signal to the indicator in the flight deck. An analog fuel pressure gauge is shown in Figure 8-4-11.

Manifold Air Pressure (MAP)

In reciprocating engine aircraft, the manifold pressure gauge indicates the pressure of the air in the engine's induction manifold. This is

Figure 8-4-11. A typical analog fuel pressure gauge.

Figure 8-4-12. An analog manifold pressure indicator.

an indication of power being developed by the engine. The higher the pressure of the fuel air mixture going into the engine, the more power it can produce.

Most manifold pressure gauges are calibrated in inches of mercury, although digital displays can have the option to display in a different scale. When atmospheric pressure acts on the aneroid inside the gauge, the connected pointer indicates the current air pressure. A line running from the intake manifold into the gauge presents intake manifold air pressure to the aneroid, so the gauge indicates the absolute pressure in the intake manifold. An analog manifold pressure gauge is shown in Figure 8-4-12.

Instruments That Use Pressure Measurements for Other Values

Reciprocating engines on some fuel-injected light aircraft use a fuel pressure gauge that is calibrated to read fuel flow. This is because the fuel flow is proportional to the fuel pressure in the system. The amount of fuel that is flowing through the fuel injectors has a direct relationship to the pressure drop across the fuel injector orifices. Therefore, monitoring fuel pressure at the injectors closely approximates fuel flow measured in gallons per hour.

One of these instruments is shown in Figure 8-4-13.

Some older aircraft have oil temperature systems that use a sealed system with a temperature bulb installed in the engine and a capillary tube that extends to the oil pressure gauge on the instrument panel. The system is

Figure 8-4-13. Fuel pressure gauge calibrated to read fuel flow.

filled with a liquid that expands and contracts with changes in temperature. Those changes register on the instrument as changes in oil temperature. The instrument uses a Bourdon tube to convert the pressure change to needle movement.

are attached to each other, the effect is that the coiled end tries to uncoil as the one metal expands faster than the other. This moves the pointer across the dial face of the instrument. When the temperature drops, the metals contract at different rates, which tends to tighten the coil and move the pointer in the opposite direction. This mechanism is illustrated in Figure 8-5-1.

Bourdon tube. A Bourdon tube can also be used as a direct reading nonelectric temperature gauge in simple, light aircraft. By calibrating the dial face of a Bourdon tube gauge with a temperature scale, it can indicate temperature. The basis for operation is the consistent expansion of the vapor produced by a volatile liquid in an enclosed area. This vapor pressure changes directly with temperature. By filling a sensing bulb with such a volatile liquid and connecting it to a Bourdon tube, the tube causes an indication of the rising and falling vapor pressure due to temperature change. Calibrating the dial face in degrees Fahrenheit or Celsius, rather than p.s.i., provides a temperature reading. In such a gauge, the sensing bulb is placed in the area needing to have temperature measured. A long capillary tube connects the bulb to the Bourdon tube in the instrument

Section 5

Temperature-Sensing Instruments

Methods of Temperature Sensing

Several very different technologies are used to measure temperatures on aircraft. Some are self-contained and require no outside power source, others operate using power provided by the aircraft's electrical system, and some even produce their own electricity. We will take a quick look at each technology and then where they are found.

Bimetallic strip. A bimetallic thermometer is very useful in aviation. The temperature-sensing element of a bimetallic thermometer is made of two dissimilar metals strips bonded together. Each metal expands and contracts at a different rate when the temperature changes. One end of the bimetallic strip is fixed; the other end is coiled. A pointer is attached to the coiled end that is set in the instrument housing. When the bimetallic strip is heated, the two metals expand. Because their expansion rates differ and they

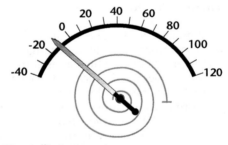

Bimetallic temperature gauge

Bimetallic coil of bonded metals with dissimilar coefficient of expansion

Figure 8-5-1. A bimetallic temperature gauge works because of the difference in the expansion rates of the two metals.

Figure 8-5-2. An electric resistance thermometer sensing bulb.

housing. The narrow diameter of the capillary tube ensures that the volatile liquid is lightweight and stays primarily in the sensor bulb. Oil temperature is sometimes measured this way.

Electrical resistance thermometer. The electrical resistance thermometer is a common temperature-measuring device on today's aircraft. The principal parts of the electrical resistance thermometer are the indicating instrument, the temperature-sensitive element (or bulb), and the connecting wires and plug connectors. Electrical resistance thermometers are used widely in many types of aircraft to measure carburetor air, oil, free air temperatures, and more. They are used to measure low and medium temperatures in the –70°C to 150°C range.

For most metals, electrical resistance changes as the temperature of the metal changes. This is the principle on which a resistance thermometer operates. Typically, the electrical resistance of a metal increases as the temperature rises. Various alloys have a high temperature-resistance coefficient, meaning their resistance varies significantly with temperature. This can make them suitable for use in temperature sensing devices. The metal resistor is subjected to the fluid or area in which temperature needs to be measured. It is connected by wires to a resistance-measuring device in the flight deck indicator. The instrument dial is calibrated in degrees Fahrenheit or Celsius as desired rather than in ohms. As the temperature to be measured changes, the resistance of the metal changes and the resistance-measuring indicator shows to what extent.

A typical electrical resistance thermometer looks like any other temperature gauge. Indicators are available in dual form for use in multiengine aircraft. Most indicators are self-compensating for changes in flight deck temperature. The heat-sensitive resistor is manufactured so that it has a definite resistance for each temperature value within its working range. The temperature-sensitive resistor element is a length or winding made of a nickel/manganese wire or other suitable alloy in an insulating material. The resistor is protected by a closed-end metal tube attached to a threaded plug with a hexagonal head (Figure 8-5-2). The two ends of the winding are brazed, or welded, to an electrical receptacle designed to receive the prongs of the connector plug.

Thermocouples. A thermocouple is used to measure high temperatures. Two common applications are to measure cylinder head temperature (CHT) in reciprocating engines and exhaust gas temperature (EGT) in turbine engines. Thermocouple leads are made from a variety of metals, depending on the maximum temperature to which they are exposed. Iron and constantan, or copper and constantan, are common for CHT measurement. Chromel and alumel are used for turbine EGT thermocouples.

A thermocouple is a circuit or connection of two unlike metals. The metals are touching at two separate junctions. If one of the junctions is heated to a higher temperature than the other, an electromotive force is produced in the circuit. This voltage is directly proportional to the temperature. So, by measuring the amount of electromotive force, temperature can be determined. A voltmeter is placed across the colder of the two junctions of the thermocouple. It is calibrated in degrees Fahrenheit or Celsius, as needed. The hotter the high temperature junction (hot junction) becomes, the greater the electromotive force produced, and the higher the temperature indication on the meter. The components and connections of a thermocouple system are shown in Figure 8-5-3.

The amount of voltage produced by the dissimilar metals when heated is measured in millivolts. Therefore, thermocouple leads are designed to provide a specific amount of resistance in the thermocouple circuit (usually very little). Their material, length, or cross-sectional size cannot be altered without compensation for the change in total resistance that would result. Each lead that makes a connection back to the voltmeter must be made of the same metal as the part of the thermocouple to which it is connected. For example, a copper wire is connected to the copper portion of the hot junction and a constantan wire is connected to the constantan part.

The hot junction of a thermocouple varies in shape, depending on its application. Two common types are the gasket and the bayonet. In the gasket type, two rings of the dissimilar metals are pressed together to form

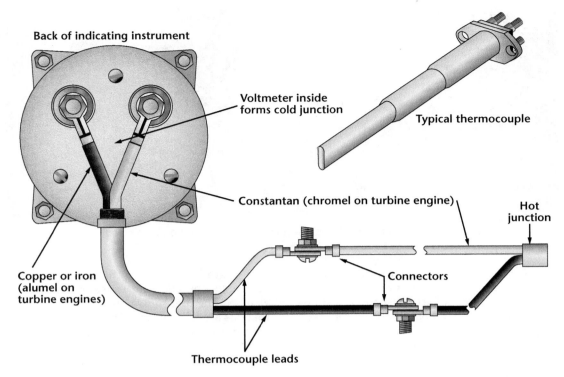

Figure 8-5-3. Thermocouples combine two unlike metals that cause current flow when heated.

a gasket that can be installed under a spark plug or cylinder hold down nut. In the bayonet type, the metals come together inside a perforated protective sheath. Bayonet thermocouples fit into a hole or well in a cylinder head. On turbine engines, they are mounted on the turbine inlet or outlet case and extend through the case into the gas stream.

The cold junction of the thermocouple circuit is inside the instrument case. Because the electromotive force set up in the circuit varies with the difference in temperature between the hot and cold junctions, it is necessary to compensate the indicator mechanism for changes in flight deck temperature that affect the cold junction. This is done by using a bimetallic spring connected to the indicator mechanism. This works the same as the bimetallic thermometer described previously. When the leads are disconnected from the indicator, the temperature of the flight deck area around the instrument panel can be read on the indicator dial. Typical CHT indicators are shown in Figure 8-5-4. Numeric light-emitting diode (LED) indictors for CHT are also common in modern aircraft.

Outside Air Temperature

Direct reading bimetallic temperature gauges are often used in light aircraft to measure free air temperature or outside air tempera-

Figure 8-5-4. Typical thermocouple temperature indicators.

Figure 8-5-5. A bimetallic type outside air temperature gauge installed on an aircraft.

ture (OAT) (Figure 8-5-5). In this application, a collecting probe protrudes through the aircraft's windshield to be exposed to the atmospheric air. The coiled end of the bimetallic strip in the instrument head is just inside the windshield where it can be read by the pilot.

Carburetor Air Temperature

Measured at the carburetor entrance, carburetor air temperature (CAT) is regarded by many as an indication of induction system ice formation. Although it serves this purpose, it also provides many other important items of information. The powerplant is a heat machine, and the temperature of its components, or the fluids flowing through it, affects the combustion process either directly or indirectly. The induction air temperature affects the charge density and the vaporization of the fuel. CAT is also useful for checking induction system condition.

The temperature reading is sensed by a bulb or electric sensor. The CAT gauge indicates the temperature of the air before it enters the carburetor. Backfiring is indicated as a momentary rise on the gauge, if it is of sufficient severity for the heat to be sensed at the carburetor air-measuring point. A sustained induction system fire shows a continuous increase of CAT.

Fuel Temperature

Turbine-powered aircraft operate at high altitudes where the temperature is very low. As the fuel in the fuel tanks cools, water in the fuel condenses and freezes. It can form ice crystals in the tank or as the fuel/water solution slows and contacts the cool filter element on its way through fuel filter to the engine. Ice formation on the filter element blocks the flow of fuel through the filter. Fuel

heaters are used to warm the fuel so that ice does not form. These heat exchanger units also heat the fuel sufficiently to melt any ice that has already formed. The flight crew uses the information supplied by the filter bypass indicating lights and fuel temperature gauge (Figure 8-5-6) to know when to heat the fuel.

Oil Temperature

In dry-sump lubricating systems, the oil temperature bulb can be anywhere in the oil inlet line between the supply tank and the engine. Oil systems for wet-sump engines have the temperature bulb where it senses oil temperature after the oil passes through the oil cooler. In either system, the bulb is placed so that it measures the temperature of the oil before it enters the engine's hot sections. The oil temperature gauge in the flight deck is usually connected to the oil temperature bulb by electrical leads. The oil temperature is indicated on the gauge.

Most oil temperature systems today operate using a temperature-sensing bulb containing a resistor with a value that varies with changes in temperature and a bridge circuit

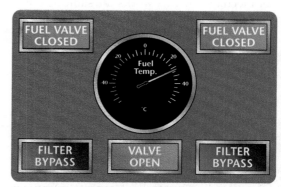

Figure 8-5-6. A large aircraft fuel panel showing fuel valve position indicators and the fuel temperature in tank No. 1.

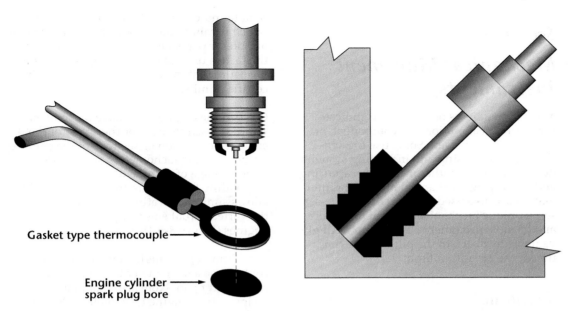

Figure 8-5-7. A CHT thermocouple with a gasket hot junction is installed under the spark plug (left). A bayonet thermocouple is installed in a bore in the cylinder wall (right).

in the instrument mounted on the panel. This allows a great deal of flexibility in the location of both the sensor and the instrument. In some older aircraft, the fixed-length sealed system using a pressure-type system is still used. This converts changes in pressure to changes in temperature on the instrument face.

Cylinder Head Temperature

Cylinder head temperature (CHT) is indicated by a gauge connected to a thermocouple attached to the cylinder. The thermocouple can be in a special gasket under a spark plug or in a special well in the top or rear of the cylinder head (Figure 8-5-7). Aircraft can be fitted with systems that measure the temperature of all cylinders, or only one cylinder. If only one cylinder is measured, it will usually be the one that is generally considered to be the hottest.

This is the one that tests show to be the hottest on an engine in each installation.

Exhaust Gas Temperature

Exhaust gas temperature (EGT) might not be measured in some low-powered training aircraft, but it becomes more important as the horsepower of reciprocating engines go up and is essential to the operation of gas turbine engines. Because of the high temperatures, the EGT systems on both reciprocating and turbine engines use thermocouple sensors. The number of sensors can vary from one on a small reciprocating engine, to one per cylinder, to a multi-sensor ring around the turbine exit of a jet engine. The system illustrated in Figure 8-5-8 is typical of a turbine engine EGT system where the sensors are connected so that the gauge is reading an average of the temperatures.

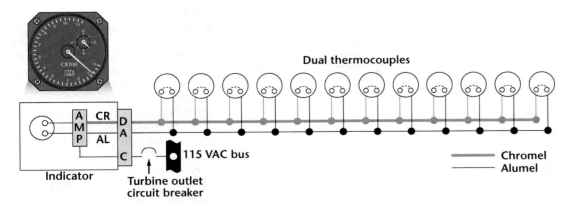

Figure 8-5-8. A typical EGT thermocouple system for a turbine engine.

Section 6

Mechanical Movement Instruments

Many instruments on an aircraft indicate the mechanical motion of a component, or even the aircraft itself. Some use the synchro remote-sensing and indicating systems described earlier. Other means for capturing and displaying mechanical movement information are also used. This section discusses some unique mechanical motion indicators and groups instruments by function. All give valuable feedback to the pilot on the condition of the aircraft in flight.

Tachometer

The tachometer, or tach, is an instrument that indicates the speed of the crankshaft of a reciprocating engine. It can be a direct- or

Figure 8-6-1. A tachometer for a reciprocating engine is calibrated in r.p.m. A tachometer for a turbine engine is calibrated in percent of r.p.m.

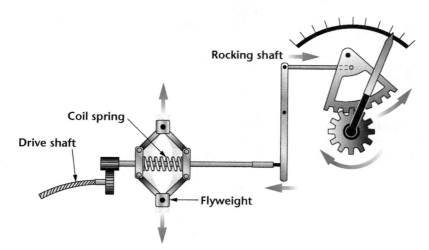

Figure 8-6-2. The simplified mechanism of a flyweight type mechanical tachometer.

remote-indicating instrument, the dial of which is calibrated to indicate revolutions per minutes (r.p.m.). On reciprocating engines, the tach is used to monitor engine power and to ensure that the engine is operated within certified limits.

Gas turbine engines also have tachometers. They are used to monitor the speed of the compressor section or sections of the engine. Turbine engine tachometers are calibrated in percentage of r.p.m. with 100 percent corresponding to optimum turbine speed. This allows similar operating procedures despite the varied actual engine r.p.m. of different engines (Figure 8-6-1).

In addition to the engine tachometer, helicopters use a tachometer to indicator main rotor shaft r.p.m. Note also that many reciprocating-engine tachometers also have built-in numeric drums that are geared to the rotational mechanism inside. These are hour meters that keep track of the time the engine is operated. Two types of tachometer systems are in wide use today: mechanical and electrical.

Mechanical tachometer indicating systems are used on small, single-engine light aircraft in which a short distance exists between the engine and the instrument panel. They consist of an indicator connected to the engine by a flexible drive shaft. The drive shaft is geared into the engine so that when the engine turns, so does the shaft. The indicator contains a flyweight assembly coupled to a gear mechanism that drives a pointer. As the drive shaft rotates, centrifugal force acts on the flyweights and moves them to an angular position. This angular position varies with the engine's speed. The amount of movement of the flyweights is transmitted through the gear mechanism to the pointer. The pointer rotates to indicate this movement on the tachometer indicator, which is directly related to the engine's r.p.m. (Figure 8-6-2).

A more common variation of this type of mechanical tachometer uses a magnetic drag cup to move the pointer in the indicator. As the drive shaft turns, it rotates a permanent magnet in a close-tolerance aluminum cup. A shaft attached to the indicating point is attached to the exterior center of the cup. As the magnet is rotated by the engine flex drive cable, its magnetic field cuts through the conductor surrounding it, creating eddy currents in the aluminum cup. This current flow creates its own magnetic field, which interacts with the rotating magnet's flux field. The result is that the cup tends to rotate, and with it, the indicating pointer. A calibrated restraining spring limits the cup's rotation to the arc of motion of the pointer across the scale on the instrument face (Figure 8-6-3).

Magnetic Compass

Having an instrument onboard an aircraft that indicates direction is invaluable to the pilot. In fact, it is a requirement that all certified aircraft have some sort of magnetic direction indicator. The magnetic compass is a direction-finding instrument that has been used for navigation for hundreds of years. It is a simple instrument that takes advantage of the earth's magnetic field.

The magnetic north pole is very close to the geographic North Pole of the globe, but they are not the same. An ordinary permanent magnet that is free to do so, aligns itself with the direction of the earth's magnetic field. On this principle, an instrument is constructed that the pilot can reference for directional orientation. Permanent magnets are attached under a float that is mounted on a pivot, so it is free to rotate in the horizontal plane. As such, the magnets align with the earth's magnetic field. A numerical compass card, usually graduated in 5° increments, is constructed around the perimeter of the float. It serves as the instrument dial. The entire assembly is enclosed in a sealed case that is filled with a liquid similar to kerosene. This dampens vibration and oscillation of the moving float assembly and decreases friction.

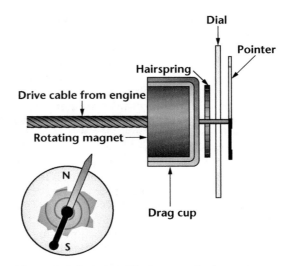

Figure 8-6-3. A simplified magnetic drag cup tachometer indicating device.

On the front of the case, a glass face allows the numerical compass card to be referenced against a vertical lubber line. The magnetic heading of the aircraft is read by noting the graduation on which the lubber line falls. Thus, direction in any of 360° can be read off the dial as the magnetic float compass card assembly holds its alignment with magnetic north, while the aircraft changes direction.

The liquid that fills the compass case expands and contracts as altitude changes and temperature fluctuates. A bellows diaphragm expands and contracts to adjust the volume of the space in the case, so it remains full (Figure 8-6-4).

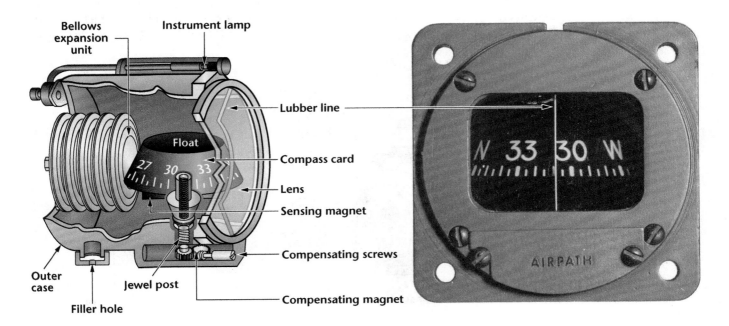

Figure 8-6-4. The parts of a typical magnetic compass.

Accuracy issues are associated with using a magnetic compass. The main magnets of a compass align with the earth's magnetic field, and they align with the composite field made up of all magnetic influences around them, including local electromagnetic influence from metallic structures near the compass and aircraft's electrical system. This is called magnetic deviation. It causes a magnet's alignment with the earth's magnetic field to be altered. Compensating screws are turned; these move small permanent magnets in the compass case to correct for the magnetic deviation. The two set-screws are on the face of the instrument and are labeled N-S and E-W. They position the small magnets to counterbalance the local magnetic influences acting on the main compass magnets.

Fuel Flow

Some reciprocating engine fuel systems use a vane-type fuel flow meter that measures the volume of the fuel the engine consumes. The fuel delivered to the engine passes through the flowmeter. Inside, the fuel pushes against the vane, which counters the force of the fuel flow with a calibrated spring. The vane shaft rotates varying degrees matching the fuel flow rate through the unit. A transmitter deflects the pointer on the fuel flow gauge the same amount as the vane deflects (Figure 8-6-5).

Another fuel flow sensor used primarily on light aircraft also detects the spinning velocity of a turbine in the fuel path. The higher the flow rate is, the faster the turbine rotates. A transducer converts the speed of the turbine to an electrical signal to be used by the fuel gauge.

Section 7

Gyroscopic Instruments

Principles of Operation

Three of the most common flight instruments, the attitude indicator, heading indicator, and the turn coordinator, are controlled by gyroscopes. To understand how these instruments operate, knowledge of gyroscopic principles and instrument power systems is required.

A mechanical gyroscope, or gyro, is composed of a wheel or rotor with its mass concentrated around its perimeter. The rotor has bearings to enable it to spin at high speeds (Figure 8-7-1).

To spin the gyro at high speed, different methods are used. In some aircraft, all the gyros are vacuum, pressure, or electrically operated. In other aircraft, vacuum or pressure systems provide the power for the heading and attitude indicators, and the electrical system provides the power for the turn coordinator. Most aircraft have at least two sources of power to ensure at least one source is available if one power source fails. The vacuum or pressure system spins the gyro by drawing a stream of air against the rotor vanes to spin the rotor at high speed, much like a waterwheel or turbine. Vacuum systems are explained in more detail later in this chapter.

Different mounting configurations are available for the rotor and axle, which allow the rotor assembly to rotate about one or two axes

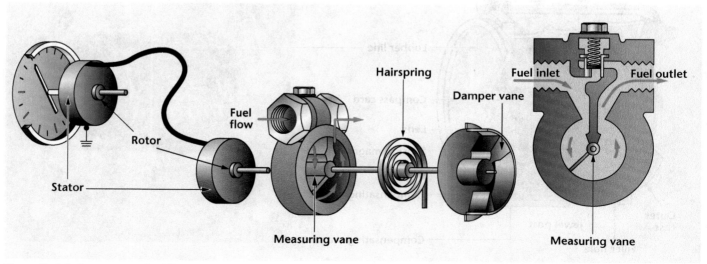

Figure 8-6-5. A vane-type fuel flow meter.

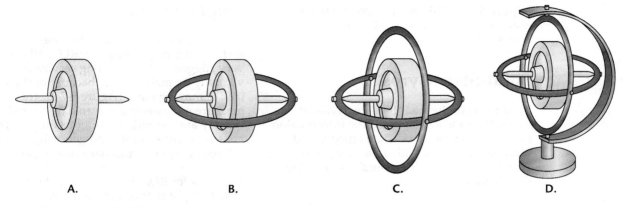

Figure 8-7-1. A free gyroscope has two rings and a mounting bracket.

perpendicular to its axis of spin. To suspend the rotor for rotation, the axle is first mounted in a supporting ring (Figure 8-7-1 view B). If brackets are attached 90° around the supporting ring from where the spin axle is attached, the supporting ring and rotor can both move freely 360°. When in this configuration, the gyro is said to be a captive gyro. It can rotate about only one axis that is perpendicular to the axis of spin (Figure 8-7-1 view C).

The supporting ring can also be mounted inside an outer ring. The bearing points are the same as the bracket just described, 90° around the supporting ring from where the spin axle attached. Attaching a bracket to this outer ring allows the rotor to rotate in two planes while spinning. Both of these are perpendicular to the spin axis of the rotor. The plane that the rotor spins in because of its rotation about its axle is not counted as a plane of rotation.

A gyroscope with this configuration—two rings plus the mounting bracket—is said to be a free gyro because it is free to rotate about two axes that are both perpendicular to the rotor's spin axis (Figure 8-7-1 view D). As a result, the supporting ring with spinning gyro mounted inside is free to turn 360° inside the outer ring.

Gyro Properties

Unless the rotor of a gyro is spinning, it has no unusual properties; it is simply a wheel universally mounted. When the rotor is spinning at a high speed, the gyro exhibits a couple of unique characteristics.

Rigidity

The first characteristic is called gyroscopic rigidity, or rigidity in space. This means that the rotor of a free gyro always points in the same direction no matter which way the base of the gyro is positioned.

Gyroscopic rigidity depends on several factors:

1. Weight—for a given size, a heavy mass is more resistant to disturbing forces than a light mass.

2. Angular velocity—the higher the rotational speed, the greater the rigidity or resistance is to deflection.

3. Radius at which the weight is concentrated—maximum effect is obtained from a mass when its principal weight is concentrated near the rim, rotating at high speed.

4. Bearing friction—any friction applies a deflecting force to a gyro. Minimum bearing friction keeps deflecting forces at a minimum.

This characteristic of gyros to remain rigid in space is exploited in the attitude-indicating instruments and directional indicators.

Precession

Precession is a second important characteristic of gyroscopes. By applying a force to the horizontal axis of the gyro, a unique phenomenon occurs. The applied force is resisted. Instead of responding to the force by moving about the horizontal axis, the gyro moves in response about its vertical axis. Stated another way, an applied force to the axis of the spinning gyro does not cause the axis to tilt. Rather, the gyro responds as though the force was applied 90° around in the direction of rotation of the gyro rotor. The gyro rotates rather than tilts

(Figure 8-7-2). This predictable controlled precession of a gyroscope is used in a turn coordinator.

Solid-State Gyros

In addition to the traditional mechanical gyros, the industry has seen the introduction of highly accurate solid-state attitude and directional devices with no moving parts. This results in very high reliability and low maintenance.

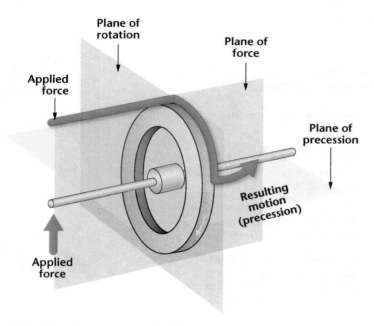

Figure 8-7-2. The plane of the applied force, the plane of rotation, and the plane of precession are all perpendicular to each other.

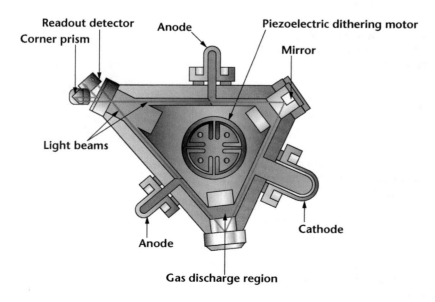

Figure 8-7-3. The ring laser gyro is rugged, accurate, and has no moving parts, which means it has no friction.

Ring Laser Gyro

The first widely adapted technology of this sort was the ring laser gyro (RLG). RLGs are very rugged and have a long service life with virtually no maintenance because of their lack of moving parts (Figure 8-7-3). They measure movement about an axis extremely quickly and provide continuous output. They are extremely accurate and generally are considered superior to mechanical gyroscopes.

The basis for RLG operation is that it takes time for light to travel around a stationary, nonrotating circular path. Light takes longer to complete the journey if the path is rotating in the same direction as the light is traveling. And, it takes less time for the light to complete the loop if the path is rotating in the direction opposite to that of the light. Essentially the path is made longer or shorter by the rotation of the path.

Slaved Gyros

The flux gate compass that drives slaved gyros uses the characteristic of current induction. The flux valve is a small, segmented ring, made of soft iron that readily accepts lines of magnetic flux. An electrical coil is wound around each of the three legs to accept the current induced in this ring by the earth's magnetic field. A coil wound around the iron spacer in the center of the frame has 400 Hz alternating current (AC) flowing through it. When this current reaches its peak, twice during each cycle, this coil produces so much magnetism that the frame cannot accept the lines of flux from the earth's field.

As the current reverses between the peaks, it demagnetizes the frame so it can accept the flux from the earth's field. As this flux cuts across the windings in the three coils, it causes current to flow in them. These three coils are connected in such a way that the current flowing in them changes as the heading of the aircraft changes (Figure 8-7-4).

MEMS

On aircraft, microelectromechanical systems (MEMS) save space and weight. Using solid-state MEMS, reliability is increased primarily because of the lack of moving parts. Tiny vibration-based units with resistance and capacitance-measuring pickups are accurate and reliable and measure only a few millimeters. You can get an idea of the size of these MEMS from Figure 8-7-5. They are normally integrated into a complete microelectronic

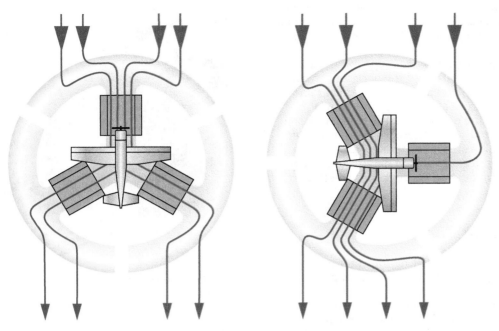

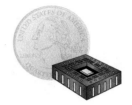

Figure 8-7-5. The relative scale of a MEMS gyro.

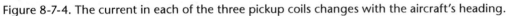

Figure 8-7-4. The current in each of the three pickup coils changes with the aircraft's heading.

solid-state chip that yields an output after performing various conditioning processes. The chips, which are similar to tiny circuit boards, are installed in a dedicated computer or module and mounted in the aircraft.

While a large mechanical gyroscope spins in a plane, its rigidity in space is used to observe and measure the aircraft's movement. The basis of operation of many MEMS gyroscopes is the same, despite their tiny size. The difference is that a vibrating or oscillating piezoelectric device replaces the spinning, weighted ring of the mechanical gyro. Still, once set in motion, any motion is detectable by varying microvoltages or capacitances detected through geometrically arranged pickups. Because piezoelectric substances have a relationship between movement and electricity, microelectrical stimulation sets a piezoelectric gyro in motion, and the tiny voltages produced via the movement in the piezo are extracted. They are input as the required variables to compute attitude or direction information.

Attitude Indicator

The attitude indicator, or artificial horizon, is one of the most essential flight instruments. It gives the pilot pitch and roll information that is especially important when flying without outside visual references. The attitude indicator, with its miniature aircraft and horizon bar, displays a picture of the aircraft's attitude. The relationship of the miniature aircraft to the horizon bar is the same as the

relationship of the real aircraft to the actual horizon. The instrument gives an instantaneous indication of even the smallest changes in attitude

The attitude indicator operates with a gyroscope rotating in the horizontal plane. Thus, it mimics the actual horizon through its rigidity in space. As the aircraft pitches and rolls in relation to the actual horizon, the gyro gimbals allow the aircraft and instrument housing to pitch and roll around the gyro rotor that remains parallel to the ground (Figure 8-7-6).

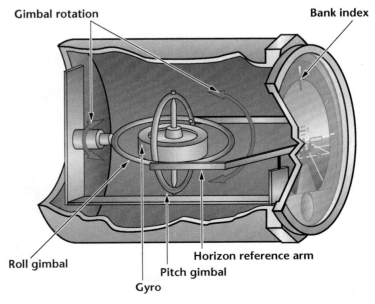

Figure 8-7-6. An attitude indicator.

A horizontal representation of the airplane in miniature is fixed to the instrument housing. A painted semisphere simulating the horizon, the sky, and the ground is attached to the gyro gimbals. The sky and ground meet at what is called the horizon bar. The relationship between the horizon bar and the miniature airplane are the same as those of the aircraft and the actual horizon. Graduated scales reference the degrees of pitch and roll. Often, an adjustment knob allows pilots of varying heights to place the horizon bar at an appropriate level (Figure 8-7-7).

Heading Indicator

The gyroscopic heading indicator or directional gyro (DG) is often the primary instrument for direction. Because a magnetic compass fluctuates so much, a gyro aligned with the magnetic compass gives a much more stable heading indication. Gyroscopic direc-

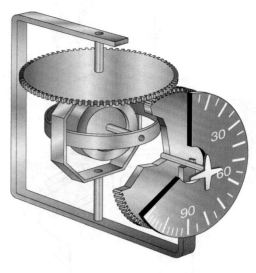

Figure 8-7-8. A typical vacuum powered heading indicator.

tion indicators are at the center base of the instrument panel basic T.

A vacuum-powered DG is common on many light aircraft. Its basis for operation is the gyro's rigidity in space. The gyro rotor spins in the vertical plane and stays aligned with the direction to which it is set. The aircraft and instrument case move around the rigid gyro. This causes a vertical compass card that is geared to the rotor gimbal to move. It is calibrated in degrees, usually with every 30° labeled. The nose of a small, fixed airplane on the instrument glass indicates the aircraft's heading (Figure 8-7-8).

Turn Coordinator

Many aircraft have a turn coordinator. The rotor of the gyro in a turn coordinator is canted upwards 30°. As such, it responds to movement about the vertical axis and to roll movements about the longitudinal axis. This is useful because it is necessary to roll an aircraft to turn it about the vertical axis. Instrument indication of roll, therefore, is the earliest possible warning of a departure from straight-and-level flight. Most turn coordinator gyros are electrically driven.

Typically, the face of the turn coordinator has a small airplane symbol. The wing tips of the airplane provide the indication of level flight and the rate at which the aircraft is turning (Figure 8-7-9).

Slip indicator. The slip indicator (ball) part of the instrument is an inclinometer. The ball responds only to gravity during coordinated straight-and-level flight. Thus, it rests in the

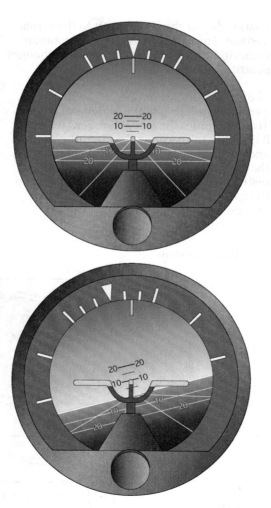

Figure 8-7-7. A typical attitude indicator showing the aircraft in level flight (top) and in a climbing right turn (bottom).

Figure 8-7-9. A turn coordinator senses and indicates the rate of both roll and yaw.

lowest part of the curved glass between the reference wires. When a turn is initiated, and the aircraft is banked, both gravity and the centrifugal force of the turn act on the ball. If the turn is coordinated, the ball remains in place. If a skidding turn takes place, the centrifugal force exceeds the force of gravity on the ball, and it moves in the direction of the outside of the turn. In a slipping turn, there is more bank than needed, and gravity is greater than the centrifugal force acting on the ball. The ball moves in the curved glass toward the inside of the turn.

Section 8

Vacuum System

Purpose

Vacuum systems are very common for driving gyro instruments. In a vacuum system, a stream of air directed against the rotor vanes turns the rotor at high speed. The action is like a water wheel. Air at atmospheric pressure is first drawn through a filter or filters. It is then routed into the instrument and directed at vanes on the gyro rotor. A suction line leads from the instrument case to the vacuum source. From there, the air is vented overboard. Either a venturi or a vacuum pump can be used to provide the vacuum required to spin the rotors.

The vacuum value required for instrument operation is usually between 3" Hg to 4.5" Hg.

Vacuum Pumps

The vane-type, engine-driven pump is the most common source of vacuum for gyros in general aviation, light aircraft. One type of engine-driven pump is geared to the engine and is connected to the lubricating system to seal, cool, and lubricate the pump. Another commonly used pump is a dry vacuum pump. It operates without external lubrication and requires no connection to the engine oil supply. It also does not need the air oil separator or gate check valve found in wet pump systems. In many other respects, the dry pump system and oil lubricated system are the same (Figure 8-8-1).

When a vacuum pump develops a vacuum (negative pressure), it also creates a positive pressure at the outlet of the pump. Sometimes, the positive pressure is used to operate pressure gyro instruments. The components for pressure systems are much the same as those for a vacuum system as listed below. Other times, the pressure developed by the vacuum pump is used to inflate deice boots, inflatable seals, or it is vented overboard.

An advantage of engine-driven pumps is their consistent performance on the ground

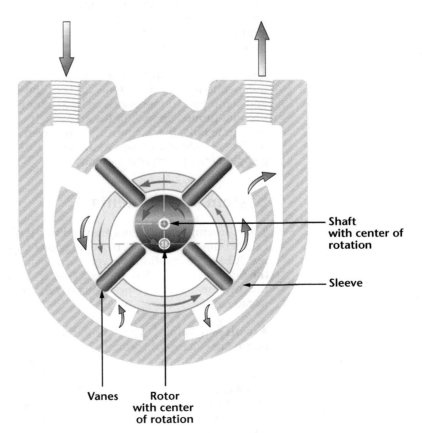

Figure 8-8-1. Cutaway view of a vane-type, engine-driven, vacuum pump used to power gyros.

Figure 8-8-2. A vacuum regulator, also known as a suction relief valve, includes a foam filter.

and in flight. Even at low engine speeds, they can produce more than enough vacuum so that a regulator in the system is needed to continuously provide the correct suction to the vacuum instruments. As long as the engine operates, the relatively simple vacuum system adequately spins the instrument gyros for accurate indications. However, engine failure, especially on single engine aircraft, could leave the pilot without attitude and directional information at a critical time. To overcome this shortcoming, many turn-and-bank indicators operate with an electrically driven gyro that can be driven by the battery for a short time. Thus, when combined with the aircraft's magnetic compass, sufficient attitude and directional information is still available.

Multiengine aircraft typically provide independent vacuum systems for the pilot and copilot instruments driven by separate vacuum pumps on each of the engines. If an engine fails, the vacuum system driven by the still operating engine supplies a full complement of gyro instruments.

System Components

The following components are used in a typical vacuum system for gyroscopic power supply. A brief description is given of each, and the figure further below shows a system with the instruments and components in relation to each other.

Air-oil separator. Oil and air in the vacuum pump are exhausted through the separator, which separates the oil from the air; the air is vented overboard, and the oil is returned to the engine sump. This component is not present with dry-type vacuum pumps. The self-lubricating nature of the pump vanes requires no oil.

Vacuum regulator or suction relief valve. Because the system capacity is more than is needed for operating the instruments, the adjustable vacuum regulator is set for the vacuum desired for the instruments. Excess suction in the instrument lines is reduced when the spring-loaded valve opens to atmospheric pressure (Figure 8-8-2).

Gate check valve. The gate check valve prevents possible damage to the instruments by engine backfire that would reverse the flow of air and oil from the pump.

Pressure relief valve. A pressure relief valve is used because a reverse flow of air from the pump would close both the gate check valve and the suction relief valve, and the resulting pressure could rupture the lines. The pressure relief valve vents positive pressure into the atmosphere.

Selector valve. In twin-engine aircraft with vacuum pumps driven by both engines, the alternate pump can be selected to provide vacuum if either engine or pump fails. A check valve is incorporated to seal off the failed pump.

Restrictor valve. Because the turn needle of the turn-and-bank indicator operates on less vacuum than that required by the other instruments, the vacuum in the main line must be reduced for use by this instrument. An in-line restrictor valve performs this function.

Air filter. A master air filter screens out foreign matter from the air flowing through all the gyro instruments.

Suction gauge. The suction gauge is a pressure gauge that indicates the difference between the pressure in the system and atmospheric or flight deck pressure. It is usually calibrated in inches of mercury.

Suction/vacuum pressures discussed in conjunction with operating vacuum systems are negative pressures, indicated as inches of mercury below that of atmospheric pressure. The minus sign is usually not presented, because the importance is placed on the magnitude of the vacuum developed. In relation to an absolute vacuum (0 p.s.i. or 0" Hg), instrument vacuum systems have positive pressure.

Figure 8-8-3 shows a typical engine-driven pump vacuum system containing the above components.

At high altitudes, pressure-driven gyros are more efficient. Pressure systems are like vacuum systems and use the same components,

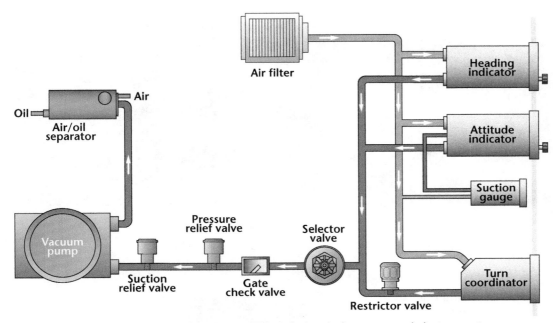

Figure 8-8-3. A typical pump-driven vacuum system for powering gyroscopic instruments.

but they are designed for pressure instead of vacuum. Thus, a pressure regulator is used instead of a suction relief valve.

Section 9

Electronic Displays

Electronic displays started appearing on aircraft instrument panels about as soon as they appeared anywhere else. Usually they just replaced the display for one instrument, and many times there was no significant advantage in size or weight. However, as the technologies advanced, the applications became more flexible, and multiple readouts became possible on one instrument (Figure 8-9-1).

Couple the solid-state measuring technology with the new displays and computer processing, and the result is the age of glass panel aircraft (Figure 8-9-2). Even training aircraft today are being made with very sophisticated electronic displays replacing much of the traditional instrumentation. This is economical, reduces maintenance costs, and prepares pilots for the flight decks of the more advanced aircraft they move into as they advance in their career.

The probes and transducers measure pressures, temperatures, fuel flow, volts, amps, fuel levels, and other engine and aircraft system functions.

In small aircraft, a data converter converts the analog signals from the probes and transducers to a digital format. This data is transmitted via a cable to the display. In large aircraft, the data concentrators throughout the aircraft collect information from probes and transducers and send information via a data bus to the computers in the electronics bay, which then process it for display.

Figure 8-9-1. Analog and digital information are both shown on this typical electronic flight instrument systems (EFIS) display.

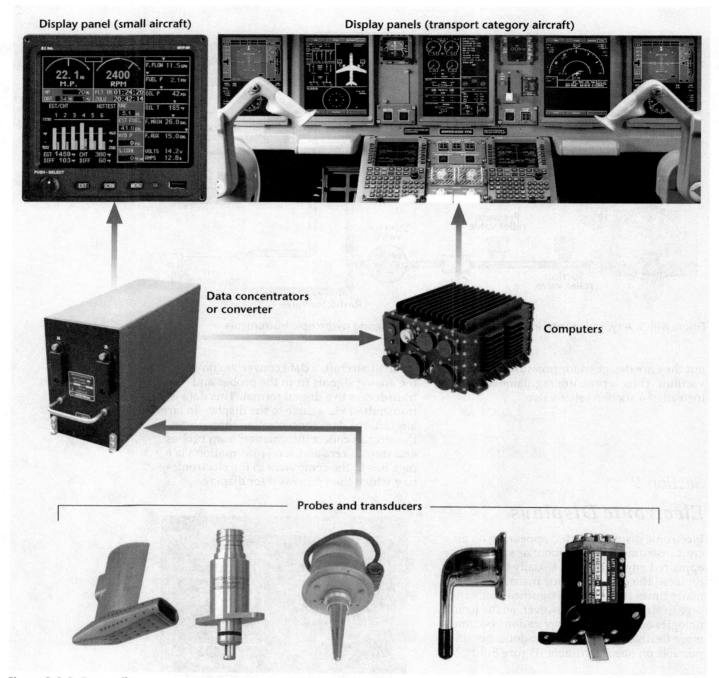

Figure 8-9-2. Data collectors or converters prepare and combine probe readings for display on one panel or several.

Section 10

Communication and Navigation Systems

The magnetic compass, clock, and ASI can be coupled with some careful calculations based on wind direction to result in a reliable navigation system, but this has many limitations. Early aviators sought solutions using radio technology. The development of electronics to be used in aviation has always been a joint effort to meet both military and civil aviation requirements.

Voice communications from ground to air and from aircraft to aircraft were established almost from the beginning of powered flight. However, World War I brought about an urgent need for communications (Figure 8-10-1). The development of aircraft reliability and use for civilian purposes in the 1920s led to increased instrumentation and set in motion the need to conquer blind flight—flight without the ground being visible. Radio beacon direction finding was developed for enroute navigation. Toward the end of the decade, instrument navigation combined with rudimentary radio use to produce the first safe blind landing of an aircraft.

In the 1930s, the first all radio-controlled blind-landing was accomplished. At the same time, radio navigation using ground-based beacons expanded. Instrument navigation certification for airline pilots began. Low- and medium-frequency radio waves were found to be problematic at night and in weather. By the end of the decade, using high-frequency radio waves was explored and included the advent of high-frequency radar.

In the 1940s, after two decades of development driven by mail carrier and passenger airline requirements, World War II injected urgency into developing aircraft radio communication and navigation. Communication radios, despite their size, were essential onboard aircraft (Figure 8-10-2). Very high frequencies were developed for communication and navigational purposes. Installation of the first instrument landing systems for blind landings began mid-decade and, by the end of the decade, the very high frequency (VHF) omni-directional range (VOR) navigational network was instituted. It was also in the 1940s that the first transistor was developed, paving the way for modern, solid-state electronics.

Civilian air transportation increased over the ensuing decades. Communication and navigation equipment were refined. Solid-state radio development, especially in the 1960s, produced a wide range of small, rugged radio and navigational equipment for aircraft. The space program began and added a need for higher level for communication and navigation. Communication satellites were also launched. The Cold War military buildup caused developments in guidance and navigation and gave birth to the concept of using satellites for positioning. This is what we know as global positioning system (GPS).

In the new millennium, the Federal Aviation Administration (FAA) assessed the national airspace system (NAS) and traffic projections for the future. Gridlock is predicted by 2022. Therefore, the FAA developed and has undertaken a complete overhaul of the NAS, including communication and navigational systems. The program is called NextGen.

NextGen uses the latest technologies to provide a more efficient and effective system of air traffic management. Heavily reliant on global satellite positioning of aircraft in flight and on the ground, NextGen combines GPS technology with automatic dependent

surveillance–broadcast technology (ADS-B) for traffic separation. A large increase in air system capacity is the planned result. Overhauled ground facilities accompany the

Figure 8-10-1. Early voice communication radio tests in 1917.
Courtesy of AT&T Archives and History Center.

Figure 8-10-2. A bomber's onboard radio station.

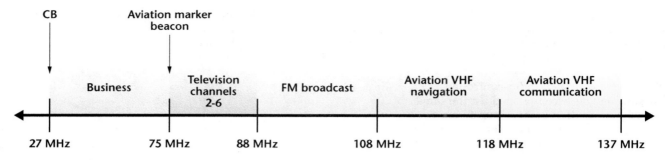

Figure 8-10-3. A section of the VHF band showing aviation frequencies.

technology upgrades mandated for aircraft. NextGen implementation has started and is scheduled through the year 2025.

For the past few decades, avionics development has increased at a faster pace than that of airframe and powerplant development. This is likely to continue. Improvements to solid-state electronics in the form of micro- and nano-technologies continue to this day. Trends are toward lighter, smaller devices with remarkable capability and reliability. A focus is to integrate the wide range of communication and navigational aids.

Voice Communication

Voice communication equipment was one of the first radio technologies to be developed for aircraft use. Lt. Paul W. Beck performed the first air-to-ground radio communication on January 21, 1911, from a Wright Model B Flyer. Flying at 400 ft. above ground level (AGL), he completed a radio communication to a ground station more than 40 miles away. The communication was done using a radio telegraph. Beck held the 29-lb. transmitter in his lap while another pilot, Phil Parmalee, flew the airplane.

Radio technology was developed quickly to make equipment smaller and more efficient. To move beyond some of the problems associated with other frequency ranges, the industry settled on the VHF range for communications and later for some navigation systems. Figure 8-10-3 shows a section of the VHF band that includes the aviation frequencies.

In the 1950s radios that operated on a 90-channel communication band ranging from 118 megahertz (MHz) to 127 MHz were widely available. Today's complete VHF aviation communication system channeling

Figure 8-10-4. A VOR ground station.

is described later in this chapter. Each channel was spaced 100 kilohertz (kHz) from the next channel. As the number of aircraft grew and as more aircraft became equipped with radios, the industry determined that 90 channels were not enough.

The communication band was expanded to 136 MHz, and the spacing between channels was cut in half to 50 kHz in the 1960s. This made 360 channels available for communication. Before the 1960s ended, the industry realized 360 channels still were not enough, and the band was subdivided yet again. In 1973 the spacing between channels was cut to 25 kHz, thus giving radios in the United States 720 available channels. The Europeans had frequencies to 137 MHz available for aviation communication use. As a result, 760 channels were available in Europe. In 1990 frequencies up to 137 MHz became available for aviation use in North America.

At the end of the twentieth century, 760 channels were no longer enough. In 1999 the Europeans began to phase in a 2,280-channel system. The United States began implementing the same system in 2007.

VHF Navigation

The aviation industry uses the VHF portion of the radio frequency spectrum for three types of navigation systems. Included in the VHF portion are the VHF omnirange (VOR), localizer, glideslope, and marker beacon systems.

VOR

VOR is a navigation system used to guide aircraft flying cross country. The VOR ground station (Figure 8-10-4) transmits an amplitude modulated signal, which is radiated from an array of antennas. The signal is fed to the antennas such that the radiation pattern is rotated electronically. The rotation rate is 1,800 r.p.m.

The key to navigating using the VOR is for the system on the aircraft to sense where the energy from the transmitter is pointed. In doing so, the system can determine the direction of the aircraft in relation to the VOR station. The onboard aircraft equipment can give the flight crew information regarding whether they are going TO or FROM the station, and on which radial.

The aircraft equipment includes a receiver with a tuning device and a VOR or omni navigation instrument. The navigation instrument

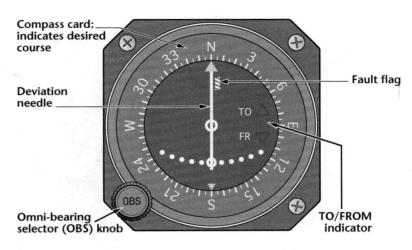

Figure 8-10-5. A CDI is used to determine the aircraft's course.

could be a course deviation indicator (CDI), horizontal situation indicator (HSI), or a radio magnetic indicator (RMI). Each of these instruments indicates the course to the tuned VOR.

CDI. The CDI is found in many training aircraft. It consists of an omni bearing selector (OBS) sometimes referred to as the course selector, a CDI needle (left-right needle), and a TO/FROM indicator. A typical CDI is shown in Figure 8-10-5.

The course selector is an azimuth dial that can be rotated to select a desired radial or to determine the radial over which the aircraft is flying. In addition, the magnetic course *TO* or *FROM* the station can be determined.

When the course selector is rotated, it moves the CDI or needle to indicate the position of the radial relative to the aircraft. If the course selector is rotated until the deviation needle is centered, the radial (magnetic course *FROM* the station) or its reciprocal (magnetic course *TO* the station) can be determined. The course deviation needle also moves to the right or left if the aircraft is flown or drifting away from the radial which is set in the course selector.

By centering the needle, the course selector indicates either the course *FROM* the station or the course *TO* the station. If the flag displays a *TO*, the course shown on the course selector must be flown to the station. If *FROM* is displayed and the course shown is followed, the aircraft is flown away from the station.

Horizontal Situation Indicator (HSI). The HSI is a direction indicator that combines the magnetic compass with navigation signals and a glideslope. The HSI gives the pilot an indication of the location of the aircraft in

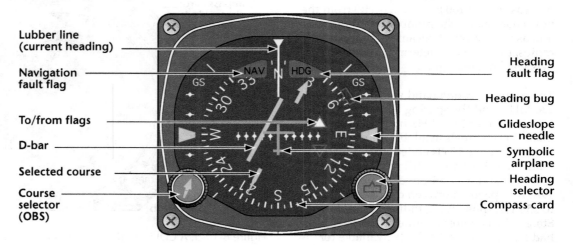

Lubber line (current heading)
Navigation fault flag
To/from flags
D-bar
Selected course
Course selector (OBS)
Heading fault flag
Heading bug
Glideslope needle
Symbolic airplane
Heading selector
Compass card

Figure 8-10-6. A typical HSI.

relation to the chosen course or radial (Figure 8-10-6).

Radio Magnetic Indicator (RMI). The RMI is a navigational aid providing aircraft magnetic or directional gyro heading and VOR, GPS, and automatic direction finder (ADF) bearing information. Remote indicating compasses were developed to compensate for errors in and limitations of older types of heading indicators (Figure 8-10-7).

Automatic Direction Finder (ADF). An older navigation aid, used in many general aviation aircraft, is ADF radio receiving equipment. To navigate using the ADF, the pilot tunes the receiving equipment to a ground station known as a nondirectional radio beacon (NDB).

Basically, the ADF aircraft equipment consists of a tuner, which is used to set the desired station frequency, and the navigational display. The navigational display consists of a dial on which the azimuth is printed and a needle that rotates around the dial and points to the station to which the receiver is tuned.

Some ADF dials can be rotated to align the azimuth with the aircraft heading; others are fixed with 0° representing the nose of the aircraft and 180° representing the tail (Figure 8-10-8).

Localizer

Closely related to the VOR, the localizer is a ground-based system used to give aircraft horizontal guidance to a runway. This is part of the instrument landing system (ILS). The localizer uses the same receiver, converter, and indicator as the VOR system. On localizer frequencies, the receiver sends an enable signal to the converter, which switches from VOR conversion to localizer conversion.

The ILS brings several different navigation methods together to provide precise guidance as an aircraft approaches an airport. ILS has different categories. Starting with Category I, each category of ILS offers higher precision, which allows aircraft to descend lower before visually sighting the runway. The most precise category is Category III, which is precise enough to allow landings under weather conditions with zero forward visibility.

Figure 8-10-9 shows an array of antennas used to transmit the localizer signals. These antennas are placed at the opposite end of the runway from the intended landing direction.

Figure 8-10-7. An RMI.

The antenna array and transmitters radiate two signals, as shown in Figure 8-10-10. The signal on the right side of the runway is amplitude modulated with a 150-Hz tone. On the left, the signal is amplitude modulated with a 90-Hz tone. The receiver receives these signals simultaneously. The LOC converter measures the signals to determine which modulation is stronger.

If the 150-Hz tone is stronger, the CDI D-bar moves to the left, indicating the aircraft is to the right of the course. If the 90-Hz tone is stronger, the CDI D-bar moves to the right, indicating the aircraft is to the left of the course. If the tones are equal, the D-bar centers, indicating the aircraft is above the extended runway centerline. Examples of indications are shown in Figure 8-10-11.

Like the VOR system, localizer signals are adversely affected by tall buildings and mountains. The service volume for localizers

Figure 8-10-8. ADF with a fixed azimuth and magnetic compass.

Figure 8-10-9. A localizer antenna array.

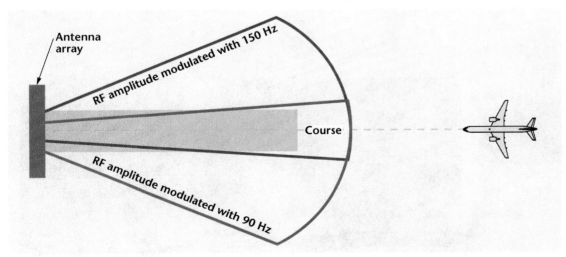

Figure 8-10-10. Localizer signals.

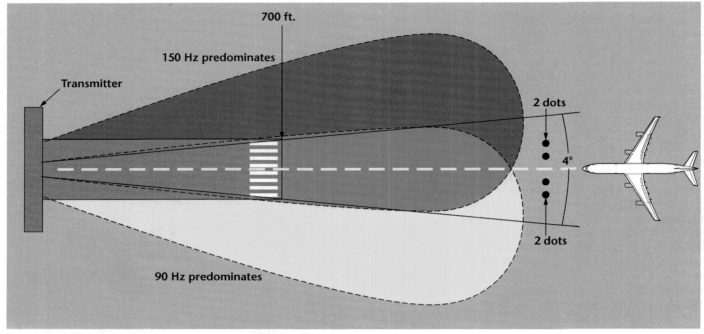

Figure 8-10-11. Navigating to the runway with the localizer.

is ±10° from the centerline out to 18 nautical miles and ±35° from the centerline out to 10 nautical miles.

Marker Beacon

The marker beacon system is used to mark specific points along the ILS approach path to a runway. The ground-based transmitters broadcast an amplitude modulated signal on 75 MHz. Figure 8-10-12 shows a marker transmitter site. Each marker point along the approach has a different name, modulating tone, and associated color.

Farthest from the runway is the outer marker. Typically, the outer marker is between four and seven miles from the landing end of the runway. The outer marker signal is modulated with a 400-Hz tone, which is turned on and off to emulate Morse code dashes. About 3,500 ft. from the landing end of the runway is the middle marker. The middle marker signal is modulated with a 1,300-Hz tone, which is turned on and off to emulate Morse code

Figure 8-10-12. A marker beacon transmitter site.

dots and dashes. Category II and Category III ILS use an inner marker. This transmitter is about 1,000 ft. along the landing end of the runway, close to where the aircraft is to touch down. The inner marker is modulated with a 3,000-Hz tone, which is turned on and off to emulate a rapid series of Morse code dots. Table 8-10-1 summarizes the location, modulating tone, and associated color of the marker system.

Glideslope

The glideslope system is another component of the ILS that provides vertical guidance to the end of the runway. Glideslope works in the ultrahigh frequency (UHF) band and has 40 frequencies, each of which is assigned, paired, or collocated with a localizer frequency. The glideslope band ranges from 329.15 MHz to 335.0 MHz and has channels every 150 kHz. An example of pairing is shown in Table 8-10-2.

The glideslope system guides the pilot along a 2.5° to 3.5° angled path descending to the runway. If the aircraft is above the path, the needle moves downward. If the aircraft is on the proper glidepath, the needle is centered. Aircraft below the glidepath have the needle swung upward. An invalid or missing signal causes the glideslope fault flag to be displayed. An illustration of the glideslope indications is in Figure 8-10-13.

Marker	Tone (Hz)	Location	Color	Morse code
Outer	400	4–7 miles	Blue	Dashes
Middle	1,300	3,500 ft.	Amber	Dots and dashes
Inner	3,000	1,000 ft. from the approach end of the runway	White	Dots

Table 8-10-1. Marker beacon system details.

Localizer VHF frequency (MHz)	Glideslope UHF frequency (MHz)
108.95	329.15
109.30	332.00
110.30	335.00

Table 8-10-2. Selected localizer and glideslope frequency pairings.

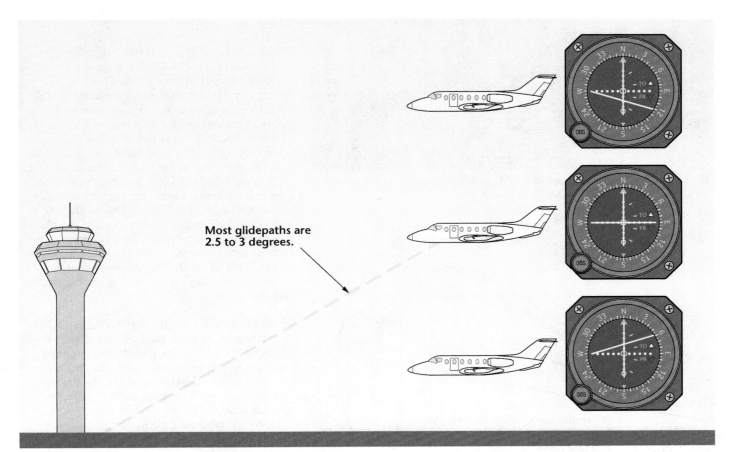

Most glidepaths are 2.5 to 3 degrees.

Figure 8-10-13. Glideslope indications.

On the ground, the glideslope transmitter is connected to an array of antennas on a small tower beside the runway (Figure 8-10-14).

These antennas radiate two signals, as shown in Figure 8-10-15. The signal on the lower side of the glidepath is amplitude modulated with a 150-Hz tone. Above the glidepath the signal is amplitude modulated with a 90-Hz tone. The receiver receives these signals simultaneously. The glideslope converter in the receiver, measures which modulation is stronger. Electronically, glideslope systems are quite like localizer systems.

Figure 8-10-14. A glideslope ground station with its antenna tower.

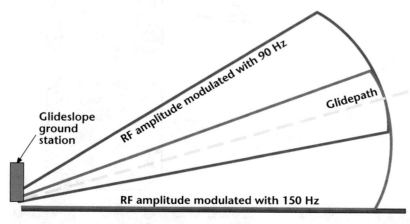

Figure 8-10-15. Radiated glideslope energy.

Distance Measuring Equipment (DME)

The navigation systems described so far are passive, in that they receive and process signals transmitted from the ground. *Distance measuring equipment* (DME) is an active system that transmits and receives information from a ground-based transceiver known as a DME transponder or TACAN transponder.

Tactical navigation (TACAN) was developed by the U.S. military in the mid-twentieth century. TACAN provides both bearing and distance information to TACAN-equipped aircraft. Many VOR sites also have a TACAN ground station at the same location. A ground station with both VOR and TACAN is known as a VORTAC. DME is designed to use the distance feature of TACAN. The technology proved popular, and the FAA equipped DME transponders at VOR and ILS sites so civilian pilots could also use distance information from non-VORTAC sites. The VOR and ILS sites with DME capabilities are known as VOR/DME or ILSDME, respectively.

Like glideslope, the DME operates on the UHF band and can be controlled using the VHF navigation system control head. An example of a DME display is shown in Figure 8-10-16. DME frequencies are not displayed to the pilot.

The basic principle of DME navigation is similar to radar. The DME transmits energy and measures the time it takes for energy to return. Unlike most radar systems, DME is active. In other words, the system in the aircraft transmits and so does the ground system. Because radio waves travel at the speed of light, physicists have calculated that a radio wave travels one nautical mile in 6.18 microseconds (µS). DME and radar work on the principle of a radar round trip nautical mile (RRTNM), or 12.36 µS. The main function of a DME is to measure the time it takes for the signal to travel to the transponder, be processed, and come back. Once the measurement is made, the DME does the necessary math and displays the result as nautical miles for the pilot.

Both pilots and technicians should note that DME measures *slant range*. Slant range is the direct distance, not map distance, from the aircraft to the ground station. The closer an aircraft gets to the transponder, the greater the slant range error gets, until the aircraft passes over the station. When the aircraft is directly over the station, the DME reads altitude in nautical miles. Figure 8-10-17 illustrates slant range error.

While it was the first system to provide speed and distance information it enjoyed wide popularity. However, the popularity of the DME has been largely replaced using satellite navigation systems, which can offer better coverage, and accuracy.

Global Positioning Satellite System (GPS)

GPS is the fastest growing type of navigation in aviation. It provides navigation by using the NAVSTAR satellites set and maintained in orbit around the earth by the U.S. government. Continuous coded transmissions from the satellites facilitate locating the position of an aircraft equipped with a GPS receiver with extreme accuracy. GPS can be used on its own for enroute navigation, or it can be integrated into other navigation systems or flight management systems.

Three segments make up the GPS: the space segment, the control segment, and the user segment. Aircraft technicians are involved only with user segment equipment such as GPS receivers, displays, and antennas.

Space segment. Twenty-four satellites (21 active, 3 spares) in six separate planes of orbit 12,625 ft. above earth make up the space segment of the GPS. The satellites are positioned such that in any place on earth at any time, at least 4 are a minimum of 15° above the horizon. Typically, between 5 and 8 satellites are in view.

Two signals loaded with digitally coded information are transmitted from each sat-

ellite. The L1 channel transmission on a 1,575.42-MHz carrier frequency is used in civilian aviation. Satellite identification, position, and time are conveyed to the aircraft GPS receiver on this digitally modulated signal along with status and other information. The military uses an L2 channel 1,227.60-MHz transmission.

Control segment. The time it takes for signals to reach the aircraft GPS receiver from transmitting satellites is combined with each satellite's exact location to calculate the aircraft's position. The GPS control segment monitors each satellite to ensure that its location and time are precise. This control is achieved with 5 ground-based receiving stations, a master control station, and 3 transmitting antennas. The receiving stations forward status information received from the satellites to the master control station. Calculations are made, and corrective instructions are sent to the satellites via the transmitters.

User segment. The GPS user segment is made up of the thousands of receivers

Figure 8-10-16. A DME display.

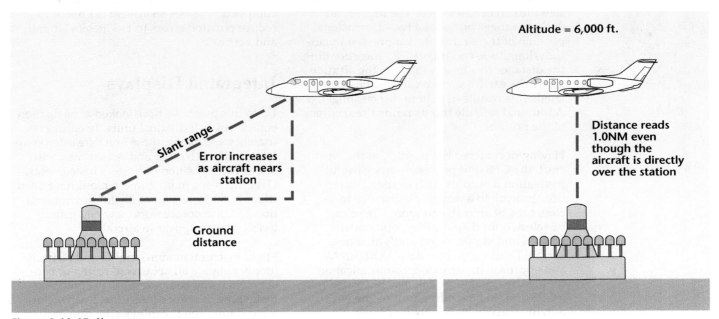

Figure 8-10-17. Slant range error.

Figure 8-10-18. A GPS unit integrated with NAV/COM circuitry.

installed in aircraft and every other receiver that uses the GPS transmissions. Specifically, for the aircraft technician, the user section consists of a control panel/display, the GPS receiver circuitry, and an antenna. The control, display, and receiver are usually in one unit that also can include VOR/ILS circuitry and a VHF communications transceiver. GPS information is integrated into the multifunctional displays of glass cockpit aircraft (Figure 8-10-18).

The GPS receiver measures the time it takes for a signal to arrive from three transmitting satellites. Because radio waves travel at 186,000 miles per second, the distance to each satellite can be calculated. The intersection of these ranges provides a two-dimensional position of the aircraft. It is expressed in latitude/longitude coordinates. By incorporating the distance to a fourth satellite, the altitude above the earth's surface can also be calculated. This results in a three-dimensional fix. Additional satellite inputs refine the accuracy of the position.

Having deciphered the position of the aircraft, the GPS unit processes many useful navigational outputs such as speed, direction, bearing to a waypoint, distance traveled, time of arrival, and more. These can be selected for display. Waypoints can be entered and stored in the unit's memory. Terrain features, airport data, VOR/RNAV and approach information, communication frequencies, and more can also be loaded into a GPS unit. Most modern units come with moving map display capability.

A main benefit of GPS use is immunity from service disruption due to weather. Errors are introduced while the carrier waves travel through the ionosphere; however, these are corrected and kept to a minimum. GPS is also relatively inexpensive. GPS receivers for instrument flight rules (IFR) navigation in aircraft must be built to TSO-129A (an FAA performance standard). This raises the price above that of handheld units used for hiking or in an automobile. But the overall cost of GPS is low because of its small infrastructure. Most of the inherent accuracy is built in to the space and control segments, permitting reliable positioning with inexpensive user equipment.

WAAS. To increase the accuracy of GPS for aircraft navigation, the wide area augmentation system (WAAS) was developed. It consists of about 25 precisely surveyed ground stations that receive GPS signals and ultimately transmit correction information to the aircraft.

WAAS ground stations receive GPS signals and forward position errors to two master ground stations. Time and location information is analyzed, and correction instructions are sent to communication satellites in geostationary orbit over the NAS. The satellites broadcast GPS-like signals that WAAS-enabled GPS receivers use to correct position information received from GPS satellites.

A WAAS-enabled GPS receiver is required to use the WAAS. If so equipped, an aircraft qualifies to perform precision approaches into thousands of airports without any ground-based approach equipment. Separation minimums are also able to be reduced between aircraft that are WAAS equipped. The WAAS system is known to reduce position errors to 1–3 meters laterally and vertically.

Integrated Displays

Up to this point, we have looked at navigation equipment as individual units. To enhance usability and safety, these units are often combined with each other and, sometimes, with one or more position indicating instruments. Over the years, many combinations have been tried. With the advent of digital instrumentation and microprocessors, new navigation tools began to appear in aircraft.

Flight instrumentation, engine and airframe monitoring are all areas well suited to benefit from using computers. They contribute by helping to reduce instrument panel clutter and focusing the pilot's attention only on matters of imminent importance. *Glass cockpit* is a term that refers to the flat-panel display screens in flight deck instrumentation. It also refers to the use of computer-produced images that have replaced individual mechanical gauges. A typical glass cockpit installation is seen in Figure 8-10-19. Moreover, computers and computer systems monitor the processes and components of an operating aircraft beyond human ability while relieving the pilot of the stress from having to do so.

These flat-panel displays can often display more than one *page* of information, giving them the possibility of offering much more information by simply moving from page to page. The same display can often give you the same data that the entire instrument panel provided in the days of *steam gauges*. Additionally, the computer system gives it capabilities far beyond any that were possible with analog instruments and individual navigation radios.

Computerized electronic flight instrument systems have additional benefits. The components' solid-state construction increases reliability. Also, microprocessors, data buses, and liquid crystal displays all save space and weight.

Figure 8-10-19. In a modern glass cockpit, digital data displays replace many older instruments and indicators of the past.

9

Ice, Rain, Smoke, and Fire Protection Systems

Section 1

Introduction

Every flight begins with the same basic goal—to complete the mission safely. All aspects of the operation must be done with safe completion of the flight in mind. Many factors can affect the safe outcome of a flight.

Rain, snow, and ice are transportation's long-time enemies. Flying has added a new dimension, especially considering ice. Today, passengers expect the flight to continue regardless of weather conditions. Aircraft can now be certified to fly into known icing conditions. This does, however, require some special equipment and training for the flight crews.

Smoke and fire are internal dangers that originate on the aircraft. Safe continuation of the flight relies on early detection and extinguishing. From the simple, handheld fire extinguisher to the sophisticated, high-rate-of-discharge (HRD) extinguishing systems, aircraft today can minimize the danger from fire.

This chapter explores some of the systems that detect, prevent, and combat these dangers.

Section 2

Ice Control Systems

Under certain atmospheric conditions, ice can build rapidly on airfoils and air inlets. On days when there is visible moisture in the air,

Learning Objectives

EXPLAIN
• Types of ice protection systems

DISCUSS
• Rain control systems

• Fire protection and smoke detection systems

Left: This Piper PA-60 aircraft incorporates ice protection for the windshield, props, and leading edges.

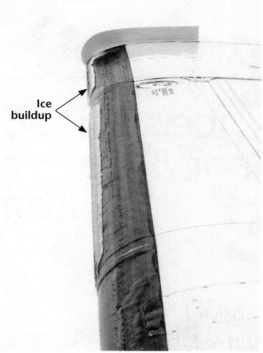

Figure 9-2-1. Ice can build up quickly in the air and on the ground.

ice can form on aircraft leading-edge surfaces at altitudes where freezing temperatures start. Water droplets in the air can be supercooled to below freezing without turning into ice unless they are somehow disturbed. This unusual occurrence is partly due to the surface tension of the water droplet not allowing the droplet to expand and freeze. However, when aircraft surfaces disturb these droplets, they immediately turn to ice on the aircraft surfaces.

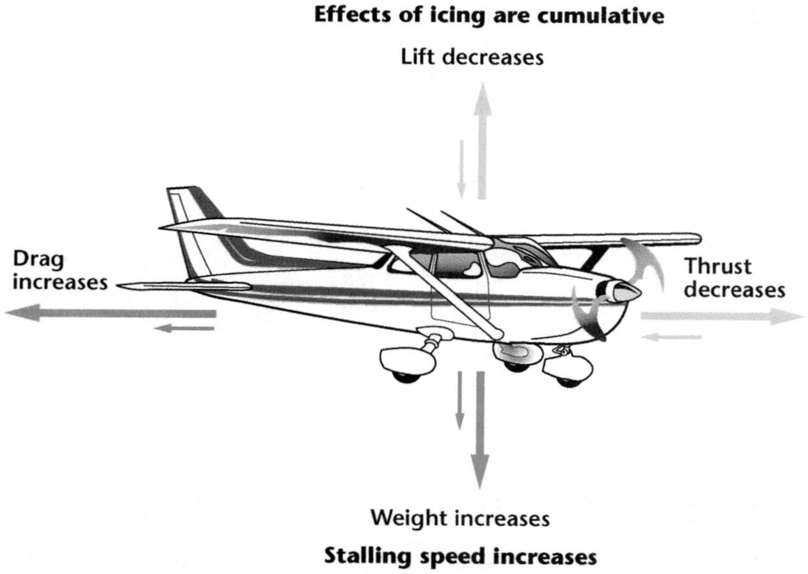

Effects of icing are cumulative

Lift decreases

Drag
increases

Thrust
decreases

Weight increases

Stalling speed increases

Figure 9-2-2. Effects of structural icing.

The two types of ice encountered during flight are clear and rime. Clear ice forms when the remaining liquid portion of the water drop flows out over the aircraft surface, gradually freezing as a smooth sheet of solid ice. Clear ice forms when droplets are large, such as in rain or in cumuliform clouds. Clear ice is hard, heavy, and tenacious. Removing it with deicing equipment is especially difficult.

Rime ice forms when water drops are small, such as those in stratified clouds or light drizzle. The liquid portion remaining after initial impact freezes rapidly before the drop has time to spread over the aircraft surface. The small frozen droplets trap air, giving the ice a white appearance. Rime ice is lighter than clear ice and its weight is of little significance. However, its irregular shape and rough surface decrease the effectiveness of the aerodynamic efficiency of airfoils, reducing lift and increasing drag. Rime ice is brittle and more easily removed than clear ice.

Mixed clear and rime icing can form rapidly when water drops vary in size or when liquid drops intermingle with snow or ice particles. Ice particles become imbedded in clear ice, building a very rough accumulation sometimes in a mushroom shape on leading edges. Ice can form whenever there is visible moisture in the air and temperature is near or below freezing. An exception is carburetor icing, which can occur in warm weather with no visible moisture present.

Ice or frost forming on aircraft creates two basic hazards:

- The resulting malformation of the airfoil that could decrease the amount of lift

- The additional weight and unequal formation of the ice that could cause the aircraft to become unbalanced, making it hard to control

Enough ice to cause an unsafe flight condition can form in a very short time; thus, some method of ice prevention or removal is necessary. Figure 9-2-1 shows the effects of ice on a leading edge.

Icing Effects

Ice buildup increases drag and reduces lift. It causes destructive vibration and hampers true instrument readings. Control surfaces can become unbalanced or frozen. Fixed slots are filled, and movable slots are jammed. Radio reception is hampered, and engine performance is affected. Ice, snow, and slush have a direct effect on the safety of flight. They degrade lift, reduce takeoff performance, and reduce the aircraft's maneuverability.

Whenever icing conditions are encountered, the performance characteristics of the airplane deteriorate (Figure 9-2-2). Increased aerodynamic drag increases fuel consumption, reducing the airplane's range and making it more difficult to maintain speed. Decreased rate of climb must be anticipated because of the decrease in wing and empennage efficiency and because of the possible reduced efficiency of the propellers and increase in gross weight. Abrupt maneuvering and steep turns at low speeds must be avoided because the airplane stalls at higher-than-published speeds with ice accumulation. On final approach for landing, stall speed increases. After touchdown with heavy ice accumulation, landing distances can be as much as twice the normal distance because of the increased landing speeds. Ice prevention and ice elimination using pneumatic pressure, applying heat, and applying fluid are discussed next.

The ice and rain protection systems used on aircraft keep ice from forming on the following airplane components:

- Wing leading edges
- Horizontal and vertical stabilizer leading edges
- Engine cowl leading edges
- Propellers
- Propeller spinners
- Air data probes
- Flight deck windows
- Water and waste system lines and drains
- Antennas

Figure 9-2-3 gives an overview of ice and rain protection systems installed in a large, transport-category aircraft. In modern aircraft, many of these systems are automatically controlled by the ice detection system and onboard computers.

Ice Prevention

Several means to prevent or control ice formation are used on aircraft:

- Heating surfaces with hot air
- Heating by electrical elements
- Breaking up ice formations, usually by inflatable boots
- Applying chemicals

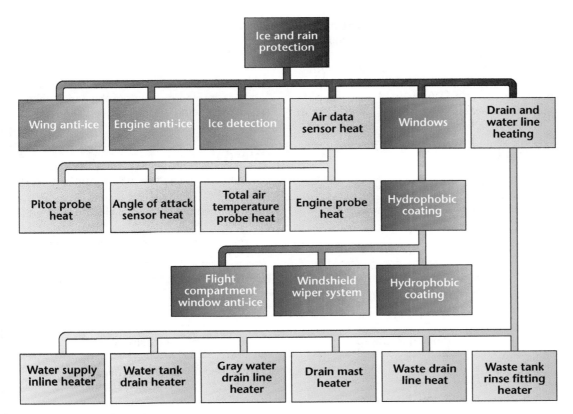

Figure 9-2-3. Ice and rain protection systems.

Equipment is designed for anti-icing or for deicing. Anti-icing equipment is turned on before entering icing conditions and is designed to prevent ice from forming. A surface can be anti-iced by keeping it dry, by heating to a temperature that evaporates water upon impingement, or by heating the surface just enough to prevent freezing, maintaining it running wet. Deicing equipment removes ice after it begins to accumulate, typically on the wings and stabilizer leading edges. Ice is controlled on aircraft structure by the methods listed in Table 9-2-1.

Thermal Electric Anti-Icing

Electricity is used to heat various components on an aircraft so that ice does not form. This type of anti-ice is typically limited to small components because of high amperage draw. Effective thermal electric anti-ice is used on most air data probes, such as pitot tubes, static air ports, total air temperature (TAT) and angle of attack (AOA) probes, ice detectors, and engine P2/T2 sensors. Water lines, waste water drains, and some turboprop inlet cowls are also heated with electricity to prevent ice from forming. Transport category and high-performance aircraft use thermal electric anti-icing in windshields.

In devices that use thermal electric anti-ice, current flows through an integral conductive element that produces heat. The component's temperature is elevated above water's freezing point, so ice cannot form. Various schemes are used, such as an internal coil wire, externally wrapped blankets or tapes, conductive films, and heated gaskets. A basic discussion of probe heat follows. Windshield heat and portable water heat anti-ice are discussed later in this chapter. Propeller deice boots, which also are used for anti-ice, are also thermal electric and discussed in this chapter.

Data probes that protrude into the ambient airstream are especially susceptible to ice formation in flight. Figure 9-2-4 shows on a large aircraft the types and locations of probes that use thermal electric heat. A pitot tube, for example, contains an internal electric element that is controlled by a switch in the flight deck. When the aircraft is on the ground, use caution checking the function of the pitot heat. The tube gets extremely hot because it must keep ice from forming at altitude in temperatures near 50°F below zero at speeds possibly over 500 miles per hour. An ammeter or load meter in the circuit can be used as a substitute to touching the probe, if so equipped.

Simple probe heat circuits exist on small aircraft with a switch and a circuit breaker to activate and protect the device. Advanced aircraft might have more complex circuitry in which control is by computer and flight condition of the aircraft is considered before thermal electric heaters are automatically activated. The primary flight computer (PFC) supplies signals for the air data computer (ADC) to energize ground and air heat control relays to activate probe heat. Factors that the ADC considers are aircraft speed, whether it is in the air or on the ground, and if the engines are running. Similar control is used for other probe heaters.

Chemical Anti-Icing

Chemical anti-icing is used in some aircraft to anti-ice the leading edges of the wing, stabilizers, windshields, and propellers. The wing

Ice location	Method of control
Leading edge of the wing	Thermal pneumatic, thermal electric, chemical, and pneumatic (deice)
Leading edges of vertical and horizontal stabilizers	Thermal pneumatic, thermal electric, and pneumatic (deice)
Windshield, windows	Thermal pneumatic, thermal electric, and chemical
Heater and engine air inlets	Thermal pneumatic and thermal electric
Pitot and static air data sensors	Thermal electric
Propeller blade leading edge and spinner	Thermal electric and chemical
Carburetors	Thermal pneumatic and chemical
Lavatory drains and portable water lines	Thermal electric

Table 9-2-1. Typical ice control methods.

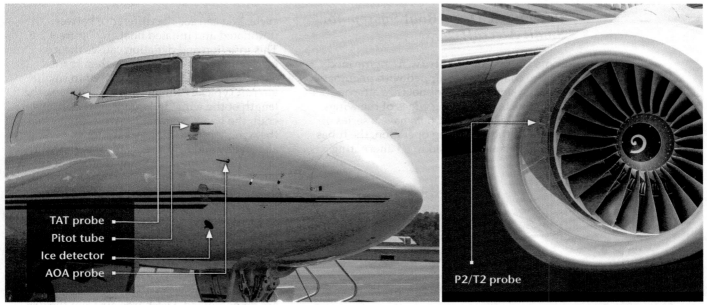

Figure 9-2-4. Probes with thermal electric anti-icing on a transport category aircraft.

and stabilizer systems are often called weeping wing systems or are known by their trade name of TKS™ systems. Ice protection is based on the concept of lowering the freezing point. An antifreeze fluid is pumped from a reservoir through a mesh screen embedded in the leading edges of the wings and stabilizers. Activated by a switch in the flight deck, the liquid flows over the wing and tail surfaces, preventing the ice from forming as it flows. The fluid mixes with the supercooled water in the cloud, lowers its freezing point, and allows the mixture to flow off the aircraft without freezing.

The system is designed to anti-ice, but it can also deice an aircraft. When ice has accumulated on the leading edges, the antifreeze fluid chemically breaks down the bond between the ice and airframe. This allows aerodynamic forces to carry the ice away. Thus, the system clears the airframe of accumulated ice before transitioning to anti-ice protection. Figure 9-2-5 shows a chemical anti-ice system.

The TKS weeping wing system contains formed titanium panels that are laser drilled with more than 800 tiny holes (0.0025 inch diameter) per square inch. These are mated with nonperforated stainless steel rear panels and bonded to wing and stabilizer leading edges. As fluid is delivered from a central reservoir and pump, it seeps through the holes. Aerodynamic forces cause the fluid to coat the upper and lower surfaces of the airfoil. The glycol-based fluid prevents ice from adhering to the aircraft structure.

Some aircraft with weeping wing systems are certified to fly into known icing conditions. Others use it as a hedge against unexpected ice encountered in flight. The systems are basically the same. Reservoir capacity permits 1-2 hours of operation. TKS weeping wings are used primarily on reciprocating aircraft that lack a supply of warm bleed air for a thermal anti-ice system. However, the system is simple and effective leading to its use on some turbine-powered corporate aircraft as well.

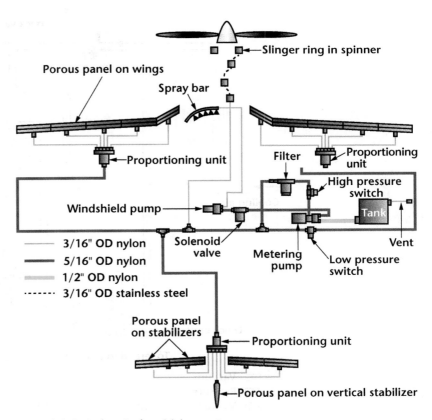

Figure 9-2-5. A chemical anti-icing system.

Pneumatic Deice Boot System for Small Aircraft

Some aircraft, especially twin-engine models, are commonly equipped with pneumatic deicer systems. Rubber boots are attached with glue to the leading edges of the wings and stabilizers. These boots have a series of inflatable tubes. During operation, the tubes are inflated and deflated in an alternating cycle. You can see the difference between the uninflated and inflated boots in Figure 9-2-6. This inflation and deflation causes the ice to crack and break off. The ice is then carried away by the airstream. Boots used in smaller aircraft typically inflate and deflate along the length of the wing. In larger turboprop aircraft, the boots are installed in sections along the wing with the different sections operating alternately and symmetrically about the fuselage. This is done so that any disturbance to airflow caused by an inflated tube is kept to a minimum by inflating only short sections on each wing at a time.

Figure 9-2-7 shows a deice system used on a light, twin-engine aircraft with reciprocating engines. The source of pneumatic air is from two engine-driven, dry air pumps. In normal flight, all the components in the deice system are de-energized. Discharge air from the dry air pumps is dumped overboard through the deice control valves. The deflate valve is open, connecting the deice boots to the suction side of the pump through the check valve manifold and the vacuum regulator. The gyroscopic instruments are also connected to the vacuum side of the dry air pump. The vacuum regulator is set to supply the optimum suction for the gyros, which is sufficient to hold the boots tightly against the airfoil surfaces.

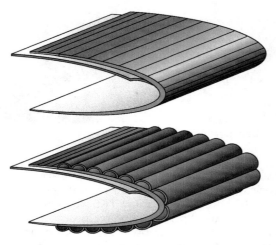

Figure 9-2-6. Cross-section of a pneumatic deicing boot uninflated (top) and inflated (bottom).

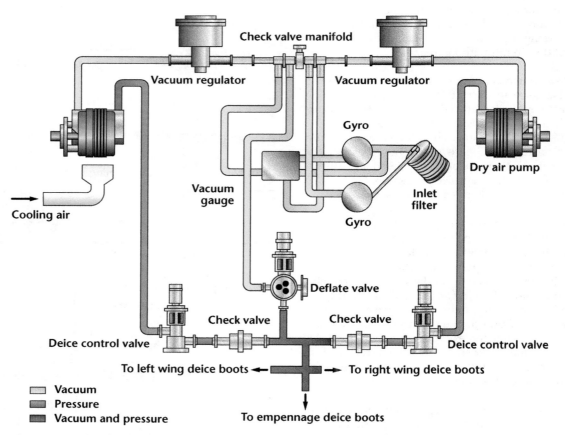

Figure 9-2-7. Pneumatic deicing system for a light twin with reciprocating engines.

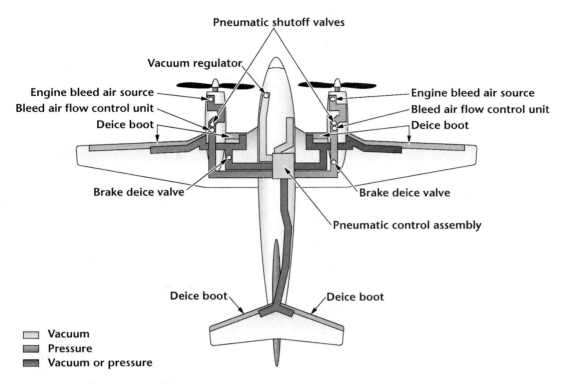

Figure 9-2-8. Wing deice system for a turboprop aircraft.

When the switch is pushed ON, the solenoid-operated deice control valves in each nacelle open, and the deflate valve energizes and closes. Pressurized air from the discharge side of the pumps is routed through the control valves to the deice boot. Pressure switches on the deflate valve de-energize the deice control valve solenoids. The valves close and route pumped air overboard. The deflate valve opens and the boots are again connected to vacuum.

On this simple system, the pilot must manually start this inflation/deflation cycle by pressing the switch each time deice is required. Larger aircraft with more complex systems can include a timer that cycles the system automatically until turned off. Using distributor valves is also common. A distributor valve is a multiposition control valve controlled by the timer. It routes air to different deice boots in a sequence that minimizes aerodynamic disturbances as the ice breaks off the aircraft. Boots are inflated symmetrically on each side of the fuselage to maintain control in flight while deicing occurs. Distributor valves are solenoid operated and incorporate the deflate valve function to reconnect the deice boots with the vacuum side of the pump after all have been inflated.

Figure 9-2-8 shows a pneumatic deice system used on a turboprop aircraft. The source of pneumatic air is engine bleed air, which is used to inflate two inboard wing boots, two outboard boots, and horizontal stabilizer

boots. Additional bleed air is routed through the brake deice valve to the brakes.

A three-position switch controls the operation of the boots. This switch is spring loaded to the center OFF position. When ice has accumulated, the flight crew moves the switch to the single-cycle (up) position and releases it (Figure 9-2-9). Pressure-regulated bleed air from the engine compressors supply air through bleed air flow control units and pneumatic shutoff valves to a pneumatic

Figure 9-2-9. Ice protection panel on a turboprop aircraft with deice boots.

control assembly that inflates the wing boots. After 6 seconds of inflation, an electronic timer switches the distributor in the control assembly to deflate the wing boots, and a 4-second inflation begins in the horizontal stabilizer boots. After these boots have been inflated and deflated, the cycle is complete, and all boots are again held down tightly against the wings and horizontal stabilizer by vacuum. The crew must select the spring-loaded switch again for another cycle to occur.

Each engine supplies a common bleed air manifold. To ensure that the system is not disabled if one engine is inoperative, a flow-control unit with check valve is used in the bleed air line from each engine to prevent the loss of pressure through the compressor of the inoperative engine. If the boots fail to function sequentially, they can be operated manually by selecting the DOWN position of the same deice cycle switch. Depressing and holding it in the manual DOWN position inflates all the boots simultaneously. When the switch is released, it returns to the (spring-loaded) off position, and each boot is deflated and held by vacuum. When operated manually, the boot should not be left inflated for more than 7 to 10 seconds because a new layer of ice can begin to form on the expanded boots and become unremovable. If one engine is inoperative, the loss of its pneumatic pressure does not affect boot operation. Electric power to the boot system is required to inflate the boots in either single-cycle

or manual operation. When electric power is lost, the vacuum holds the boots tightly against the leading edge.

Propeller Deice Systems

Ice forming on the propeller leading edges, cuffs, and spinner reduces the powerplant's efficiency. Typical propeller deice systems include those that use electrical heating elements and chemical deicing fluid.

Many propellers are deiced by an electrically heated boot on each blade. The boot, firmly cemented in place, receives current from a slip ring and brush assembly on the spinner bulkhead. The slip ring transmits current to the deice boot. These components are shown in Figure 9-2-10. The centrifugal force of the spinning propeller and air blast breaks the ice loose from the heated blades.

On some aircraft, the boots are heated in a preset sequence, which is an automatic function controlled by a timer. This sequence is as follows: 30 seconds for the right prop outer elements, 30 seconds for the right prop inner elements, 30 seconds for the left prop outer elements, and 30 seconds for the left prop inner elements. Once the system is turned on automatic, it cycles continuously. A manual bypass of the timer is incorporated.

Some aircraft models, especially single-engine aircraft, use a chemical deicing system for the

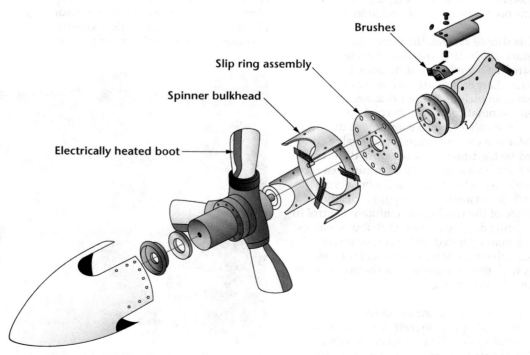

Figure 9-2-10. Electro thermal propeller deice system components.

propellers. Ice usually appears on the propeller before it forms on the wing. The glycol-based fluid is metered from a tank by a small, electrically driven pump through a microfilter to the slinger rings on the prop hub. The propeller system can be a standalone system, or it can be part of a chemical wing and stabilizer deicing system such as the TKS weeping system.

Section 3

Rain Control Systems

Rain is removed from aircraft windshields in several ways. Most aircraft use one or a combination of the following systems: windshield wipers, chemical rain repellent, pneumatic rain removal (jet blast), or windshields treated with a hydrophobic surface seal coating.

Windshield Wiper Systems

In an electrical windshield wiper system, the wiper blades are driven by an electric motor that receives power from the aircraft's electrical system. On some aircraft, the pilot's and copilot's windshield wipers are operated by separate systems to ensure that clear vision is maintained through one of the windows if one system fails. This type of assembly is shown in Figure 9-3-1. Each windshield wiper assembly consists of a wiper, wiper arm, and a wiper motor/converter. Almost all windshield wiper systems use electrical motors. Some older aircraft might be equipped with hydraulic wiper motors.

Chemical Rain Repellent

Water poured onto clean glass spreads out evenly. Even when the glass is held at a steep angle or subjected to air velocity, the glass remains wetted by a thin film of water. However, when glass is treated with certain chemicals, a transparent film is formed that causes the water to behave very much like mercury on glass. That is, the water draws up into beads that cover only a portion of the glass and the area between beads is dry. The water is readily removed from the glass. This principle lends itself quite naturally to removing rain from aircraft windshields. The high-velocity slipstream continually removes the water beads, leaving a large part of the window dry.

A switch or pushbutton control in the flight deck allows the flight crew to apply chemical repellent. The system applies the proper

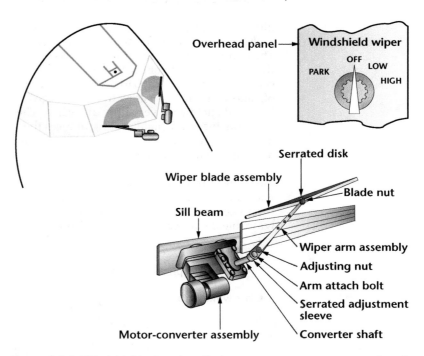

Figure 9-3-1. Windshield wiper installation on a transport category aircraft.

amount of repellant regardless of how long the switch is held. On some systems, a solenoid valve controlled by a time-delay module meters the repellent to a nozzle that sprays it on the outside of the windshield. Two such units exist—one each for the forward glass of the pilot and copilot.

This system should be used only in very wet conditions. Do not use the rain repellant system on dry windows because heavy, undiluted repellant restricts window visibility. If the system is operated inadvertently, the windshield wipers or rain clearing systems should not be operated because doing so tends to increase smearing. Also, the rain repellant residues caused by applying it in dry weather or very light rain can cause staining or minor corrosion of the aircraft skin. To prevent this, any concentrated repellant or residue should be removed by a thorough fresh water rinse at the earliest opportunity. After it is applied, the repellant film slowly deteriorates with continuing rain impingement. This makes it necessary to periodically reapply the repellant. The time between applications depends on rain intensity, the type of repellant used, and whether windshield wipers are used.

Windshield Surface Seal Coating

Some aircraft use a surface seal coating, also called hydrophobic coating, that is on the outside of the flight deck windshield. The layers of the windshield including this coating are illustrated in Figure 9-3-2. The word *hydro-phobic* means to repel or not absorb water. The windshield hydrophobic coating is on the external surface of the windshields. The coatings cause raindrops to bead up and roll off, allowing the flight crew to see through the windshield with very little distortion. The hydrophobic windshield coating reduces the need for wipers and gives the flight crew better visibility in heavy rain.

Most new aircraft windshields are treated with surface seal coating. The manufacturer's coating process deeply penetrates the windshield surface, providing hydrophobic

action for quite some time. When effectiveness declines, products are used that can be applied in the field. These liquid treatments rubbed onto the windshield surface maintain the beading action of rain water. They must be applied periodically or as needed.

Pneumatic Rain Removal Systems

Windshield wipers have two basic problems. One is the tendency of the slipstream aerodynamic forces to reduce the wiper blade loading pressure on the window, causing ineffective wiping or streaking. The other is in achieving fast enough wiper oscillation to keep up with high rain impingement rates in heavy rainfall. As a result, most aircraft wiper systems fail to provide satisfactory vision in heavy rain.

The rain removal system shown in Figure 9-3-3 controls windshield icing and removes rain by directing a flow of heated air over the windshield. This heated air serves two purposes. First, the air breaks the rain drops into small particles that are then blown away. Second, the air heats the windshield to prevent the moisture from freezing. The air can be supplied by an electric blower or by bleed air.

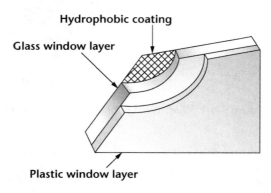

Figure 9-3-2. Hydrophobic coating on a windshield.

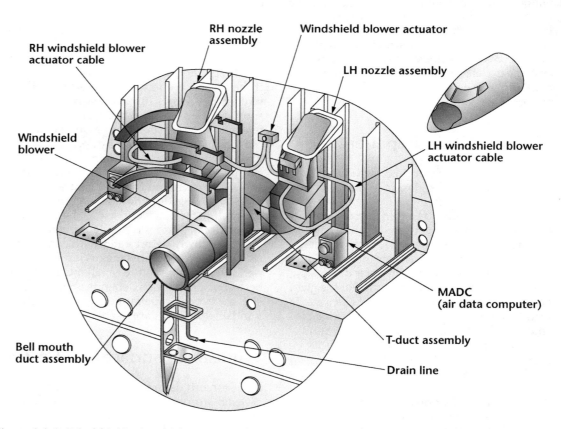

Figure 9-3-3. Windshield rain and frost removal system.

Electric Windshield Systems

High-performance and transport category aircraft windshields are typically made of laminated glass, polycarbonate, or similar ply material. Typically, clear vinyl plies are also included to improve performance characteristics. The laminations create the strength and impact resistance of the windshield assembly. These are a critical feature for windshields because they are subject to a wide range of temperatures and pressures. To be certified, they must also withstand the force of a 4-lb. bird strike at cruising speed.

The laminated construction facilitates the inclusion of electric heating elements into the glass layers, which are used to keep the windshield clear of ice, frost, and fog. The elements used as one of the window plies can be in the form of resistance wires or a transparent conductive material. To ensure that enough heat is applied to the outside of the windshield, heating elements are placed on the inside of the outer glass ply.

Windshields are typically bonded together by applying pressure and heat without using cement. Figure 9-3-4 illustrates the plies in a transport category aircraft windshield. Whether resistance wires or a laminated conductive film are used, aircraft window heat systems have transformers to supply power and feedback mechanisms, such as thermistors, to provide a window heat control unit with information used to keep operating temperature within acceptable limits. Some

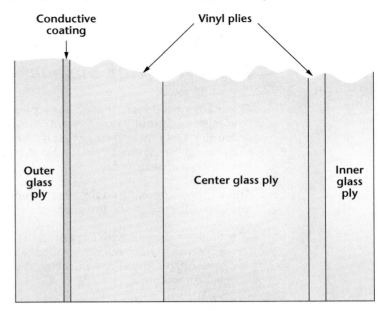

Figure 9-3-4. Cross-section of a transport category aircraft windshield.

systems are automatic; others are controlled by flight deck switches.

Separate circuits for the pilot and co-pilot are common to ensure visibility in case of a malfunction. Some windshield heating systems can be operated at two heat levels. In such systems, NORMAL heating supplies heat to the broadest area of windshield. HIGH heating supplies a higher intensity of heat to a smaller but more essential viewing area. Figure 9-3-5 illustrates a simplified windshield heat system of this type.

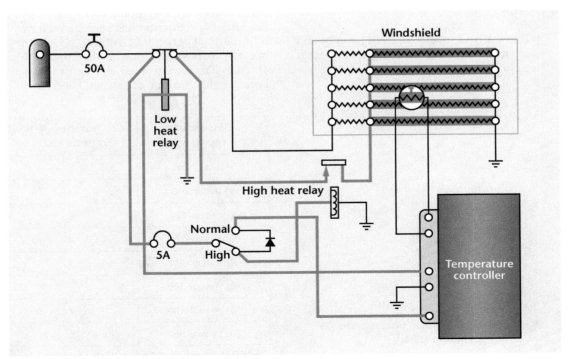

Figure 9-3-5. Electric windshield heat schematic.

Section 4

Fire Protection Systems

Fire is always a danger that no one—pilots, passengers, or ground crew—wants to encounter. Only by knowing what it takes to sustain a fire can we begin to understand how to protect against fire.

Three things are required for a fire; remove any one of these and the fire goes out:

- Fuel—combines with oxygen in the presence of heat, releasing more heat. As a result, it reduces itself to other chemical compounds.
- Heat—accelerates the combining of oxygen with fuel, in turn releasing more heat.
- Oxygen—the element that combines chemically with another substance through the process of oxidation.

Rapid oxidation, accompanied by a noticeable release of heat and light, is called combustion or burning. Figure 9-4-1 illustrates the three elements of fire.

Classification of Fires

For commercial purposes, the National Fire Protection Association (NFPA) has classified fires into three basic types: Class A, Class B, and Class C.

- Class A fires involve ordinary combustible materials, such as wood, cloth, paper, upholstery materials, and the like.

- Class B fires involve flammable petroleum products or other flammable or combustible liquids, greases, solvents, paints, and such.
- Class C fires involve energized electrical wiring and equipment.

A fourth class of fire, the Class D fire, involves flammable metal. The NFPA does not consider Class D fires to be a basic type of fire because they are caused by a Class A, B, or C fire. Usually Class D fires involve magnesium in the shop, or in aircraft wheels and brakes, or are the result of improper welding operations.

At least one handheld, portable fire extinguisher must be available for use in the pilot compartment that is within easy access of the pilot while seated. At least one convenient handheld fire extinguisher must be in the passenger compartment of each airplane that can hold more than 6 and fewer than 30 passengers. Each extinguisher for use in a personnel compartment must be designed to minimize the hazard of toxic gas concentrations. The numbers of portable, handheld fire extinguishers that are required for transport aircraft are listed in Table 9-4-1.

Halogenated Hydrocarbon Extinguishers

For more than 45 years, halogenated hydrocarbons (Halons) have been practically the only fire extinguishing agents used in civil transport aircraft. However, Halon is an ozone-depleting and global warming chemical, and its production has been banned by international agreement. Although Halon use has been banned in some parts of the world, aviation has been granted an exemption because of its unique operational and fire

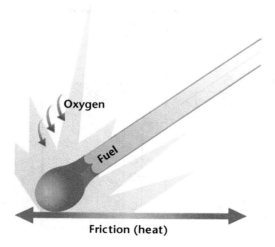

Figure 9-4-1. Three elements of fire.

Passenger capacity	Number of extinguishers
7 through 30	1
31 through 60	2
61 through 200	3
201 through 300	4
301 through 400	5
401 through 500	6
501 through 600	7
601 through 700	8

Table 9-4-1. Handheld fire extinguisher requirements for transport aircraft.

safety requirements. Halon has been the fire extinguishing agent of choice in civil aviation because it is extremely effective for its weight over a wide range of aircraft environmental conditions. It is a clean agent (no residue), electrically nonconducting, and has relatively low toxicity.

Two types of Halon are used in aviation: Halon 1301 ($CBrF_3$) a total flooding agent, and Halon 1211 ($CBrClF_2$) a streaming agent. Class A, B, and C fires are appropriately controlled with Halons. However, do not use Halons on a class D fire. Halon agents can react vigorously with the burning metal.

> NOTE: Although Halons are still in service and are appropriate agents for these classes of fires, production of these ozone-depleting agents has been restricted.

Inert Cold Gas Extinguishers

Carbon dioxide (CO_2) is an effective extinguishing agent. It is most often used in fire extinguishers that are available on the ramp to fight fires on the exterior of the aircraft, such as engine or auxiliary power unit (APU) fires. CO_2 has been used for many years to extinguish flammable fluid fires and fires involving electrical equipment. It is noncombustible and does not react with most substances. It provides its own pressure for discharge from the storage vessel, except in extremely cold climates where a booster charge of nitrogen can be added to winterize the system. Normally, CO_2 is a gas, but it is easily liquefied by compression and cooling. After liquification, CO_2 remains in a closed container as both liquid and gas. When CO_2 is then discharged to the atmosphere, most of the liquid expands to gas. Heat absorbed by the gas during vaporization cools the remaining liquid to –110°F, and it becomes a finely divided, white-solid, dry-ice snow.

CO_2 is about 1.5 times as heavy as air, which gives it the ability to replace air above burning surfaces and maintain a smothering atmosphere. CO_2 is effective as an extinguishing agent primarily because it dilutes the air and reduces the oxygen content so that combustion is no longer supported. Under certain conditions, some cooling effect is also realized. CO_2 is considered only mildly toxic, but it can cause unconsciousness and death by suffocation if the victim breathes it in fire-extinguishing concentrations for 20 to 30 minutes. CO_2 is not effective as an extinguishing agent on fires involving chemicals containing their own oxygen supply, such as cellulose nitrate (used in some aircraft paints). Also, fires involving magnesium and titanium cannot be extinguished by CO_2.

Dry Powder Extinguishers

Class A, B, and C fires can be controlled by dry chemical extinguishing agents. The only all-purpose (class A, B, C rating) dry chemical powder extinguishers contain monoammonium phosphate. All other dry chemical powders have a Class B, C U.S. Underwriter's Laboratory fire rating only. Dry powder chemical extinguishers best control class A, B, and C fires, but their use is limited because of the residue and cleanup that is required after it is used.

Water Extinguishers

Class A type fires are best controlled with water by cooling the material below its ignition temperature and soaking the material to prevent reignition.

Flight Deck and Cabin Interior Requirements

All materials used in the flight deck and cabin must conform to strict standards to prevent fire. In case of a fire, several types of portable fire extinguishers are available to fight the fire. The most common types are Halon 1211 and water.

Extinguisher Choices for Flight Deck and Cabin

Portable fire extinguishers are used to extinguish fires in the flight deck or cabin. Figure 9-4-2 shows a Halon fire extinguisher used in small aircraft. The Halon extinguishers are used on electrical and flammable liquid fires. Some transport aircraft also use water fire extinguisher for use on nonelectrical fires.

The following is a list of extinguishing agents and the type (class) fires for which each is appropriate.

- Water—class A. Water cools the material below its ignition temperature and soaks it to prevent reignition.

- CO_2—class B or C. CO_2 acts as a blanketing agent.

> NOTE: CO_2 is not recommended for handheld extinguishers for internal aircraft use.

Figure 9-4-2. A portable fire extinguisher.

- Dry chemicals—class A, B, or C. Dry chemicals are the best control agents for these types of fires.

- Halons—only class A, B, or C.

- Halocarbon clean agents—only class A, B, or C.

- Specialized dry powder—class D. Follow the extinguisher manufacturer's recommendations because of the possible chemical reaction between the burning metal and the extinguishing agent.

The following handheld extinguishers are not suitable as cabin or flight deck equipment.

- CO_2

- Dry chemicals, because of the potential for corrosion damage to electronic equipment, the possibility of visual obscuration if the agent were discharged into the flight deck area, and the cleanup problems from their use

- Specialized dry powder is suitable for use in ground operations

Installed Fire Protection Systems

Because fire is one of the most dangerous threats to an aircraft, the potential fire zones of larger aircraft are protected by a fixed fire protection system. The term *fixed* describes a permanently installed system, in contrast to any portable fire extinguishing equipment, such as a handheld Halon or a water fire extinguisher. A complete fire protection system includes a fire detection system and a fire extinguishing system (Figure 9-4-3).

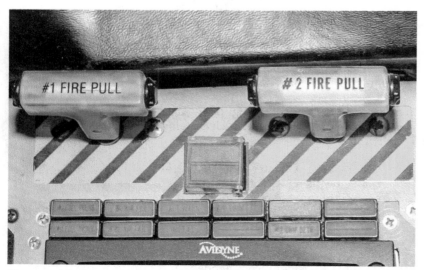

Figure 9-4-3. On some aircraft, pulling the fire handle shuts down the engine, closes the fuel supply line, and discharges the fire extinguisher.

In accordance with Title 14 of the *Code of Federal Regulations* (CFR) parts 23 and 25, engine fire protection systems are mandatory on multiengine, turbine-powered airplanes; multiengine, reciprocating-engine powered airplanes incorporating turbochargers; airplanes with engines that are not readily visible from the flight deck; all commuter and transport category airplanes; and the APU compartment of any airplane with an APU. Fire protection systems are not mandatory for many small aircraft with single and twin reciprocating-engines.

Fire Protection System Components

To detect fires or overheat conditions, detectors are placed in the various zones to be monitored. Fires are detected in aircraft by using one or more of the following: overheat detectors, rate-of temperature rise detectors, and flame detectors. In addition to these detectors, other types are used in aircraft fire protection systems but are not used to detect engine fires. For example, smoke detectors are better suited to monitor areas such as baggage compartments or lavatories, where materials burn slowly or smolder. Other types of detectors in this category include carbon monoxide detectors. Fire protection systems on current-production aircraft do not rely on observation by crewmembers as a primary method of fire detection. An ideal fire detector system includes as many of the following features as possible:

- Does not cause false warnings under any flight or ground condition.

- Rapid indication of a fire and accurate location of the fire.

- Accurate indication that a fire is out.

- Indication that a fire has reignited.

- Continuous indication for the duration of a fire.

- Means for electrically testing the detector system from the flight deck.

- Detectors that resist damage from exposure to oil, water, vibration, extreme temperatures, or handling.

- Detectors that are light and easily adaptable to any mounting position.

- Detector circuitry that operates directly from the aircraft power system without inverters.

- Minimum electrical current requirements when not indicating a fire.

- Turns on a flight deck light to indicate the location of the fire and provides an audible alarm.

- A separate detector system for each engine.

Engine Fire Detection Systems

A fire detection system should indicate the presence of a fire. Units of the system are installed where possibilities of a fire are greater. Several types of fire detection system are installed in aircraft to detect engine fires. Two common types used are spot detectors and continuous-loop systems. Spot detector systems use individual sensors to monitor a fire zone. Examples of spot detector systems are the thermal switch system, the thermocouple system, the optical fire detection system, and the pneumatic-based thermal fire detection system.

Thermal Switch Systems

A thermal switch system has one or more lights energized by the aircraft power system and thermal switches that control operation of the lights. These thermal switches are heat-sensitive units that complete electrical circuits at a certain temperature. They are connected in parallel with each other but in series with the indicator lights (Figure 9-4-4). If the temperature rises above a set value in any one section of the circuit, the thermal switch closes, completing the light circuit to indicate a fire or overheat condition. On some installations, all the thermal detectors are connected to one light; on others, a thermal switch might be used for each indicator light.

Some warning lights are push-to-test lights. The bulb is tested by pushing it in to check an auxiliary test circuit. The circuit shown in Figure 9-4-4 includes a test relay. With the relay contact in the position shown, current can flow in two possible paths from the switches to the light. This is an additional safety feature. Energizing the test relay completes a series circuit and checks all the wiring and the light bulb. Also included in the circuit shown in Figure 9-4-4 is a dimming relay. By energizing the dimming relay, the circuit is altered to include a resistor in series with the light. In some installations, several circuits are wired through the dimming relay, and all the warning lights can be dimmed at the same time.

Thermocouple Systems

The thermocouple fire warning system operates on an entirely different principle from the thermal switch system. A thermocouple depends on the rate of temperature rise and does not give a warning when an engine slowly overheats or a short circuit develops. The system consists of a relay box, warning lights, and thermocouples. The wiring system of these units can be divided into the following circuits:

- Detector circuit

- Alarm circuit

- Test circuit

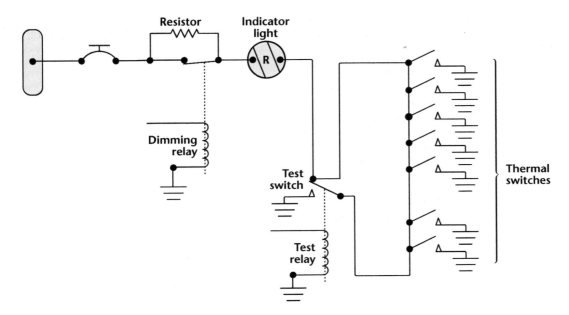

Figure 9-4-4. Thermal switch fire circuit.

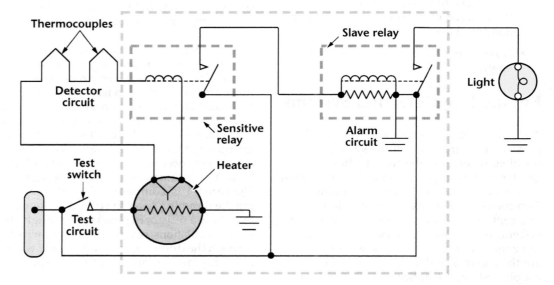

Figure 9-4-5. Thermocouple fire warning system.

These circuits are shown in Figure 9-4-5. The relay box contains two relays—the sensitive relay and the slave relay—and the thermal test unit. Such a box can contain from one to eight identical circuits, depending on the number of potential fire zones. The relays control the warning lights. In turn, the thermocouples control the operation of the relays. The circuit consists of several thermocouples in series with each other and with the sensitive relay.

The thermocouple is constructed of two dissimilar metals, such as chromel and constantan. The point at which these metals are joined and exposed to the heat of a fire is called a hot junction. It also has a reference junction enclosed in a dead air space between two insulation blocks. A metal cage surrounds the thermocouple to give mechanical protection and allow air to move freely to the hot junction.

If the temperature rises rapidly, the thermocouple produces a voltage due to the temperature difference between the reference junction and the hot junction. If both junctions are heated at the same rate, no voltage results. In the engine compartment, it is normal for the temperature to gradually rise from engine operation; because it is gradual, both junctions heat at the same rate and no warning signal is given. If a fire occurs, however, the hot junction heats more rapidly than the reference junction. The resulting voltage causes a current to flow in the detector circuit.

Continuous-Loop Systems

Continuous-loop systems are typically installed on transport type aircraft and provide more complete fire detection coverage by using several loop sensors. They are often used for powerplant and wheel well protection.

A continuous-loop detector or sensing system permits more complete coverage of a fire hazard area than any of the spot-type temperature detectors. Two widely used continuous-loop systems are the thermistor detectors, such as the Kidde and the Fenwal systems, and the pneumatic pressure detector, such as the Lindberg system. The Lindberg system is also known as Systron-Donner and, more recently, Meggitt Safety Systems.

Fenwal. The Fenwal system uses a slender Inconel tube packed with thermally sensitive eutectic salt and a nickel wire center conductor (Figure 9-4-6). Lengths of these sensing elements are connected in series to a control unit. The elements can be of equal or varying

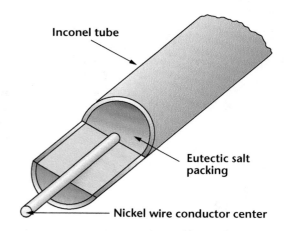

Figure 9-4-6. Fenwall sensing element.

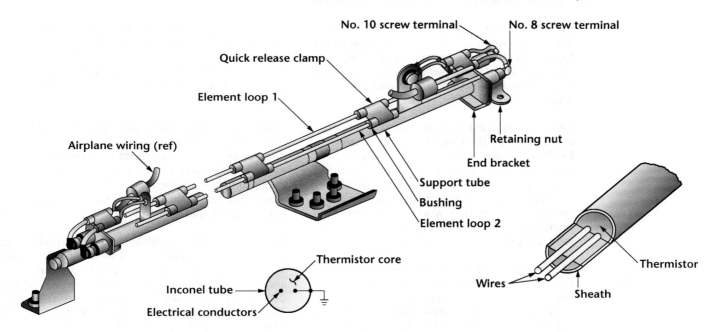

Figure 9-4-7. Kidde continuous-loop system.

length and of the same or different temperature settings.

The control unit, operating directly from the power source, impresses a small voltage on the sensing elements. When an overheat condition occurs at any point along the element length, the resistance of the eutectic salt in the sensing element drops sharply, causing current to flow between the outer sheath and the center conductor. The control unit senses this current flow and produces a signal to actuate the output relay and activate the alarms.

When the fire has been extinguished or the critical temperature lowered below the set point, the Fenwal system automatically returns to standby alert, ready to detect any subsequent fire or overheat condition. The Fenwal system can be wired to employ a loop circuit. In such a case, if an open circuit occurs, the system still signals fire or overheat. If multiple open circuits occur, only that section between breaks becomes inoperative.

Kidde. In the Kidde continuous-loop system, two wires are imbedded in an Inconel tube filled with a thermistor core material (Figure 9-4-7). Two electrical conductors go through the length of the core. One conductor has a ground connection to the tube, and the other conductor connects to the fire detection control unit. As the temperature of the core increases, electrical resistance to the ground decreases.

The fire detection control unit monitors this resistance. If the resistance decreases to the overheat setpoint, an overheat indication is given in the flight deck. Typically, a time delay is incorporated for the overheat indication. If the resistance decreases more to the fire setpoint, a fire warning is given. When the fire or overheat condition is gone, the resistance of the core material increases to the reset point and the flight deck indications disappear.

Pneumatic Single Point Systems

Some smaller turboprop aircraft are outfitted with pneumatic single point detectors. The design of these detectors is based on the principles of gas laws. The sensing element consists of a closed, helium-filled tube connected at one end to a responder assembly (Figure 9-4-8). As the element is heated, the gas pressure inside the tube increases until the alarm

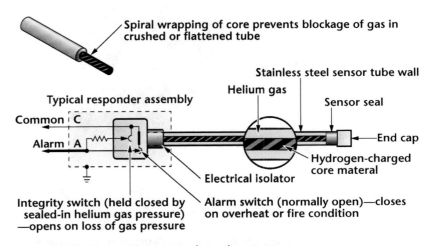

Figure 9-4-8. Pneumatic pressure loop detector system.

threshold is reached. At this point, an internal switch closes and triggers an alarm in the flight deck. Continuous fault monitoring is included. This type of sensor is designed as a single-sensor detection system and does not require a control unit.

The pneumatic continuous-loop systems are also known by their manufacturers' names Lindberg, Systron-Donner, and Meggitt Safety systems. These systems are used for engine fire detection of transport type aircraft and have the same function as the Kidde system; however, they work on a different principle. They are typically used in a dual-loop design to increase system reliability.

The pneumatic detector has two sensing functions. It responds to an overall average temperature threshold and to a localized discrete temperature increase caused by impinging flame or hot gases. Both the average and discrete temperature are factory set and are not field adjustable.

Smoke Detectors

A smoke detection system monitors the lavatories and cargo baggage compartments for smoke, which is indicative of a fire condition. Smoke detection instruments that collect air for sampling are mounted in the compartments in strategic locations (Figure 9-4-9). A smoke detection system is used where the

Figure 9-4-9. A smoke detector in the baggage compartment of a large aircraft.

type of fire anticipated is expected to generate a substantial amount of smoke before temperature changes are enough to actuate a heat detection system. Two common types of smoke detectors are light refraction and ionization.

Light refraction smoke detectors. The light refraction type of smoke detector contains a photoelectric cell that detects light refracted by smoke particles. Smoke particles refract the light to the photoelectric cell and, when it senses enough of this light, it creates an electrical current that sets off a light.

Ionization smoke detectors. Some aircraft use an ionization type smoke detector. The system generates an alarm signal (both horn and indicator) by detecting a change in ion density due to smoke in the monitored space. The system is connected to the aircraft's 28-volt direct current electrical power. Alarm output and sensor sensitive checks are performed simply with the test switch on the control panel.

Flame Detectors

Optical sensors, often referred to as flame detectors, are designed to trigger an alarm when they detect the presence of prominent, specific radiation emissions from hydrocarbon flames. The two types of optical sensors available are infrared (IR) (Figure 9-4-10) and ultraviolet (UV), based on the emission wavelengths that they are designed to detect. IR-based optical flame detectors are used primarily on light turboprop aircraft and helicopter engines. These sensors have proven to be very dependable and economical for these applications.

When radiation emitted by the fire crosses the airspace between the fire and the detector, it impinges on the detector front face and window. The window allows a broad spectrum of radiation to pass into the detector where it strikes the sensing device filter. The filter allows only radiation in a tight waveband centered on 4.3 micrometers in the IR band to pass on to the sensing device's radiation-sensitive surface. The radiation striking the sensing device minutely raises its temperature causing small thermoelectric voltages to be generated. These voltages are fed to an amplifier whose output is connected to various analytical electronic processing circuits. The processing electronics are tailored exactly to the time signature of all known hydrocarbon flame sources and ignores false alarm sources, such as incandescent lights and sunlight. Alarm sensitivity level is accurately controlled by a digital circuit.

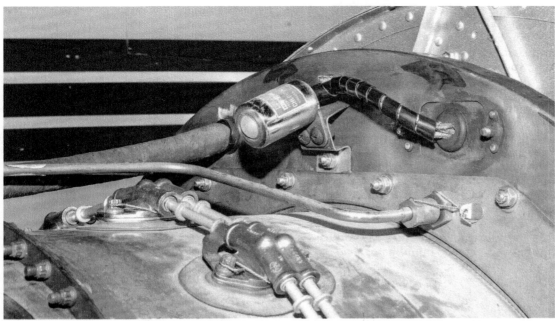

Figure 9-4-10. An infrared sensor is seen here installed on a Beechcraft Model E90.

Carbon Monoxide Detectors

Carbon monoxide is a colorless, odorless gas that is a by-product of incomplete combustion. For humans, its presence in the breathing air can be deadly. To ensure crew and passenger safety, carbon monoxide detectors are used in aircraft cabins and flight decks. They are most often found on reciprocating engine aircraft with exhaust shroud heaters and on aircraft equipped with a combustion heater. In turbine-powered aircraft, turbine bleed air, if used for heating the cabin, is obtained from the engine upstream of the combustion chamber. Therefore, no threat of carbon monoxide presence is posed.

Carbon monoxide gas is found in varying degrees in all smoke and fumes of burning carbonaceous substances. Exceedingly small amounts of the gas are dangerous if inhaled. A concentration of as little as 2 parts in 10,000 can produce headache, mental dullness, and physical lethargy in a few hours. Prolonged exposure or higher concentrations can cause death.

Several types of carbon monoxide detectors are made. Electronic detectors are common. Some are panel mounted and others are portable. Chemical color-change types are also common. These are mostly portable. Some are simple buttons, cards, or badges that have a chemical applied to the surface (Figure 9-4-11). Normally, the color of the chemical is tan. If carbon monoxide is present, the chemical darkens to gray or even black. The transition time required to change color is inversely related to the concentration of CO present. At 50 parts per million, the indication is apparent in 15 to 30 minutes. A concentration of 100 parts per million changes the color of the chemical in as little as 2 to 5 minutes. As concentration increases or duration of exposure is prolonged, the color evolves from gray to dark gray to black.

Installed Fire Extinguishing Systems

Transport aircraft have fixed fire extinguishing systems installed in these areas:

- Turbine engine compartments
- APU compartments
- Cargo and baggage compartments
- Lavatories

Figure 9-4-11. Carbon monoxide detector patch.

Older aircraft with reciprocating engines used CO_2 as an extinguishing agent, but all newer aircraft designs with turbine engines use a Halon or equivalent extinguishing agent, such as halocarbon clean agents.

The fixed, Halon fire extinguisher systems used in most engine and cargo compartment fire protection systems are designed to dilute the atmosphere with an inert agent that does not support combustion. Many systems use perforated tubing or discharge nozzles to distribute the extinguishing agent. HRD systems use open-end tubes to deliver extinguishing agent in 1 to 2 seconds.

Fire extinguisher containers (HRD bottles) (Figure 9-4-12) store a liquid halogenated extinguishing agent and pressurized gas (typically nitrogen). They are normally made of stainless steel. Depending on the design, alternate materials are used, including titanium. Containers are also available in a wide range of capacities. They are produced under the U.S. Department of Transportation specifications or exemptions. Most aircraft containers are spherical, which are lightest; however, cylinders are available for where space is limited. Each container incorporates a temperature- or pressure-sensitive safety

relief diaphragm that prevents pressure from exceeding container test pressure if exposed to excessive temperatures.

This system uses discharge indicators to provide immediate visual evidence that the container discharged its contents. Two kinds of indicators can be used: thermal and discharge. Both types are designed for aircraft and skin mounting and can easily be checked in the preflight inspection.

The thermal discharge indicator is connected to the fire container relief fitting and ejects a red disk to show when container contents have dumped overboard because of excessive heat. The agent discharges through the opening left when the disk blows out. This gives the flight and maintenance crews an indication that the fire extinguisher container needs to be replaced before the next flight.

If the flight crew activates the fire extinguisher system, a yellow disk is ejected from the skin of the aircraft fuselage. This is an indication for the maintenance crew that the flight crew activated the fire extinguishing system, and the fire extinguishing container needs to be replaced before the next flight.

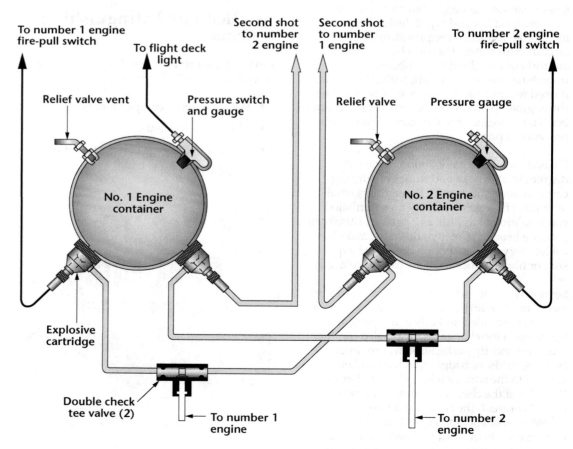

Figure 9-4-12. Diagram of fire extinguisher containers (HRD bottles).

Cargo and Baggage Compartment Fire Detection and Extinguishing System

The cargo compartment smoke detection system gives warnings in the flight deck if smoke is present in a cargo compartment. Each compartment is equipped with a smoke detector, and the smoke detector monitors the air for smoke.

The cargo compartment extinguishing system is activated by the flight crew if the smoke detectors detect smoke there. Some aircraft are equipped with two types of fire extinguisher containers. The first is the dump system that releases the extinguishing agent directly when the cargo fire discharge switch is activated. This action extinguishes the fire.

The second system is the metered system. After a time-delay, the metered bottles discharge slowly and at a controlled rate through the filter regulator. Halon from the metered bottles replaces the extinguishing agent leakage. This keeps the correct concentration of extinguishing agent in the cargo compartment to keep the fire extinguished for 180 minutes.

The fire extinguishing bottles contain Halon 1301 or equivalent fire extinguishing agent pressurized with nitrogen. Tubing connects the bottles to discharge nozzles in the cargo compartment ceilings.

Lavatory Smoke Detectors

Airplanes that have a passenger capacity of 20 or more are equipped with a smoke detector system that monitors the lavatories for smoke. Smoke indications provide a warning light in the flight deck or provide a warning light or audible warning at the lavatory and at flight attendant stations that are readily detected by a flight attendant. Each lavatory must have a built-in fire extinguisher that discharges automatically. The smoke detector is in the ceiling of the lavatory. The details of this installation are shown in Figure 9-4-13.

Lavatory Fire Extinguisher System

The lavatory compartment is outfitted with a fire extinguisher bottle to extinguish fires in the waste compartment (Figure 9-4-14). The fire extinguisher is a bottle with two nozzles. The bottle contains pressurized Halon 1301 or equivalent fire extinguishing agent. When the temperature in the waste compartment reaches about 170°F, the solder that seals the nozzles melts and the Halon is discharged. Weighing the bottle is often the only way to determine if it is empty or full.

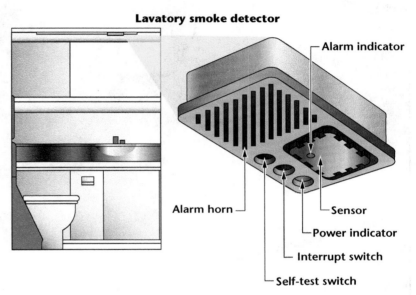

Figure 9-4-13. Lavatory smoke detector.

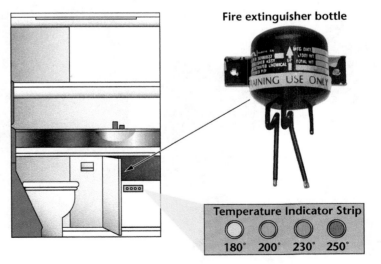

Figure 9-4-14. Lavatory fire extinguisher bottle.

10
Aircraft Powerplants Overview

Section 1

Propulsion/Powerplant

All aircraft require a means of propulsion. Propulsion means to push or drive an object forward. A propulsion system is a device that produces thrust to push an object forward. Thrust is generated by applying Newton's second and third laws of motion. A gas, or working fluid, is accelerated by an engine or propeller that produces a force referred to as thrust. The reaction to the force (thrust) results in the engine and aircraft moving forward.

The source of propulsion for an aircraft is referred to as a *powerplant*. The Federal Aviation Administration (FAA) defines an aircraft powerplant as "the engine, propeller, and the components to make the engine operate."

Aircraft require thrust to produce enough speed for the wings to provide lift or enough thrust to overcome the aircraft's weight for vertical takeoff. For an aircraft to remain in level flight, thrust must be provided that is equal to and in the opposite direction of the aircraft drag (Figure 10-1-1).

For acceleration, thrust must exceed the aircraft's drag. The greater the difference between the thrust and the drag, called the excess thrust, the faster the airplane accelerates (Figure 10-1-2). If drag exceeds thrust, the airplane slows down.

This thrust, or propulsive force, is provided by a suitable type of aircraft heat engine. Heat engines convert a fuel's chemical energy into heat energy, and then convert the heat energy into mechanical energy.

Left: From the largest jet transports to the smallest piston-powered aircraft, a safe, reliable, powerplant is a necessity.

Figures 10-1-1 through 10-1-4

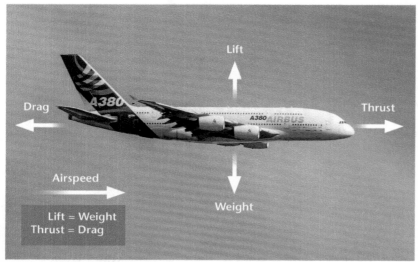

Figure 10-1-1. An aircraft flies at constant airspeed when thrust and drag are equal.

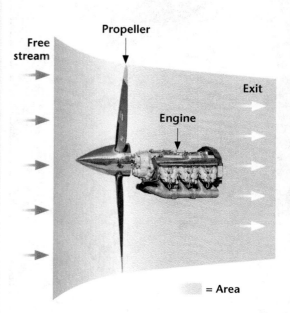

Figure 10-1-3. Many small airplanes are powered by engines that turn a propeller to accelerate a mass of air to generate thrust.

Figure 10-1-2. An aircraft accelerates when thrust exceeds drag.

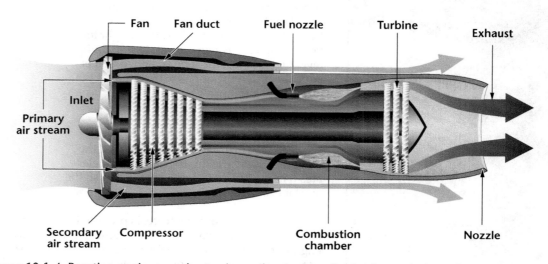

Figure 10-1-4. Reaction engines accelerate air or other working fluid as it travels through the engine to generate thrust.

Engines vary in how they generate thrust. Shaft engines generate thrust by turning a propeller, which accelerates a mass of air to produce thrust (Figure 10-1-3). Reaction engines directly generate thrust by accelerating a mass of air through the engine (Figure 10-1-4). In engines with propellers and reaction engines, both generate thrust by accelerating a mass of air. This concept is demonstrated in Newton's second law of motion, which is expressed as

Force = Mass × Acceleration

By accelerating a mass of air, either with a propeller or by passing through a reaction engine, a force referred to as *thrust* is generated.

Newton's third law of motion states that "for every action there is an equal and opposite reaction." When a propeller or thrust-producing engine is providing enough thrust (force) to overcome drag, the engine and aircraft moves in the opposite direction; therefore, if the engine accelerates a mass of air (action), it applies a force on the aircraft (reaction) (Figure 10-1-5).

Section 2

History

The first practical engines developed were steam engines. The first steam engine to do actual work was invented in 1698; it was developed to pump water out of flooded mines. Steam engine refinements were made by James Watt in 1769. These engines worked by introducing steam into a cylinder and then cooling it, causing the steam to condense. This created a rapid decrease in the volume of gas present and thus caused a piston to move. Watt's improvement, condensing the steam outside the working cylinder, was so efficient that he is often credited with inventing the steam engine. His work brought on the Industrial Revolution. Factories and mills no longer had to be at a source of water power, and the way was opened to create self-propelled vehicles.

By 1840, steam power was in regular use in steam coaches, railroads, and steamboats. Experimental aircraft using steam engines to turn large fans for propulsion appeared as early as 1882. Using steam engines for aircraft was not very practical, however, because steam engines were heavy and required both fuel and water.

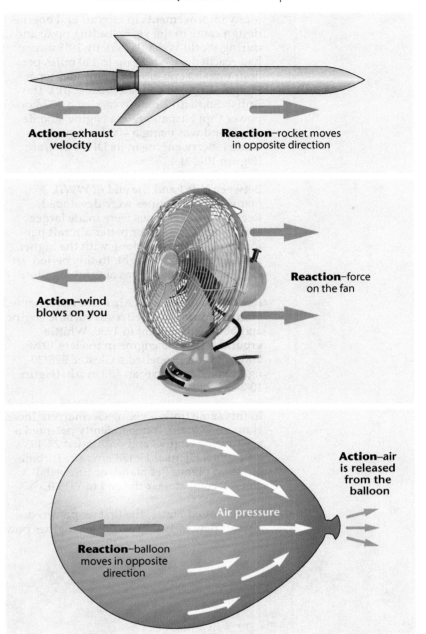

Figure 10-1-5. Examples of an action resulting in an equal and opposite reaction.

From 1860 to 1900, several people developed a variety of reciprocating piston engines that burned fuel in cylinders. In Germany in 1876, Nikolaus Otto patented the Otto cycle four-stroke engine consisting of intake, compression, ignition, and exhaust. Most cars and small aircraft still use the Otto cycle today. Gottlieb Daimler invented what most consider to be the first modern gasoline engine with vertical cylinders and a carburetor, which he patented in 1887.

Wilbur and Orville Wright along with their mechanic, Charlie Taylor, built a lightweight engine and propeller used for their historic first flight on December 17, 1903.

Many improvements in aircraft and engine design came in the years leading up to and during World War I (WWI). By 1918 aircraft had reached speeds of up to 140 miles per hour (m.p.h.) and effective altitudes (operating ceilings) of over 20,000 feet (ft.). The British Sopwith Dolphin carried a 300-horsepower (hp) Hispano-Suiza engine, and de Havilland was using a 400-hp American-made Liberty engine in its DH–4 aircraft (Figure 10-2-1)

Between WWI and the end of WWII, many aircraft engines were developed. Reciprocating engines were made larger and more powerful for better aircraft performance. However, along with the higher power came more weight. In this period, jet engine development was also taking place.

In 1928 a young Royal Air Force cadet named Frank Whittle designed a gas turbine engine and obtained a patent in 1930. Whittle ground tested his engine in the late 1930s, and in 1941 it propelled a Gloster E28/39 fighter plane faster than 400 m.p.h. (Figure 10-2-2).

In this same time, a young German engineer, Hans von Ohain, independently patented a gas turbine engine, and on August 27, 1939, it flew in a Heinkel He178 aircraft. Turbine-powered planes (jet planes or turbojets) entered combat near the end of WWII.

In the United States, the first jet-powered aircraft flew in 1942. Two GE jet engines pow-

Figure 10-2-2. The Whittle Supercharger Type W1, which powered the Gloster E28/39 on its maiden flight.

ered the Bell XP-59A aircraft. The GE engine was based on Whittle's engine.

After the war, turbine engine development greatly accelerated because they had many advantages over reciprocating engines, including better power-to-weight ratios and were not limited by the inefficiencies of a propeller at high speed. Turbine engines for commercial use were developed. The first turboprop airline service began in 1948. The first turbojet powered aircraft began airline service in 1952 with the de Havilland Comet. Soon, turbine powered engines became the engine of choice for larger commercial aircraft, with reciprocating engines mostly used for smaller aircraft operated at low speeds.

Section 3

Engine Design Requirements

All aircraft engines must meet certain general requirements of efficiency, economy, and reliability. Besides being economical in fuel consumption, an aircraft engine must be economical in the cost of original procurement and the cost of maintenance; it must also meet exacting requirements of efficiency and low weight-to-horsepower ratio. It must be

Figure 10-2-1. A de Havilland DH-4.

Courtesy of USAF

capable of sustained high-power output with no sacrifice in reliability; it must also have the durability to operate for long periods between overhauls. It needs to be as compact as possible, yet have easy accessibility for maintenance. It must be as vibration free as possible and able to provide a wide range of power output at various speeds and altitudes.

Weight

If a manufacturer can decrease an engine's weight and keep its power output the same, the useful load that an aircraft can carry and the aircraft's performance, obviously, are increased. Every excess pound of weight carried by an aircraft engine reduces its performance. Tremendous reductions in engine weight through improved design and metallurgy have resulted in reciprocating engines with a much-improved power-to-weight ratio.

Fuel Economy

The basic parameter for describing the fuel economy of aircraft engines is usually specific fuel consumption. Specific fuel consumption is based on how much fuel an engine uses compared to the amount of power the engine produces.

Reliability

An aircraft engine is reliable when it can perform at the specified ratings in widely varying flight attitudes and in extreme weather conditions. Standards of powerplant reliability are agreed on by the FAA, the engine manufacturer, and the airframe manufacturer. The engine manufacturer ensures the engine's reliability by design, research, and testing. Close control of manufacturing and assembly procedures is maintained, and each engine is tested before it leaves the factory.

Durability

Durability is the amount of engine life obtained while maintaining the desired reliability. Reliability and durability are built into the engine by the manufacturer, but the engine's continued reliability is determined by the maintenance, overhaul, and operating personnel. Careful maintenance and overhaul methods, thorough sheduled and preflight inspections, and strict observance of the operating limits established by the engine manufacturer make engine failure a rare occurrence.

Operating Flexibility

Operating flexibility is an engine's ability to run smoothly and give desired performance at all speeds from idle to full-power. The aircraft engine must also function efficiently through all the variations in atmospheric conditions encountered in widespread operations.

Compactness

For proper streamlining and balancing of an aircraft, the engine's shape and size must be as compact as possible. In single-engine aircraft, the shape and size of the engine also affect the pilot's forward view. A smaller engine is better from this standpoint, and it reduces the drag created by a large frontal area.

Weight limitations, naturally, are closely related to the compactness requirement. The more elongated and spread out an engine is, the more difficult it becomes to keep the weight within the allowable limits.

Section 4

Types of Engines

Aircraft engines can be classified in several ways: operating cycles, cylinder arrangement, or the method of thrust production. All are heat engines that convert fuel into heat energy that is converted to mechanical energy to produce thrust. Almost all aircraft engines are of the internal combustion type because the combustion process takes place inside the engine.

As discussed, aircraft engines need to generate thrust. This can be done by turning a propeller or directly produced by the engine. Shaft engines are torque producing engines that spin a propeller, accelerating a mass of air, generating thrust. Reaction engines accelerate an air mass inside the engine to generate thrust.

Shaft Engines

Reciprocating

A reciprocating engine, also known as a piston engine, is an engine in which the up-and-down or back-and-forth motion of one or more pistons is transformed into a

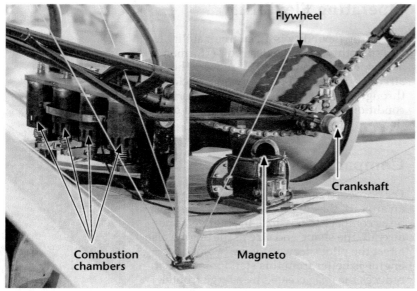

Figure 10-4-1. The reciprocating engine developed by Charles Taylor, the Wright brothers' mechanic.

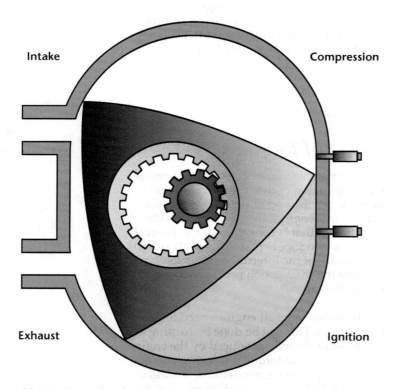

Figure 10-4-2. Example of a Wankel engine.

Figure 10-4-3. Example of a turboprop engine.

rotary motion by a crankshaft. A propeller is turned by attaching it to the crankshaft. Such an engine (Figure 10-4-1) powered the first, heavier than air, self-propelled, maneuverable, piloted aircraft—the 1903 Wright Flyer.

Aircraft reciprocating engines are similar to most auto engines. The combustion process takes place in an enclosed cylinder where chemical energy is converted to mechanical energy. Inside the cylinder is a moving piston that compresses a mixture of fuel and air before combustion and is then forced back down the cylinder after combustion. The piston turns a crankshaft, which turns the aircraft propeller. The piston's motion is repeated in a thermodynamic cycle called the Otto cycle.

Wankel

Wankel engines also convert pressure developed inside the engine to rotary motion that turns an output shaft. Instead of using pistons, these engines use eccentric rotors (Figure 10-4-2).

Turboprop

The turboprop engine is a gas turbine (jet) engine that turns a propeller through a speed-reduction gear box (Figure 10-4-3). This type of engine is most efficient in the 300 m.p.h. to 400 m.p.h. speed range and can use shorter runways than other aircraft.

Turboshaft

Similar to a turboprop is the turboshaft (jet) engine. Instead of driving a propeller, the shaft is used to power such things as helicopters, tanks, train engines, and even race cars. Turboshaft engines are frequently used in aircraft to turn a helicopter rotors; they are also used as an auxiliary power unit (APU). APUs are used on aircraft to provide electrical power and bleed air on the ground and a backup generator in flight. Turboshaft engines can come in many different styles, shapes, and horsepower ranges.

Reaction Engines

Turbojet

The term *turbojet* was originally used to describe any gas turbine engine used in aircraft. As gas turbine technology evolved, these other engine types were developed to take the place of the pure turbojet engine (Figure 10-4-4). The turbojet engine has problems with noise and fuel consumption in the speed range that airliners fly (Mach 0.8). Because of these problems, pure turbojet engine use is very limited. Almost all transport category aircraft use a turbofan engine.

Turbofan

A turbofan is a modified version of a turbojet engine. Both share the same basic parts, however, the turbofan engine was developed to turn a fan or set of fans at the front of the engine (Figure 10-4-5). These fans are capable of producing a large percentage of the engine's thrust. Turbofan engines are also called bypass engines. They are quieter and have better fuel consumption in the speed range of most airliners.

Rocket

During and after WWII, several rocket-powered aircraft were built to explore high speed flight. The X-1A (Figure 10-4-6), used to break the sound barrier, and the X-15 were rocket-powered airplanes. In a rocket engine, fuel and a source of oxygen, called an oxidizer, are mixed and exploded in a combustion chamber. The combustion produces hot exhaust is passed through a nozzle to accelerate the flow and produce thrust.

Two main types of rocket engines are made: liquid rockets and solid rockets. In a liquid rocket (Figure 10-4-7), the propellants—the fuel and the oxidizer—are stored separately as liquids and are pumped into the combustion chamber of the nozzle where burning occurs. In a solid rocket, the propellants are mixed together and packed into a solid cylinder.

Turbine engines and propellers use air from the atmosphere as the working fluid, but rockets use the combustion exhaust gases. In outer space there is no atmosphere so turbines and propellers cannot work there. This explains why a rocket works in space but a turbine engine or a propeller does not work.

Figure 10-4-4. Example of a turbojet engine.

Figure 10-4-5. Example of a turbofan engine.

Figure 10-4-6. The X-1A in flight.

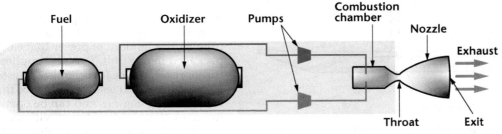

Figure 10-4-7. Example of a liquid rocket engine.

Ramjet

Rockets are a proven way to accelerate aircraft to very high speeds, but rockets must carry their own supply of oxidizer and fuel. Ramjets are designed to scoop up their oxygen from the atmosphere and eliminate this extra weight.

Ramjets produce thrust, like other reaction engines, by passing the hot exhaust from the combustion of a fuel through a nozzle (Figure 10-4-8). In a ramjet the high-pressure air used for combustion is produced by *ramming* external air into the combustor using the aircraft's forward speed. The combustion process in a ramjet occurs at subsonic speeds in the combustor. For an aircraft traveling supersonically, the air entering the engine must be slowed to subsonic speeds by shock waves generated in the aircraft inlet. Much above Mach 5, the performance losses from the shock waves become so great that the engine can no longer produce net thrust.

The downside is that ramjet engines can work only when the aircraft is already moving at a considerable speed. A ramjet produces little thrust below about half the speed of sound and works best when operating at low supersonic speeds.

Scramjet

In the 1960s an improved ramjet was proposed in which the combustion in the burner would occur supersonically. In the supersonic combustion ramjet, or scramjet, the losses associated with slowing the flow would be minimized and the engine could produce net thrust for a hypersonic aircraft. Because the scramjet uses external air for combustion, it is a more efficient propulsion system for flight in the atmosphere than a rocket, which must carry all of its oxygen. Scramjets are ideally suited for hypersonic flight in the atmosphere.

Like ramjets, scramjets can work only when the aircraft is already moving at a high speed.

Section 5
Selecting a Powerplant

For aircraft whose cruising speed does not exceed 250 m.p.h., the reciprocating engine is the usual powerplant choice. For this speed range, the conventional reciprocating engine is reliable and has a relatively low cost. When higher altitude performance is desired, a turbocharged reciprocating engine might be chosen because it can maintain rated power to a high altitude (above 30,000 ft.). Turbochargers are devices that can be installed on a reciprocating engine to increase performance.

In the cruising speed range of 180 m.p.h. to 350 m.p.h., turboprop engines perform very well. Turboprops develop more power per pound of weight than a reciprocating engine, thus allowing a greater fuel load or payload for engines of a given power.

Both reciprocating and turboprop engines require a propeller to produce thrust, which limits propulsive efficiency. As propeller tip speeds approach the speed of sound, shock waves develop, which causes a loss of performance. At airspeeds faster than 375 m.p.h., the propulsive efficiency of propellers drops very rapidly (Figure 10-5-1).

In the cruising speed range of 350 m.p.h. up to Mach 0.8–0.9, turbofan engines are generally chosen. One of the important advantages of jet propulsion systems is that because they do not need to use a propeller to generate thrust, they avoid the compressibility problem that limits the speed at which the propeller can be efficiently used. Thus, jet propulsion systems are more efficient a high airspeeds.

Another advantage of jet propulsion systems is the low weight per unit power and the tremendous amount of power that can be packaged in one unit. This also applies to turboprop engines. Jet propulsion systems also require much less maintenance than do reciprocating engines and can be operated for many thousands of hours without major overhaul. Engine failures are also relatively rare with jet propulsion systems.

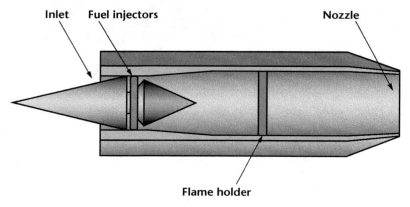

Inlet   **Fuel injectors**   **Nozzle**

Flame holder

Figure 10-4-8. A ramjet uses the aircraft's forward speed to compress the incoming air; therefore, it has few moving parts.

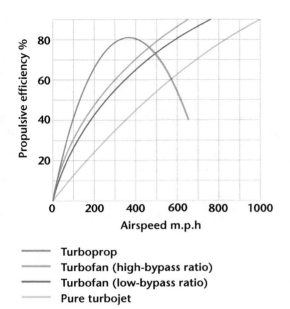

Figure 10-5-1. Propulsive efficiency of engines.

- Turboprop
- Turbofan (high-bypass ratio)
- Turbofan (low-bypass ratio)
- Pure turbojet

Section 6
Fuel and Oil

Fuel and oil are included here because they are common to both reciprocating and turbine powerplants. We discuss how they are made, their functions and properties, and the different types and how to identify them.

Petroleum Production

Petroleum is a naturally occurring hydrocarbon material that is believed to have formed from organic sources in deep sedimentary beds. It has been found seeping to the surface, and in deposits very deep in the earth. You can find petroleum deposits of some sort in nearly every area of the planet. People have been harvesting and using petroleum products for heat, light, and many other things for centuries.

Oil has been extracted from the ground in many ways. This includes harvesting from deposits open to the surface, to both shallow and deep wells. As early as 600 B.C. the Chinese were pumping oil from the ground and transporting it in pipelines made from bamboo. However, it was much later, and here in the United States, that large-scale production of petroleum products really got a start. Colonel Drake's heralded discovery of oil in Pennsylvania in 1859 and the Spindletop discovery in Texas in 1901 set the stage for widespread use of oil products.

The product that is extracted from the ground varies depending on the location and the depth from which it comes. Generally, it is all referred to as crude oil, which is a product containing various combinations of carbon and hydrogen atoms, along with some sulfur and metal content. The process of turning this crude oil into gasoline, jet fuel, motor oil, and other products is called *refining.*

Petroleum products are produced by distilling the crude oil. The crude oil is heated until it turns into a vapor. The vapor is then directed into a condensing unit known as a fractionating column. Various fractions condense and are collected at different temperatures that correspond to the height of collection in the distillation tower. For this reason, the process is known as fractional distillation (Figure 10-6-1).

Types of Fuel

Fuel is a substance that when combined with oxygen burns and produces heat. Fuels can be classified according to their physical state as solid, gaseous, or liquid. Liquid fuels, in many respects, are the ideal fuel for use in internal combustion engines. Aviation fuels are made up almost entirely of hydrocarbons—molecules consisting of hydrogen and carbon.

For the first few decades of flight, aircraft engines simply used the same kind of gasoline that powered automobiles. But simple gasoline was not necessarily the best fuel for the large, powerful engines used by piston-driven airplanes that were made in the 1930s and 1940s, and certainly not for the new gas turbine engines that were increasingly being made. Today, in general, two types of aviation fuel are used. Aviation gasoline, also known as AVGAS, is used in most reciprocating engine aircraft, and turbine fuel or jet fuel is used to power all types of gas turbine engines and reciprocating diesel engines.

AVGAS is used primarily in piston engine powered aircraft in the general aviation community. Activities such as personal travel, recreational flying, flight training, and agricultural application fall into this category. Piston engines operate using the same basic principles as automobile engine, but they have a much higher performance requirement. Except for a few recently certificated light-aircraft engines, auto fuel is not acceptable for aircraft use. However, some older, low-powered aircraft engines may also be operated on auto fuel if approved by a supplemental type certificate.

Fractionating column

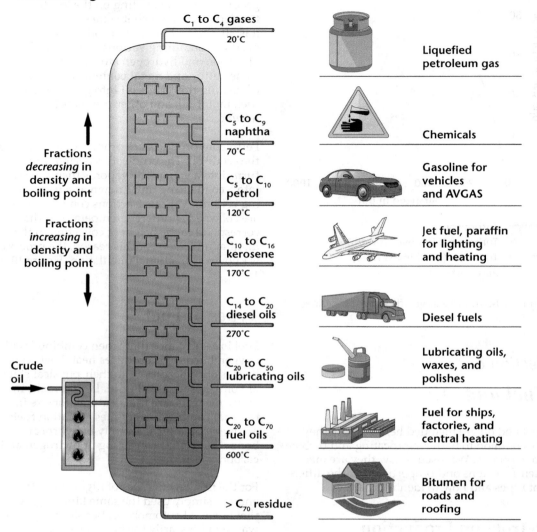

Figure 10-6-1. Fractional distillation yields many products from crude oil.

Jet fuel is used to power all types of gas turbine engines. Three types of turbine fuel generally used in civilian aviation are JET A and JET A-1, which are kerosene based, and JET B, a blend of jet fuel and AVGAS.

Most turbine engines are certified to run on both JET A and JET B, and some can operate with gasoline, usually for a limited time. Gasoline-powered reciprocating engines, however, cannot be run on jet fuel. Gasoline contaminated with jet fuel causes a decrease in the power developed by a piston engine and could cause damage to the engine and engine failure.

Identifying Fuels

Aircraft and engine manufacturers designate approved fuels for each aircraft and engine. Because several fuel types are made, it is

imperative that you positively identify fuel and never introduce it into a fuel system that is not designed for it. Dyes are added to fuel to help identify fuel type.

In the past, many grades of AVGAS were produced. However, with decreasing demand these have been reduced to one principle grade: 100LL.

Below are details of the various aviation fuels and the properties that define them. We have included types that are no longer in production but are likely to still be seen on fuel placards and in pilot's operating handbooks. Keep in mind that many of these fuels will not be available at your local airport. Most times, the only options will be 100LL and Jet A-1.

80/87 AVGAS. 80/87 AVGAS is no longer available. It was dyed red. Many supplemental type certificates have been issued for engine and engine/airframe combinations that permit using automobile gasoline in engines originally designed for 80/87 AVGAS.

82UL. A new fuel specification for 82UL (unleaded) was introduced in the late 1990s for use in relatively low-compression engines. Although, in practical terms, 82UL comes from basic unleaded automotive gasoline stock. Requirements and specifications distinguish it from unleaded auto gasoline. For example, adding alcohol is prohibited, as are deposit-control additives (an EPA requirement in auto gas); stability test requirements are more stringent; and the vapor pressure limits are different. It is dyed purple.

100 AVGAS. The 100 AVGAS has a high lead content and is dyed green.

100LL AVGAS. The grade of AVGAS most readily available and used in the United States is 100LL AVGAS. This is the low lead version of AVGAS 100. Low lead is a relative term. Up to 0.56 g/liter of lead is in 100LL AVGAS. The 100LL AVGAS is dyed blue.

115/145 AVGAS. A fuel designed for large, high-performance reciprocating engines from the World War II era is 115/145 AVGAS. It also is dyed purple.

Jet A, Jet A-1, and Jet B. Three basic turbine engine fuel types are available worldwide; although, some countries have their own unique fuels. The first is Jet A. It is the most common turbine engine fuel available in the continental United States. The second is Jet A-1, which is the most popular globally. Jet A-1 has a slightly lower freezing point than Jet A. Most engine operations manuals permit either Jet A or Jet A-1 to be used.

The third type of turbine engine fuel available is Jet B. It is a blend of jet fuel and gasoline. Jet B is primarily available in parts of the world that are consistently cold because of its low freezing point, and its higher volatility yields better cold-weather performance.

Fuel colors and labeling. All grades of jet fuel are colorless or straw colored. This distinguishes them from AVGAS of any kind that contains dye of some color. Compare fuel colors in Figure 10-6-2 in the fuel color column. If AVGAS fuel is not a recognizable color, the cause should be investigated. Some color change might not affect the fuel. Other times, a color change can be a signal that fuels have been mixed or contaminated in some way.

Identifying fuel and ensuring that the correct fuel is delivered into storage tanks, fuel trucks, and aircraft fuel tanks is a process aided by color-coded labeling on the fueling equipment. Decals and markings with the same colors as the AVGAS colors are used. AVGAS is identified by name in white letters on a red background. In contrast, turbine engine fuels are identified by white letters on a black background. Delivery trucks and hoses are marked, as are aircraft tank fuel caps and fill areas. Jet fuel fill hose nozzles are made too large to fit into an AVGAS tank fill opening. Figure 10-6-2 shows examples of color-coded fuel labeling.

Fuel Properties

A fuel's properties such as the energy content, octane rating, and volatility make the fuel suitable or unsuitable for use in an aircraft. Using an improper fuel and allowing contamination in the fuel can damage an engine. Therefore, it is worth understanding these properties.

Energy Content (BTUs)

The energy content and combustion quality are key performance properties of the fuel used in any engine. An aircraft engine generates power by converting a fuel's stored chemical energy (potential energy) into a combination of mechanical energy and heat energy. Because space on an aircraft is at a premium, the amount of energy contained in fuel is very important.

The *energy content* of a fuel sample can be measured in the lab. It is the heat released (also called the heat of combustion) when a known quantity of fuel is burned under specific conditions. As mentioned, aviation gasoline has potential energy because of its chemical nature. Several units of measurement can be used to measure this potential energy, but in aviation the common unit used to is based on a British thermal unit (BTU).

One BTU is defined as the amount of heat required to change the temperature of 1 lb. of water 1 degree Fahrenheit (1°F).

Energy content can be expressed either gravimetrically (energy per unit mass of fuel) or volumetrically (energy per unit volume of fuel).

Generally, less dense fuels have a higher gravimetric energy content, and more dense jet fuels have a higher volumetric energy content. This effect is more pronounced when

Fuel type and grade	Color of fuel	Equipment control color	Pipe banding and marketing	Refueler decal
AVGAS 82UL	Purple	 82UL AVGAS	 AVGAS 82UL	 82UL AVGAS
AVGAS 100	Green	 100 AVGAS	 AVGAS 100	 100 AVGAS
AVGAS 100LL	Blue	 100LL AVGAS	 AVGAS 100LL	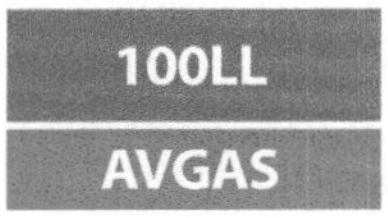 100LL AVGAS
Jet A	Colorless or straw	 JET A	 JET A	 JET A
Jet A-1	Colorless or straw	 JET A-1	 JET A-1	 JET A-1
Jet B	Colorless or straw	 JET B	 JET B	 JET B

Figure 10-6-2. Color-coded labeling and markings used on fueling equipment.

comparing the types of fuel, such as the typical values of AVGAS and jet fuel BTUs (Table 10-6-1).

Octane Rating

AVGAS is identified by an octane number (grade). The grade designates a fuel's resistance to detonation. Detonation is when a fuel explodes inside a reciprocating engine, as opposed to the normal controlled burning (more information about detonation, is in chapter 11). Detonation results in reduced engine power, high engine temperatures, and possible engine damage. The higher the grade, the greater the fuel's resistance to detonation. A referencing system is used to rate the fuel.

Traditionally, aviation grades were often expressed using two numbers such as 80/87, 100/130, or 115/145. The two numbers indicate the lean mixture octane and rich mixture octane numbers of a specific fuel. In other words, with 80/87 AVGAS, the 80 is the lean

mixture octane rating and 87 is the rich mixture octane rating. To avoid confusing types of AVGAS, it is generally identified using only the lean mixture rating number, as grade 80, 100, 100LL, or 115.

Additives can be used to increase a fuel's antidetonation characteristics. Tetraethyl lead (TEL) is added to AVGAS to increase the octane rating. Adding a small amount of TEL to a gallon of gasoline increases the fuel's octane number and its anitdetonation characteristics.

Because of the small size of the worldwide AVGAS market, 100LL AVGAS is the reciprocating engine fuel most readily available and used in the United States. 100LL has the same antidetonation characteristics as 100 octane, but it contains less lead (hence the LL designation for *low lead*. To ensure that the correct aviation grade is being used for the type of engine, exercise care. The proper fuel grade is stated in the aircraft flight manual, pilot's operating handbook, on placards in the flight deck, and next to the filler caps. Using the proper fuel is critical; never use unapproved fuel.

Although lead is an economical way to increase a fuel's octane rating, it is detrimental to human health and the environment. Leaded fuel contributes to air, water, and soil pollution. Lead dust can remain in the environment indefinitely. Lead is a known health hazard for humans (lead poisoning). In the United States, lead has been banned in automobiles since the mid-1990s. For environmental purposes, unleaded AVGAS with no TEL is sought for the aviation fleet of the future.

Volatility

One of the most important characteristics of an aircraft fuel is its volatility. Volatility describes how readily a substance changes from liquid into a vapor. Fuel with high volatility vaporizes at relatively low temperatures. Higher temperatures are required for low volatility fuel to vaporize.

For reciprocating engines, highly volatile fuel is desired. Liquid gasoline delivered to the engine must vaporize and mix with oxygen to burn in the engine. Fuel with low volatility vaporizes slowly. This can cause hard engine starting, slow warmup, and poor acceleration. However, fuel can also be too volatile, causing detonation and vapor lock. Vapor lock is a condition in which a liquid fuel vaporizes in the fuel line or other fuel system components. Vapor lock prevents the proper fuel amount from reaching the engine by restricting or completely blocking flow, resulting in loss of engine power and possible engine shutdown.

Jet fuel is much less volatile than AVGAS. If a few drops of AVGAS are placed on a surface,

they evaporate quickly. In comparison, jet fuel is much slower to evaporate. Although it is desirable to use a fuel that is low in volatility to resist vapor lock and evaporation while it is in the aircraft's fuel tanks, turbine engine aircraft operate in cold environments, making in flight starts more difficult. Turbine engines must start readily and be able to restart while in flight. Fuel with high volatility makes this easier.

AVGAS has a relatively low volatility compared to automotive gasoline. Jet A has a much lower volatility than AVGAS. Jet B volatility, a blend of Jet A and gasoline, is more volatile than Jet A, but less so than AVGAS.

Contamination

Checking for water and other sediment contamination is a key preflight task. Water tends to accumulate in fuel tanks from condensation, especially in partially filled tanks. Because water is heavier than fuel, it collects in the low points of the fuel system. Water can also be introduced into the fuel system from deteriorated gas cap seals exposed to rain, or from the supplier's storage tanks and delivery vehicles. Sediment contamination can arise from dust and dirt entering the tanks during refueling or from deteriorating rubber seals or tank sealant. The presence of water is more prominent in jet fuel, which has different molecular structure and retains water in two principal ways. Some water is dissolved into the fuel. Other water also is entrained in the fuel, which is more viscous than AVGAS. The greater presence of water in jet fuel allows microbes to assemble, grow, and live in the fuel.

During preflight and after refueling, each fuel tank sump should be drained from all sump drains into a transparent container. Check

Fuel	Typical density at 60°F (15°C)		Typical energy content	
			Gravimetric	Volumetric
	g/mL	lb./U.S. gal	BTU/lb.	BTU/gal
Aviation gasoline (AVGAS)	0.715	5.97	18,800	112,500
Jet fuel				
Jet B	0.762	6.36	18,720	119,000
Jet A	0.810	6.76	18,610	125,800

Table 10-6-1. Typical fuel energy content vs. density.

for fuel grade/color, water, dirt, and smell (Figure 10-6-3). Water is the principal fuel contaminant. Suspended water droplets in the fuel can be identified by a cloudy appearance or by the clear separation of water from the colored fuel, which occurs after the water has settled to the bottom of the tank. In extreme cases, do not overlook the possibility that the entire sample, especially a small sample, is water. If water is found in the first fuel sample, take further samples until no water appears.

Lubrication and Friction

A lubricant's primary purpose is to reduce friction between moving parts. Because liquid lubricants or oils can be circulated readily, they are used universally in aircraft engines. In theory, fluid lubrication is based on the actual separation of the surfaces so that no metal-to-metal contact occurs. If the oil film remains unbroken, metallic friction is replaced by the lubricant's internal fluid friction. Under ideal conditions, friction and wear are held to a minimum. Oil is generally pumped throughout the engine to all areas that require lubrication. Overcoming the friction of the engine's moving parts consumes energy and creates unwanted heat. Reducing friction in engine operation increases the overall potential power output. Engines are subjected to several types of friction.

Friction can be defined as rubbing one object or surface against another. One surface sliding over another surface causes sliding friction, as found in using plain bearings. The surfaces are not completely flat or smooth and have microscopic defects that cause friction between the two moving surfaces. Rolling friction is created when a

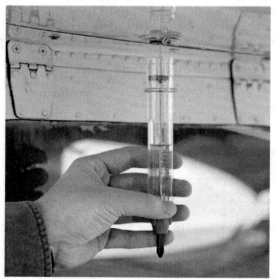

Figure 10-6-3. Checking for fuel grade/color, water, dirt, or other contamination.
Courtesy of Sporty's Pilot Shop

roller or sphere rolls over another surface, such as with ball or roller bearings, also referred to as antifriction bearings. The amount of friction created by rolling friction is less than that created by sliding friction, and this bearing uses an outer race and an inner race with balls, or steel spheres, rolling between the moving parts or races. Another type of friction is wiping friction, which occurs between gear teeth. With this type of friction, pressure can vary widely, and loads applied to the gears can be extreme, so the lubricant must be able to withstand the loads.

Functions of Oil

In addition to reducing friction, the oil film acts as a cushion between metal parts. This cushioning effect is especially important for such parts as reciprocating engine crankshafts and connecting rods, which are subject to shock loading. As the piston is pushed down on the power stroke, it applies loads between the connecting rod bearing and the crankshaft journal. The load-bearing qualities of the oil must prevent the oil film from being squeezed out, causing metal-to-metal contact in the bearing.

As oil circulates through the engine, it absorbs heat from the pistons and cylinder walls. In reciprocating engines, these components are especially dependent on the oil for cooling. Oil cooling can account for up to 50 percent of the total engine cooling and is an excellent medium to transfer the heat from the engine to the oil cooler. Oil also helps form a seal between the piston and the cylinder wall to prevent gases from leaking from the combustion chamber.

Oils clean the engine by reducing abrasive wear by picking up foreign particles and carrying them to a filter where they are removed. The dispersant, an additive, in the oil holds the particles in suspension and allows the filter to trap them as the oil passes through the filter.

The oil also works to prevent corrosion on the interior of the engine by leaving a coating of oil on parts when the engine is shut down. This is one of the reasons why the engine should not be shut down for long times. The oil coating preventing corrosion does not last on the parts, allowing them to rust or corrode. Unless they have been treated with special products designed for long-term storage, engines should be started and run occasionally, even if the aircraft is not flown.

Viscosity

A satisfactory reciprocating engine oil must have several important properties, but its viscosity is most important in engine operation. The oil's resistance to flow is known as its viscosity. Oil that flows slowly is viscous or has a high viscosity; if it flows freely, it has a low viscosity. Unfortunately, the oil viscosity is affected by temperature. It was somewhat common for earlier grades of oil to become practically solid in cold weather, increasing drag and making circulation almost impossible. Other oils can become so thin at high temperatures that the oil film is broken, reducing its load-carrying ability and resulting in rapid wear of the moving parts.

The oil selected for aircraft engine lubrication must be light enough to circulate freely at cold temperatures, yet heavy enough to provide the proper oil film at engine operating temperatures. Because lubricants vary in properties and because no one oil is satisfactory for all engines and all operating conditions, it is extremely important that only the approved grade be used.

When determining the proper grade of oil to use in an engine, manufacturers must consider several factors. The most important of these are the operating load, rotational speeds, and operating temperatures. The grade of the lubricating oil to be used is determined by the operating conditions to be met in the various types of engines. The oil used in aircraft reciprocating engines has a relatively high viscosity required by the following:

- Large engine operating clearances due to the relatively large size of the moving parts, the different materials used, and the different expansion rates of the various materials

- High operating temperatures

- High bearing pressures

Viscosity classification or grade. Several methods are used to express or designate reciprocating engine oil viscosity. Generally, commercial aviation oils are classified by a number (such as 65, 80, 100, 120, 140). Also, an SAE grade or an Army and Navy Specification number could be used to designate viscosity. The lower numbers designate low viscosity or less resistance to flow; the higher numbers are high-viscosity oils with more resistance to flow. The correlation among these grade numbering systems is shown in Table 10-6-2.

Types of Oil

A single-grade (monograde) oil is a lubricant with one viscosity grade. Single-grade oils are sometimes considered to be better in warmer climates. They function well in these locations but cannot provide the flow needed for cold-weather startups without using a heated

Commercial aviation no.	Commercial SAE no.	Army and Navy spec no.
65	30	1065
80	40	1080
100	50	1100
120	60	1120
140	70	

Table 10-6-2. Grade designations for aviation oil.

hangar or engine preheaters. These oils are labled with single-grade designations (SAE 40 or Aviation 80).

Multigrade oils are primarily designed for all-season operation. They meet the requirements of more than one SAE viscosity grade classification and are, therefore, more suitable for use over a wider temperature range than single-grade oil. Multigrade oils contain additives that reduce the oil's tendency to lose viscosity or thin out at different temperatures. These oils are labled with two grade designations (SAE 20W-40).

Straight mineral oil is usually recommended by manufacturers for the break-in period on new or newly overhauled engines. This allows faster piston ring seating that leads to better oil loss control.

Ashless dispersant (AD) oils are commonly used in aircraft engines after the break-in period. They are available in both multigrade and single-grade versions. Oil requrements vary by manufacurer and engine model. In all cases, refer to the manufacturers' information when determining proper oil type to use.

Many additives are used in engine oil to help improve characteristics and performance. One such additive used in AD oils is a *dispersant* designed to minimize deposit formation. The dispersants help the oil suspend combustion by-products, keeping them dispersed until trapped in the filter or until the oil is drained. This helps prevent contaminants from forming sludge buildup that could plug oil passageways. Straight minerail oils contain no dispersant additives.

Synthetic oils are polyalphaolefins produced from chemical synthesis rather than from refining petroleum oils. In the manufacturing process, molecules are made to a uniform size and structure. Depening on the application, synthetic oil provides better lubricating properties, are more stable than mineral-based oils.

Some synthetic blend oils (part synthetic oil and part mineral oil) are available for use in aircraft reciprocating engines. Almost all turbine engines use synthetic oil.

11

Reciprocating Engines

Aircraft reciprocating engines are a type of internal combustion engine. Many types of aircraft reciprocating engines have been designed over the years; however, manufacturers have developed some designs that are more commonly used than others. Reciprocating engines are often referred to as *piston engines* because the reciprocating motion, or up-and-down motion of one or more pistons is transformed into the rotary motion by a crankshaft.

Combustion, or burning, inside a reciprocating engine is a basic chemical process. Energy is released from a mixture of air and fuel. Internal combustion engines are engines in which the combustion of the air and fuel occurs inside the engine. The main parts of a reciprocating engine are a cylinder, piston, crankcase, connecting rod, crankshaft, and two valves. The piston moves inside the cylinder. The cylinder is attached to the crankcase that houses and supports a crankshaft. A connecting rod connects the piston to the crankshaft. An intake valve allows air and fuel to enter the cylinder, and an exhaust valve allows the burned gases to exit the cylinder (Figure 11-0-1).

The engine converts the energy from the combustion process into heat and work. A mixture of air and fuel enters the cylinder and is ignited. When the air and fuel burn, the heat causes the combustion gases to expand, and pressure in the cylinder increases significantly. The pressure in the cylinder pushes the piston and rotates the crankshaft. A propeller can be attached to the crankshaft and when the crankshaft rotates, so does the propeller, generating thrust. The propeller can also be attached to reduction gearing, which allows the propeller to rotate more slowly than the engine.

Learning Objectives

IDENTIFY
- Aircraft engines by cylinder arrangement
- Location of the main parts of an aircraft reciprocating engine

EXPLAIN
- Engine operating principles
- Functions of the main parts of an aircraft reciprocating engine

DISCUSS
- Things that affect engine power output

Left: These two Beechcraft classics—the Model 18 Twin Beech (top) and the Model 35 Bonanza—are powered by reciprocating engines.

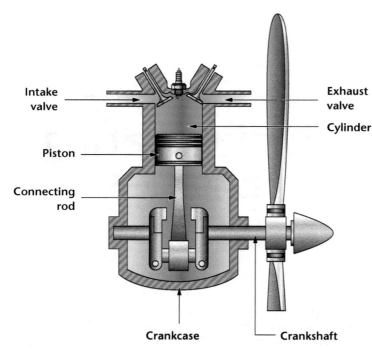

Figure 11-0-1. The major components of a reciprocating engine.

Section 1

Types of Engines/Engine Classification

Reciprocating engines can be classified according to the cylinder arrangement (inline, V-type, radial, and opposed), method of cooling (liquid cooled or air cooled), or type of fuel used and ignition source.

Classification by Type of Fuel and Ignition Source

Two fuel types (gasoline and diesel) are used in reciprocating engines currently in production that are used in small aircraft: spark ignition gasoline engines and the compression ignition diesel engines. The difference between gasoline and diesel engines is when in the cycle the fuel is introduced into the air and ignited. In gasoline engines, the fuel is mixed with air and then and the mixture is introduced into the cylinder. After the piston compresses the fuel-air mixture, a spark plug ignites it, burning the air/fuel mixture. In a diesel engine, only air is introduced into cylinder and the air (without fuel) is compressed. When the air is compressed sufficiently, fuel is sprayed into the hot compressed air, causing it to ignite.

In both cases, the heat produced causes the air-fuel mixture to expand, significantly increasing cylinder pressure and pushing the piston down. The piston movement ultimately causes the crankshaft and propeller to rotate. Gasoline engines are, by far, the most popular for small aircraft. Historically, diesel engines were rarely used in aircraft. However, their popularity has increased in recent years.

Classification by Type of Cooling

Piston engines are cooled by transferring excess heat to the surrounding air or another fluid. With air-cooled engines, this heat transfer is direct from the cylinders to the air. Therefore, it is necessary to provide thin metal fins on the cylinders of an air-cooled engine to have increased surface for enough heat transfer. This is the most common design today (Figure 11-1-1).

While most reciprocating aircraft engines are air cooled, a few use a liquid-cooling system. In liquid-cooled engines, the heat is transferred from the cylinders to the coolant, which is then sent through tubing and cooled in a radiator (heat exchanger) placed in the airstream. The coolant is then recirculated to the engine. The coolant radiator must be large enough to cool the liquid efficiently.

The main problem with liquid cooling is the complexity and added weight of coolant, radiator, and tubing to connect the components. This was a popular choice for engines used on military fighter aircraft in the 1920s and 1930s.

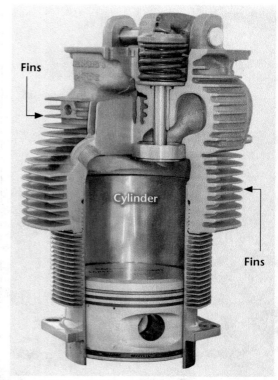

Figure 11-1-1. An air-cooled cylinder's fins add surface area for cooling.

Classification by Cylinder Arrangement

Cylinder arrangement refers to the relationship of how the cylinders are mounted on the crankcase. Many cylinder arrangements for reciprocating engines have been used on aircraft. The arrangements were varied to accommodate many factors, including cooling, ground clearance, pilot visibility, and frontal area subject to drag. Many designs have been tried, but only a few have survived the test of time and are still in use: inline, opposed, V-type, and radial.

Inline Engines

An inline engine usually has an even number of cylinders, although some three-cylinder engines have been constructed. This engine can be either liquid cooled or air cooled and has only one crankshaft, either above or below the cylinders. If the engine cylinders are below the crankshaft, it is called an inverted engine (Figure 11-1-2).

The inline engine has a small frontal area and is better adapted to streamlining. With increase in engine size, the air cooled, inline engines

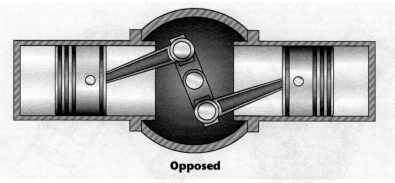

Opposed

Figure 11-1-3. Examples of an opposed engine.

present additional problems to provide proper cooling; therefore, this type of engine is associated with low- and medium-horsepower engines used on some older light aircraft.

Opposed or O-Type Engines

The opposed-type engine has two banks of cylinders directly opposite each other with a crankshaft in the center (Figure 11-1-3). The pistons of both cylinder banks are connected to one crankshaft. Although the engine can be either liquid cooled or air cooled, the air-

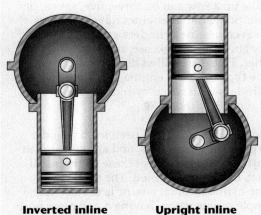

Inverted inline   **Upright inline**

Figure 11-1-2. Examples of an inline engine.

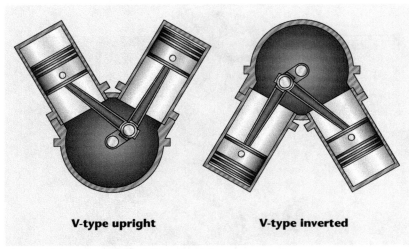

Figure 11-1-4. Examples of V-type engines.

V-type upright   **V-type inverted**

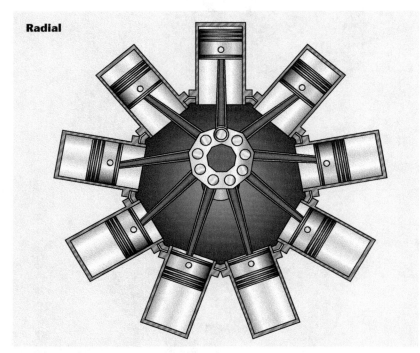

Radial

Figure 11-1-5. Radial engine.

cooled version is used predominantly in aviation. It is usually mounted with the cylinders in a horizontal position. The opposed-type engine has a low weight-to-horsepower ratio, and its narrow silhouette makes it ideal for horizontal installation on the aircraft wings, in twin-engine applications. Another advantage is its low vibration characteristics.

V-Type Engines

In V-type engines, the cylinders are arranged in two inline banks usually set 60° apart (Figure 11-1-4). This type of engine was used mostly during World War II, mainly limited to older aircraft.

Radial Engines

The radial engine consists of a row, or rows, of cylinders arranged radially about a central crankcase (Figure 11-1-5). This type of engine has proven to be very rugged and dependable. The number of cylinders that make up a row can be three, five, seven, or nine. Some radial engines have two rows of seven or nine cylinders arranged radially about the crankcase, one in front of the other. These are called double-row radials. One type of radial engine has four rows of cylinders with seven cylinders in each for a total of 28 cylinders.

Radial engines are still used in some older cargo planes, war birds, and agricultural aircraft. Although many of these engines still exist, their use is limited. The single-row, nine-cylinder radial engine is of relatively simple construction, having a one-piece nose and a two-section main crankcase. The larger double-row engines are slightly more complex than the single-row engines.

Section 2

Getting around the Engine

For best understanding when discussing engines and locations of an engine, we must have a common method of determining which direction we are referring to. For example, sometimes, it is necessary to refer to the left or right side of the engine or to one of the cylinders. Therefore, we must know the engine directions and how cylinders of an engine are numbered. The propeller shaft end of the engine is always the front end, and the accessory end is the rear end, regardless of how the engine is mounted in an aircraft. When referring to the right side or left side of an engine, always assume the view is from the rear of the engine. As seen from this position, the crankshaft rotation is referred to as either clockwise/right or counterclockwise/left (Figure 11-2-1).

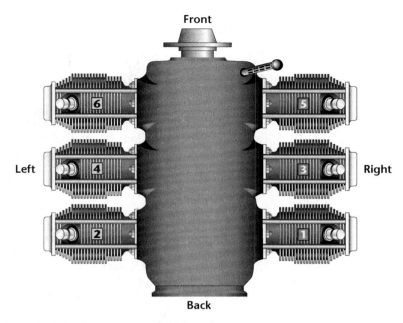

Figure 11-2-1. Directions of a reciprocating engine.

Cylinder Numbering

A cylinder number is used to identify each cylinder (Figure 11-2-2). Inline and V-type engine cylinders are usually numbered from the rear. In V-engines, the cylinder banks are known as the right bank and the left bank, as viewed from the back of the engine.

Single-row radial engine cylinders are numbered clockwise when viewed from the back. Cylinder No. 1 is the top cylinder. In double-row engines, the same system is used. The No. 1 cylinder is the top one in the back row. No. 2 cylinder is the first one clockwise from

No. 1, but No. 2 is in the front row. No. 3 cylinder is the next one clockwise to No. 2 but is in the back row. Thus, all odd-numbered cylinders are in the back row, and all even-numbered cylinders are in the front row.

The cylinder numbering of the opposed engine shown begins with the right back as No. 1 and the left back as No. 2. The one forward of No. 1 is No. 3; the one forward of No. 2 is No. 4, and so on. The numbering of opposed engine cylinders is by no means standard. Some manufacturers number their cylinders with the No. 1 cylinder at the back and others at the front of the engine.

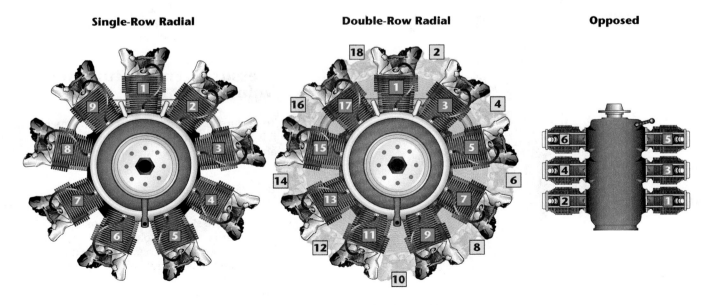

Figure 11-2-2. Numbering engine cylinders; radial engines are viewed from the back.

Section 3

Terms, Theory, and Operating Principles

The relationships among pressure, volume, and temperature of gases are the basic principles of engine operation. An internal combustion engine is a device for converting heat energy into mechanical energy. Gasoline is vaporized and mixed with air, forced or drawn into a cylinder, compressed by a piston, and then ignited by an electric spark. In the cylinder, the resultant heat energy is converted into mechanical energy and then into work. Figure 11-3-1 illustrates the various engine components necessary to perform this conversion and presents the principal terms used to indicate engine operation.

The operating cycle of an internal combustion reciprocating engine involves the series of events required to induct the gas and air; compress, ignite, and burn them; and then expel the burned gases. When the compressed mixture is ignited, the resultant gases of combustion expand very rapidly and force the pis-

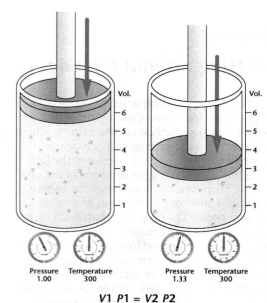

$$V1\ P1 = V2\ P2$$

For a given mass, at a constant temperature, the pressure times the volume is a constant

Figure 11-3-2. Boyle's law.

ton to move away from the cylinder head. This downward motion of the piston, acting on the crankshaft through the connecting rod, is converted to a circular or rotary motion by the crankshaft. A valve in the top or head of the cylinder opens to allow the burned gases to escape, and the momentum of the crankshaft and the propeller forces the piston back up in the cylinder where it is ready for the next event in the cycle. Another valve in the cylinder head then opens to let in a fresh charge of the air/fuel mixture. The valve that allows the burning exhaust gases to escape is called the exhaust valve, and the valve that lets in the fresh charge of the air/fuel mixture is called the intake valve. These valves are opened and closed mechanically at the proper times by the valve-operating mechanism.

Pressure, Temperature, and Volume

To understand reciprocating engine operation, it is helpful to understand the relationships among pressure, volume, and temperature.

Boyle's Law

Robert Boyle studied the relationship between the pressure and the volume of a confined gas held at a constant temperature. He discovered that when the temperature of a combined sample of gas was kept constant and the absolute pressure doubled, the volume was reduced to half the former value. As the applied abso-

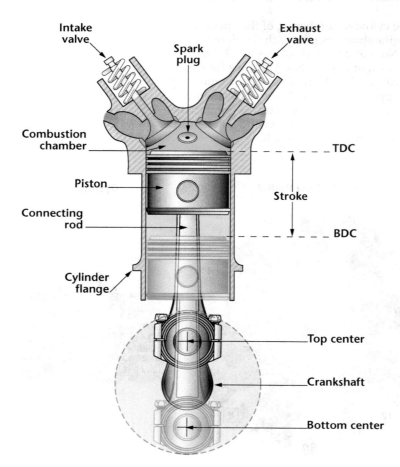

Figure 11-3-1. Components and terminology of engine operation.

lute pressure was decreased, the resulting volume increased. From these observations, he concluded that for a constant temperature, the product of the volume and absolute pressure of an enclosed gas remains constant. Boyle's law is normally stated: "The volume of an enclosed dry gas varies inversely with its absolute pressure, provided the temperature remains constant."

The following formula is used for Boyle's law calculations. Note, the pressure used needs to be absolute pressure (Figure 11-3-2).

Volume 1 × Pressure 1 = Volume 2 × Pressure 2

or

$V1\ P1 = V2\ P2$

This relationship is also illustrated as shown in Figure 11-3-3.

Charles's Law

Jacques Charles, found that all gases expand and contract in direct proportion to the change in the absolute temperature as long as the pressure is held constant. If the temperature goes up, the volume goes up (Figure 11-3-4).

As a formula, this law is shown as follows:

Volume 1 × Absolute temperature 2
= Volume 2 × Absolute temperature 1

or

$V1\ T2 = V2\ T1$

This relationship expressed in Charles's law is also illustrated as shown in Figure 11-3-5.

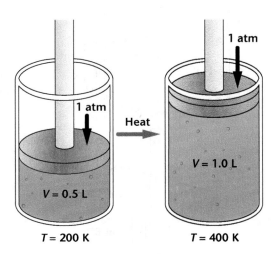

$V1\ T2 = V2\ T1$

Figure 11-3-4. Charles's law.

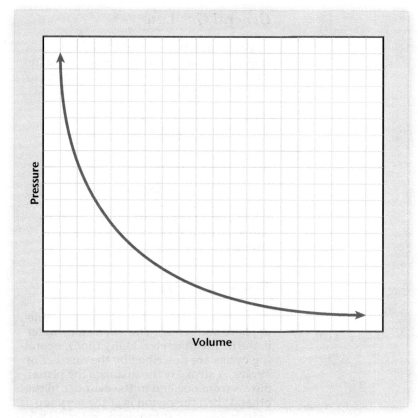

Figure 11-3-3. Boyle's law illustrated: if the volume decreases, pressure increases and vice versa.

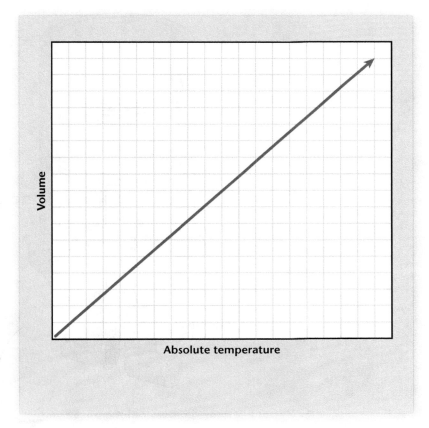

Figure 11-3-5. Charles's law illustrated: if the absolute temperature increases, volume increases and vice versa.

General Gas Law

By combining Boyle's and Charles's laws, a single expression can be derived that states all the information in both. The formula to express the general gas law is as follows:

$$\frac{\text{Pressure 1 (Volume 1)}}{\text{Temperature 1}} = \frac{\text{Pressure 2 (Volume 2)}}{\text{Temperature 2}}$$

or

$$P1\ (V1)\ (T2) = P2\ (V2)\ (T1)$$

When using the general gas law formula, temperature and pressure must be in the absolute.

Bore and Stroke

Two terms useful in describing an engine are bore and stroke. The *bore* of a cylinder is the inside diameter. Many times, operating cycles are described by the number of *strokes*. A stroke is the distance the piston moves from one end of the cylinder to the other. When the piston is at the very top of its travel, it is at top dead center (TDC). When the piston is at the very bottom of its

travel, it is at bottom dead center (BDC). The stroke is the distance between TDC and BDC (Figure 11-3-6).

Operating Cycles

Several operating cycles are used in reciprocating engines:

- Four-stroke
- Two-stroke
- Diesel

Four-Stroke Cycle

The vast majority of certified aircraft reciprocating engines operate on the four-stroke cycle, sometimes called the Otto cycle after its originator, Nikolaus Otto, a German physicist. The four-stroke cycle engine has many advantages for use in aircraft.

In the Otto engine, four strokes are required to complete the required series of events or operating cycle of each cylinder. These four strokes are illustrated in Figure 11-3-7. Two complete revolutions of the crankshaft (720°)

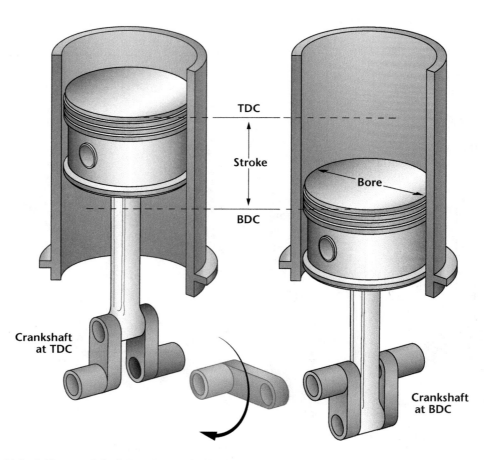

Figure 11-3-6. The crankshaft rotates one half of a rotation for each stroke.

Intake Stroke

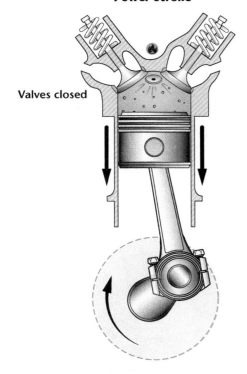

Intake open

Compression Stroke

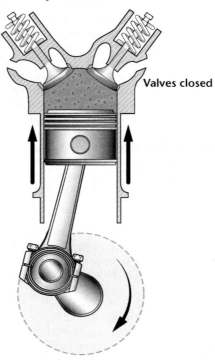

Valves closed

Power Stroke

Valves closed

Exhaust Stroke

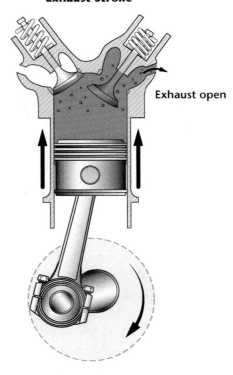

Exhaust open

Figure 11-3-7. The four-stroke cycle.

are required for the four strokes; thus, each cylinder in an engine of this type fires once in every two revolutions of the crankshaft.

Intake stroke. The first stroke of this four-stroke process is called the intake stroke.

The intake stroke starts with the piston at TDC, with the intake valve open. During the intake stroke, the piston is pulled downward in the cylinder by the crankshaft's rotation. This reduces the pressure in the cylinder and causes air under atmospheric pressure to flow through the induction system, and the fuel metering device introduces the correct amount of fuel into the air. The air/fuel mixture passes through the intake pipes and intake valves into the cylinders (Figure 11-3-8). The quantity or weight of the air/fuel charge depends on the degree of throttle opening. The intake stroke is complete when the piston reaches BDC. The crankshaft rotates from 0° to 180° on the intake stroke.

Compression stroke. The second stroke is the compression stroke. In the compression stroke, the intake valve closes, the piston moves from BDC to TDC, and the crankshaft rotates from 180° to 360°.

After the intake valve is closed, the continued upward travel of the piston compresses the air/fuel mixture to obtain the desired burning and expansion characteristics (Figure 11-3-9).

Ignition event: The ignition event occurs as the piston nears the end of its travel on the compression stroke. A surge of high-voltage current is sent to the spark plug. This produces a high-energy spark in the combustion chamber, igniting the compressed air-fuel mixture and leading to the next engine stroke.

Power stroke. The third stroke is the power stroke. In the power stroke, the piston moves from TDC to BDC. When the air-fuel mixture is ignited on the compression stroke, it burns rapidly and creates extreme temperature in the cylinder. The temperature of these burning gases can be between 3,000°F and 4,000°F. These hot gases expand rapidly, greatly increasing pressure in the cylinder. Pressure in the cylinder can reach a force of more than 15 tons (30,000 p.s.i.) at maximum power output of the engine.

The ignition event is timed so that peak pressure occurs just as the piston is passing TDC at the beginning of the power stroke. The high pressure exerts tremendous force on the piston, forcing the piston and connecting rod down. That downward movement is changed to rotary movement by the crankshaft, causing the propeller to spin (Figure 11-3-10). In the power stroke, the crankshaft moves from 360° to 540° of travel.

Exhaust stroke. The fourth and last stroke is the exhaust stroke (Figure 11-3-11). As the piston moves from BDC to TDC, the exhaust valve is open, and the piston's movement pushes the burned exhaust gases out of the

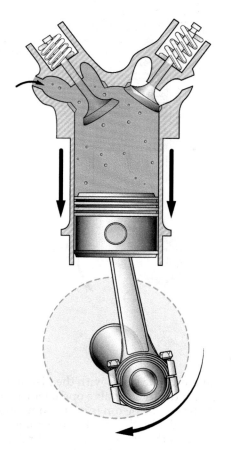

Figure 11-3-8. The intake stroke.

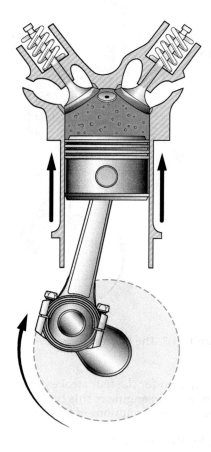

Figure 11-3-9. The compression stroke.

cylinder through the exhaust valve. The crankshaft rotates from 540° to 720°. This completes the four strokes, and the process is ready to start the next cycle.

This entire four-stroke cycle is summarized in Figure 11-3-12.

Four-Stroke Cycle: Valve Timing, Ignition Timing, and Firing Order

As the piston approaches TDC on the compression stroke, the air/fuel mixture is ignited by means of a spark plug that provides an electric spark in the cylinder. The timing of the ignition event is specified in degrees of crankshaft travel. The time of ignition varies from 20° to 35° of crankshaft travel before TDC, on the compression stroke, depending on the requirements of an engine model.

The firing order of an engine is the sequence in which the power event occurs in the different cylinders. The firing order is designed to provide for balance and to eliminate vibration as much as possible.

Opposed Engines

The firing order of many six-cylinder opposed engine is 1-4-5-2-3-6 (Figure 11-3-13). The firing order of some four-cylinder opposed engines is 1-4-2-3, and other models use 1-3-2-4. The engine's firing order varies by manufacturer and model. The firing orders presented here are only examples of some engines.

Single-Row Radial Engines

On a single-row radial engine, all the odd-numbered cylinders fire in numerical succession; then the even-numbered cylinders fire in numerical succession. On a five-cylinder radial engine, for example, the firing order is 1-3-5-2-4, and on a seven-cylinder radial engine, it is 1-3-5-7-2-4-6. The firing order of a nine-cylinder radial engine is 1-3-5-7-9-2-4-6-8.

Double-Row Radial Engines

On a double-row radial engine, the firing order is somewhat complicated. It is arranged with the firing impulse occurring in a cylinder

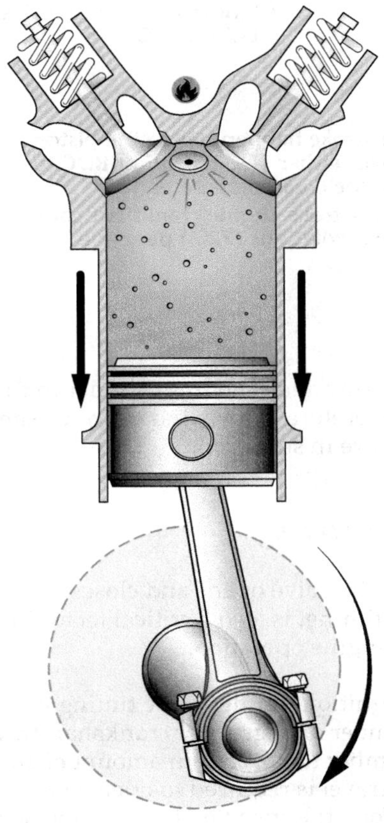

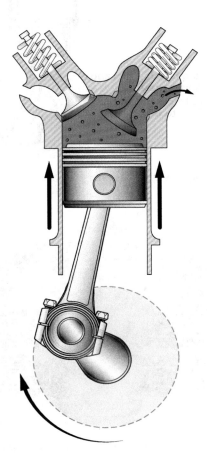

Figure 11-3-10. The power stroke.

Figure 11-3-11. The exhaust stroke.

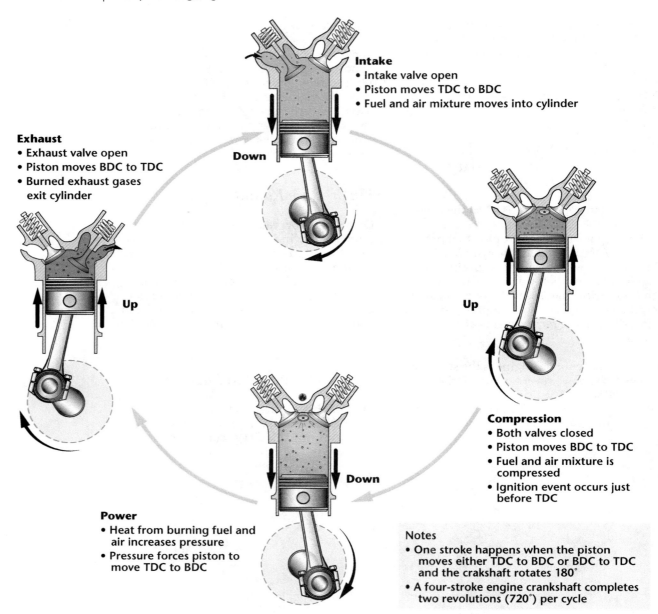

Intake
- Intake valve open
- Piston moves TDC to BDC
- Fuel and air mixture moves into cylinder

Down

Exhaust
- Exhaust valve open
- Piston moves BDC to TDC
- Burned exhaust gases exit cylinder

Up

Up

Compression
- Both valves closed
- Piston moves BDC to TDC
- Fuel and air mixture is compressed
- Ignition event occurs just before TDC

Down

Power
- Heat from burning fuel and air increases pressure
- Pressure forces piston to move TDC to BDC

Notes
- One stroke happens when the piston moves either TDC to BDC or BDC to TDC and the crankshaft rotates 180°
- A four-stroke engine crankshaft completes two revolutions (720°) per cycle

Figure 11-3-12. The four-stroke engine's cycle summary.

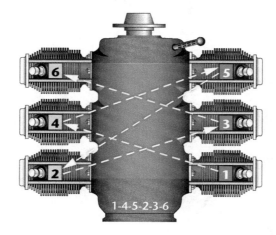

Figure 11-3-13. A six-cylinder opposed engine firing order.

in one row and then in a cylinder in the other row; therefore, two cylinders in the same row never fire in succession.

Valve Timing

When the valve opens and closes, called valve timing, is also a critical factor in efficient engine operation.

Like ignition timing, valve timing is specified in number of degrees of crankshaft travel. Remember that a certain amount of crankshaft travel is required to open a valve fully; therefore, the specified timing represents the start of opening rather than the fully opened

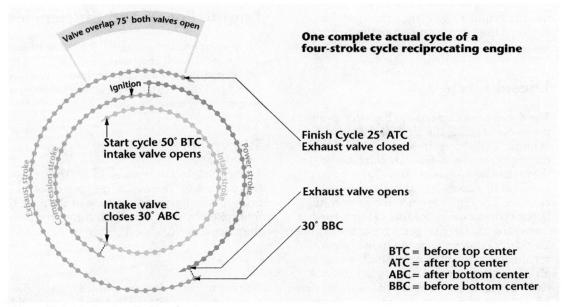

Figure 11-3-14. A valve timing chart.

position of the valve. An example valve timing chart is in Figure 11-3-14.

To induce a greater quantity of the air/fuel charge into the cylinder and thus increase the horsepower, the intake valve is opened considerably before the piston reaches TDC on the exhaust stroke. The opening of the valve before the stroke begins is called *valve lead*. The distance the valve can be opened before TDC, however, is limited by several factors such as hot gases still in the cylinder from the previous cycle that could flash back into the intake pipe and the induction system.

At the start of the intake stroke, both the intake and the exhaust valves are off the valve seats at TDC. As mentioned earlier, the intake valve opens before TDC on the exhaust stroke (valve lead), and the closing of the exhaust valve is delayed considerably after the piston has passed TDC and has started the intake stroke. The delay in closing the valve is referred to as *valve lag*, and the period that both valves are open is called valve overlap. The timing is designed to help cool the cylinder internally by circulating the cool incoming air/fuel mixture, to increase the amount of the air/fuel mixture induced into the cylinder, and to help scavenge the by-products of combustion from the cylinder.

The intake valve is timed to close after BDC (valve lag) on the compression stroke, depending on the engine, to allow the momentum of the incoming gases to charge the cylinder more completely. Because of the comparatively large volume of the cylinder above the piston when the piston is near

BDC, the slight upward travel of the piston at this time does not have a great effect on the incoming flow of gases. This late timing can be carried too far because the gases can be forced back through the intake valve and defeat the purpose of the late closing.

The timing of the exhaust valve opening is determined by, among other considerations, the desirability of using as much of the expansive force as possible and of scavenging the cylinder as completely and rapidly as possible. The valve is opened considerably before BDC (valve lead) on the power stroke while some pressure still exists in the cylinder. This timing is used so that the pressure can force the gases out of the exhaust port as soon as possible. This process frees the cylinder of waste heat after the desired expansion has been obtained and avoids overheating the cylinder and the piston. Thorough scavenging is very important, because any exhaust products remaining in the cylinder dilute the incoming air/fuel charge at the start of the next cycle.

Two-Stroke Cycle

The two-stroke cycle engine has re-emerged being used in ultra-light, light sport, and many experimental aircraft. As the name implies, two-stroke cycle engines require only one upstroke and one downstroke of the piston to complete the required series of events in the cylinder. Thus, the engine completes the operating cycle in one revolution of the crankshaft. The intake and exhaust functions are performed in the same stroke. These engines can be either air or water cooled and usually require a gear reduction gearbox between the engine and propeller (Figure 11-3-15).

Diesel Cycle

The diesel cycle depends on high-compression pressures to ignite the air/fuel charge in the cylinder. Only air is drawn into the cylinder during the intake stroke. It is compressed by the piston (compression stroke) and when pressure is at its maximum, fuel is sprayed in the cylinder. The high pressure and temperature in the cylinder cause the fuel to burn, further increasing the internal pressure of the cylinder. This drives down the piston (power stroke), turning or driving the crankshaft. Water- and air-cooled engines that can operate on Jet A fuel (kerosene) use a version of the diesel cycle. Many types of diesel cycles are used, including two-stroke and four-stroke diesels. Figure 11-3-16 illustrates a four-stroke diesel cycle.

Stroke 1

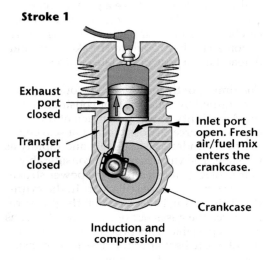

Exhaust port closed

Transfer port closed

Inlet port open. Fresh air/fuel mix enters the crankcase.

Crankcase

Induction and compression

Stroke 2

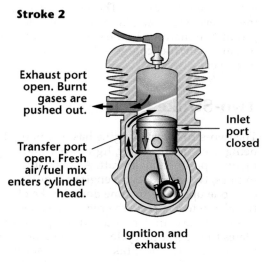

Exhaust port open. Burnt gases are pushed out.

Transfer port open. Fresh air/fuel mix enters cylinder head.

Inlet port closed

Ignition and exhaust

Figure 11-3-15. The two-stroke cycle.

Engine Power and Efficiencies

All aircraft engines are rated according to their ability to do work and produce power. This section explains work and power, how to calculate them, and the various efficiencies that govern a reciprocating engine's power output.

Work

A physicist defines work as force times distance. Work (w) done by a force acting on a body is equal to the magnitude of the force (f) multiplied by the distance (d) through which the force acts. This is expressed as

$$w = f \times d$$

Work is measured by several standards. The most common unit is called the foot-pound (ft-lb). If a 1-lb. mass is raised 1 ft., 1 ft-lb of work has been performed. The greater the mass is or the greater the distance is, the greater the work performed.

Horsepower

The common unit of mechanical power is the horsepower (hp). Late in the 18th century, James Watt, the inventor of the steam engine, found that an English workhorse could work at the rate of 550 ft-lb per second, or 33,000 ft-lb per minute, for a reasonable time. From his observations came the unit of horsepower, which is the standard unit of mechanical power in the English system of measurement. To calculate the horsepower rating of an engine, divide the power developed in ft-lb per minute by 33,000, or the power in ft-lb per second by 550.

$$\text{One hp} = \frac{\text{ft-lb per min}}{33,000}$$

or

$$\text{One hp} = \frac{\text{ft-lb per sec}}{550}$$

As stated above, work is the product of force and distance, and power is work per unit of time. Consequently, if a 33,000-lb. weight is lifted vertically by 1 ft. in 1 minute, the power expended is 33,000 ft-lb per minute, or exactly 1 hp (Figure 11-3-17).

Types of Horsepower

When discussing an engine's horsepower output, several types of horsepower can be

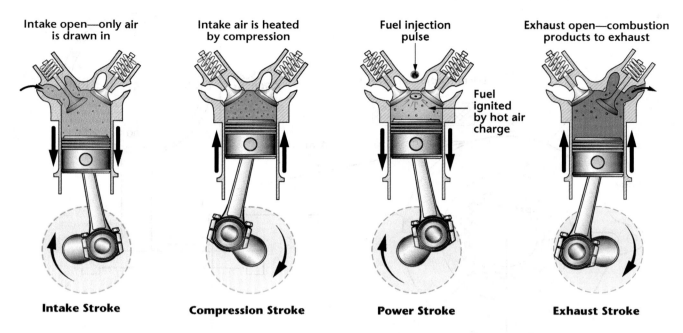

| Intake open—only air is drawn in | Intake air is heated by compression | Fuel injection pulse | Exhaust open—combustion products to exhaust |

Fuel ignited by hot air charge

| Intake Stroke | Compression Stroke | Power Stroke | Exhaust Stroke |

Figure 11-3-16. The four-stroke diesel operation.

used. You might hear the terms indicated horsepower, brake horsepower, friction horsepower, and thrust horsepower. We will look at each type so that you can better understand exactly what kind of power is being discussed.

Indicated horsepower. The indicated horsepower (ihp) produced by an engine is the horsepower calculated from the indicated mean effective pressure and the other factors that affect the engine's power output. Indicated horsepower is the power developed in the combustion chambers without reference to friction losses in the engine. This horsepower is calculated as a function of the actual cylinder pressure recorded during engine operation. The indicated horsepower calculation provides the theoretical power of a frictionless engine.

Brake horsepower. To calculate the actual horsepower delivered to the propeller, the total horsepower lost in overcoming friction must be subtracted from the indicated horsepower. The power delivered to the propeller for useful work is known as brake horsepower (bhp). Measuring an engine's bhp involves measuring a quantity known as torque or twisting moment. Torque is the product of a force and the distance of the force from the axis about which it acts.

Numerous devices are used for measuring torque, such as a dynamometer or a torque meter. One very simple type of device that can be used to demonstrate torque calcula-

tions is the Prony brake (Figure 11-3-18). A prony brake consists of a hinged collar, or brake, that can be clamped to a drum splined to the propeller shaft. The collar and drum form a friction brake that can be adjusted by a wheel. An arm of a known length is rigidly attached to or is a part of the hinged collar and terminates at a point that rests on a set of scales. As the propeller shaft rotates, it tends to carry the brake's hinged collar with it and is prevented from doing so only by the arm that rests on the scale. The scale indicates the force needed to arrest the arm's motion. If the resulting force registered on the scale is multiplied by the arm length, the resulting product is the torque exerted by the rotating shaft.

1 hp = 550 ft-lb per second

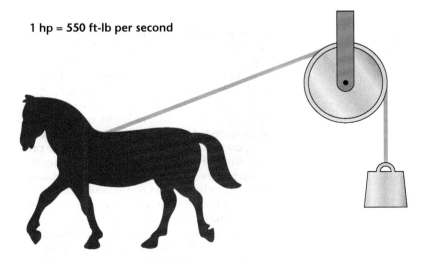

Figure 11-3-17. One hp = 550 ft-lb per second.

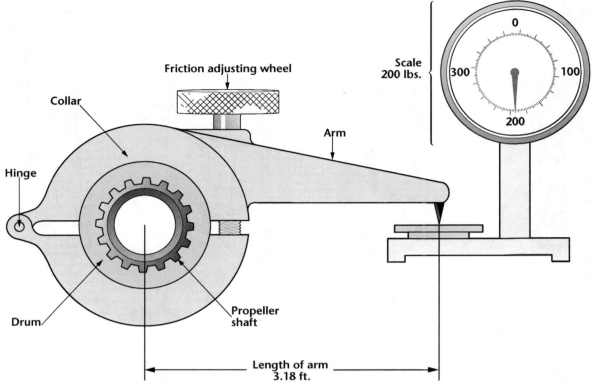

Figure 11-3-18. A typical prony brake.

Friction horsepower. The difference between indicated and brake horsepower is known as friction horsepower, which is the horsepower required to overcome mechanical losses, such as the pumping action of the pistons, the friction of the pistons, drawing in fuel, expelling exhaust, driving oil and fuel pumps, and other engine accessories; it is the friction of all other moving parts. It is calculated as the indicated horsepower minus brake horsepower. On modern aircraft engines, this power loss through friction can be as high as 10 to 15 percent of the indicated horsepower.

Thrust horsepower. Thrust horsepower can be considered the result of the engine and the propeller working together. If a propeller could be 100 percent efficient, the thrust and the bhp would be the same. However, the efficiency of the propeller varies with the engine speed, attitude, altitude, temperature, and airspeed. Thus, the ratio of the thrust horsepower and the bhp delivered to the propeller shaft are never equal. For example, if an engine develops 1,000 bhp, and it is used with a propeller that is 85 percent efficient, the thrust horsepower of that engine-propeller combination is 85 percent of 1,000, or 850 thrust hp. Of the four types of horsepower discussed, the thrust horsepower is what determines the performance of the engine-propeller combination.

Piston Displacement

When other factors remain equal, the greater the piston displacement, the greater the maximum horsepower an engine can develop. When a piston moves in the cylinder, it displaces a set volume. The volume displaced by the piston is known as piston displacement and is expressed in cubic inches for most U.S.-made engines and cubic centimeters for others (Figure 11-3-19).

To calculate piston displacement of one cylinder, you multiply the area of the cylinder bore by the stroke. To get the engine's total piston displacement, multiply this by the number of cylinders.

Displacement is the volume (V) of a geometric cylinder equals the area (A) of the base multiplied by the height (h) and is expressed as

$$V = A \times h$$

The area of the base is the area of the cross-section of the cylinder.

For engine displacement, the formula is the same but expressed as

Displacement of one cylinder
= Area of the bore × stroke

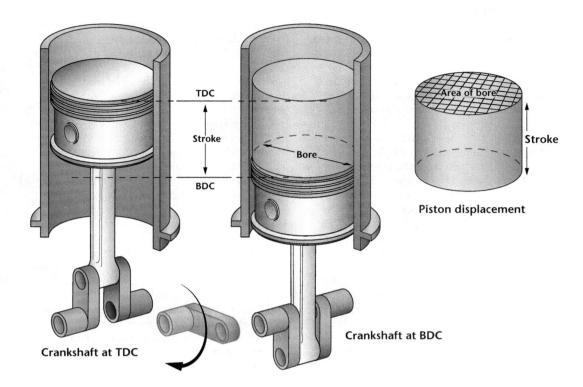

Figure 11-3-19. Piston displacement.

Total engine displacement
= Area of the bore × stroke × number of cylinders

Area of a Circle

To find the area of a circle and, likewise, the area of the cylinder bore, it is necessary to use a number called pi (π). This number represents the ratio of the circumference to the diameter of any circle. Pi cannot be stated exactly because it is a never-ending decimal. It is 3.1416 expressed to four decimal places, which is accurate enough for most computations.

The area of a circle, as in a rectangle or triangle, must be expressed in square units. The distance that is one-half the diameter of a circle is known as the radius (r). The area of any circle is found by squaring the radius and multiplying by pi. The formula is

$A = \pi r^2$

The radius of a circle or radius of the bore is equal to half the diameter:

r = diameter of the bore / 2

Example. Compute the piston displacement of the PWA 14-cylinder engine, which has a cyl-

inder with a 5.5-inch (in.) diameter bore and a 5.5-in. stroke. Formulas required are

r = diameter of the bore / 2

Area of the bore = πr^2

Displacement (one cylinder) = area of the bore × stroke

Total displacement = area of the bore × stroke × number of cylinders

Substitute values into these formulas and complete the calculation.

Radius of the bore = d / 2 = 5.5 in. / 2 = 2.75 in.

Area of the bore = πr^2 = 3.1416 (2.75 in. × 2.75 in.)

Area of the bore = 3.1416 × 7.5625 square in. (in.^{2})
 = 23.7584 in.^{2}

Cylinder displacement = area of the bore × stroke = 23.7584 in.^{2} × 5.5 in. = 130.6712 cubic inches (in.^{3})

Total displacement = cylinder displacement × number of cylinders = 130.6712 in.^{3} × 14

Total displacement = 1,829.3968 in.^{3}

Rounded off to the nearest whole number, total piston displacement equals 1,829 in.^{3}

Compression Ratio

All internal combustion engines must compress the air/fuel mixture to receive a reasonable amount of work from each power stroke. The air/fuel charge in the cylinder can be compared to a coil spring in that the more it is compressed, the more work it is capable of doing.

The *compression ratio* of an engine is a comparison of the volume of space in a cylinder when the piston is at the bottom of the stroke to the volume of space when the piston is at the top of the stroke. This comparison is expressed as a ratio, hence the term compression ratio. The compression ratio is a controlling factor in the maximum horsepower an engine can develop, but it is limited by present day fuel grades, the high engine speeds, and manifold pressures required for takeoff. For example, if the cylinder has 140 in.^{3} of space when the piston is at the bottom and 20 in.^{3} of space when the piston is at the top of the stroke, the compression ratio would be 140 to 20. If this ratio is expressed in fraction form, it is 140/20 or 7 to 1, usually represented as 7:1 (Figure 11-3-20).

Thermal Efficiency

Any study of engines and power involves consideration of heat as the source of power. The heat produced by gasoline burning in the cylinders causes a rapid expansion of the gases in the cylinder, and this, in turn, moves the pistons and creates mechanical energy. It has long been known that mechanical work can be converted into heat and that a given amount of heat contains the energy equivalent of a certain amount of mechanical work. Heat and work are theoretically interchangeable and bear a fixed relation to each other. Heat can therefore be measured in work units (for example, ft-lb) and in heat units.

The British thermal unit (BTU) of heat is the quantity of heat required to raise the temperature of 1 lb of water by 1°F. It is equivalent to 778 ft-lb of mechanical work. A pound of petroleum fuel, when burned with enough air to consume it completely, gives up about 20,000 BTU, the equivalent of 15,560,000 ft-lb of mechanical work. These quantities express the heat energy of the fuel in heat and work units, respectively.

The ratio of useful work done by an engine to the heat energy of the fuel it uses, expressed in work or heat units, is called the *thermal efficiency* of the engine. If two similar engines use equal amounts of fuel, the engine that converts into work the greater part of the energy in the fuel (higher thermal efficiency) delivers the greater amount of power. Furthermore, the engine that has the higher thermal efficiency has less waste heat to dispose of to the valves, cylinders, pistons, and cooling system of the engine. A high thermal efficiency also means low specific fuel consumption and, therefore, less fuel for a flight of a given distance at a given power. Thus, the practical importance of a high thermal efficiency is threefold, and it constitutes one of the most desirable features in an aircraft engine's performance.

The portion of the total heat of combustion that is turned into mechanical work depends to a great extent on the compression ratio. The compression ratio is the ratio of the piston displacement plus combustion chamber space to

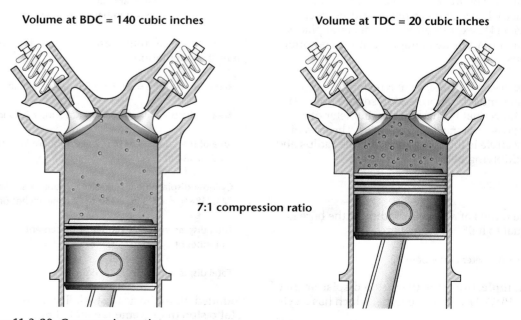

Volume at BDC = 140 cubic inches   **Volume at TDC = 20 cubic inches**

7:1 compression ratio

Figure 11-3-20. Compression ratio.

the combustion chamber space, as discussed earlier. Other things being equal, the higher the compression ratio is, the larger is the proportion of the heat energy of combustion turned into useful work at the crankshaft. On the other hand, increasing the compression ratio increases the cylinder head temperature. This is a limiting factor because the extremely high temperature created by high compression ratios causes the material in the cylinder to deteriorate rapidly and the fuel to detonate instead of burning at a controlled rate.

The thermal efficiency of an engine can be based on either bhp or ihp and is represented by the formula

$$\text{indicated thermal efficiency} = \frac{\text{ihp} \times 33,000}{\text{weight of fuel burned}/\text{min.} \times \text{heat value} \times 778}$$

The formula for brake thermal efficiency is the same as shown above, except the value for bhp is inserted instead of the value for ihp.

Example. An engine delivers 85 bhp for 1 hour and in that time consumes 50 lbs. of fuel. Assuming the fuel has a heat content of 18,800 BTU per pound, find the thermal efficiency of the engine.

$$\frac{85 \text{ ihp} \times 33,000}{0.833 \times 18,800 \text{ BTU} \times 778} = \frac{2,805,000}{12,184,569}$$

Brake thermal efficiency = 0.23 or 23 percent

Aircraft reciprocating engines are only about 25 percent to 30 percent thermally efficient; that is, they transform only about 25 percent to 30 percent of the total heat potential of the burning fuel into mechanical energy. The remainder of the heat is lost through the exhaust gases, the cooling system, and the friction in the engine. Thermal distribution in a reciprocating engine is noted in Figure 11-3-21.

Specific Fuel Consumption

Another useful measure of fuel use is called specific fuel consumption (SFC), which is the fuel weight in pounds per hour per horsepower. For reciprocating engines, this is also referred to as brake specific fuel consumption (BSFC)

SFC = pounds of fuel per hour / horsepower

Mechanical Efficiency

Mechanical efficiency is the ratio that shows how much of the power developed by the expanding gases in the cylinder is delivered to the output shaft. It is a comparison between the bhp and the ihp. It can be expressed by this formula:

Mechanical efficiency = bhp / ihp

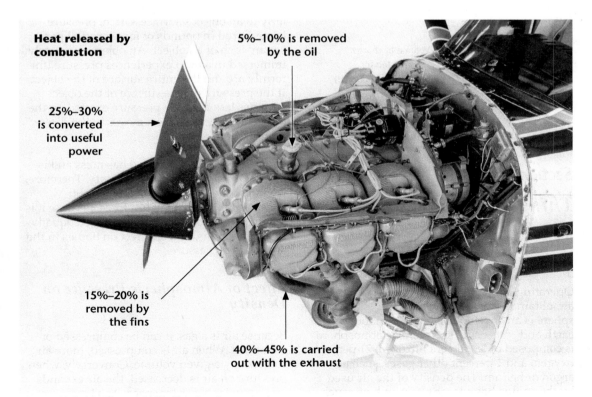

Heat released by combustion

5%–10% is removed by the oil

25%–30% is converted into useful power

15%–20% is removed by the fins

40%–45% is carried out with the exhaust

Figure 11-3-21. Thermal distribution in an engine.

Brake horsepower is the useful power delivered to the propeller shaft. Indicated horsepower is the total horsepower developed in the cylinders. The difference between the two is friction horsepower (fhp), which is the power lost in overcoming friction. The factor that has the greatest effect on mechanical efficiency is the friction in the engine itself. The friction between moving parts in an engine remains practically constant throughout an engine's speed range. Therefore, the mechanical efficiency of an engine is highest when the engine is running at the r.p.m. at which maximum bhp is developed. Mechanical efficiency of the average aircraft reciprocating engine approaches 90 percent.

Volumetric Efficiency

Volumetric efficiency is a ratio expressed in terms of percentages. It is a comparison of the volume of air and fuel charge (corrected for temperature and pressure) inducted into the cylinders to the total piston displacement of the engine. If the engine draws in a volume of charge (corrected), exactly equal to its piston displacement, it is said to be operating at 100 percent volumetric efficiency. An engine drawing in less volume than this has a volumetric efficiency lower than 100 percent. Some things that decrease volumetric efficiency include valve timing, induction system design, and throttle position.

The equation for volumetric efficiency is as follows:

$$\text{Volumetric efficiency} = \frac{\substack{\text{Volume of charge} \\ \text{(corrected for} \\ \text{temperature and pressure)}}}{\text{Piston displacement}}$$

Section 4

Things that Affect Power

The Atmosphere and Air Density

Operating an engine requires a great deal of air, obtained from the atmosphere. The atmosphere is an envelope of air that surrounds the earth and rests on its surface. The atmosphere is composed of 78 percent nitrogen, 21 percent oxygen, and 1 percent other gases, such as argon or helium. The density of the air used by the engine has a large effect on how much power an engine produces. As air density decreases, engine power and propeller thrust are reduced. Increased air density results in higher engine power and propeller thrust.

Air density is affected by changes in altitude, temperature, and humidity. Air density decreases at high elevations, low atmospheric pressures, high temperatures, high humidity, or some combination of these factors. Air density increases at high atmospheric pressures, low temperatures, and low humidity.

Standard Day Conditions

Because aircraft engines operate in many conditions, standards for atmospheric pressure and temperature had to be established. The U.S. standard atmosphere was established in 1958 and provides the necessary pressure and temperature values to calculate volumetric efficiency (Figure 11-4-1). The standard atmosphere at sea level has a surface temperature of 59°F (15°C) and a surface pressure of 29.92 inches of mercury ("Hg). This is equal to 14.69 lbs. per square inch (p.s.i.) or 1,013.2 millibars (mb). Engine performance can be compared and evaluated only when corrected to standard day conditions.

Pressure and Atmospheric Pressure

Pressure is the force applied perpendicularly to an object's surface. Often, pressure is measured in pounds of force exerted per square inch of an object. An object completely immersed in a fluid experiences pressure uniformly around the entire surface of the object. If the pressure on one surface of the object becomes less than the pressure exerted on the other surfaces, the object moves in the direction of lower pressure.

Although air is very light, it has mass and is affected by the attraction of gravity. Therefore, like any other substance, it has weight; because it has weight, it has force. Because it is a fluid substance, this force is exerted equally in all directions, and its effect on bodies in the air is called pressure.

Effect of Atmospheric Pressure on Density

Because air is a gas, it can be compressed or expanded. When air is compressed, more air can occupy a given volume. Conversely, when pressure on air is decreased, the air expands and occupies a greater space. At a lower pressure, the original column of air contains a smaller mass of air. The density is decreased because density is directly proportional to pressure. If the pressure is doubled, the density is doubled; if the pressure is lowered, the density is lowered. This statement is true only at a constant temperature.

Effect of Temperature on Density

Increasing the temperature of a substance decreases its density. Conversely, decreasing the temperature increases the density. Thus, the density of air varies inversely with temperature. This statement is true only at a constant pressure.

Effect of Altitude on Density

In the atmosphere, both temperature and pressure decrease with altitude and have conflicting effects on density. The thickness of the atmosphere is limited; therefore, the higher the altitude, the less air there is above. For this reason, the weight of the atmosphere at 18,000 ft. is one-half what it is at sea level. As altitude increases, the temperature decreases steadily at a rate of about 3.5°F (2°C) per thousand ft. increase in altitude, up to 36,000 ft. On a day when the temperature is 59°F at sea level, it would be 5°F at 15,000 ft.

The rapid drop in pressure as altitude increases has a dominating effect, and engine power decreases as altitude increases.

Effect of Humidity (Moisture) on Density

Although changes in atmospheric pressure and temperature have the greatest effect on engine performance, humidity also contributes to changes in engine performance. The earlier sections refer to air that is perfectly dry. In reality, it is never completely dry. The small amount of water vapor suspended in the atmosphere might be almost negligible under certain conditions, but in other conditions, humidity affects engine performance. Water vapor is lighter than air; consequently, moist air is lighter than dry air. Therefore, as the water content of the air increases, the air becomes less dense, decreasing engine performance.

Ignition Timing

As discussed, the ignition event is timed to the engine's crankshaft position. The time of

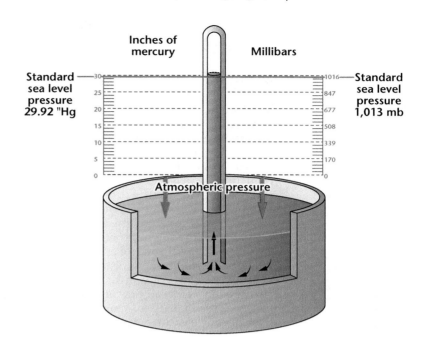

Figure 11-4-1. Standard sea level pressure.

ignition varies from 20° to 35° before TDC, depending on the engine requirements to ensure complete combustion of the air-fuel mixture by the time the piston is slightly past the TDC at the beginning of the power stroke.

Proper ignition timing is critical to an engine operating efficiently. If the ignition event occurs too early or too late, the piston is in the wrong position to take full advantage of the high pressures developed in the cylinder and engine performance decreases.

When ignition in the cylinder occurs before the optimum crankshaft position is reached, the timing is said to be early. If ignition occurs too early, the piston movement toward TDC is opposed by the force of combustion. This condition results in overheating and a loss of engine power.

If ignition occurs after the optimum crankshaft position is reached, the ignition timing is said to be late. If it is too late, not enough time is allowed to consume the air/fuel charge, and combustion is incomplete. As a result, the engine loses power.

Many factors affect ignition timing, and engine manufacturers spend considerable time researching and testing to determine the best setting. All engines incorporate devices for adjusting the ignition timing, and it is most important that the ignition system be timed correctly.

Effect of R.P.M., MAP, and Compression Ratio

Manifold Absolute Pressure

MAP stands for manifold absolute pressure. MAP is the average absolute pressure in the intake manifold; it is measured in units of "Hg. Manifold pressure is dependent on throttle position. The throttle valve is in the induction system and is connected to the throttle control lever (Figure 11-4-2). The throttle valve controls the airflow through the induction system, controlling engine speed and power. When the engine is not operating, MAP is the same as local atmospheric pressure. With the engine operating and the throttle valve in a mostly closed position (the throttle valve always allows some air flow and never completely closes), it does not allow much air into the induction system and manifold pressure, fuel flow, and r.p.m. are low.

With the throttle lever in the most aft position, the throttle valve is in its most closed position, the engine operates at idle r.p.m., or the lowest operating r.p.m. Idle r.p.m. varies with engine model but is typically in the 600 r.p.m. to 700 r.p.m. range, and MAP is low. MAP and r.p.m. are low because the pistons are trying to pull air into the engine, but the position of the throttle valve is allowing only a small amount of air into the induction system. At idle, the engine should still run smoothly. If idle r.p.m. is set too low, the engine can stall. If idle r.p.m. is too high, it makes it more difficult to descend and stop after landing because the propeller is providing more thrust than needed.

As the throttle lever is moved forward, the throttle valve allows more air into the induction system, increasing manifold pressure, fuel flow, and r.p.m. When the throttle lever at the full forward position, or full throttle, the throttle valve is fully open, allowing the maximum amount of air flow into the induction system. At full throttle, a typical aircraft engine speed is around 2,700 r.p.m. and manifold pressure is near ambient. Engines that are turbocharged or equipped with a propeller reduction system have different engine parameters than those discussed here.

Compression ratio and manifold pressure determines the pressure in the cylinder in that portion of the operating cycle when both valves are closed. The pressure of the air/fuel mix before compression is determined by manifold pressure, whereas the pressure just before ignition is determined by the manifold pressure times the compression ratio. The higher the cylinder pressure is before the ignition event, the higher the pressure is when combustion is complete, increasing engine power.

One of the reasons for using engines with high compression ratios is to obtain long-range fuel economy to convert more heat energy into useful work than is done in engines with a low compression ratio. Because more heat of the charge is converted into useful work, less heat is absorbed by the cylinder walls. This factor promotes cooler engine operation, which, in turn, increases the thermal efficiency. Here again, a compromise is needed between the demand for fuel economy and the demand for maximum horsepower without exceeding cylinder pressure and temperature limits.

Air to Fuel Ratio

Gasoline and other liquid fuels do not burn at all unless they are mixed with air. If the mixture is to burn properly in the engine cylinder, the ratio of air to fuel must be kept within a certain range. It would be more accurate to state that the fuel is burned with the oxygen in the air. Seventy-eight percent of air by volume is nitrogen, which is inert and does not participate in the combustion process, and 21 percent is oxygen. Heat is generated by burning the mixture of gasoline and oxygen. Nitrogen and gaseous by-products of combustion absorb this heat energy and turn it into power by expansion. The mixture proportion of fuel and air by weight is of extreme importance to engine performance. The characteristics of a mixture can be measured in terms of flame speed and combustion temperature.

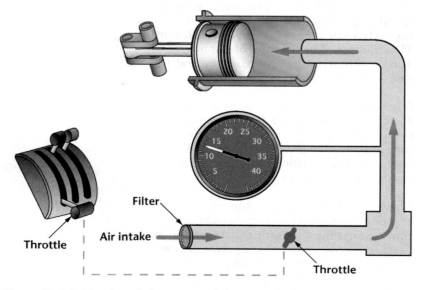

Figure 11-4-2. The throttle lever controls how much air makes it to the cylinder.

The composition of the air/fuel mixture is described by the mixture ratio. For example, a mixture with a ratio of 12 to 1 (12:1) is made up of 12 lbs. of air and 1 lb. of fuel. The ratio is expressed in weight because the volume of air varies greatly with temperature and pressure. The mixture ratio can also be expressed as a decimal. Thus, an air to fuel ratio of 12:1 and an air to fuel ratio of 0.083 describe the same mixture ratio. Mixtures of air and gasoline as rich as 8:1 and as lean as 18:1 will burn in an engine cylinder; but beyond these mixtures, the engine runs rough or might not run at all.

In a laboratory, the perfect mixture for combustion of air and fuel would be 1 lb. of air to 0.067 lb. of fuel (a mixture ratio of 15:1). This chemically correct combination is called a stoichiometric mixture (pronounced stoy-key-o-metric). With such a mixture (given sufficient time and turbulence), all the fuel and all the oxygen in the air is completely used in the combustion process. The stoichiometric mixture produces the highest combustion temperatures because the proportion of heat released to a mass of charge (fuel and air) is the greatest.

Because of combustion inefficiencies, engines develop maximum power with a mixture of around 12 parts of air and 1 part of gasoline by weight. The extra fuel (over the stoichiometric mixture) makes the combustion process more efficient, providing the most engine power for the amount of fuel. This point is referred to as *best power*.

When leaning the mixture beyond best power, even though the power diminishes, the amount of fuel required to support each horsepower hour (SFC) also is lowered. The loss of power occurs at a rate lower than the reduction of fuel flow. This favorable tendency continues until a mixture known as *best economy* is reached.

The best power air to fuel ratio is desirable when the greatest power is required. The best economy mixture results from obtaining the given power output with the least fuel flow. These are shown in Figure 11-4-3. The air to fuel ratio that gives most efficient operation varies with engine speed and power output.

Manufacturers write specific instructions for mixture ratios for each engine under various operating conditions. Failure to follow these instructions results in poor performance and possible engine damage. Excessively rich mixtures result in power loss and fuel waste. With the engine operating near its maximum

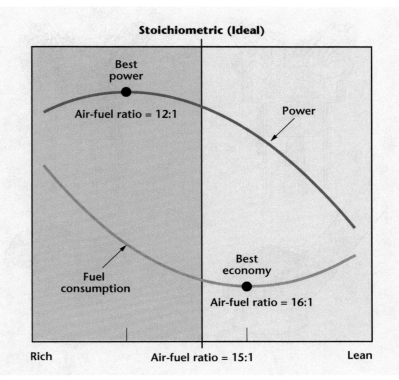

Figure 11-4-3. Air to fuel ratios for best power and best economy.

output, very lean mixtures cause power loss and, under certain conditions, serious overheating.

Detonation and Preignition

In normal combustion, the air/fuel mixture's burning is very controlled and predictable. In a spark ignition engine, the process occurs in a fraction of a second. The mixture actually begins to burn at the point where it is ignited by the spark plugs. It then burns away from the plugs until it is completely consumed. Such combustion causes a smooth buildup of temperature and pressure and ensures that the expanding gases deliver the maximum force to the piston at exactly the right time in the power stroke.

Detonation

Detonation is an uncontrolled, explosive ignition of the air/fuel mixture in the cylinder's combustion chamber (Figure 11-4-4). It causes excessive temperatures and pressures that, if not corrected, can quickly cause the piston, cylinder, or valves to fail. In less severe cases, detonation causes engine overheating, roughness, or loss of power. Detonation is characterized by high cylinder head temperatures and is most likely to occur when operating at high power settings.

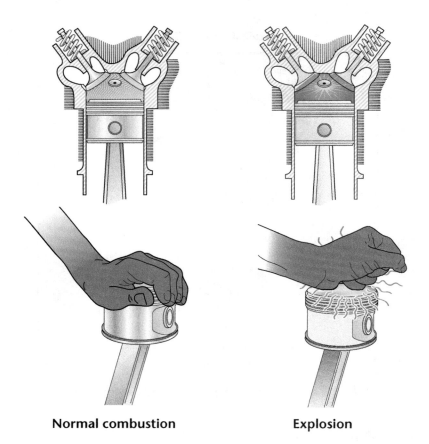

Normal combustion   **Explosion**

Figure 11-4-4. Normal combustion versus detonation

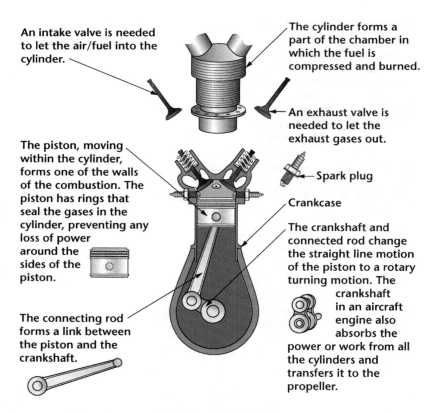

An intake valve is needed to let the air/fuel into the cylinder.

The cylinder forms a part of the chamber in which the fuel is compressed and burned.

An exhaust valve is needed to let the exhaust gases out.

The piston, moving within the cylinder, forms one of the walls of the combustion. The piston has rings that seal the gases in the cylinder, preventing any loss of power around the sides of the piston.

Spark plug

Crankcase

The crankshaft and connected rod change the straight line motion of the piston to a rotary turning motion. The crankshaft in an aircraft engine also absorbs the power or work from all the cylinders and transfers it to the propeller.

The connecting rod forms a link between the piston and the crankshaft.

Figure 11-5-1. Basic parts of a reciprocating engine.

Preignition

Preignition occurs when the air/fuel mixture ignites before the engine's normal ignition event. Premature burning is usually caused by a residual hot spot in the combustion chamber, often created by a small carbon deposit on a spark plug, a cracked spark plug insulator, or other damage in the cylinder. Such a spot causes a part to heat sufficiently to ignite the air/fuel charge. Preignition causes the engine to lose power and produces high operating temperature. As with detonation, preignition can also cause severe engine damage because the expanding gases exert excessive pressure on the piston while still on its compression stroke.

Because either condition causes high engine temperature accompanied by decreased engine performance, it is often difficult to distinguish between the two. Using the recommended grade of fuel and operating the engine within its proper temperature, pressure, and speed ranges reduce the chance of detonation or preignition.

Section 5

Main Parts of a Reciprocating Engine

The major components of a reciprocating engine are the crankcase, cylinders, pistons, connecting rods, valves, valve-operating mechanism, and crankshaft. Figure 11-5-1 illustrates these.

Crankcase

The foundation of an engine is the crankcase. It contains the bearings and bearing supports in which the crankshaft revolves. Besides supporting itself, the crankcase must provide a tight enclosure for the lubricating oil and must support various external and internal mechanisms of the engine. It also provides support for attaching the cylinder assemblies and the powerplant to the aircraft. It must be sufficiently rigid and strong to prevent the crankshaft and its bearings from misaligning. Cast or forged aluminum alloy is usually used for crankcase construction because it is light and strong.

The crankcase is subjected to many variations of mechanical loads and other forces. Because

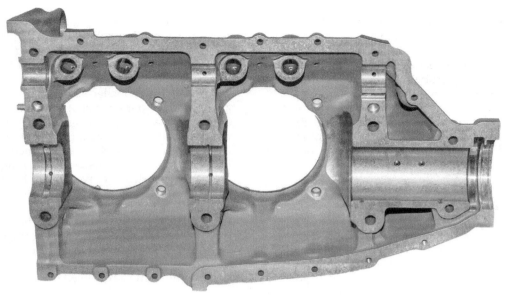

Figure 11-5-2. The crankcase.

the cylinders are fastened to the crankcase, the tremendous forces placed on the cylinder tend to pull the cylinder off the crankcase. The unbalanced centrifugal and inertia forces of the crankshaft acting through the main bearings subject the crankcase to bending moments that change continuously in direction and magnitude. The crankcase must be stiff enough to withstand these bending moments without major deflections (Figure 11-5-2).

If the engine is equipped with propeller-reduction gearing, the front or drive end is subjected to additional forces. In addition to the thrust forces developed by the propeller under high-power output, severe centrifugal and gyroscopic forces are applied to the crankcase from sudden changes in the direction of flight, such as those occurring when the aircraft maneuvers. Gyroscopic forces are especially severe when a heavy propeller is installed. To absorb centrifugal loads, a large centrifugal bearing is used in the nose section.

The machined surfaces on which the cylinders are mounted are called cylinder pads. They are provided with a suitable means of retaining or fastening the cylinders to the crankcase. The general practice in securing the cylinder flange to the pad is to mount studs in threaded holes in the crankcase. The inner portion of the cylinder pads are sometimes chamfered or tapered to allow a large rubber O-ring to be installed around the cylinder skirt, which effectively seals the joint between the cylinder and the crankcase pads against oil leakage.

Mounting lugs are used to attach the engine assembly to the engine mount or framework

for attaching the powerplant to the fuselage of single-engine aircraft or to the wing nacelle structure of multiengine aircraft. The mounting lugs can be integral with the crankcase or diffuser section or they can be detachable, as in the case of flexible or dynamic engine mounts. The mounting arrangement supports the entire powerplant including the propeller and, therefore, is designed to provide ample strength for rapid maneuvers or other loadings.

Accessory Section

The accessory (rear) section usually is of cast construction of either aluminum alloy, which is used most widely, or magnesium, which has been used to some extent. On some engines, the section is cast in one piece and has means for mounting the accessories, such as magnetos, carburetors, fuel, oil, vacuum pumps, starter, generator, tachometer drive, and such, in the various locations needed for accessibility. Other adaptations consist of an aluminum alloy casting and a separate cast magnesium cover plate on which the accessory mounts are arranged. Accessory drive shafts are mounted in suitable drive arrangements that are carried out to the accessory mounting pads. This allows the various gear ratios to be obtained for the proper drive speed to magnetos, pumps, and other accessories to obtain correct timing or functioning.

Accessory Gear Train

Gear trains with both spur gears and bevel gears are used in the different types of engines for driving engine components and accessories. Spur gears are generally used to drive the heavier loaded accessories or those requiring the least play or backlash in the gear train. Bevel gears permit angular location of short stub shafts leading to the various accessory mounting pads. On opposed, reciprocating engines, the accessory gear trains are usually simple arrangements. Many of these engines use simple gear trains to drive the engine's accessories at the proper speeds.

Crankshaft

The crankshaft is mounted along the longitudinal axis of the crankcase and is supported by the main bearings (Figure 11-5-3). The crankshaft main bearings must be supported rigidly in the crankcase—usually with transverse webs in the crankcase, one for each main bearing. The webs form an integral part of the structure and, in addition to supporting the main bearings, strengthen the entire case.

The crankshaft is the backbone of the reciprocating engine. It is subjected to most of the forces an engine develops. Its main purpose is to transform the reciprocating motion of the piston and connecting rod into rotary motion for turning the propeller. The crankshaft, as the name implies, is a shaft made of one or more cranks along its length. The cranks, referred to as throws, are formed by forging offsets into a shaft before it is machined. Because crankshafts must be very strong, they are typically forged from a strong alloy, such as chromium-nickel-molybdenum steel.

In all cases, the type of crankshaft must correspond with the engine's cylinder arrangement (Figure 11-5-4). The position of the cranks on the crankshaft in relation to the other cranks of the same shaft is expressed in degrees.

The crankshaft is supported by, and rotates in, the main bearings. They serve as the crankshaft's center of rotation. They are surface hardened to reduce wear. The crankpin, or

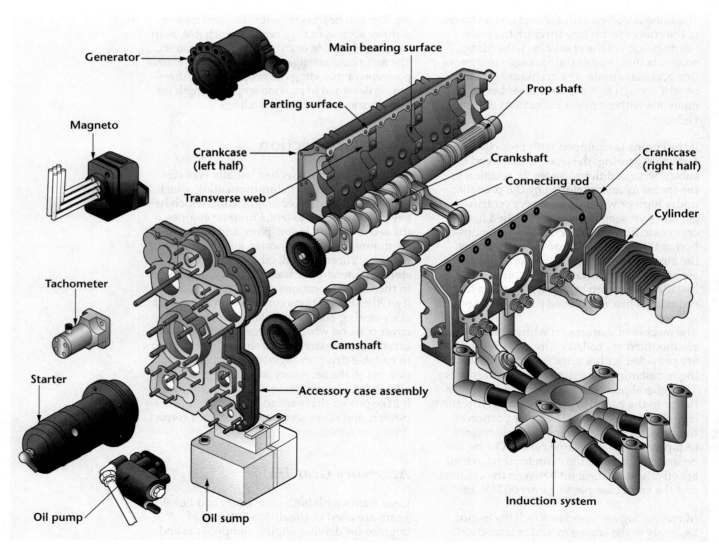

Figure 11-5-3. Typical opposed engine exploded into component assemblies.

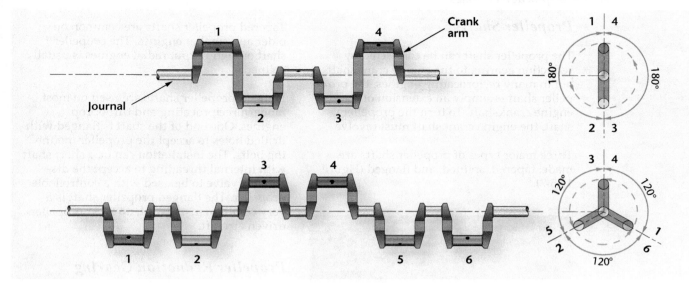

Figure 11-5-4. Solid crankshafts.

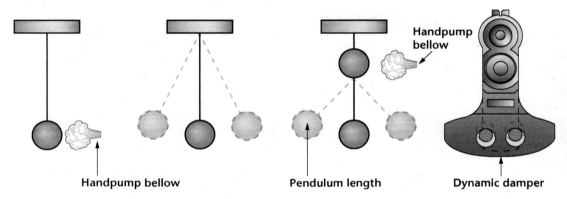

Figure 11-5-5. Principles of a dynamic damper.

connecting rod journal, is the section to which the connecting rod is attached. It is off-center from the main journals and is often called the throw. Two crank cheeks and a crankpin make a throw. When a force is applied to the crankpin in any direction other than parallel or perpendicular to and through the center line of the crankshaft, it causes the crankshaft to rotate.

Excessive vibration in an engine results in fatigue failure of the metal structures, and it causes the moving parts to wear rapidly. Counterweights and dampers are sometimes used to reduce engine vibration. A dynamic damper is merely a pendulum that is fastened to the crankshaft so that it is free to move in a small arc (Figure 11-5-5).

Radial Engine Crankshaft

The crankshaft for a radial engine is different from those used in other type engines. In the radial-type engine, only one throw is provided for each row of cylinders (Figure 11-5-6).

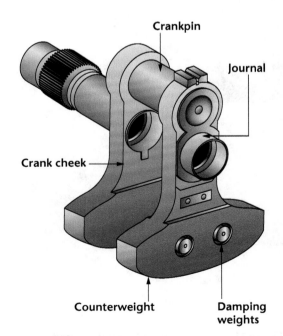

Figure 11-5-6. Example of a crankshaft used for a single-row radial engine.

Propeller Shafts

The propeller shaft can be connected by reduction gearing to the engine crankshaft, but in many reciprocating engines, the propeller shaft is simply an extension of the engine crankshaft. To turn the propeller shaft, the engine crankshaft must revolve.

Three major types of propeller shafts are made: tapered, splined, and flanged (Figure 11-5-7).

Figure 11-5-7. Examples of tapered, splined, flanged shafts.

Tapered propeller shafts are common on older and smaller engines. The propeller shaft of high-output radial engines is usually splined.

Flanged propeller shafts are used on most modern reciprocating and turboprop engines. One end of the shaft is flanged with drilled holes to accept the propeller mounting bolts. The installation can be a short shaft with internal threading to accept the distributor valve to be used with a controllable propeller. The flanged propeller shaft is a very common installation on most propeller-driven aircraft.

Propeller Reduction Gearing

The increased brake horsepower delivered by a high-horsepower engine results partly from increased crankshaft speed. Therefore, reduction gears are needed to limit the propeller rotation speed to a value at which efficient operation is obtained. Whenever the speed of the blade tips approaches the speed of sound, the propeller's efficiency decreases rapidly. Reduction gearing for engines allows the engine to operate at a higher speed, developing more power while slowing down the propeller speed. This prevents the propeller efficiency from decreasing.

Many types of reduction gearing systems are used. The three types most commonly used are spur planetary, bevel planetary, and spur and pinion (Figure 11-5-8).

Connecting Rods

The connecting rod is the link that transmits forces between the piston and the crankshaft. Connecting rods must be strong enough to remain rigid under load and yet be light enough to reduce the inertia forces that are produced when the rod and piston stop, change direction, and start again at the end of each stroke.

Plain connecting rods. Plain connecting rods are used in inline and opposed engines. The end of the rod attached to the crankpin is fitted with a cap and a two-piece bearing. The bearing cap is held on the end of the rod by bolts or studs. To maintain proper fit and balance, connecting rods should always be replaced in the same cylinder and in the same relative position (Figure 11-5-9, top).

Master and articulated connecting rods. Master and articulated rods are used in radial engines. In a radial engine, the piston

Spur Planetary

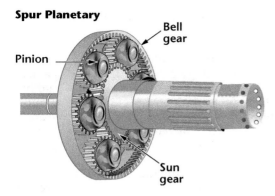

Bevel Planetary

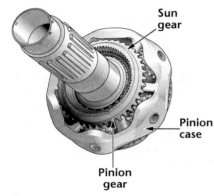

Spur and Pinion

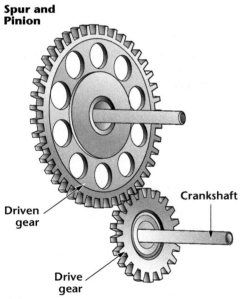

Figure 11-5-8. Propeller reduction gearing types.

in one cylinder in each row is connected to the crankshaft by a master rod. All other pistons in the row are connected to the master rod by articulated rods (Figure 11-5-9, middle).

Fork-and-blade rod. The V-type engine uses a connecting rod called a fork-and-blade rod (Figure 11-5-9, bottom).

Plain Rod

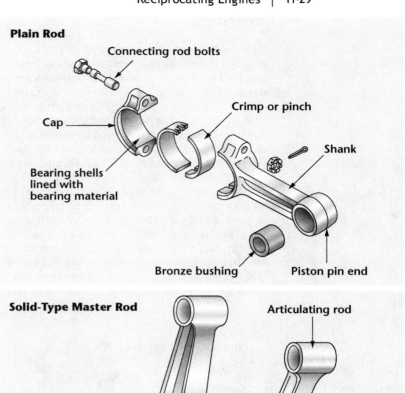

Solid-Type Master Rod

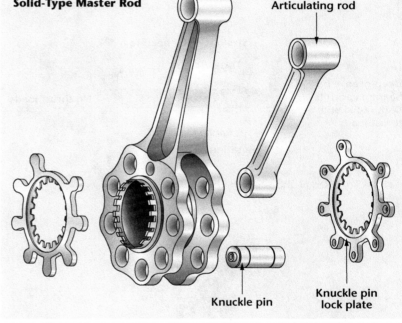

Fork-and-Blade Rod

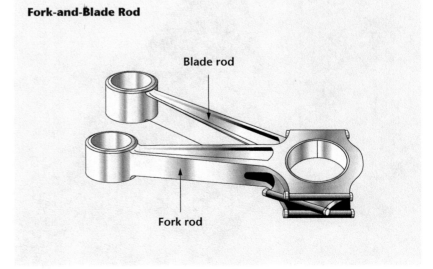

Figure 11-5-9. Connecting rods.

Bearings

Bearings are used at various places in an engine. The crankshaft rotates on bearings inserted in the crankcase, and bearings are used at both the small and large end of the connecting rod. A bearing is any surface that supports, or is supported by, another surface. A good bearing must be made of material that is strong enough to withstand the pressure imposed on it and should permit the other surface to move with a minimum of friction and wear. The parts must be held in position within very close tolerances to provide efficient and quiet operation and yet allow freedom of motion. To achieve this, and at the same time reduce friction of moving parts so that power loss is not excessive, lubricated bearings of many types are used. Bearings must take radial loads, thrust loads, or a combination of the two. These two types of loads are illustrated in Figure 11-5-10.

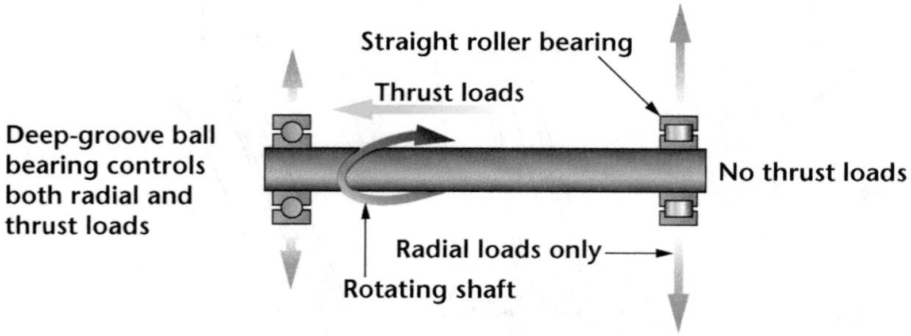

An example of a radial load would be a rotating shaft being held or contained in one position on a radial plane. Thrust load would be the rotating shaft being contained from moving axially along the shaft's axis. There are two ways in which bearing surfaces move in relation to each other.

The type of bearing most frequently used in aircraft reciprocating engines are referred to as plain bearings (Figure 11-5-11).

Plain Bearings

Plain bearings are generally used for the crankshaft, camshaft, connecting rods, and the accessory drive shaft bearings. Such bearings are usually subjected to radial loads only, although some have been designed to take thrust loads. Plain bearings are usually made of nonferrous (containing no iron) metals, such as silver, bronze, aluminum, and various alloys of copper, tin, or lead.

Smaller bearings, such as those used to support various shafts in the accessory section, are called bushings. Porous Oilite bushings are widely used in such cases. They are impregnated with oil so that the heat of friction brings the oil to the bearing surface during engine operation.

Figure 11-5-10. Radial and thrust loads.

Pistons

The piston of a reciprocating engine is a cylindrical part that moves back and forth in a steel cylinder. The piston acts as a moving wall in the combustion chamber. As the piston moves down in the cylinder, it draws in the air/fuel mixture. As it moves up, it compresses the charge, ignition occurs, and the expanding gases force the piston down. This force is transmitted to the crankshaft through the connecting rod. On the return upward stroke, the piston forces the exhaust gases from the cylinder, and the cycle repeats.

Piston Construction

Most aircraft engine pistons are machined from aluminum alloy forgings. Grooves are machined in the outside surface to receive the piston rings. The top of the piston, or head, can be flat, convex, or concave. Recesses can be machined in the piston head to prevent interference with the valves (Figure 11-5-12).

Figure 11-5-11. Plain bearing.

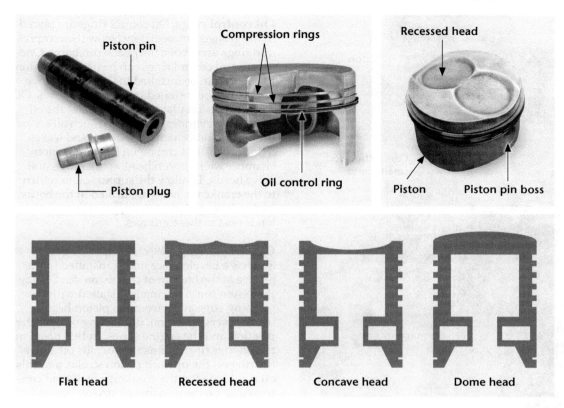

Figure 11-5-12. Piston assembly and types of pistons.

The grooves around the piston's circumference accommodate the piston rings. Up to six grooves can be machined into the piston. The portions of the piston walls between ring grooves are called the ring lands. The bottom sides of the piston are referred to as the piston skirt. In addition to acting as a guide for the piston, the piston skirt incorporates the piston-pin bosses. The piston-pin bosses are of heavy construction to enable the heavy load on the piston to be transferred to the piston pin, which connects the piston to the connecting rod (Figure 11-5-12, top right).

Piston Rings

Up to six rings can be used on a piston. They consist of compression rings and oil rings (Figure 11-5-13).

Piston ring construction. Most piston rings are made of high-grade cast iron. After the rings are made, they are ground to the cross-section desired. Then they are split so that they can be slipped over the outside of the piston and into the ring grooves that are machined in the piston wall. Because their purpose is to seal the clearance between the piston and the cylinder wall, they must fit the cylinder wall snugly enough to provide a gastight fit. They must exert equal pressure at all points on the cylinder wall and must

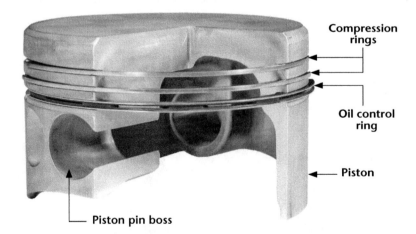

Figure 11-5-13. Piston ring locations and types.

make a gastight fit against the sides of the ring grooves.

Compression ring. The purpose of the compression rings is to prevent combustion gases from escaping past the piston during engine operation. They are placed in the ring grooves immediately below the top of the piston. The manufacturer determines the number of compression rings used on each piston according to the type of engine and its design, although most aircraft engines have two compression rings and one or more oil control rings.

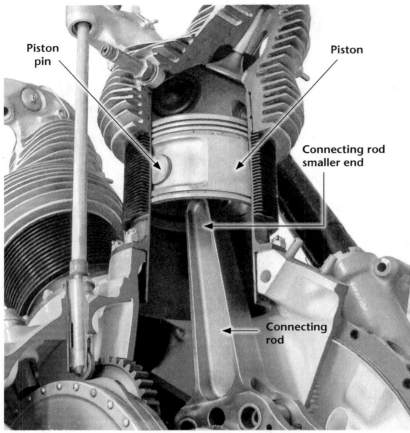

Figure 11-5-14. The piston pin joins the piston to the connecting rod.

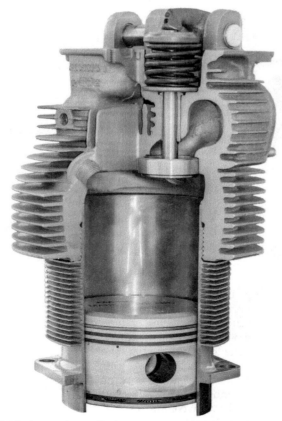

Figure 11-5-15. An engine cylinder.

Oil control rings. Oil control rings are placed in the grooves immediately below the compression rings and above the piston pin bores. One or more oil control rings can be used per piston; two rings can be installed in the same groove, or they can be installed in separate grooves. Oil control rings regulate the thickness of the oil film on the cylinder wall. If too much oil enters the combustion chamber, it burns and leaves a thick coating of carbon on the combustion chamber walls, piston head, spark plugs, and valve heads. To allow the surplus oil to return to the crankcase, holes are drilled in the bottom of the oil control piston ring grooves or in the lands next to these grooves.

Oil scraper ring. The oil scraper ring usually has a beveled face and is installed in the groove at the bottom of the piston skirt, below the piston pin. The ring is installed with the scraping edge away from the piston head or in the reverse position, depending on cylinder position and the engine series. In this position, the scraper ring retains the surplus oil above the ring on the upward piston stroke, and this oil is returned to the crankcase by the oil control rings on the downward stroke.

Piston Pin

The piston pin as seen in Figure 11-5-14 joins the piston to the connecting rod. It is machined as a tube from a nickel steel alloy forging, case hardened, and ground. The piston pin is sometimes called a wristpin because of the similarity between the relative motions of the piston and the articulated rod and that of the human arm. The piston pin used in modern aircraft engines is the full-floating type, so called because the pin is free to rotate in both the piston and in the connecting rod piston-pin bearing. The piston pin must be held in place to prevent the pin ends from scoring the cylinder walls. A plug of relatively soft aluminum in the pin end provides a good bearing surface against the cylinder wall.

Cylinders

The portion of the engine in which the power is developed is called the cylinder (Figure 11-5-15). The cylinder is a combustion chamber where gas burns and expands, and it houses the piston and the connecting rod.

Manufacturers must consider four major factors when designing and constructing the cylinder assembly. It must have these qualities:

- Be strong enough to withstand the internal pressures developed during engine operation

- Be constructed of a lightweight metal to keep down engine weight

- Have good heat-conducting properties for efficient cooling

- Be comparatively easy and inexpensive to manufacture, inspect, and maintain

The cylinders of air-cooled engines are subjected to extreme temperatures. They are made of metals that conduct heat rapidly. Cooling fins are incorporated into the cylinder, providing additional surface area to ensure adequate cooling.

The cylinder used in the air-cooled engine is the overhead valve type (Figure 11-5-16). Each cylinder is an assembly of two major parts: cylinder head and cylinder barrel. At assembly, the cylinder head is expanded by heating and then screwed down on the cylinder barrel, which has been chilled. When the head cools and contracts and the barrel warms up and expands, a gastight joint results. Most of the cylinders used are constructed in this manner using an aluminum head and a steel barrel.

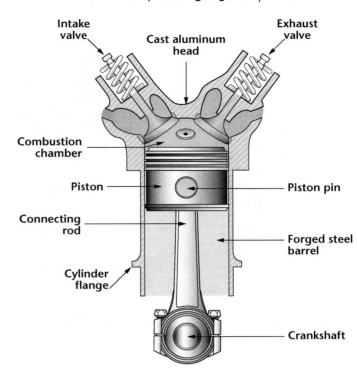

Figure 11-5-16. Cutaway of the cylinder assembly.

Cylinder Heads

The cylinder head of an air-cooled engine is usually made of aluminum alloy because it is a good conductor of heat and its light weight reduces the overall engine weight. Cylinder heads are usually cast or forged. The cylinder head's inner shape is usually semispherical.

The intake and exhaust valve ports are in the cylinder head along with the spark plugs and the intake and exhaust valve actuating mechanisms.

Cylinder Barrels

The cylinder barrel in which the piston operates must be made of a high-strength material, usually steel. It must be as light as possible yet have the proper characteristics for operating under high temperatures. It must be made of a good bearing material and have high tensile strength. The cylinder barrel is made of a steel alloy forging with the inner surface hardened to resist wear of the piston and the piston rings that bear against it.

Valves

The air/fuel mixture enters the cylinders through the intake valve ports, and burned gases are expelled through the exhaust valve ports. The flow of the incoming air/fuel mixture and the outgoing burned gases, through

the ports, is controlled by a poppet valve (Figure 11-5-17, left). Poppet valves consist of a long stem and a disk perpendicular to the stem, referred to as the valve head.

Aircraft reciprocating engines have two valves in each cylinder. One valve is the intake valve and the other is the exhaust valve. When the intake valve is open, the air/fuel mixture is allowed to enter the cylinder. When the exhaust valve is open, the burned gases escape the cylinder and flow into the exhaust system. When the valves are closed, or seated, the flow into and out of the cylinder is stopped and pressure from the combustion process is trapped in the combustion chamber (Figure 11-5-17).

Valve Construction

The valves in the cylinders of an aircraft engine are subjected to high temperatures, corrosion, and operating stresses; thus, the metal alloy in the valves must be able to resist all these factors. Because intake valves operate at lower temperatures than exhaust valves, they can be made of chromic-nickel steel. Exhaust valves are usually made of nichrome, silchrome, or cobalt-chromium steel because these materials are much more heat resistant.

The valve head has a machined face that forms a seal against the cylinder head when the valve is closed. The valve stem acts as a pilot for the valve head. The valve stem, face and tip are surface hardened to resist wear.

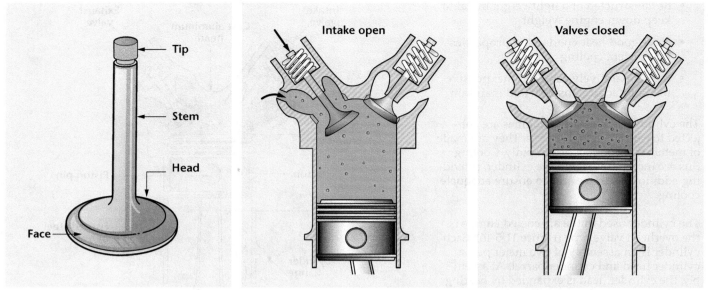

Figure 11-5-17. A poppet valve (left). Intake valve is open (middle), allowing the air-fuel mixture into the cylinder, exhaust valve is closed, blocking the exhaust port. Both valves are closed (right), keeping combustion pressure inside the cylinder and blocking the ports.

Valve Operating Mechanism

For a reciprocating engine to operate properly, each valve must open at the proper time, stay open for the required time, and close at the proper time. Intake valves are opened just before the piston reaches TDC, and exhaust valves remain open after TDC. For a short time, both valves are open (end of the exhaust stroke and beginning of the intake stroke). This valve overlap permits better volumetric efficiency and lowers the cylinder operating temperature.

The valve operating mechanism in an opposed engine consists of a camshaft equipped with lobes that move a *tappet* (also known as a *lifter*) (Figure 11-5-18). The tappet pushes a push rod that actuates a rocker arm that, in turn, pushes the valve open. Springs that slip over the valve stem push the valve mechanism in the opposite direction.

Camshaft

The valve mechanism of an opposed engine is operated by a camshaft. The camshaft is driven by a gear that mates with another gear attached to the crankshaft (Figure 11-5-19). The camshaft always rotates at half the crankshaft speed.

Cam lobes. Cam lobes are incorporated into the camshaft. The opening of the valves starts with the cam lobe. The size of the cam lobe determines how far a valve opens and how long it stays open. The valve lift (distance that the valve is lifted off its seat) and the valve duration (how long the valve is held open) are both determined by the shape of the cam lobes. Typical cam lobes are shown in Figure 11-5-20.

Tappets/Lifters

The tappet, also referred to as lifter or follower, slides on the cam lobe, following the cam lobe profile. The tappet's function is to convert the cam lobe's rotational movement into linear motion and to transmit this motion to the push rod, rocker arm, and then

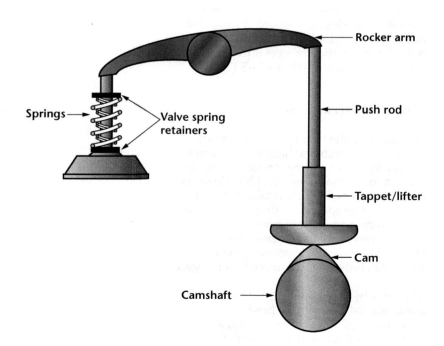

Figure 11-5-18. Valve-operating mechanism for an opposed engine.

to the valve tip, opening the valve head at the proper time. As the camshaft revolves, the lobes cause the tappet to rise, transmitting the force required through the push rod and rocker arm to open the valve.

A hole is drilled through the tappet to allow engine oil to flow to the hollow push rods to lubricate the rocker arm.

Solid lifters/tappets. Solid lifters generally require the valve clearance to be adjusted manually by adjusting a screw and lock nut. Valve clearance is needed to ensure that the valve has enough clearance in the valve train to close completely. This adjustment or inspection was a continuous maintenance item until hydraulic lifters were devised.

Hydraulic valve tappets/lifters. Most aircraft engines incorporate hydraulic tappets that automatically keep the valve clearance at zero, eliminating the necessity for any valve clearance adjustment mechanism. A typical hydraulic tappet (zero-lash valve lifter) is shown in Figure 11-5-21. When the engine valve is closed, the face of the tappet body (cam follower) is on the base circle or back of the cam.

The light plunger spring lifts the hydraulic plunger so that its outer end contacts the push rod socket, exerting a light pressure against it, thus eliminating any clearance in the valve linkage. As the plunger moves outward, the ball check valve moves off its seat. Oil from the supply chamber, which is directly connected with the engine lubrication system, flows in and fills the pressure chamber. As the camshaft rotates, the cam pushes the tappet body and the hydraulic lifter cylinder outward. This action forces the ball check valve onto its seat; thus, the oil trapped in the pressure chamber acts as a cushion.

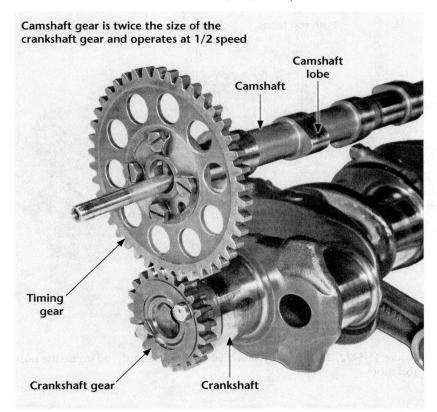

Figure 11-5-19. The cam drive mechanism for an opposed engine.

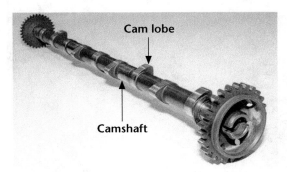

Figure 11-5-20. A typical cam lobe; its shape is referred to as the profile.

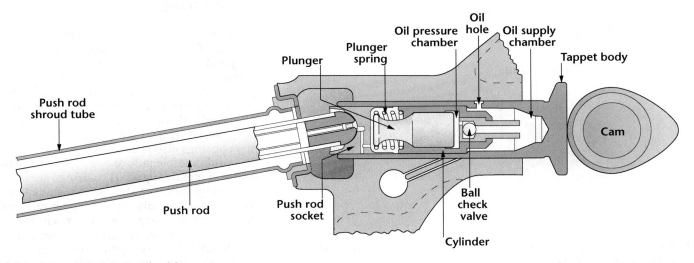

Figure 11-5-21. Hydraulic valve lifters.

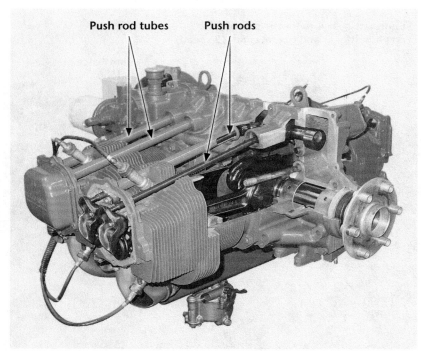

Figure 11-5-22. This cutaway allows you to see the push rod inside the push rod tubes.

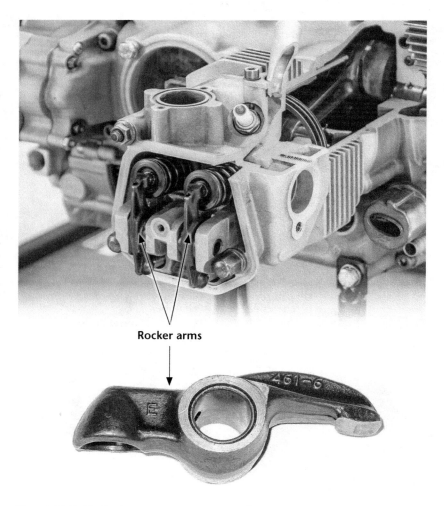

Figure 11-5-23. Rocker arms on an opposed engine (top) and one before being installed (bottom).

In the interval when the engine valve is off its seat, a predetermined leakage occurs between plunger and cylinder bore, which compensates for any expansion or contraction in the valve train. Immediately after the engine valve closes, the amount of oil required to fill the pressure chamber flows in from the supply chamber, preparing for another cycle of operation.

Hydraulic valve lifters require less maintenance, are better lubricated, and operate more quietly than the screw adjustment type.

Push Rods

The push rod, tubular in form, transmits the lifting force from the valve tappet to the rocker arm. A hardened-steel ball is pressed over or into each end of the tube. One ball end fits into the socket of the rocker arm. In some cases, the balls are on the tappet and rocker arm, and the sockets are on the push rod. The tubular form is used because it is light and strong. It permits the engine lubricating oil under pressure to pass through the hollow rod and the drilled ball ends to lubricate the ball ends, rocker-arm bearing, and valve stem guide. The push rod is enclosed in a tubular housing that extends from the crankcase to the cylinder head, referred to as push rod tubes (Figure 11-5-22).

Rocker Arms

The rocker arms transmit the lifting force from the cams to the valves (Figure 11-5-23). Generally, one end of the arm bears against the push rod, and the other bears on the valve stem. In some cases, one end of the rocker arm is slotted to accommodate a steel roller.

Valve Springs

Each valve is closed by two or three helical springs. If one spring is used, it vibrates or surges at certain speeds. To eliminate this problem, two or more springs (one inside the other) are installed on each valve. Each spring vibrates at a different engine speed; this rapidly dampens out all spring-surge vibrations during engine operation. Two or more springs also reduce danger of weakness and possible failure by breakage due to heat and metal fatigue. The springs are held in place by split ring stem keys installed in the recess of the valve spring upper retainer or washer and engage a groove machined into the valve stem. The stem keys form a lock to hold the valve spring retainers in place. The valve springs close the valve and hold the valve securely on the valve seat (Figure 11-5-24).

Valve Guides and Valve Seats

Valve guides and valve seats are installed into the cylinder head.

Valve seats. The valve seats are circular rings of hardened metal that the valve closes against and seals off the combustion chamber. The valve seats protect the relatively soft metal of the cylinder head from the hammering action of the valves as they close.

Bronze/steel valve guides. Bronze or steel valve guides are installed into drilled openings in the cylinder head to hold the valve stems in the correct position as they move up and down. The valve stem acts as a pilot for the valve head, keeping the head parallel to the seat. The guides also help to protect the cylinder head (Figure 11-5-25).

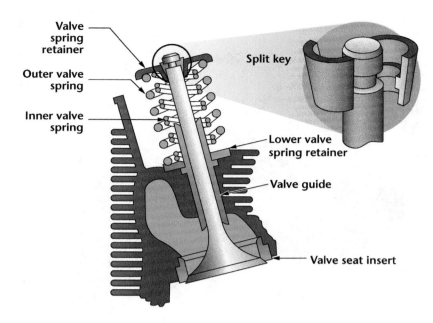

Figure 11-5-24. The valve springs close the valve. The valve spring split key retainer (inset) holds springs in place.

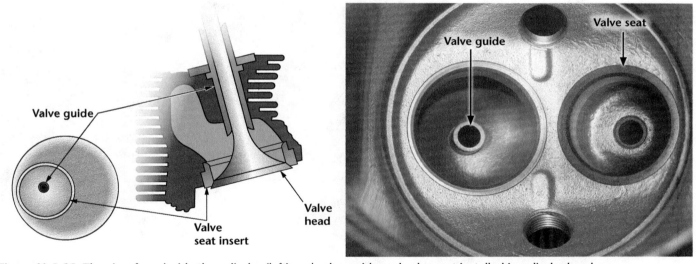

Figure 11-5-25. The view from inside the cylinder (left) and valve guide and valve seat installed in cylinder head.

Reciprocating Engine Systems

Section 1

Induction, Fuel Metering, and Exhaust

The induction system brings in air from the atmosphere, mixes it with fuel, and delivers the air/fuel mixture to the cylinder where combustion occurs. The induction system of an aircraft using a reciprocating engine consists of an air inlet scoop (Figure 12-1-1) used to collect the inlet air and ducting that transfers the air into an inlet filter. After the filter is a fuel metering device, either a carburetor or fuel injection system, and an intake manifold with long curved pipes or passages that completes path for the air/fuel mixture to get to the cylinders. The air/fuel mix is burned in the cylinders, and the burned exhaust gases exit the engine through the exhaust system.

Induction System

Induction systems can have different arrangements. Two common ones are the updraft and downdraft induction systems. Figure 12-1-2 shows an example of an updraft system. The carburetor is below the engine and air flows up and into the cylinders. The flow for a downdraft is the opposite, with the air flowing down into the cylinders. Induction systems can also be *naturally aspirated* (also called *normally aspirated*) or forced induction. Naturally aspirated systems are those that are not supercharged or turbocharged.

Air is admitted into the induction system through the air scoop (Figure 12-1-1), which is typically on the engine cowling below the propeller spinner. The air scoop helps to col-

Learning Objectives

DISCUSS
- Reciprocating engine induction, fuel metering, and exhaust systems
- Operation of turbochargers
- Reciprocating engine lubrication and cooling systems
- Ignition and starting systems
- Propellers and propeller governors

Left: Many additional systems are used to keep a reciprocating engine running well.

Figure 12-1-1. Inlet scoop.

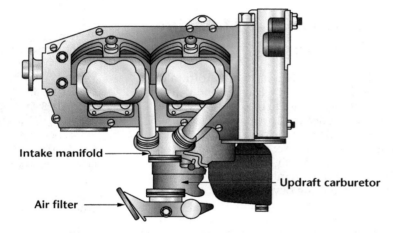

Figure 12-1-2. Induction system using a carburetor.

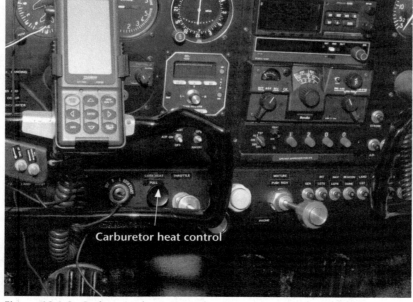

Figure 12-1-3. Carburetor heat control.

lect intake air and directs it into the induction system. The inlet placement takes advantage of the slipstream so the air is forced into the induction system, maximizing airflow into the engine.

Dust and dirt in the incoming air can be a serious source of trouble for an aircraft engine. Dust consists of small particles of hard, abrasive material that can be carried by the air and drawn into the engine cylinders, causing cylinder wear and damage. It can also collect, causing problems in the fuel-metering device and in the engine oil. The air filter, shown in Figure 12-1-2, prevents dirt and other foreign matter from entering the engine. Several types of air filters are used. Filters made from paper and foam are common.

In flight, the filter can become restricted by dirt, but more likely by icing. Ice can build up on the filter surface when operating in icing conditions or if the filter element freezes after it was rain soaked.

Because it is possible for the air filter to become clogged, an alternate source of air must be available. Usually, the alternate air is from inside the engine cowling, bypassing the clogged air filter. Because carburetor systems are also prone to carburetor icing, a carburetor heat air valve is near the carburetor for selecting a warm air source (carburetor heat) to prevent carburetor icing. Carburetor heat is operated by a control in the flight deck (Figure 12-1-3).

The carburetor heat valve can also be used as an alternate air source if the intake filter clogs. Fuel-injected systems use an alternate air door or valve to provide an alternate path for the intake air to bypass a clogged filter. On fuel injected engines, some alternate air doors function automatically; others operate manually (similar to the carburetor heat valve and control shown in Figure 12-1-3).

The air passes through the air ducts to the fuel-metering device. Two types of fuel-metering systems are used for reciprocating aircraft engines:

- The carburetor system mixes the air and fuel in the carburetor before this mixture enters the intake manifold.

- The fuel injection system mixes the fuel and air at each cylinder.

Filtered air enters the fuel-metering device (carburetor or fuel injection system) where the throttle valve controls the amount of air flowing to the engine (Figure 12-1-4). The throttle valve is connected to and actuated by the throttle lever inside the airplane (Figure 12-1-5).

In addition to controlling airflow, the fuel metering system also meters the fuel in proportion to the air. A mixture control lever (Figure 12-1-5) controls a fuel-metering valve that adjusts fuel flow, keeping the proper air to fuel ratio as the aircraft climbs to higher altitudes.

Pressure inside the intake manifold between the throttle valve and the cylinder is referred to manifold pressure. The absolute pressure in the manifold can be measured and is referred to as manifold absolute pressure (MAP). This pressure is measured in inches of mercury ("Hg). The pilot controls the throttle valve from the flight deck, regulating the flow of air which determines MAP and, thus, controls the engine power output.

From the fuel-metering device, the air or air/fuel mixture (depending on type of fuel metering device) travels to the engine cylinders and is distributed by the intake manifold. As mentioned, in carbureted engines, the air and fuel are mixed at the carburetor and then move through the intake manifold to the cylinders. Engines that have a fuel injection system, only air flows through the induction manifold and flows to the cylinders. Just before the intake valve, the air is mixed with fuel, and the combustible mixture enters the cylinder as the valve opens.

Fuel Metering for Reciprocating Engines

The engine fuel system must supply fuel to the engine's fuel metering device under all conditions of ground and air operation. It must function properly at constantly changing altitudes and in any climate.

The reciprocating engine's basic requirement of a fuel metering system is the same, regardless of the type of system used or the model engine on which it is equipped. It must control the airflow (throttle valve and throttle lever) and meter the fuel proportionately to the amount of air, establishing the proper air/fuel mixture ratio for the engine at all speeds and altitudes at which the engine can be operated. The fuel metering system also atomizes and distributes the air and fuel to the cylinders. It is desirable that the air/fuel mixture delivered to each cylinder has equal amounts of air and fuel.

Fuel flow is normally calibrated at sea-level air pressure where the correct air/fuel mixture ratio is established with the mixture control set in the most forward or *full rich* position. However, as altitude increases, the density of air entering the induction system decreases,

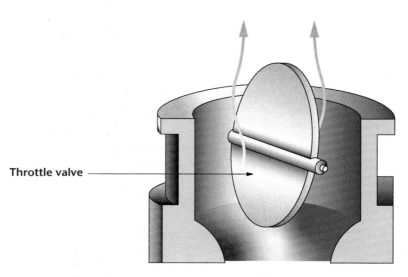

Figure 12-1-4. Throttle valve controls airflow through the induction system.

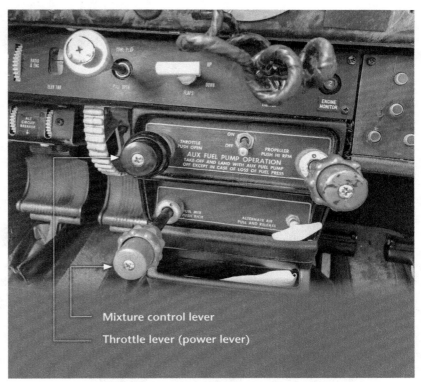

Figure 12-1-5. The throttle lever controls the throttle valve. The mixture control lever adjusts fuel flow.

but the fuel flow remains the same. This creates a progressively richer mixture as the aircraft's altitude increases. This results in a rich mixture that wastes fuel and can result in engine roughness and an appreciable loss of power at high altitudes.

To maintain the correct air/fuel mixture, the mixture must be leaned using the mixture control lever. Leaning the mixture decreases fuel flow, which compensates for the decreased air density at high altitude.

During a descent from high altitude, the air/fuel mixture must be enriched, using the mixture control lever, or it could become too lean.

When the mixture lever is moved all the way forward, it is in what is called the full rich position. The full rich position provides maximum fuel flow. The mixture is leaned by moving the lever aft. When the mixture lever is moved full aft, it is in the *idle cutoff* position. With the mixture lever in the idle cutoff position, all fuel flow stops.

Carburetors

Aircraft carburetors are separated into two categories: float-type and pressure-type. Float-type carburetors are the most common of the two carburetor types. The basic difference between a float-type and a pressure-type carburetor is in how the fuel is delivered. The pressure-type carburetor delivers fuel under pressure by using a fuel pump; a float-type carburetor relies on a pressure drop inside the carburetor venturi.

Carburetor principles. The carburetor measures the airflow through the induction system and uses this measurement to regulate the amount of fuel discharged into the airstream. The air-measuring unit is the venturi, which makes use of a basic law of physics: as the velocity of a gas or liquid increases, the pressure decreases. As shown in Figure 12-1-6, a simple venturi is a passageway or tube that has a narrow portion called the throat. As the velocity of the air increases to get through the narrow portion, its pressure drops. Note that the pressure in the throat is lower than that in any other part of the venturi. This pressure drop is proportional to the velocity and is, therefore, a measure of the airflow. The

basic operating principle of most carburetors depends on the differential pressure between the inlet and the venturi throat.

The carburetor is mounted on the engine so that air to the cylinders passes through the barrel, which is the part of the carburetor housing the venturi. The venturi's size and shape depends on the requirements of the engine. A carburetor for a high-powered engine might have one large venturi or several small ones. The air can flow either up or down through the venturi, depending on the design of the engine and the carburetor. Those in which the air passes down are known as downdraft carburetors, and those in which the air passes upward are called updraft carburetors. Some carburetors are even made to use a side draft or horizontal air entry into the engine induction system.

When a piston moves toward the crankshaft (down) on the intake stroke, the pressure in the cylinder lowers. Air rushes through the carburetor and intake manifold to the cylinder to replace the air displaced by the piston as it moves down on the intake stroke. With this low-pressure area, the higher-pressure air in the atmosphere flows in to fill the low-pressure area. As it does, the air must pass through the carburetor venturi.

The throttle valve is between the venturi and the engine. Mechanical linkage connects this valve with the throttle lever in the flight deck. The throttle regulates airflow to the cylinders and controls the power output of the engine. More air is admitted to the engine, and the carburetor automatically supplies enough additional gasoline to maintain the correct air to fuel ratio. This is because as the volume of airflow increases, the velocity in the venturi increases, lowering the pressure and allowing more fuel to be forced into the airstream. The throttle valve obstructs air passage very little when it is parallel with the flow, in the wide-open throttle position.

The float-type carburetor is the most common of all carburetors. In Figure 12-1-7 we see one type of float carburetor where the fuel moves through the float chamber and a regulated amount exits through the discharge nozzle. The float-operated needle valve regulates the flow through the inlet, which maintains the correct level in the fuel float chamber. This level must be slightly below the outlet of the discharge nozzle to prevent overflow when the engine is not running.

The discharge nozzle is in the throat of the venturi at the point where the lowest drop in pressure occurs as air passes through the carburetor to the engine cylinders. Two different pressures are acting on the fuel in the carburetor—a low pressure at the discharge

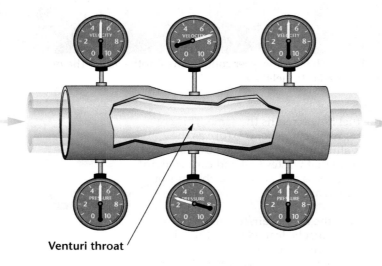

Venturi throat

Figure 12-1-6. A simple venturi.

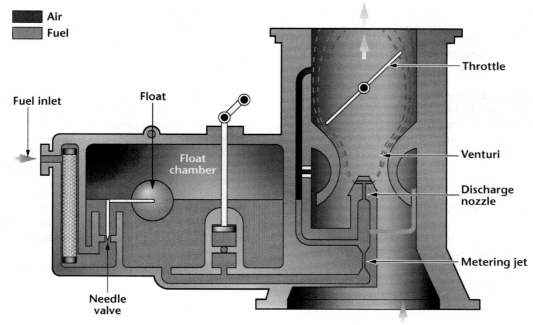

Air
Fuel

Fuel inlet

Float

Float chamber

Throttle

Venturi

Discharge nozzle

Metering jet

Needle valve

Figure 12-1-7. Fuel discharge in an updraft carburetor.

nozzle and a higher (atmospheric) pressure in the float chamber. The higher pressure in the float chamber forces the fuel through the discharge nozzle into the airstream. If the throttle is opened wider to increase the airflow to the engine, a greater drop in pressure exists at the venturi throat. Because of the higher differential pressure, the fuel discharge increases in proportion to the increase in airflow. If the throttle is moved toward the closed position, the airflow and fuel flow decrease.

The fuel must pass through the metering jet to reach the discharge nozzle (Figure 12-1-7). A metering jet is really a certain sized hole through which the fuel passes. The size of this jet determines the rate of fuel discharged at each differential pressure. If the jet is replaced with a larger one, the fuel flow increases, resulting in a richer mixture. If a smaller jet is installed, fuel flow decreases, creating a leaner mixture.

Carburetor Systems

To provide for engine operation under various loads and at different engine speeds, a carburetor can have up to six systems built into it.

- Main metering
- Idling
- Accelerating
- Mixture control
- Idle cutoff
- Power enrichment or economizer

Each of these systems has a definite function and is described below. It can act independently or with one or more of the others.

Main metering system. The main metering system supplies fuel to the engine at all speeds above idling. The fuel discharged by this system is determined by the drop in pressure in the venturi throat. A separate system is necessary for idling because the main metering system can be erratic at very low engine speeds. Therefore, most carburetors have an idling system to supply fuel to the engine at low engine speeds.

Idling system. With the throttle valve closed at idling speeds, air velocity through the venturi is so low that it cannot draw enough fuel from the main discharge nozzle; in fact, the spray of fuel can stop altogether. To allow the engine to idle, a fuel passageway is incorporated to discharge fuel from an opening in the low-pressure area near the edge of the throttle valve. This opening is called the idling jet.

Accelerating system. The accelerating system supplies extra fuel during sudden increases in engine power. When the throttle is opened, the airflow through the carburetor increases to obtain more power from the engine. The main metering system then increases the fuel discharge. During sudden acceleration, however, the increase in airflow is so rapid that there is a slight lag before the increase in fuel discharge is enough to provide the correct mixture ratio with the new airflow. By supplying extra fuel in this period, the accelerating system prevents a temporary leaning out of the mixture and gives smooth acceleration.

Mixture control system. The mixture control system determines the ratio of air to fuel in the mixture. Using the manual flight deck control, the pilot selects the mixture ratio to suit operating conditions.

Idle cutoff system. The carburetor has an idle cutoff system so that the fuel can be shut off to stop the engine. This system, incorporated in the manual mixture control, stops the fuel discharge from the carburetor completely when the mixture control lever is set to the *idle cutoff* position. The safest way to stop an aircraft engine is to shut off the fuel; do not simply turn off the ignition.

If the ignition is turned off with the carburetor still supplying fuel, fresh air/fuel mixture continues to pass through the induction system to the cylinders. As the engine is coasting to a stop and if it is excessively hot, local hotspots in the cylinder can ignite this combustible mixture. This can cause the engine to continue running or kick backward. Also, the mixture can pass through the cylinders unburned but be ignited in the hot exhaust manifold. Or the engine can come to an apparently normal stop, but a combustible mixture remains in the induction passages, the cylinders, and the exhaust system. This is an unsafe condition because the engine can kick over after it has been stopped and seriously injure anyone near the propeller.

When the engine is shut down by using the idle cutoff system, the spark plugs continue to ignite the air/fuel mixture until the fuel discharge from the carburetor ceases. The engine basically runs out of fuel. After the engine has come to a complete stop, the ignition switch is turned off.

Power enrichment system. The power enrichment system automatically increases the richness of the mixture during high-power operation. It makes possible the variation in air to fuel ratio necessary to fit different operating conditions. Essentially, it is a valve that is closed at cruising speeds and opened to supply extra supply extra fuel to the mixture during high power operation. The power enrichment system is sometimes called an economizer or a power compensator.

Although the various systems are discussed separately, the carburetor functions as a unit. The fact that one system is in operation does not necessarily prevent another from functioning. While the main metering system is discharging fuel in proportion to the airflow, the mixture control system determines whether the resultant mixture is rich or lean. If the throttle is suddenly opened wide, the accelerating and power enrichment systems act to add fuel to that already being discharged by the main metering system.

Carburetor Icing

The main disadvantage of the float-type carburetor is its tendency for ice to form inside. Carburetor ice as a result of the fuel vaporization and the decrease in air pressure in the venturi causes a sharp temperature drop in the carburetor. If water vapor in the air condenses when the carburetor temperature is at or below freezing, ice can form on the carburetor's internal surfaces, including the throttle valve. If enough ice builds up, the engine begins to run rough and can even stop.

Three general types of carburetor icing occur (Figure 12-1-8):

- Fuel evaporation ice
- Throttle ice
- Impact ice

Fuel evaporation ice. Fuel evaporation ice is formed with the decrease in air temperature resulting from fuel evaporating after it is introduced into the airstream. As the fuel evaporates, the temperature is lowered in the area where the evaporation takes place. Reduced air pressure in the venturi also contributes to a drop in temperature as the temperature drops as pressure decreases. Any

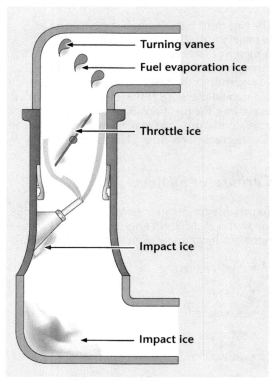

Figure 12-1-8 Three types of carburetor ice.

moisture in the incoming air can form ice in this area. Ice generally forms in the vicinity of the fuel discharge nozzle and in the venturi throat. This restricts the flow of the air/fuel mixture and reduces power. If enough ice builds up, the engine can cease to operate.

Carburetor ice is most likely to occur when outside air temperatures are below 70 degrees Fahrenheit (°F) or 21 degrees Celsius (°C) and the relative humidity is above 80 percent. Because of the cooling that takes place in the carburetor, icing can occur even in outside air temperatures as high as 100°F (38°C) and humidity as low as 50 percent. An induction system like that shown in Figure 12-1-9 likely has icing occurring on the inside.

Throttle ice. Throttle ice is formed on the rear side of the throttle, usually when the throttle is in a partially closed position. The rush of air across and around the throttle valve causes a low pressure on the rear side; this sets up a pressure differential across the throttle, which has a cooling effect on the air/fuel charge. Moisture freezes in this low-pressure area and collects as ice on the low-pressure side. Throttle ice tends to accumulate in a restricted passage. A small amount of ice here can cause a relatively large reduction in airflow and MAP. A large amount of ice can jam the throttles and cause them to become inoperable. Throttle ice seldom occurs with outside air above 38°F (3°C).

Impact ice. Impact ice is formed either from water present in the atmosphere as snow, sleet, or from liquid water that impinges on surfaces that are at temperatures below 32°F (0°C). Because of inertia effects, impact ice collects on or near a surface that changes the direction of the airflow. This type of ice can build up on the carburetor elbow and the carburetor air filter and metering elements. The most dangerous impact ice is that which collects on the carburetor air filter and causes a very rapid reduction of airflow and power. In general, danger from impact ice normally exists only when ice forms on the leading edges of the aircraft structure. Under some conditions, ice can enter the carburetor in a comparatively dry state and does not adhere to the inlet air filter or walls or affect engine airflow or MAP. This ice can enter the carburetor and gradually build up internally in the carburetor air metering passages and affect carburetor metering characteristics.

Most aircraft are equipped with an outside air temperature (OAT) gauge. It indicates the outside or ambient air temperature for calculating and is useful in detecting potential icing conditions.

Some engines are also equipped with carburetor air temperature indicating system. This temperature sensor informs the flight crew of conditions where induction system icing could occur.

Figure 12-1-9. An example of ice buildup on the outside of an induction system.   *Courtesy of Mark Stoltzfus*

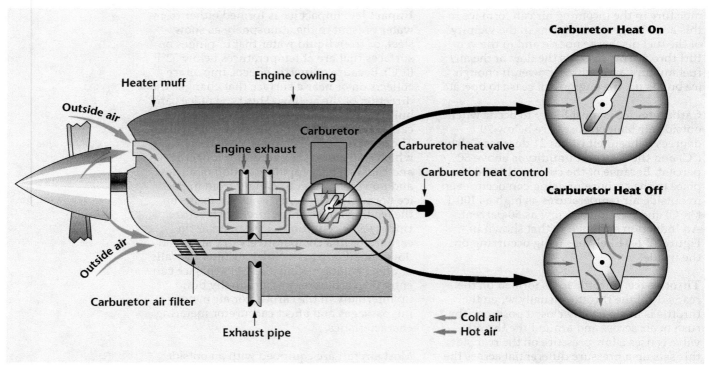

Figure 12-1-10. Air is heated by circulating outside the muffler and into the carburetor.

Carburetor heat. Induction system ice can be prevented or eliminated by raising the temperature of the air that passes through the system, using a carburetor heat system that is upstream near the induction system inlet and well ahead of the dangerous icing zones. This air is collected by a duct surrounding the muffler and is controlled with a valve that allows warm air into the induction system (Figure 12-1-10).

Carburetor heat can be used to preheat the air before it reaches the carburetor and keeps the air/fuel mixture above freezing, thus preventing carburetor ice from forming. Carburetor heat can also be used to melt ice that has already formed in the carburetor if the accumulation is not too great, but using carburetor heat as a preventative measure is the better option.

It is important to recognize carburetor ice when it forms in flight to prevent a loss in power, altitude, or airspeed. These symptoms can be accompanied by vibration or engine roughness. Once the pilot notices a power loss, he or she should take immediate action to eliminate ice already formed in the carburetor and to prevent further ice formation. This is done by applying full carburetor heat, which further reduces power and can cause engine roughness as melted ice goes through the engine. These symptoms can last from 30 seconds to several minutes, depending on the severity of the icing.

Using carburetor heat causes a decrease in engine power because the heated air is less dense than the outside air that had been entering the engine. This enriches the mixture. When ice is present in an aircraft with a fixed-pitch propeller and carburetor heat is being used, the r.p.m. slows, then gradually speeds up as the ice melts. The engine also should run more smoothly after the ice has been removed. If ice is not present, the r.p.m. slows and then remains constant. When carburetor heat is used on an aircraft with a constant-speed propeller and ice is present, MAP decreases, followed by a gradual increase. If carburetor icing is not present, the gradual increase in MAP is not apparent until the carburetor heat is turned off.

Pressure Injection Carburetors

Although not as common as they once were, some aircraft might have a pressure injection carburetor. Pressure injection carburetors are distinctly different from float-type carburetors because they do not incorporate a float chamber or a discharge nozzle in the venturi tube. Instead, they provide a pressurized fuel system that is closed from the engine fuel pump to the discharge nozzle. The venturi serves only to create pressure differentials for controlling the quantity of fuel to the metering jet in proportion to airflow to the engine.

The operating parameters of these carburetors are very different from float carburetors and are more like some types of fuel injection systems.

Fuel Injection Systems

In a fuel injection system, the fuel is injected directly into the cylinders, just outside of the intake valve. The air intake for the fuel injection system is similar to that used in a carburetor system, with an alternate air source in the induction system. This source is used if the external air source is obstructed. The alternate air source is usually operated automatically with a backup manual system that can be used if the automatic feature malfunctions.

A fuel injection system usually incorporates six basic components: an engine-driven fuel pump, an air/fuel control unit, a fuel manifold (fuel distributor), discharge nozzles, an auxiliary fuel pump, and fuel pressure/flow indicators.

The auxiliary fuel pump provides fuel under pressure to the air/fuel control unit for engine starting or emergency use. After starting, the engine-driven fuel pump provides fuel under pressure from the fuel tank to the air/fuel control unit.

This control unit, which essentially replaces the carburetor, meters fuel according to the mixture control setting and sends it to the fuel manifold valve at a rate controlled by the throttle.

After reaching the fuel manifold valve, the fuel is distributed to the individual fuel discharge nozzles. The discharge nozzles, which are in each cylinder head, inject the air/fuel mixture directly into each cylinder intake port.

The fuel-injection system has many advantages over a float carburetor. It has less chance of induction system icing because the drop in temperature from fuel vaporization takes place in or near the cylinder. Acceleration is also improved because of the positive action of the injection system. In addition, fuel injection improves fuel distribution. This reduces individual cylinder overheating, often caused by a variation in mixture from uneven distribution. The fuel-injection system also gives better fuel economy than a system in which the mixture to most cylinders must be richer than necessary so that the cylinder with the leanest mixture operates properly.

Fuel-injection systems vary in their construction, arrangement, and operation. The Bendix and Continental fuel-injection systems are introduced next.

Bendix fuel injection. Today, Precision Airmotive manufactures the RSA fuel injection system; Bendix is the former name. This series consists of an injector, flow divider, and fuel discharge nozzle (Figure 12-1-11). It is a continuous-flow system that measures engine air consumption and uses airflow forces to control fuel flow to the engine.

The heart of the RSA system is the regulator, which you can see in Figure 12-1-11. The regulator section uses two diaphragms to control fuel flow. The air diaphragm reacts to the difference between the pressure of air at the intake of the carburetor, and the pressure at the throat of the venturi. The fuel metering diaphragm reacts to the difference between

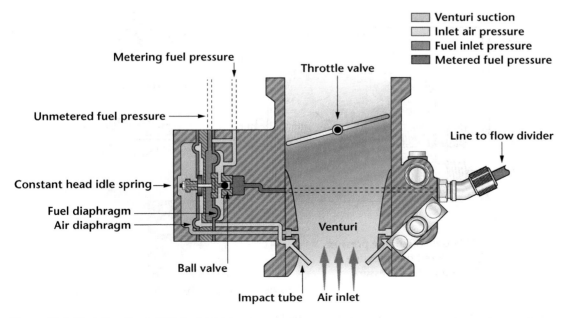

Figure 12-1-11. A Bendix or RSA fuel injector.

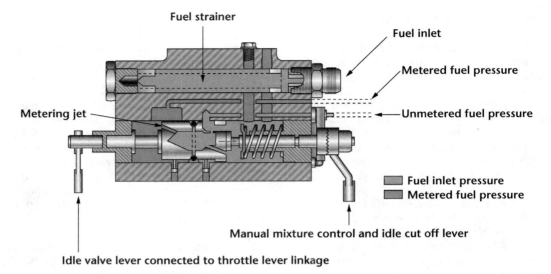

Figure 12-1-12. Fuel metering section of a Bendix fuel injection system.

the unmetered fuel pressure (supplied by the fuel pump) and metered fuel pressure (which is supplied to the fuel metering section).

The ball valve attached to the fuel diaphragm controls the orifice opening and fuel flow through the forces placed on it. The distance the ball valve opens is determined by the difference between the pressures acting on the diaphragms. This difference in pressure is proportional to the airflow through the injector. Thus, the volume of airflow determines the rate of fuel flow.

The fuel metering section is attached to the air metering section and contains an inlet

fuel strainer, a manual mixture control valve, an idle valve, and the main metering jet. This unit is illustrated in Figure 12-1-12. The fuel metering section meters and controls the fuel flow to the flow divider. The manual mixture control valve produces full rich condition when the lever is against the rich stop and a progressively leaner mixture as the lever is moved toward idle cutoff. Both idle speed and idle mixture can be adjusted externally to meet individual engine requirements.

The metered fuel is delivered from the fuel control unit to a pressurized flow divider. This unit keeps metered fuel under pressure, divides fuel to the various cylinders at all

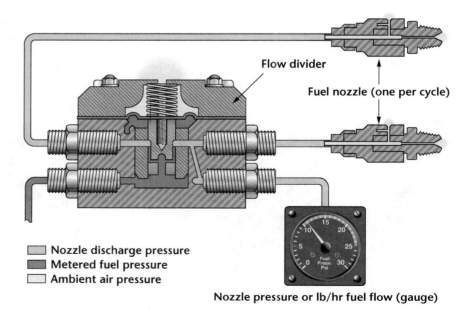

Figure 12-1-13. The Bendix system flow divider, fuel flow indicator, fuel nozzle.

engine speeds, and shuts off the individual nozzle lines when the control is moved to idle cutoff (Figure 12-1-13).

A fuel pressure gauge, calibrated in pounds per hour fuel flow, can be used as a fuel flow meter. This gauge is connected to the flow divider and senses the pressure being applied to the discharge nozzle. This pressure is in direct proportion to the fuel flow and indicates the engine fuel flow.

The fuel is discharged through a fuel nozzle. One nozzle for each cylinder is in the cylinder head. The nozzle outlet is directed into the intake port.

Continental/TCM fuel-injection system.
The Continental fuel-injection system injects fuel into the intake valve port in each cylinder head. This system is illustrated in Figure 12-1-14. The system consists of a fuel injector pump, a control unit, a fuel manifold, and

a fuel discharge nozzle. It is a continuous-flow type, which controls fuel flow to match engine airflow.

Ignoring the effect of altitude or ambient air conditions, using a positive-displacement, engine-driven pump means that changes in engine speed affect total pump flow proportionally. Because the pump provides greater capacity than is required by the engine, a recirculation path is required. By arranging a calibrated orifice and relief valve in this path, the pump delivery pressure is also maintained in proportion to engine speed. These provisions ensure proper pump pressure and fuel delivery for all engine speeds.

The function of the air/fuel control assembly is to control engine air intake and to set the metered fuel pressure for proper air/fuel ratio. The air throttle is mounted at the manifold inlet and its butterfly valve, positioned by the throttle control inside the aircraft

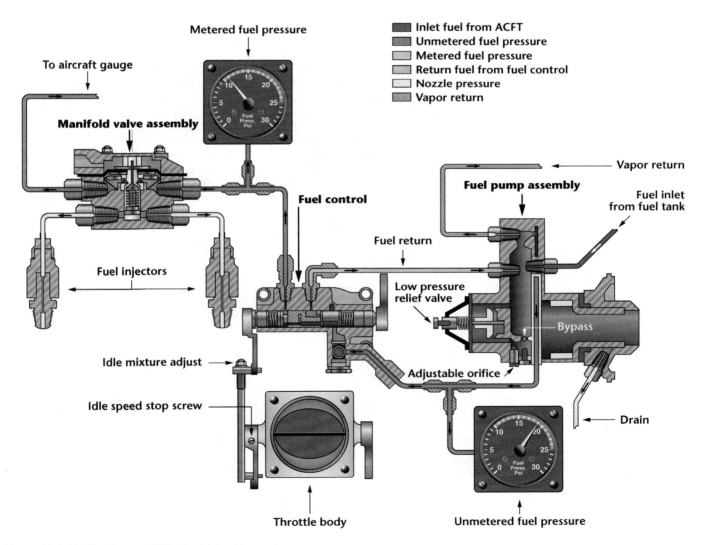

Figure 12-1-14. Continental/TCM fuel-injection system.

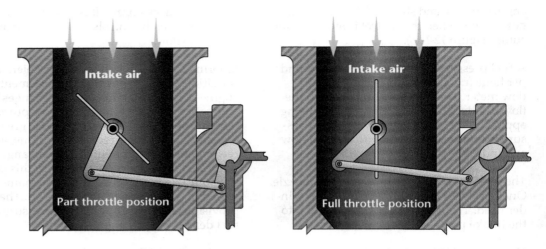

Figure 12-1-15. Continental/TCM system fuel air control unit.

(Figure 12-1-15), controls the flow of air to the engine. The air throttle assembly contains the shaft and butterfly-valve assembly. The casting bore size is tailored to the engine size, and no venturi or other restriction is used.

Fuel enters the control unit through a strainer and passes to the metering valve (Figure 12-1-16). This rotary valve has a cam-shaped edge on the outer part of the end face. The position of the cam at the fuel delivery port controls the fuel passed to the manifold valve and the nozzles. The fuel return port connects to the return passage of the center metering plug. The alignment of the mixture control valve with this passage determines the amount of fuel returned to the fuel pump.

By connecting the metering valve to the air throttle, the fuel flow is properly proportioned to airflow for the correct air to fuel ratio. A control level is mounted on the mixture control valve shaft and connected to the flight deck mixture control.

The fuel manifold valve contains a fuel inlet, a diaphragm chamber, and outlet ports for the lines to the individual nozzles (Figure 12-1-17). The spring-loaded diaphragm operates a valve in the central bore of the body. Fuel pressure provides the force for moving the diaphragm. The diaphragm is enclosed by a cover that retains the diaphragm loading spring. When the valve is down against the lapped seat in the body, the fuel lines to the

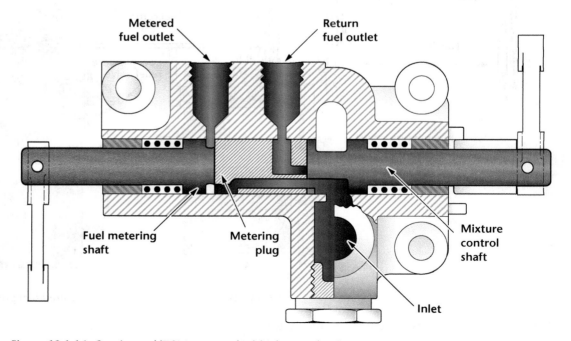

Figure 12-1-16. Continental/TCM system dual fuel control unit.

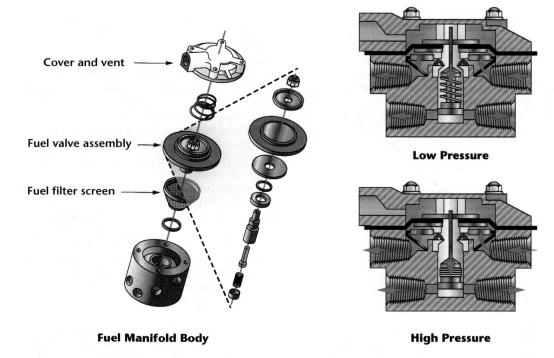

Figure 12-1-17. Continental/TCM system fuel manifold valve assembly.

cylinders are closed off. The valve is drilled for fuel to pass from the diaphragm chamber to its base, and a ball valve is installed in the valve. All incoming fuel must pass through a fine screen installed in the diaphragm chamber.

From the fuel-injection control valve, fuel is delivered to the fuel manifold valve, which provides a central point for dividing fuel flow to the individual cylinders. In the fuel manifold valve, a diaphragm raises or lowers a plunger valve to open or close the individual cylinder fuel supply ports simultaneously.

The fuel discharge nozzle is mounted in the cylinder head with its outlet directed into the intake port. A fuel nozzle is illustrated in Figure 12-1-18.

Exhaust Systems

Engine exhaust systems vent the burned combustion gases overboard and provide heat for the cabin and carburetor heat system. Most exhaust systems have exhaust piping attached to the cylinders and a muffler, muffler shroud, and additional piping required to allow the exhaust to exit to the atmosphere.

Many exhaust systems have an exhaust gas temperature (EGT) probe installed on the hottest cylinder, or sometimes a probe for each cylinder. The probes transmit the exhaust temperature to an EGT indicator in the air-

plane. This temperature varies with the ratio of air to fuel entering the cylinders and can be used as a basis for regulating the air/fuel mixture.

Two general types of exhaust systems are used on reciprocating engines: the short stack (open) system and the collector system.

Short stack system. The short stack system is relatively simple and consists of one exhaust pipe attached to each cylinder. Each pipe carries the exhaust gases away from the engine to where it enters the atmosphere.

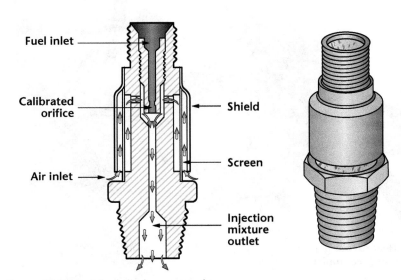

Figure 12-1-18. A fuel discharge nozzle.

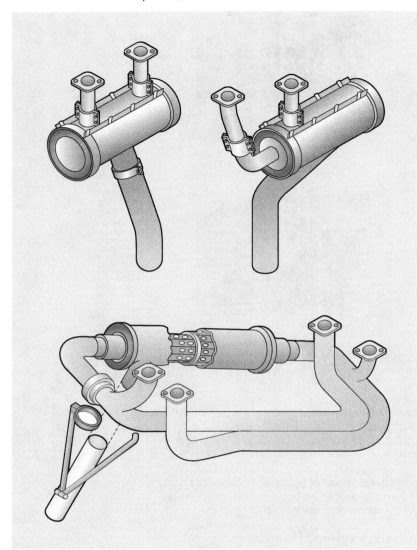

Figure 12-1-19. Exhaust collector systems. The left and right sides of a four-cylinder collector system (top), and a crossover system that collects from all cylinders (bottom).

Heat exchanger
shroud (heat muff)

Figure 12-1-20. Heat exchanger around muffler.

Collector system. Various configurations of collector systems are used. These systems use a manifold or riser pipe to collect the exhaust gas at each cylinder and then route it into a larger collector pipe or muffler before going into the atmosphere. Many engines use a collection system for the cylinders on each side of the engine, some collect the exhaust from all the cylinders into a common pipe or muffler. Figure 12-1-19 shows two types of collector systems for a four-cylinder engine. The top drawing shows a system collecting exhaust gas from the two cylinders on the right side of an engine, through a muffler, and an additional pipe for the exhaust to exit the muffler. An identical system is on the left side cylinder. The bottom drawing shows exhaust gas collected from each cylinder into one muffler and then an additional pipe to carry the exhaust from the muffler. The mufflers reduce engine noise.

Heat exchangers. For cabin heat, and for engines with carburetors, outside air drawn into an air inlet is ducted through a shroud around the muffler. The muffler, heated by the exiting exhaust gases, heats the air around the muffler. This heated air is then ducted to the cabin for heat and defrost applications. The heat and defrost are controlled in the flight deck and can be adjusted to the desired level. The heated air also provides carburetor heat to prevent carb ice (Figure 12-1-20).

Failures (cracks) in the exhaust system could allow exhaust gases to escape into the cabin heat system. Exhaust gases contain much carbon monoxide, which is odorless and colorless. Carbon monoxide is deadly, and its presence is virtually impossible to detect. To ensure that exhaust gases are properly expelled, the exhaust system must be in good condition and free of cracks.

Section 2

Superchargers and Turbochargers

Forced induction systems incorporate a supercharger or turbocharger to increase engine horsepower. Both turn a compressor in the induction system that compresses the intake air to increase its density, increasing engine power. The key difference lies in the method of turning the compressor. A supercharger relies on an engine-driven compressor. A turbocharger gets its power from a turbine in the exhaust system, which spins the compressor (Figure 12-2-1).

Aircraft with these systems have a MAP gauge, which displays MAP in the engine's intake manifold. As a naturally aspirated aircraft climbs, it eventually reaches an altitude where the MAP is insufficient for a normal climb. This altitude limit is known as the aircraft's service ceiling, and it is directly affected by the engine's ability to produce power. If the induction air entering the engine is pressurized, by either a supercharger or a turbocharger, the aircraft's service ceiling can be increased. Both increase engine power by increasing MAP. The increase in MAP is referred to as amount of *boost*.

Superchargers

A supercharger is an engine-driven air pump or compressor that provides additional pressure to the induction air as compressed air so that the engine can produce additional power. It increases MAP and forces the air/fuel mixture into the cylinders. Higher MAP increases the density of the air/fuel mixture and increases the power an engine can produce.

Engine-driven superchargers were used primarily on radial engines and certain large horizontally opposed engines. The major disadvantage of a supercharger is that it uses much of the engine's power output to turn the compressor, which reduces amount of power increase produced.

Turbochargers

Turbochargers, sometimes referred to as turbosuperchargers, are more efficient than superchargers because turbochargers are powered by an engine's exhaust gases. This means a turbocharger recovers energy from hot exhaust gases that would otherwise be lost.

A second advantage of turbochargers over superchargers is that they can maintain an engine's rated sea-level horsepower from sea level up to the engine's critical altitude. Critical altitude is the maximum altitude at which a turbocharged engine can produce its rated horsepower. Above the critical altitude, power output begins to decrease like it does for a naturally aspirated engine.

A turbocharger has two main elements: a compressor and turbine, linked by a shaft. As the compressor section spins, induction

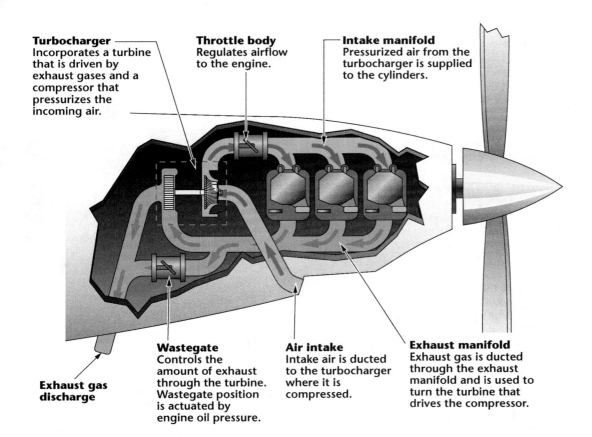

Turbocharger Incorporates a turbine that is driven by exhaust gases and a compressor that pressurizes the incoming air.

Throttle body Regulates airflow to the engine.

Intake manifold Pressurized air from the turbocharger is supplied to the cylinders.

Exhaust gas discharge

Wastegate Controls the amount of exhaust through the turbine. Wastegate position is actuated by engine oil pressure.

Air intake Intake air is ducted to the turbocharger where it is compressed.

Exhaust manifold Exhaust gas is ducted through the exhaust manifold and is used to turn the turbine that drives the compressor.

Figure 12-2-1. Turbocharger components.

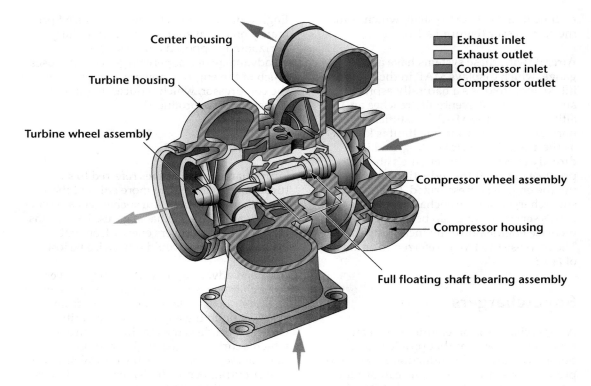

Figure 12-2-2. A typical turbosupercharger and its main parts.

air is drawn into the center of the compressor and is accelerated toward the outside of the compressor. The air then passes through a diffuser that slows the air and increases pressure. The high-pressure, high-density air is then delivered to the engine through the intake manifold. To turn the compressor, the engine's exhaust gases are used to drive a turbine wheel that is mounted on the opposite end of the compressor's drive shaft (Figure 12-2-2).

Another component in the exhaust system is the wastegate (Figure 12-2-3). The wastegate, essentially an adjustable butterfly valve installed in the exhaust system, is used to vary how much exhaust gas flows to the turbine. By varying the amount of exhaust gases over the turbine, the turbine and linked compressor r.p.m. are controlled, thus varying the pressure change in the intake manifold.

When closed, most of the exhaust gases from the engine flow through the turbine, increasing compressor r.p.m. and the amount of boost. When open, the exhaust gases bypass the turbine by flowing directly out through the engine's exhaust pipe, decreasing compressor r.p.m. and amount of boost (Figure 12-2-4). When the wastegate valve is fully closed, r.p.m. is high, producing the largest amount of boost. When the wastegate valve is fully open, r.p.m. is low, producing little boost.

Because gas temperature increases when the gas is compressed, turbocharging raises the induction air temperature. To reduce this temperature and lower the risk of detonation, many turbocharged engines use an intercooler. This small heat exchanger uses outside air to cool the hot compressed air.

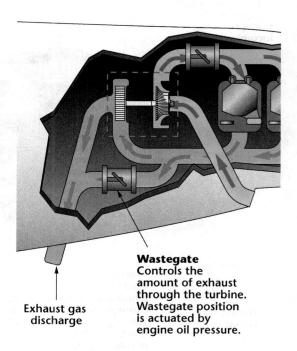

Wastegate
Controls the amount of exhaust through the turbine. Wastegate position is actuated by engine oil pressure.

Exhaust gas discharge

Figure 12-2-3. The wastegate controls exhaust airflow over the turbine.

System Operation

On most modern turbocharged engines, wastegate valve position is governed by a pressure-sensing control mechanism coupled to an actuator. Engine oil directed into or away from this actuator moves the wastegate position. The wastegate actuator is physically connected to the wastegate by mechanical linkage and controls the wastegate butterfly valve's position. On these systems, the actuator is automatically positioned to produce the desired MAP simply by changing the position of the throttle control.

Altitude turbocharging or turbo-normalizing is achieved by using a turbocharger that maintains maximum allowable sea-level MAP (normally 29 "Hg to 30 "Hg) up to a certain altitude. As an aircraft equipped with a turbo-normalizing system climbs, the wastegate is gradually closed to maintain the maximum allowable MAP. At some point, the wastegate is fully closed and further increases in altitude cause the MAP to decrease. This altitude is specified by the airplane manufacturer and is referred to as the airplane's critical altitude. Above the critical altitude, the MAP decreases with higher altitude.

Ground boosting, on the other hand, is an application of turbocharging that MAP is

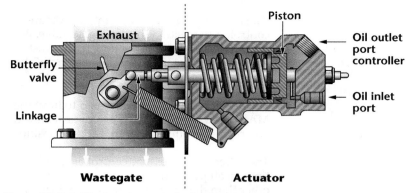

Figure 12-2-4. Wastegate control of exhaust.

increased in flight from sea level up. These engines, sometimes called sea-level-boosted engines, can develop more power at sea level than an engine without turbocharging. Airplanes using ground boosting, takeoff MAPs exceed the normal 29 "Hg to 30 "Hg limits and can go as high as 45 "Hg.

Wastegate Control

Most aircraft use an automatic wastegate control. Figure 12-2-5 is a schematic of one type of turbocharger system. This system uses a

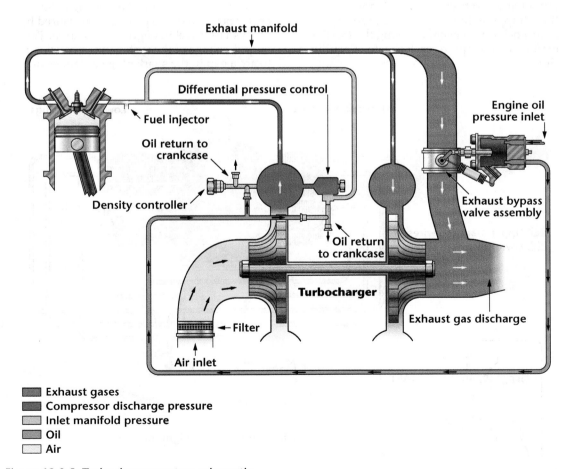

Exhaust gases
Compressor discharge pressure
Inlet manifold pressure
Oil
Air

Figure 12-2-5. Turbocharger system schematic.

density controller and differential pressure controller to position the wastegate valve. Both controllers regulate the oil flow to the wastegate actuator, determining the position of the actuator and the wastegate valve.

The density controller is designed to limit the MAP below the turbocharger's critical altitude and regulates only at the full throttle position.

The differential pressure controller functions in all positions of the wastegate valve other than the fully open position, which is controlled by the density controller. The two controllers operate independently to control turbocharger operation at all positions of the throttle.

Operating characteristics. *Bootstrapping* is an indication of unregulated power change that results in the continual drift of MAP. This condition can be illustrated by considering the operation of a system when the wastegate is fully closed. Any slight change in power caused by a change in temperature or r.p.m. fluctuation is magnified and results in MAP change because the slight change causes a change in the amount of exhaust gas flowing to the turbine. Any change in exhaust gas flow to the turbine causes a change in power output and is reflected in MAP indications. Bootstrapping, then, is an undesirable cycle of turbocharging events causing the MAP to drift in an attempt to reach a state of equilibrium.

Bootstrapping is sometimes confused with the condition known as *overboost*, but bootstrapping is not a condition that is detrimental to engine life. An overboost condition is one in which MAP exceeds the limits prescribed for an engine and can cause serious damage. Pressure relief valves are used in some systems to prevent damaging overboost if a system malfunction occurs.

Section 3

Ignition and Starting

Ignition Systems

In a spark ignition engine, the ignition system provides a spark that ignites the air/fuel mixture in the cylinders. The basic requirements for reciprocating engine ignition systems are similar regardless of the type of engine. All ignition systems must deliver a high-voltage spark at a spark plug in each engine cylinder, in the correct firing order. The spark timing must also take place at a predetermined number of degrees ahead of the top dead center position of the piston, as measured by crankshaft travel in degrees of rotation. The output voltage of the system must be adequate to arc a gap in the spark plug electrodes under

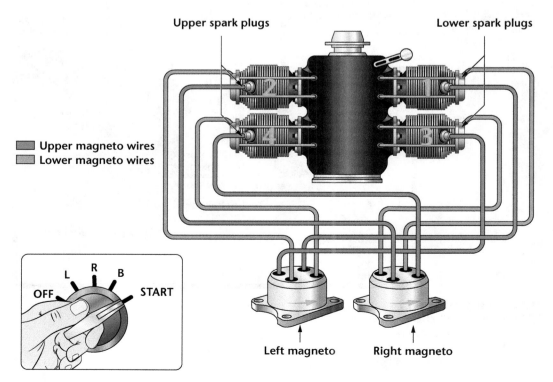

Figure 12-3-1. A magneto ignition system.

all operating conditions. The spark plug is threaded into the cylinder head with the electrodes exposed to the combustion area of the engine's cylinder.

Magneto Ignition

A magneto ignition system is made up of two magnetos, two spark plugs per cylinder, two ignition harnesses, and an ignition switch (Figure 12-3-1). A magneto is an engine-driven generator that uses a permanent magnet to generate an electrical current completely independent of the aircraft's electrical system. The magneto generates sufficiently high voltage to jump a spark across the spark plug gap in each cylinder. The system begins to fire when the starter is engaged and the crankshaft begins to turn. It continues to operate whenever the crankshaft is rotating. The ignition harness is the electrical connection between the magneto and spark plug.

Most standard certificated aircraft incorporate a dual ignition system with two individual magnetos, separate ignition harness, and two spark plugs in each cylinder to increase reliability of the ignition system. Each magneto operates independently to fire one of the two spark plugs in each cylinder. Firing two spark plugs improves combustion of the air/fuel mixture and results in a slightly higher power output. If one of the magnetos fails, the other is unaffected. The engine contin-

ues to operate normally, although a slight decrease in engine power can be expected. The same is true if one of the two spark plugs in a cylinder fails.

Magneto. The magneto is a special type of engine-driven alternating current (AC) generator (Figure 12-3-2). Using a permanent magnet, coil of wire, and the relative movement of the magnetic field, current is generated in the wire. At first, the magneto generates electrical power by the engine rotating the permanent magnet and inducing a current to flow in the coil windings. As current flows through the coil windings, it generates its own magnetic field that surrounds the coil windings. At the correct time, this current flow is stopped and the magnetic field collapses across a second set of windings in the coil. This action causes a high-voltage to be generated in the coil's secondary winding. This is the voltage used to arc across the spark plug gap. The three basic things needed to generate electrical power are present to develop the high voltage that forces a spark to jump across the spark plug gap in each cylinder. Magneto operation is timed to the engine so that a spark occurs only when the piston is on the proper stroke at a specified number of crankshaft degrees before the top dead center piston position.

The magneto system can be divided, for purposes of discussion, into three distinct circuits: magnetic, primary electrical, and secondary electrical circuits.

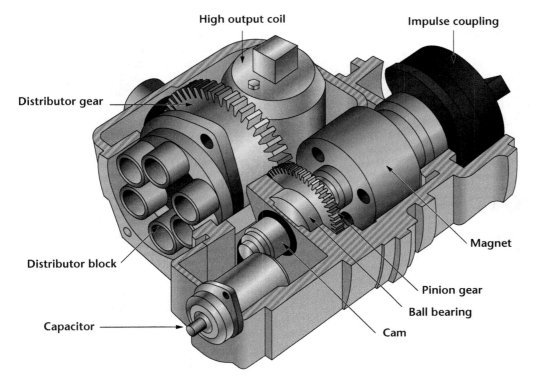

Figure 12-3-2. A magneto.

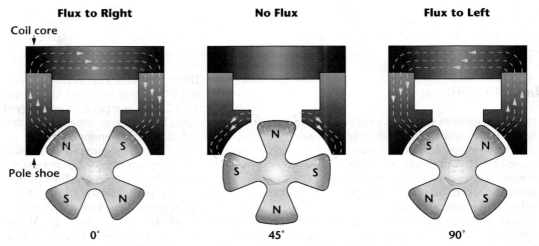

Figure 12-3-3. Magnetic flux at three positions of the rotating magnet.

The magnetic circuit consists of a permanent multi-pole rotating magnet, a soft iron core, and pole shoes (Figure 12-3-3). The magnet is geared to the aircraft engine and rotates in the gap between two pole shoes to furnish the magnetic lines of force (flux) needed to produce an electrical voltage.

The primary electrical circuit consists of a set of breaker contact points, a condenser, and an insulated winding (Figure 12-3-4). The third unit in the circuit, the condenser (capacitor), prevents arcing at the points when the circuit is opened and hastens the collapse of the magnetic field about the primary winding.

The secondary circuit contains the secondary windings, distributor rotor, distributor cap, ignition lead, and spark plug (Figure 12-3-5).

When the breaker points are closed, the primary electrical circuit is completed, and the rotating magnet induces current flow in the primary circuit. This current flow generates its own magnetic field.

Opening the breaker points stops the flow of current in the primary circuit and allows the magnetic rotor to quickly reverse the field through the winding. This sudden flux reversal produces a high rate of flux change in the winding that cuts across the secondary winding of the magneto (wound over and insulated from the primary winding) (Figure 12-3-5), inducing the pulse of high-voltage electricity in the secondary needed to fire a spark plug. As the rotor continues to rotate, the primary breaker points close again, and the cycle is repeated to fire the next spark plug in firing order.

The high voltage induced in the secondary winding is directed to the distributor, which consists of two parts: revolving and stationary. The revolving part is called a distributor rotor and the stationary part is called a distributor block. The rotating part, which can take the shape of a disk, drum, or finger, is made of a nonconducting material with an embedded conductor. The stationary part consists of a block also made of nonconducting material that contains terminals and terminal receptacles into which the ignition lead wiring that connects the distributor to the spark plug is attached.

Because the distributor rotates at one-half crankshaft speed on all four-stroke cycle engines, the distributor block has as many electrodes as there are engine cylinders, or as many electrodes as cylinders served by the magneto. The electrodes are located circumferentially around the distributor block so that, as the rotor turns, a circuit is completed to a different cylinder and spark plug each time there is alignment between the rotor finger and an electrode in the distributor block. The electrodes of the distributor block are numbered consecutively in the direction of distributor rotor travel.

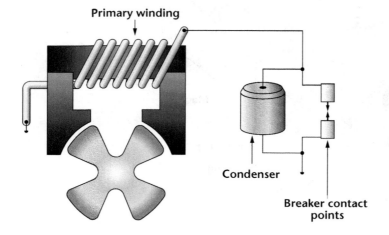

Figure 12-3-4. Primary electrical circuit of a high-tension magneto.

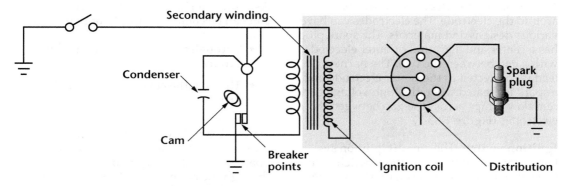

Figure 12-3-5. The magneto's secondary circuit.

Ignition harness. The ignition harness contains an insulated wire or lead for each cylinder. One end of each lead is connected to the magneto distributor block, and the other end is connected to the proper spark plug.

The ignition lead directs the electrical energy from the magneto to the spark plug. The ignition harness contains an insulated wire for each cylinder that the magneto serves in the engine. Figure 12-3-6 shows a typical lead wire construction. The ignition harness provides the conductor path for the voltage to the spark plug. It also serves as a shield for stray magnetic fields that surround the wires as they momentarily carry high-voltage current. By conducting these magnetic lines of force to the ground, the ignition harness cuts down electrical interference with the aircraft radio and other electrically sensitive equipment.

Spark plugs. The spark plug in an ignition system provides a short impulse of high-voltage current in the combustion chamber. There, the high-voltage current jumps across the spark plug's air gap, producing an electric spark to ignite the air/fuel charge.

Spark plugs operate in extreme temperatures, electrical pressures, and very high cylinder pressures. A cylinder of an engine operating at 2,100 r.p.m. must produce about 17 separate high-voltage sparks that bridge the air gap of one spark plug each second. Because of the extremes in which spark plugs must operate and because the engine loses power if one spark does not occur correctly, it is imperative that the spark plug functions properly.

The three main components of a spark plug are the electrode, insulator, and outer shell (Figure 12-3-7). The outer shell is threaded into the cylinder. Close-tolerance screw threads and a copper gasket prevent cylinder gas pressure from escaping around the plug. The other end is threaded to receive the ignition lead from the magneto (Figure 12-3-8).

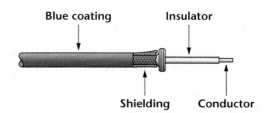

Figure 12-3-6. Ignition lead.

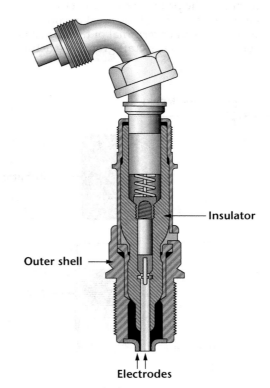

Figure 12-3-7. Spark plug.

Figure 12-3-8. Ignition lead spark plug end.

The insulator provides a protective core around the electrode. The electrodes can have various designs and materials. The spark plug has a center and a ground or outer electrode with a gap between the two. The harness lead is connected to the center electrode and a spark is created when the high voltage current flow jumps across the gap between the electrodes (Figure 12-3-7).

Ignition switch. The aircraft ignition system is controlled by an ignition switch. The type of switch used varies with the number of engines on the aircraft and the type of magnetos used. On some aircraft, this switch also provides power for turning the starter. All switches, however, control the ignition system in the same way. The ignition switch is different from most other types of switches: when the ignition switch is in the OFF position, a circuit is completed through the switch to ground (Figure 12-3-9). In other electrical switches, the OFF position normally breaks or opens the circuit.

The ignition switch has one terminal connected to the primary electrical circuit between the coil and the breaker contact points. The other terminal of the switch is connected to the aircraft ground structure.

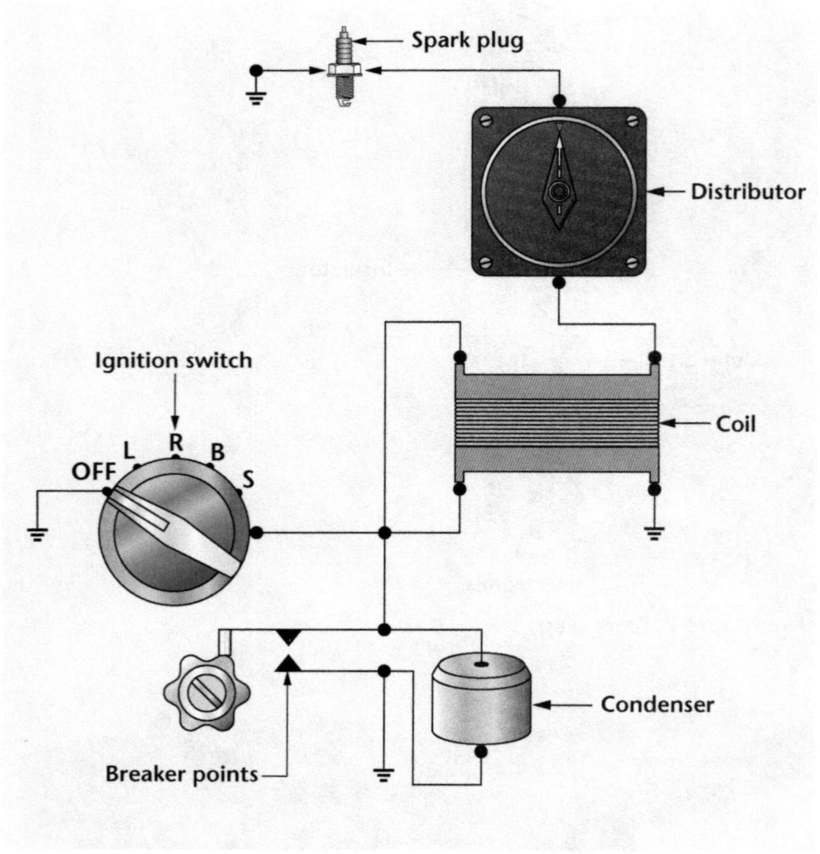

As shown in Figure 12-3-9, the primary circuit can be completed in one of two ways:

- Through the closed breaker points to ground
- Through the closed ignition switch to ground

Figure 12-3-9 shows that the primary current is not interrupted when the breaker contacts open because there is still a path to ground through the closed, or OFF, ignition switch. This path ground is provided by the magneto ground lead, usually referred to as the P-lead. Because primary current is not stopped when the contact points open, there can be no sudden collapse of the primary winding flux field and no high voltage is induced in the secondary winding to fire the spark plug, and the magneto is inoperative.

When the ignition switch is placed in the on position, the interruption of primary current and the rapid collapse of the primary winding flux field is once again controlled or triggered by the opening of the breaker contact points. When the ignition switch is in the on position, the switch has absolutely no effect on the primary circuit.

Ignition System Control and Checks

The operation of the magneto is controlled in the flight deck by the ignition switch (Figure 12-3-10). A common switch has five positions:

- OFF
- R (right)
- L (left)
- B or BOTH
- START

With RIGHT or LEFT selected, only the associated magneto is activated. The system operates on both magnetos when BOTH or START is selected. In the START position, both magnetos are activated and also the starter. Moving the switch to the BOTH position deactivates the starter, and both magnetos remain (activated (switch moves from start to both). With the switch in the R position, the right magneto is active and the left magneto is deactivated. With the switch in the L position, the left magneto is activated and the right magneto is deactivated. Both magnetos are deactivated if the switch is in the OFF position.

To ensure that the ignition system is operating properly, checks are performed during

Figure 12-3-9. Typical ignition switch in the off position.

the aircraft engine run-up, which is the engine check before each flight and before engine shutdown. The magneto check, as it is usually referred to, is performed during the engine run-up checklist.

The ignition system check is used to check the individual magnetos, harnesses, and spark plugs. Before flight and after the engine is properly warmed up, the engine r.p.m. is increased to a specified r.p.m. for the ignition system check and allowed to stabilize. The r.p.m. is specified in the aircraft flight manual (AFM) or pilot's operating handbook (POH), usually around 1,700 to 1,800 r.p.m. When the ignition switch is placed the ignition in the R position, a small drop in the r.p.m. should be noted. Then the switch is returned to the BOTH position, and engine speed should return to the original setting. Allow the switch to remain in the both position for a few seconds so that the r.p.m. stabilizes again. Place the ignition switch in the L position and again note the r.p.m. drop. Return the ignition switch to the BOTH position. Note the amount of total r.p.m. drop that occurs for each magneto position. Generally a 150 to 200 r.p.m. drop is acceptable. The r.p.m. drop for both magnetos should be similar, generally within 25 to 75 r.p.m. of each other. Always refer to the AFM or POH for specific information about an acceptable drop. This r.p.m. drop is because operating on one magneto, the combustion is not as efficient as it is with two magnetos providing sparks in the cylinder. Note that *no drop* in r.p.m. is not normal, and in that instance, the aircraft should not be flown.

Remember, this checks the magnetos and the ignition leads and spark plugs. If either magneto has excessive r.p.m. drop, or no r.p.m. drop while operating in the R or L position, the ignition system must be checked for problems.

Another check is performed to see that all magneto ground leads are electrically grounded. The ignition switch check is usually made at 700 r.p.m. On those aircraft engine installations that do not idle at this low r.p.m., set the engine speed to the lowest possible to perform this check. When the proper speed is obtained, momentarily turn the ignition switch to OFF. The engine should completely quit firing. After a drop of 200–300 r.p.m. is observed, return the switch to BOTH as rapidly as possible. If the ignition switch is not returned quickly enough, the engine r.p.m. drops off completely and the engine stops.

If the engine does not cease firing with the switch in the OFF position, the magneto

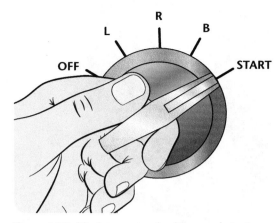

Figure 12-3-10. A common ignition and start switch.

P-lead is disconnected or broken, and one or both of the magnetos are not deactivated even with the ignition switch in the OFF position. This can be a dangerous situation because the engine could accidentally start if the propeller is moved and there is residual fuel in the cylinder.

Starting Help

When starting the engine, the magneto's output is low because the engine's cranking speed is low. This is understandable because the strength of the rotating magnet and the number of turns in the coil are constant factors in magneto ignition systems. The voltage produced depends on the speed at which the rotating magnet is turned. When the engine is being cranked for starting, the magnetos are rotating at a low speed compared to when the engine is running. At this low speed, the magnetos cannot produce enough voltage to jump the spark plug gap. This results in a weak or no spark.

To facilitate engine starting, impulse couplings or a starter vibrator can be used to improve the spark intensity.

Impulse coupling. Many opposed reciprocating engines are equipped with an impulse coupling as the auxiliary starting system. The impulse coupling performs two functions: rotating the magneto fast enough to produce a good spark and retarding the timing of the spark during the start cycle.

An impulse coupling gives one of the magnetos attached to the engine, generally the left, a brief acceleration, that produces an intense spark for starting. This device consists of a cam and flyweight assembly, spring,

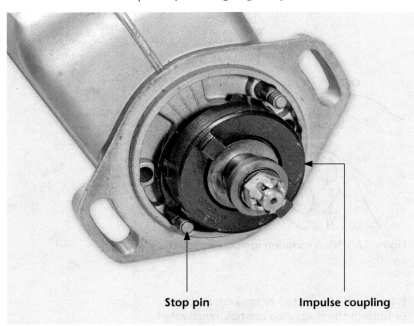

Figure 12-3-11. Impulse coupling installed on magneto.

and a body assembly. An assembled impulse coupling is shown installed on a magneto in Figure 12-3-11.

The magneto is flexibly connected through the impulse coupling with a spring so that at low speeds the magneto is temporarily held. The flyweight, because of slow rotation, catches on a stud or stop pins (Figure 12-3-12) and the magneto spring is wound as the engine continues to turn. The engine continues to rotate until the piston of the cylinder to be fired nears a top dead center position. At this point, the magneto flyweight contacts the body of the impulse coupling and is released. The spring kicks back to its original position, resulting in a quick twist of the rotating magnet of the magneto (Figure 12-3-13). This magneto speed is equivalent to high-speed magneto rotation in normal engine operation.

After the engine is started, centrifugal force on the flyweights causes them to no longer engage the stop pin. This makes it a solid unit, returning the magneto to a normal timing position relative to the engine. The presence of an impulse coupling is identified by a sharp clicking noise when the propeller is turned by hand.

Starter vibrator (shower of sparks). To provide for more spark power in the starting cycle, a starter vibrator or shower of sparks system (Figure 12-3-14) was developed that provides several sparks at the spark plug electrodes.

This starting vibrator changes the DC of the battery into a pulsating DC and delivers it to the magneto's primary winding. Placing the ignition switch to the START position energizes the starter and causes the engine to rotate. At the same time, current also flows through the starter vibrator, and sends the pulsating DC to the magneto winding.

Because this current is being interrupted many times per second, the resulting magnetic field is building and collapsing across the primary and secondary windings of the magneto. The rapid successions of separate voltages induced in the secondary winding produces a shower of sparks across the selected spark plug air gap.

Usually the starter vibrator is used only with the left magneto, with the right magneto deactivated during starting. The magneto used with the starter vibrator has an extra set of breaker points referred to as retard breaker points. With this system installed, an impulse coupling is not needed.

During start, after the engine begins to accelerate, the manual starter switch is released, causing both the vibrator and retard breaker points to become inoperative. It also removes the ground from the right magneto. Both

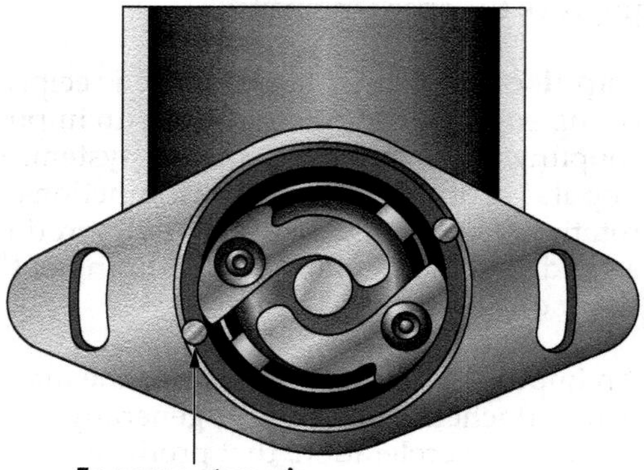

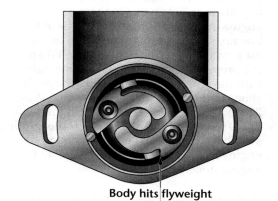

Figure 12-3-12. The flyweight engages the stop pin.

Figure 12-3-13. The impulse coupling body hits the flyweight and releases.

Figure 12-3-14. A starter vibrator produces sparks that ignite the combustible mixture.

magnetos now fire at the normal set degrees of crankshaft rotation before top dead center.

Full Authority Digital Engine Control (FADEC) System

Some aircraft use a newer system to control the ignition timing and fuel delivery schedule. A Full Authority Digital Engine Control (FADEC) is a solid-state digital electronic ignition and electronic sequential port fuel injection system. A FADEC system continuously monitors and controls ignition and fuel delivery. It is an integrated control system. The FADEC system monitors engine operating conditions and then automatically adjusts the air to fuel ratio mixture and ignition timing accordingly for any

power setting to attain optimum engine performance. As a result, engines equipped with a FADEC system require neither magnetos or a manual mixture control.

The components of one type of FADEC system are shown in Figure 12-3-15.

In this system, the engine control unit (ECU) is at the heart, providing both ignition and fuel injection control. The system sensors continuously monitor various engine parameters such as r.p.m., crank position, fuel pressure, intake MAP, intake manifold temperature, cylinder head temperatures (CHT), and EGT.

Using this information, the ECU can determine the fuel required for the combustion cycle for either best power or best economy mode of operation. The computer precisely times the injection event, and the duration of the injector should be on for the correct air to fuel ratio. Then, the computer sets the spark ignition event and ignition timing, again using the percentage of power calculation. EGT is measured after the burn to verify that the air to fuel ratio calculations were correct for that combustion event.

The computers can also vary the amount of fuel to control the air to fuel ratio for each cylinder, thus controlling both CHT and EGT.

An ECU is assigned to a pair of engine cylinders. Each ECU contains an electronic circuit board. Each electronic control board contains two independent microprocessor controllers that serve as control channels. During engine operation, one control channel is assigned to

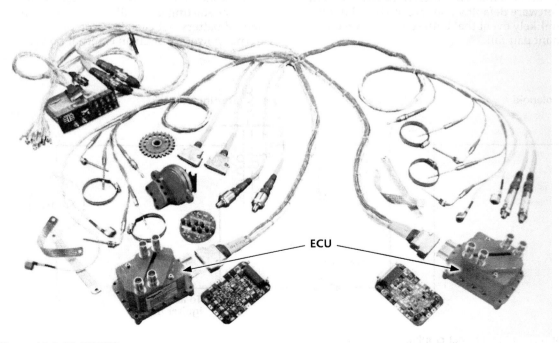

ECU

Figure 12-3-15. FADEC system components.

Figure 12-3-16. Example of an ECU.

operate one engine cylinder. Therefore, one ECU can control two engine cylinders, one control channel per cylinder. The control channels are independent, and there are no shared electronic components in one ECU. They also operate on independent and separate power supplies. However, if one control channel fails, the other control channel in the pair in the same ECU can operate both its assigned cylinder and the other opposing engine cylinder as backup control for fuel injection and ignition timing. An example ECU is shown in Figure 12-3-16.

All critical sensors are dually redundant with one sensor from each type of pair connected to control channels in different ECUs. Synthetic software default values are also used in the unlikely event that both sensors of a redundant pair fail.

Starting Systems

A starter is an electric motor capable of developing large amounts of mechanical energy that can be applied to the engine crankshaft, through a gear system, causing it to rotate. Reciprocating engines need to be turned at only a relatively slow speed until the engine starts and turns on its own. Once the reciprocating engine has fired and started, the starter is disengaged and has no further function until the next start.

In the early stages of aircraft development, relatively low-powered reciprocating engines were started by pulling the propeller through a part of a revolution by hand. This was often difficult in cold weather when lubricating oil temperatures were near the congealing point. The magneto systems also delivered a weak starting spark at the very low cranking speeds. This was often compensated for by providing a hot spark using such ignition system devices as the induction vibrator or impulse coupling.

As the aircraft reciprocating engine was developed from the earliest use of starting systems to the present, several starter systems have been used. Even today, some small, low-powered aircraft use hand cranking of the propeller, or "propping," for starting. However, most reciprocating engine starters are the direct-cranking electric type. This type of starter provides instant and continual cranking when energized.

A typical circuit for a direct cranking electric starter is shown in Figure 12-3-17. Electrical power for starting is usually supplied by an onboard battery but can also be supplied by external power through an external power

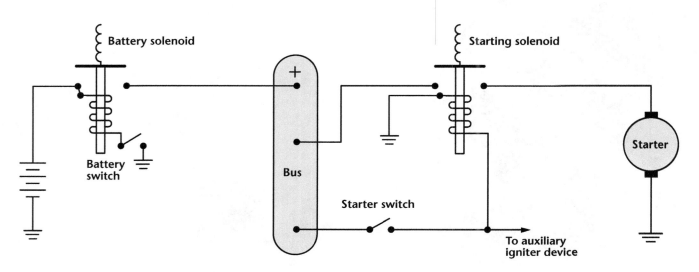

Figure 12-3-17. Typical starting circuit in a direct cranking electric starter.

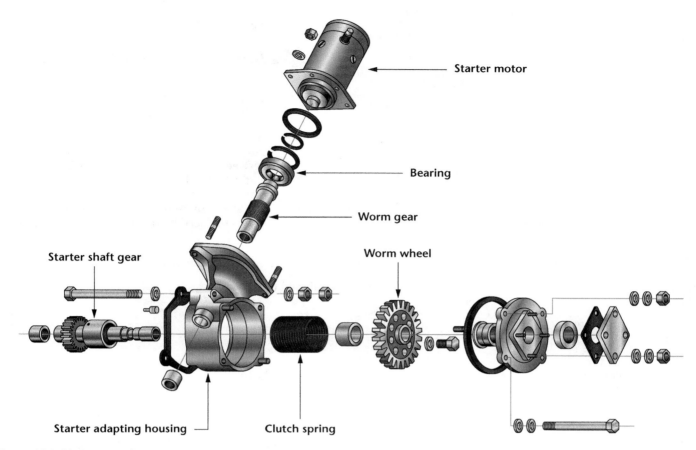

Figure 12-3-18. Starter adapter.

receptacle. When the battery switch is turned on, electricity is supplied to the main power bus bar through the battery solenoid.

The starting solenoid is energized by turning the starter switch (or ignition switch) to the START position, completing the circuit to the starter motor, rotating the starter motor. When the starter switch is released from the START position, the solenoid removes power from the starter motor. The starter motor is protected from being driven by the engine through a clutch in the starter drive that allows the engine to run faster than the starter motor.

When starting an engine, the rules of safety and courtesy should be strictly observed. One of the most important safety rules is to ensure that no one is near the propeller before starting the engine. In addition, the wheels should be chocked and the brakes set to avoid hazards caused by unintentional movement.

Some engines use an electric starter motor mounted on a right-angle drive adapter at the back of the engine attached to the accessory case (Figure 12-3-18).

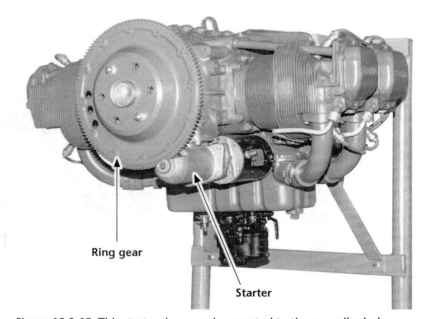

Figure 12-3-19. This starter ring gear is mounted to the propeller hub.

Other engines use a starter that drives a ring gear mounted to the propeller hub (Figure 12-3-19). In both cases, the starter turns the engine crankshaft until the engine is started.

Oil film between parts preventing
metal-to-metal contact,
which reduces friction

Figure 12-4-1. Oil reduces friction by preventing
metal surfaces from contacting each other.

Section 4
Lubrication and Cooling

Lubrication System

As discussed in chapter 10, the primary purpose of a lubricant is to reduce friction between moving parts. Engine oil coats an engine's metal surfaces so that no metal-to-metal contact occurs (Figure 12-4-1). As long as the oil film remains unbroken, metallic friction is replaced by the internal fluid friction of

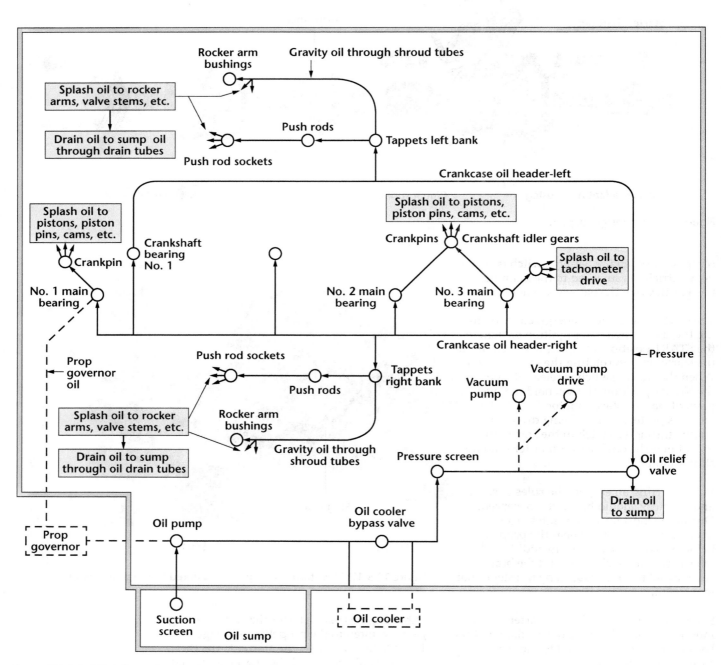

Figure 12-4-2. Oil delivered under pressure.

the lubricant. The lubrication or oil system circulates oil throughout the engine to all areas requiring lubrication.

Aircraft reciprocating engine pressure lubrication systems can be divided into two basic classifications: wet sump and dry sump. The main difference is that the wet-sump system stores oil in a reservoir inside the engine. After the oil is circulated through the engine, it is returned to this crankcase-based reservoir. A dry-sump engine pumps the oil from the engine's crankcase to an external tank that stores the oil. The dry-sump system uses a scavenge pump, some external tubing, and an external tank to store the oil. Wet-sump engines are generally not used for aerobatic aircraft because the entire oil supply would flood the engine with oil, when inverted.

One of the main components in an oil system, wet or dry, is the oil supply or pressure pump. This pump moves oil to various engine components. Two methods are used in aircraft engines to deliver oil to the parts: pressure and splash.

Engine parts that have oil delivered under pressure are said to be pressure lubricated. Other parts are lubricated by oil splash, which is not pressurized. Figure 12-4-2 shows how oil moves through internal passageways in the engine, providing pressurized oil to the engine bearings and other components by splash.

Oil System Components

The following components are used in a typical oil system:

- Oil pressure pump (supply pump)
- Oil scavenge pump (dry sump only)
- Oil tank (dry sump only)
- Pressure relief valve
- Oil filter
- Oil filter bypass
- Oil cooler
- Oil cooler control valve
- Oil pressure sensor and indicator
- Oil temperature sensor and indicator

Oil pump, relief valve, oil filter, filter bypass valve. Oil entering the engine is pressurized, filtered, and regulated as it flows through the engine. Figure 12-4-3 shows example oil flow through the oil pump, relief valve, oil filter, filter bypass valve.

As oil enters the engine, it is pressurized by an engine-driven, gear-type pump. This pump is a positive displacement pump consisting of two meshed gears that revolve inside the housing. The clearance between the teeth and housing is small. The pump inlet is on the left and the discharge port is connected to the engine's system pressure line. One gear is attached to a splined drive shaft that extends from the pump housing to an accessory drive shaft on the engine. The lower gear rotates counterclockwise, and the driven idler gear turns clockwise.

As oil enters the gear chamber, it is picked up by the gear teeth, trapped between them and the sides of the gear chamber, is carried around the outside of the gears, and discharged from the pressure port into the

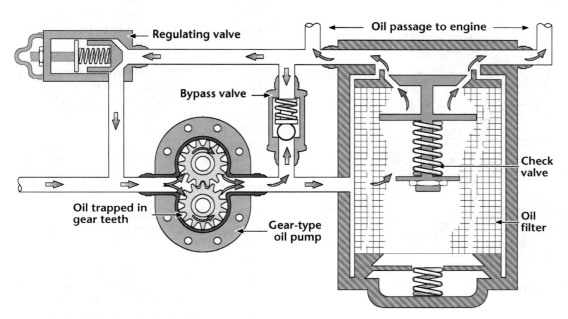

Figure 12-4-3. Pump, relief valve, filter, filter bypass.

oil filter passage. The pressurized oil flows to the oil filter, where any solid particles suspended in the oil are separated from it, preventing possible damage to engine moving parts. Several types of filters are used: cleanable or disposable. Figure 12-4-4 shows an example of a common spin-on, disposable oil filter.

The oil filter bypass valve, between the pressure side of the oil pump and the oil filter, permits unfiltered oil to bypass the filter and enter the engine if the oil filter is clogged or during cold weather if congealed oil is blocking the filter during engine start. The spring loading

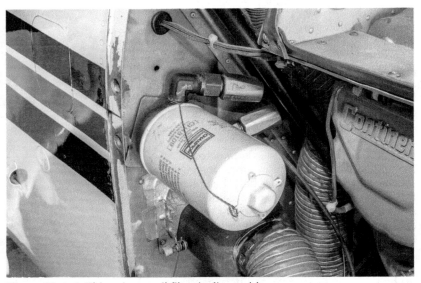

Figure 12-4-4. This spin-on oil filter is disposable.

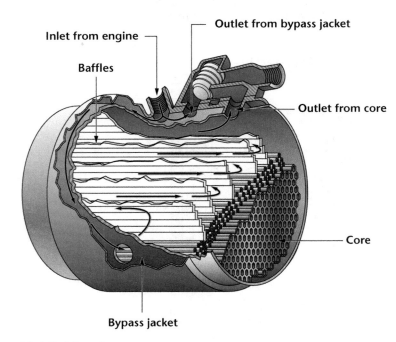

Figure 12-4-5. Oil cooler.

on the bypass valve allows the valve to open before the oil pressure collapses the filter; in the case of cold, congealed oil, it provides a low-resistance path around the filter. Dirty oil in an engine is better than no lubrication.

An oil pressure relief valve limits oil pressure to a predetermined value, depending on the installation. This valve is usually referred to as a relief valve, but its real function is to regulate the oil pressure at a preset pressure level. The oil pressure must be sufficiently high to ensure adequate lubrication of the engine and its accessories at high speeds and powers. This pressure helps ensure that the oil film between the crankshaft journal and bearing is maintained. However, the pressure must not be too high, because leakage and damage to the oil system could result.

Oil cooler and oil cooler control valve. The coolers consist of a core enclosed in a double-walled shell. The core is built of copper or aluminum tubes with the tube ends formed to a hexagonal shape and joined together in the honeycomb effect (Figure 12-4-5).

Oil flows through the spaces between the tubes as the cooling air passes through the tubes, cooling the oil.

The oil viscosity varies with the temperature. Because the viscosity affects its lubricating properties, the temperature at which the oil enters an engine must be held within close limits. The amount of cooling must be controlled if the oil is to return to the engine at the correct temperature. The oil cooler flow control valve determines which of the two possible paths the oil takes through the oil cooler. Different valve designs are used, but the idea is to allow hot oil to go through the oil cooler and cold oil to bypass the oil cooler.

When the oil is cold, the valve directs the oil flow around the outside of the tubes or bypasses the tubes altogether, depending on valve design. This allows the oil to warm up quickly and, at the same time, heat the oil in the core. As the oil warms up and reaches its operating temperature, the valve position changes and directs the oil flow through the oil cooler core.

Oil pressure indication system. The oil pressure indicator is the most important instrument to perceive the health of an engine. Usually, the oil pressure gauge indicates the pressure that oil enters the engine from the pump. This gauge warns of possible engine failure caused by an exhausted oil supply, oil pump failure, burned-out bearings, ruptured oil lines, or other causes that could be indicated by a loss of oil pressure.

Several methods are used to measure oil pressure. Bourdon tubes and electrical transmitters are common. The oil pressure is displayed on an indicator inside the aircraft. Oil pressure is usually indicated in p.s.i. (Figure 12-4-6).

Oil Temperature Indication System

The oil temperature sensor is located so that it measures the temperature of the oil before it enters the engine's hot sections. An oil temperature indicator in the flight deck is commonly connected to the oil temperature sensor by electrical leads. Reciprocating engine oil temperature is generally indicated in degrees Fahrenheit. Any malfunction of the oil cooling system appears as an abnormal reading.

Example Oil System

Other than location of the oil storage and a scavenge pump for a dry-sump system, wet and dry-sump systems use similar components. Because the dry-sump system contains all the components of the wet-sump system,

Figure 12-4-6. An analog oil pressure indicator.

the dry-sump system is explained as an example system.

An example dry-sump lubrication system used for a small, single-engine aircraft is shown in Figure 12-4-7. In a typical dry-sump pressure-lubrication system, a mechanical, engine-driven pump, supplies oil under pressure to the bearings throughout the engine. The oil flows into the inlet or suction side of an engine the pump, through a suction screen and exits the pressure side of the pump and into the oil filter. If the filter becomes clogged,

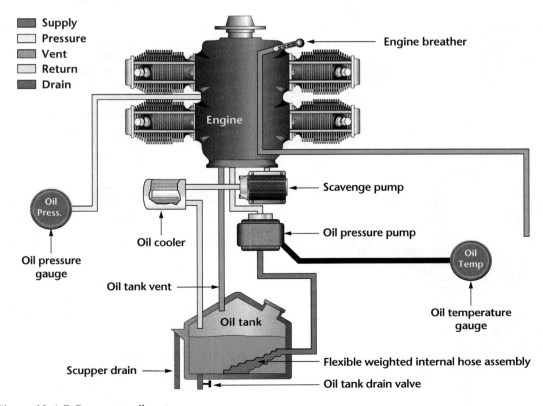

Figure 12-4-7. Dry-sump oil system.

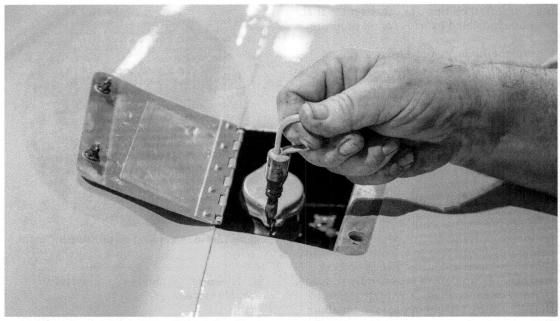

Figure 12-4-8. Checking the engine oil level before operating the engine.

the filter bypass valve opens and bypasses the filter. A pressure relief (regulating) valve senses when system pressure is reached and opens enough to bypass oil back to the inlet side of the oil pump. Then, the oil flows into a manifold that distributes the oil through drilled passages to the various engine parts.

When the circulating oil has lubricated and cooled the moving parts of the engine, it drains by gravity into the lowest parts of the engine. Oil collected at the bottom of the engine is picked up by engine-driven scavenge pumps as quickly as it accumulates. These pumps have a greater capacity than the pressure pump. This is needed because the oil volume has generally increased because of foaming (mixing with air). On dry-sump engines, this oil leaves

the engine, passes through or bypasses the oil cooler, depending on temperature, and returns to the supply tank. A thermostat attached to the oil cooler controls oil temperature by allowing part of the oil to flow through the cooler and part to flow directly into the oil supply tank.

Oil Change and Checking Quantity

Oil, in service, is constantly exposed to many harmful substances that reduce its ability to protect moving parts. The main contaminants include gasoline, moisture, acids, dirt, carbon, and metallic particles.

Because these harmful substances accumulate, a common practice is to drain the entire lubrication system at regular intervals and refill it with new oil. The time between oil changes varies, but a typical interval is 25 to 50 hours, depending on the type of oil filter used. Oil changes include oil filter replacement for disposable filters and cleaning a cleanable filter.

The oil filler cap and the dipstick used to measure the oil quantity are usually accessible through a panel in the engine cowling (Figure 12-4-8). If the quantity does not meet the manufacturer's recommended operating levels, oil should be added before any engine operation.

Engine Cooling

The burning fuel in the cylinders produces intense heat, most of which is expelled through the exhaust system. Much of the remaining heat, however, must be removed,

Cooling fins

Figure 12-4-9. Cooling fins increase surface area.

or at least dissipated, to prevent the engine from overheating. Otherwise, the extremely high temperatures can lead to loss of power, excessive oil consumption, detonation, and serious engine damage.

Most aircraft reciprocating engines are air cooled. Some older aircraft engines and many diesel aircraft engines use liquid cooling. In a liquid-cooled engine, liquid coolant is circulated and the coolant takes away the excess heat. The excess heat is then dissipated by a heat exchanger or radiator.

Air Cooling System

Cooling is a matter of transferring the excess heat from the cylinders to the air, but there is more to this job than just placing the cylinders in the airstream. Much of the wasted heat from the combustion process is absorbed by the cylinders. To help transfer heat from the engine cylinder to the surrounding air manufacturers incorporate cooling fins in the cylinder (Figure 12-4-9). Cooling fins increase the cylinder outside surface area. The increased surface area increases heat transfer to the surrounding air.

Air cooling is achieved by flowing air into the engine compartment through openings in the cowling. Baffles divide the inside of the cowl into an area of high pressure above the engine and low pressure below the engine. The pressure differential keeps the air moving through the inside of the cowl and over the engine. Baffles also route air through the cooling fins on the engine cylinders and other parts of the engine. The cooling air absorbs heat from the engine. The air exits through one or more openings in the lower, aft portion of the engine cowling (Figure 12-4-10). Cowl flaps can be used to vary the size of the opening, varying airflow through the cowl.

The air cooling system is less effective during ground operations, takeoffs, go-arounds, and other periods of high-power, low-airspeed operation. Conversely, high-speed descents provide excess air and can shock cool the engine, subjecting it to abrupt temperature fluctuations.

Operating the engine at temperatures higher than it is designed for can cause loss of power, excessive oil consumption, and detonation. It also leads to serious permanent damage, such as scoring the cylinder walls, damaging the pistons and rings, and burning and warping the valves. Monitoring the engine temperature instruments helps avoid high operating temperature. CHT and EGT systems can be used monitor engine temperatures.

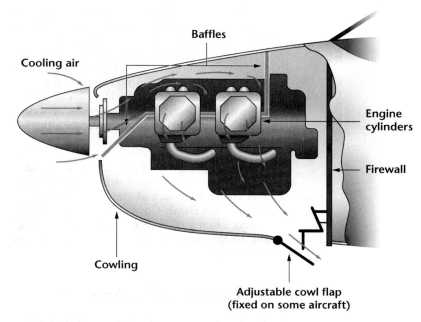

Figure 12-4-10. Airflow through the inside of the engine cowling.

In aircraft not equipped with cowl flaps, the engine temperature can be controlled by changing the airspeed or the engine's power output. High engine temperatures can be decreased by increasing the airspeed or reducing the power or a combination of both.

On aircraft equipped with cowl flaps, the cowl flap position helps control the engine temperature. Cowl flaps are hinged covers that fit over the opening through which the cooling air is expelled. The controllable cowl flaps provide a means of decreasing or increasing the exit area at the rear of the engine cowling. On small aircraft, the cowl flaps are generally opened and closed with a manual system (Figure 12-4-11).

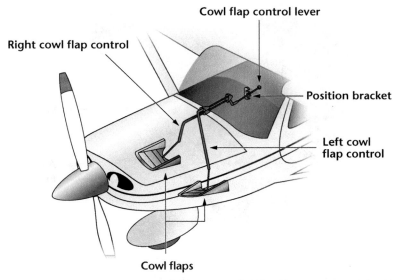

Figure 12-4-11. Small aircraft cowl flaps.

Closing the cowl flaps decreases the exit area, which effectively decreases the amount of air that moves over or between the cylinder fins. The decreased airflow cannot carry away as much heat; therefore, the engine temperature tends to increase. Opening the cowl flaps makes the exit area larger. The flow of cooling air over the cylinders increases, absorbing more heat and the engine temperature tends to decrease.

Cowl flaps are generally open when operating the aircraft and there is little cooling air over the engine such as starting, taxiing, takeoff, and climb. Cowl flaps are generally closed when airflow through the cowl is high and temperatures are low, for example cruise and descent.

Augmentor Cooling Systems

Augmentor cooling systems are used on a few light aircraft models. As shown in Figure 12-4-12, the engine is pressure cooled by air taken in through two openings in the nose cowling, one on each side of the propeller spinner. A pressure chamber is sealed off on the top side of the engine with baffles properly directing the flow of cooling air to all parts of the engine compartment. Warm air is drawn from the lower part of the engine compartment by pumping exhaust gases through the exhaust ejectors. This type of cooling system eliminates using controllable cowl flaps and ensures adequate engine cooling at all operating speeds.

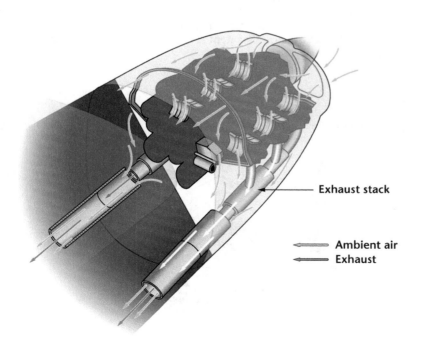

Figure 12-4-12. Augmentor cooling system.

Exhaust stack

⇐ Ambient air
⇐ Exhaust

Section 5
Propellers and Propeller Governors

The propeller is used to convert the rotational motion of the engine's crankshaft into thrust to move the aircraft forward. A pressure difference is produced between the forward and rear surfaces of the airfoil-shaped propeller blade. Propeller dynamics, like those of the aircraft's wing can be modeled by either or both Bernoulli's principle and Newton's third law of motion. In this section, we examine the parts of a propeller, basic propeller theory, and some common types of propellers you might see in use today.

Several forces act on the propeller as it turns; a major one is centrifugal force. This force at high speeds tends to pull the blades out of the hub, so blade weight is very important in propeller design. Excessive blade tip speed (rotating the propeller too fast) can result in poor blade efficiency and in fluttering and vibration. Because the propeller speed is limited, the aircraft speed of a propeller-driven aircraft is also limited to about 400 miles per hour (mph). Even with that speed limit, propeller-driven aircraft still have several advantages and are widely used in turboprop and reciprocating engine installations. The big advantage of propellers is high propulsive efficiency at low airspeeds, making propellers well suited for aircraft designed for lower cruise airspeeds.

Basic Propeller Principles

The aircraft propeller consists of two or more blades and a central hub to which the blades are attached. Each blade of a propeller is essentially a rotating wing. Because of their shape, the propeller blades produce forces that generate thrust, very similar to

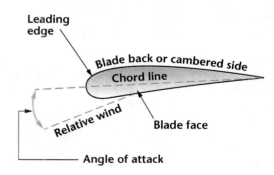

Figure 12-5-1. Cross-sectional area of a propeller blade airfoil.

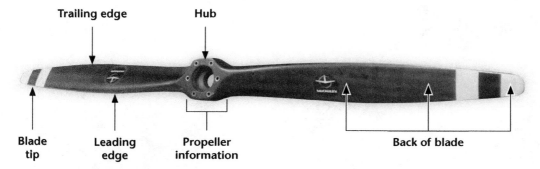

Trailing edge **Hub**

Blade tip **Leading edge** **Propeller information** **Back of blade**

Figure 12-5-2. Propeller nomenclature.

how a wing produces lift, to pull or push the airplane through the air. The amount of thrust produced depends on the airfoil's shape; the angle of air as it strikes the propeller, referred to as angle of attack (AOA); and the r.p.m. of the engine. The blade's aerodynamic cross-section is shown in Figure 12-5-1. The propeller's cross-section is comparable to an aircraft wing cross-section. One surface of the blade is cambered or curved, similar to the upper surface of an aircraft wing, and the other surface is flat like the bottom surface of a wing. As in a wing, the leading edge is the thick edge of the blade that meets the air as the propeller rotates.

The basic parts of a propeller are the hub, leading edge, trailing, blade tip, blade back, and blade face as shown in Figure 12-5-2. The face of the blade is not shown but is opposite the back.

The typical propeller blade can be described as a twisted airfoil. Two views of a propeller blade are shown in Figure 12-5-3.

The reason a propeller is "twisted" is that the outer parts of the propeller blades, like all things that turn about a central point, travel faster than the portions near the hub (Figure 12-5-4). If the blades had the same geometric pitch throughout their lengths, portions near the hub could have negative AOAs, and the propeller tips would be stalled at cruise speed. Twisting or variations in the geometric pitch of the blades permits the propeller to operate with a relatively constant AOA along its length when in cruising flight. Propeller blades are twisted to change the blade angle in proportion to the differences in speed of rotation along the length of the propeller, keeping thrust more nearly equalized along this length.

The engine furnishes the power to rotate the propeller blades. The propeller is mounted on the propeller shaft, and the engine rotates the airfoils of the blades through the air

at high speeds. The propeller converts the rotary power of the engine into thrust. In this conversion, some power is wasted. For most efficiency, the propeller must be designed to minimize this waste. Propeller efficiency varies depending on how much the propeller slips.

Propeller slip is the difference between the geometric pitch of the propeller and its effec-

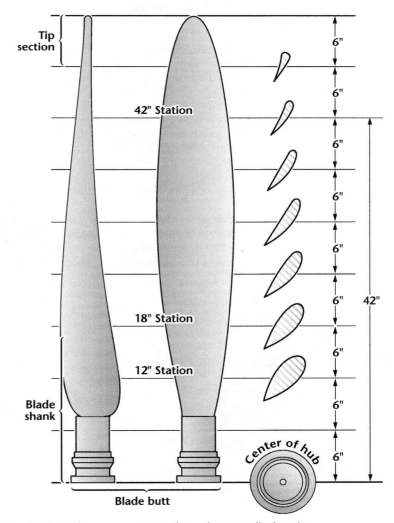

Figure 12-5-3. The cross-sections show the propeller's twist.

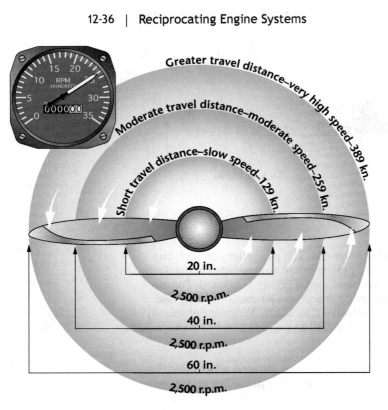

Figure 12-5-4 Propeller tips travel faster than the hub.

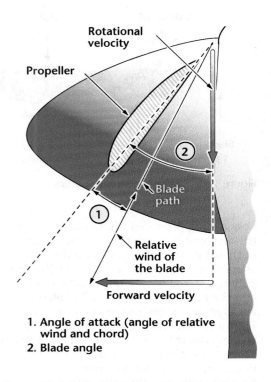

1. Angle of attack (angle of relative wind and chord)
2. Blade angle

Figure 12-5-6. Propeller aerodynamic factors.

tive pitch. This can be seen in Figure 12-5-5. Geometric pitch is the distance a propeller should advance in one revolution with no slippage; effective pitch is the distance it actually advances. Thus, geometric or theoretical pitch is based on no slippage. Actual, or effective, pitch recognizes propeller slippage in the air. The relationship can be expressed as the following equation:

Slip = Geometric pitch – Effective pitch

Although blade angle and propeller pitch are closely related, blade angle is the angle between the face or chord of a blade section and the plane in which the propeller rotates (Figure

12-5-6). Blade angle, usually measured in degrees, is the angle between the chord line of the blade and the plane of rotation. The chord line is an imaginary line drawn through the blade from its leading edge to its trailing edge.

Because most propellers have a flat blade face, the chord line is often drawn along the face of the propeller blade.

Pitch is not the same as blade angle, but because pitch is largely determined by blade angle, the two terms are used interchangeably. An increase or decrease in one is usually associated with an increase or decrease in the other.

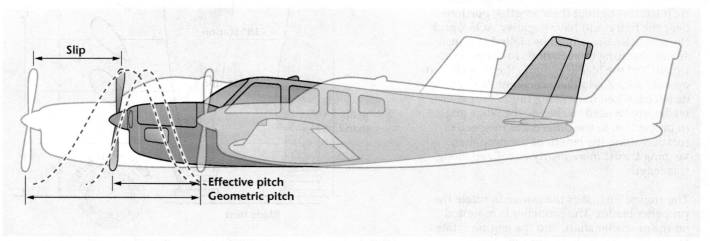

Figure 12-5-5. Effective pitch and geometric pitch.

Propeller Location

As a result of their construction, the propeller blades produce forces that create thrust to pull or push the airplane through the air. Propellers a can be classified as tractor or pusher propellers.

Tractor propeller. Tractor propellers are those mounted with the propeller shaft pointing forward in front of the supporting structure. Most aircraft are equipped with this type of propeller. A major advantage of the tractor propeller is that lower stresses are induced in the propeller as it rotates in relatively undisturbed air.

Pusher propeller. Pusher propellers are those mounted with the propeller shaft pointing aft behind the supporting structure. Seaplanes and amphibious aircraft have used a greater percentage of pusher propellers than other kinds of aircraft. Many times, engines with pusher propellers are mounted above and behind the wings to increase propeller-to-water clearance to minimize propeller damage from water spray.

Forces Acting on a Rotating Propeller

A rotating propeller is acted on by centrifugal twisting, aerodynamic twisting, torque bending, and thrust bending forces. The principal forces acting on a rotating propeller are illustrated in Figure 12-5-7.

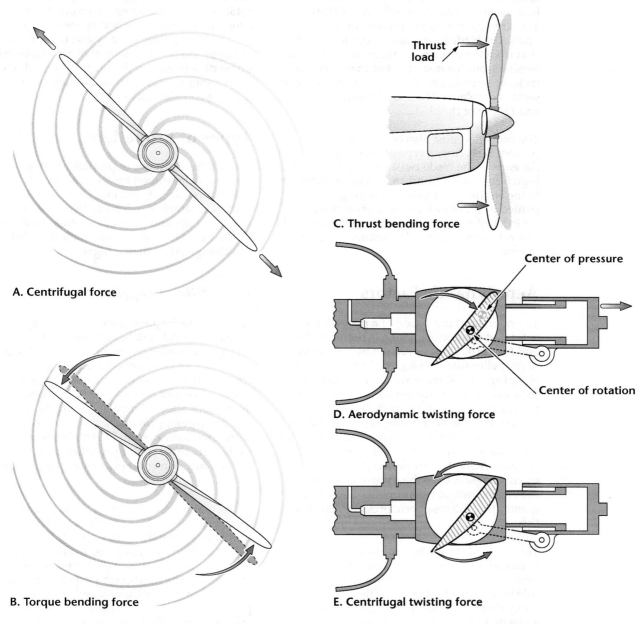

A. Centrifugal force

B. Torque bending force

C. Thrust bending force

D. Aerodynamic twisting force

E. Centrifugal twisting force

Figure 12-5-7. Forces acting on a rotating propeller.

Centrifugal force is a physical force that tends to throw the rotating propeller blades away from the hub (Figure 12-5-7 view A). This is the most dominant force on the propeller. Torque-bending force, in the form of air resistance, tends to bend the propeller blades in the direction opposite that of rotation (view B). Thrust-bending force is the thrust load that tends to bend propeller blades forward as the aircraft is pulled through the air (view C). Aerodynamic twisting force tends to turn the blades to a high blade angle (view D). Centrifugal twisting force, being greater than the aerodynamic twisting force, tends to force the blades toward a low blade angle (view E).

A propeller must be capable of withstanding severe stresses, which are greater near the hub, caused by centrifugal force and thrust. The stresses increase in proportion to the r.p.m. The blade face is also subjected to tension from the centrifugal force and additional tension from the bending. For these reasons, nicks or scratches on the blade can cause very serious problems. These could lead to cracks and failure of the blade.

The propeller must also be rigid enough to prevent fluttering, a type of vibration in which the ends of the blade twist back and forth at high frequency around an axis perpendicular to the engine crankshaft. Fluttering is accompanied by a distinctive noise, often mistaken for exhaust noise. The constant vibration tends to weaken the blade and eventually causes failure.

Aerodynamic Factors

To understand the action of a propeller, consider first its motion, which is both rotational and forward. Thus, as shown by the vectors of propeller forces in Figure 12-5-6, a section of a propeller blade moves downward and forward. As far as the forces are concerned, the result is the same as if the blade were stationary and the air coming at it from a direction opposite its path. The angle at which this air (relative wind) strikes the propeller blade is called AOA. The air deflection produced by this angle causes the dynamic pressure at the engine side of the propeller blade to be greater than atmospheric pressure, creating thrust.

The shape of the blade also creates thrust because it is shaped like a wing. As the air flows past the propeller, the pressure on one side is less than that on the other. As in a wing, this difference in pressure produces a reaction force in the direction of the lesser pressure. The area above a wing has less pressure, and the force (lift) is upward. The area of decreased pressure is in front of a propeller which is mounted vertically instead of horizontally, and the force (thrust) is in a forward direction. Aerodynamically, thrust is the result of the propeller shape and the AOA of the blade.

Another way to consider thrust is in terms of the mass of air handled. In these terms, thrust is equal to the mass of air handled multiplied by the slipstream velocity minus the velocity of the airplane. Thus, the power expended in producing thrust depends on the mass of air moved per second. On the average, thrust constitutes about 80 percent of the torque (total horsepower absorbed by the propeller). The other 20 percent is lost in friction and slippage. For any speed of rotation, the horsepower absorbed by the propeller balances the horsepower delivered by the engine. For any one revolution of the propeller, the amount of air displaced (moved) depends on the blade angle, which determines the quantity or amount of mass of air the propeller moves.

Types of Propellers

Many different types of propeller systems have been developed for specific aircraft installation, speed, and mission. Propellers started as simple fixed-pitch, two-bladed, wooden units and have advanced to multiple blades made from composite materials that can change pitch during flight.

Fixed Pitch Propellers

As the name implies, a fixed-pitch propeller has the blade pitch, or blade angle, built into the propeller (Figure 12-5-8). The blade angle cannot be changed after the propeller is built. Generally, this type of propeller is one piece and is constructed of wood or aluminum alloy. Many single-engine aircraft use fixed-pitch propellers; the advantages to these are lower cost and their simple operation. Also, this type of propeller does not require any control inputs from the pilot in flight.

When making the propeller, the manufacturer chooses the blade angle according to the propeller's normal use on an aircraft in level flight when the engine performs at maximum efficiency. Because blade pitch cannot be changed on the fixed-pitch propeller, its use is restricted to small aircraft with low-horsepower engines in which maximum engine efficiency in all flight conditions is of lesser importance than in larger aircraft.

Usually propellers are designed with a pitch that operates efficiently at normal aircraft cruising speeds. Some propellers might be designed for better efficiency while the aircraft is taking off and climbing. Every fixed-pitch propeller must be a compromise because it can be efficient at only a certain combination of airspeed and r.p.m.

Whether the airplane has a climb or cruise propeller installed depends on its intended use. The climb propeller has a lower pitch, therefore less drag. Less drag results in higher r.p.m. and more horsepower capability, which increases performance in takeoffs and climbs but decreases performance in cruising flight. The cruise propeller has a higher pitch and, therefore, more drag. More drag results in lower r.p.m. and less horsepower capability, which decreases performance in takeoffs and climbs but increases efficiency in cruising flight.

Ground-Adjustable Pitch Propellers

The ground-adjustable propeller operates as a fixed-pitch propeller while the engine is running. The pitch, or blade angle, can be changed only when the propeller is not turning. This is done by loosening a clamping mechanism holding the blades in place and adjusting blade pitch to desired angle. After the clamping mechanism has been tightened, the pitch of the blades cannot be changed in flight to meet variable flight requirements. The ground-adjustable propeller is not often used on airplanes today.

Controllable-Pitch Propellers

The controllable-pitch propeller permits a change of blade pitch, or angle, while the propeller is rotating. This allows the pilot to choose a blade angle that gives the best performance for flight conditions. Using controllable-pitch propellers also makes it possible to attain the desired engine r.p.m. for the flight condition.

With a controllable-pitch propeller, the blade angle can be changed in flight, but the pilot must change the propeller blade angle directly. The blade angle does not change again until the pilot changes it. This type of propeller is not in wide use today.

Constant-Speed Propellers

A constant-speed propeller is a controllable-pitch propeller whose pitch is automatically varied in flight by a governor maintaining constant r.p.m. despite varying air loads. It is the most common type of adjustable-pitch propeller. A

Figure 12-5-8. A fixed-pitch, aluminum alloy propeller.

constant-speed propeller is efficient over a wide range of r.p.m. and airspeed combinations.

Most aircraft with a constant-speed propeller have two controls: the throttle and the propeller control. The throttle controls power output, and the propeller control regulates engine r.p.m. This regulates propeller r.p.m., which is registered on the tachometer. Some aircraft have the propeller control connected to the throttle lever, eliminating the propeller control lever.

Once a specific r.p.m. is selected, a governor automatically adjusts the propeller blade angle as needed to maintain the selected r.p.m. For example, after setting the desired r.p.m. in cruising flight, an increase in airspeed or decrease in propeller load causes the propeller blade angle to increase to maintain the selected r.p.m.

The propeller has a natural tendency to slow down as the aircraft climbs and to speed up as the aircraft dives because the load on the engine varies. By increasing or decreasing propeller pitch, the engine speed is held constant. When the airplane goes into a climb, the blade angle decreases just enough to prevent the engine speed from decreasing. The engine can maintain its power output if the throttle setting is not changed. When the airplane goes into a dive, the blade angle increases sufficiently to prevent overspeeding and, with the same throttle setting, the power output remains unchanged. If the throttle setting is changed instead of changing the speed of the airplane by climbing or diving, the blade angle increases or decreases as needed to maintain a constant engine r.p.m. The power output (not the r.p.m.) changes in accordance with changes in the throttle setting. The governor-controlled,

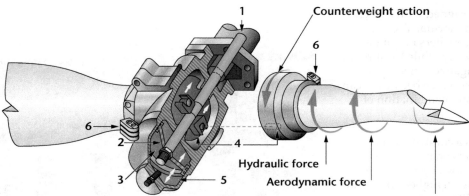

1 High-pressure oil enters the cylinder through the center of the propeller shaft and piston rod. The propeller control regulates the flow of high-pressure oil from a governor.

2 A hydraulic piston in the hub of the propeller is connected to each blade by a piston rod. This rod is attached to forks that slide over the pitch-change pin mounted in the root of each blade.

3 The oil pressure moves the piston toward the front of the cylinder, moving the piston rod and forks forward.

4 The forks push the pitch-change pin of each blade toward the front of the hub causing the blades to twist toward the low-pitch position.

5 A nitrogen pressure charge or mechanical spring in the front of the hub opposes the oil pressure and causes the propeller to move toward high-pitch.

6 Counterweights also cause the blades to move toward the high-pitch and feather positions. The counterweights counteract the aerodynamic twisting force that tries to move the blades toward a low-pitch angle.

Figure 12-5-9. Example of a constant-speed propeller hub

constant-speed propeller changes the blade angle automatically, keeping engine r.p.m. constant.

The pitch-changing mechanisms are housed in the propeller hub. Many types of pitch-changing mechanisms are made but are generally operated by oil pressure (hydraulically) supplied from the propeller governor and use a piston-and-cylinder arrangement. The piston in the cylinder responds to changes in oil pressure from the governor. The piston is mechanically linked to the blade hub, so when the piston moves, the blade angle changes. An example of one type of propeller hub is shown in Figure 12-5-9. Note that the position of the piston, and therefore blade angle, is controlled by several forces in addition to the oil from the propeller governor.

During takeoff, when maximum power and thrust are required, the constant-speed propeller is at a low propeller blade angle or pitch. The low blade angle keeps the AOA small and efficient with respect to the relative wind. At the same time, it allows the propeller to handle a smaller mass of air per revolution. This light load allows the engine to turn at high speed, maximizing thrust.

At cruising altitude, when the airplane is in level flight and less power is required than in takeoff or climb, engine power is reduced by lowering the MAP and increasing the blade angle to decrease the r.p.m. The AOA is still small because the blade angle has been increased with an increase in airspeed.

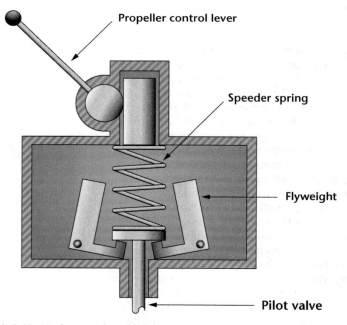

Figure 12-5-10. Underspeed condition.

Propeller governors. Constant speed operations of a propeller are normally controlled by the propeller governor. A governor is an engine r.p.m.-sensing device and high-pressure oil pump. In a constant-speed propeller system, the governor responds to a change in engine r.p.m. by directing oil under pressure to the propeller hydraulic cylinder or by releasing oil from the hydraulic cylinder. The change in oil volume in the hydraulic cylinder, moves the piston, and changes the blade angle and maintains the propeller system r.p.m.

The governors are geared to the engine crankshaft and are, therefore, sensitive to changes in engine r.p.m. When engine r.p.m. increases above the value for which a governor is set, the governor causes the propeller pitch-changing mechanism to turn the blades to a higher angle. This angle increases the load on the engine, and the r.p.m. decreases. When r.p.m. decreases below the value for which a governor is set, the governor causes the pitch-changing mechanism to turn the blades to a lower angle; the load on the engine is decreased and r.p.m. increases. Thus, a propeller governor tends to keep engine r.p.m. constant.

The engine-driven governor receives oil from the lubricating system and boosts its pressure to that required to operate the pitch-changing mechanism. The governor consists of a gear pump to increase the pressure of the engine oil, a pilot valve controlled by flyweights to control the flow of oil to and away from the propeller, and a relief valve system that regulates the operating oil pressures in the governor. A spring called the speeder spring opposes the governor flyweight's ability to fly outward when turning. The tension on this spring is adjusted by the propeller control on the control quadrant. Next, we explain three conditions and how the governor features work in each.

- Underspeed condition. When the engine is operating below the r.p.m. set by the pilot using the flight deck control, the governor is operating in an underspeed condition. In this condition, the flyweights tilt inward because there is not enough centrifugal force on the flyweights to overcome the force of the speeder spring. The pilot valve, forced down by the speeder spring, meters oil flow to decrease propeller pitch and raise engine r.p.m. (Figure 12-5-10).

- Overspeed condition. When the engine is operating above the r.p.m. set by the pilot using the flight deck control, the governor is operating in an overspeed condition. In an overspeed condition, the centrifugal force acting on the flyweights is greater than the speeder spring force. The flyweights tilt outward and raise the pilot valve. The pilot valve then meters oil flow to increase propeller pitch and lower engine r.p.m. (Figure 12-5-11).

- On-speed condition. When the engine is operating at the r.p.m. set by the pilot using the flight deck control, the governor is operating on speed (Figure 12-5-12). In an on-speed condition, the centrifugal

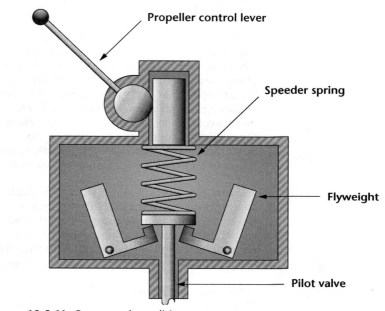

Figure 12-5-11. Overspeed condition.

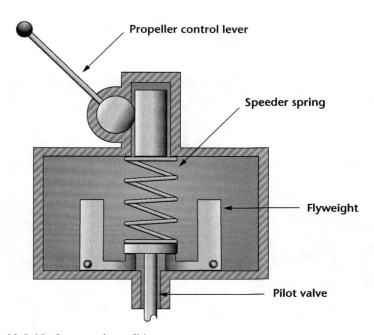

Figure 12-5-12. On-speed condition.

force acting on the flyweights is balanced by the speeder spring, and the pilot valve maintains its current position. In the on-speed condition, the forces of the governor flyweights and the tension on the speeder spring are equal; the propeller blades are not moving or changing pitch. If something happens to unbalance these forces, such as if the aircraft dives or climbs, or the pilot selects a new r.p.m. range through the propeller control (changes tension on the speeder spring), these forces are unequal and an underspeed or overspeed condition results.

Power Setting and Propeller Control

Fixed-pitch propellers have no controls and require no adjustments in flight. In a fixed-pitch propeller, the tachometer is the indicator of engine power. A tachometer is calibrated in hundreds of r.p.m. and gives a direct indication of the engine and propeller r.p.m. The instrument is color coded with a green arc denoting the maximum continuous operating r.p.m. Some tachometers have additional markings to reflect engine or propeller limitations, or both.

As mentioned, most aircraft with a constant-speed propeller have a propeller control in the center pedestal between the throttle and the mixture control, and some aircraft have the propeller control connected to the throttle lever, eliminating the propeller control lever.

A propeller control lever is shown in Figure 12-5-13. The two positions for the control are increase r.p.m. (push forward) and decrease r.p.m. (pull aft). This control is directly connected to the propeller governor and, by moving the control, adjusts the tension on the governor speeder spring.

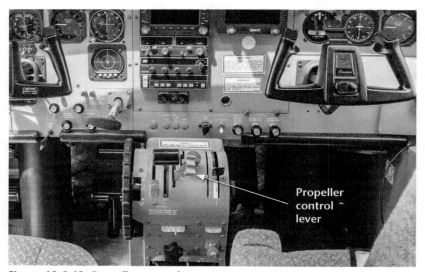

Figure 12-5-13. Propeller control.

The two main instruments used with the constant-speed propeller are the engine tachometer and the MAP gauge. The propeller control adjusts the r.p.m., and the throttle adjusts the MAP. Power output is controlled by the throttle and indicated by the MAP indicator, as r.p.m. remains constant. At a constant r.p.m. and altitude, the amount of power produced is directly related to MAP (Figure 12-5-14).

For any given r.p.m., a MAP exists that should not be exceeded. If MAP is excessive for an r.p.m., the pressure in the cylinders could be exceeded, placing undue stress on the cylinders. If repeated too frequently, this stress can weaken the cylinder components and eventually cause engine failure.

A pilot can avoid conditions that overstress the cylinders by being constantly aware of the r.p.m., especially when increasing the MAP.

When both MAP and r.p.m. need to be changed, avoid engine overstress by making power adjustments in the proper order. Generally, changes are made as follows:

- When power settings are being decreased, reduce MAP before reducing r.p.m. If r.p.m. is reduced before MAP, MAP automatically increases, possibly exceeding the manufacturer's tolerances.

- When power settings are being increased, reverse the order—increase r.p.m. first, then MAP.

Feathering and Reverse Pitch Propellers

Feathering propellers are used on multiengine aircraft to reduce propeller drag to a minimum under one or more engine failure conditions. A feathering propeller is a constant-speed propeller that has a mechanism to change the pitch to an angle of about 90° (Figure 12-5-15). A propeller is feathered when the pilot moves the propeller control into the feather position. By rotating the propeller blade angle parallel to the line of flight, the drag on the aircraft caused by the propeller is greatly reduced. With the blades parallel to the airstream, the propeller stops turning and minimizes windmilling. The blades are held in feather by aerodynamic forces.

Autofeathering System

An autofeather system is used normally only during takeoff, approach, and landing. It is used to feather the propeller automatically if power is lost from either engine. If two torque switches sense low torque from the engine, the system uses a solenoid valve to dump oil pressure from the propeller cylinder (this allows the prop to feather). This system has a test-off-arm switch that is used to arm the system.

Reversible Pitch

Additional refinements, such as reverse-pitch propellers (mainly used on turboprop engines), are included in some propellers to improve their operational characteristics. A reverse pitch propeller is a controllable propeller in which the blade angles can be changed to a negative value during operation.

The purpose of the reversible pitch feature is to produce a negative blade angle that produces reverse thrust. Normally, when the landing gear contacts with the runway after landing, the propellers blades can be moved to negative pitch (reversed) and engine power applied, which slows the aircraft. This aerodynamically brakes the aircraft, reduces ground roll after landing, and minimizes aircraft brake wear.

Other Propeller Systems

With the variety of propeller systems installed on aircraft, you might encounter several other auxiliary systems associated with propeller operation. These include propeller anti-icing, or deicing, systems. Multiengine aircraft could be equipped with synchronizing or synchrophasing systems.

Synchronizing

Many multiengine airplanes have a propeller synchronizer (prop sync) installed to elimi-

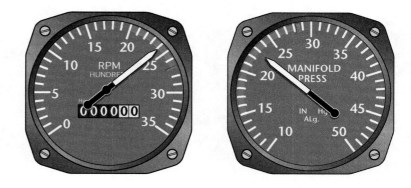

Figure 12-5-14. Engine r.p.m. is indicated on the tachometer (left) used in conjunction with a MAP gauge (right) to indicate engine power on an engine with a constant-speed prop.

nate the annoying *drumming* or *beat* of propellers whose r.p.m. are close, but not precisely the same. To use prop sync, the propeller r.p.m. are coarsely matched by the pilot and the system is engaged. The prop sync adjusts the r.p.m. of the *slave* engine to precisely match the r.p.m. of the *master* engine, and then maintains that relationship. The pilot should consult the AFM/POH should for system description and limitations.

A variation on the propeller synchronizer is the propeller synchrophaser. Prop sychrophase acts much like a synchronizer to precisely match r.p.m., but the synchrophaser goes one step further. It matches r.p.m. and actually compares and adjusts the positions of the individual blades of the propellers in their arcs. Significant propeller noise and vibration reductions can be made with a propeller synchrophaser. From the pilot's perspective, operation of a propeller synchronizer and a propeller syncrophaser are very similar. A synchrophaser is also commonly referred to as prop sync.

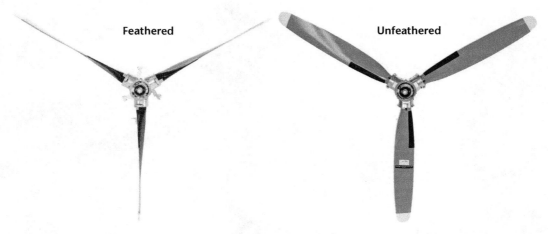

Figure 12-5-15. A propeller in the feathered position (left) reduces drag if it is not turning, compared to the unfeathered propeller (right).

Turbine Engines and Systems

Section 1

Turbine Engine Types and Classification

Some gas turbine engines are able to produce thrust by increasing the velocity of the air flowing through the engine. Others have similar operation but rely on a propeller to produce thrust. Reciprocating engines and gas turbine engines have operating similarities in that both use the functions of air intake, compression, combustion, and exhaust. In a reciprocating engine, each of these events is a separate distinct occurrence taking place in each cylinder. A significant difference with the gas turbine engine is that separate sections are devoted to each function, allowing all functions to be performed simultaneously and continuously.

A typical gas turbine engine consists of the following:

- Air inlet
- Compressor section
- Combustion section
- Turbine section
- Exhaust section
- Accessory section
- The systems necessary for starting, lubrication, fuel supply, and auxiliary purposes, such as anti-icing, cooling, and pressurization

The major components of all gas turbine engines are basically the same; however, the component part nomenclature of various engines varies slightly with each manufacturer.

Left: Modern turbine engines provide safe, reliable, and efficient propulsion for business and transport aircraft.

Using aircraft turbine engines has several advantages when compared to reciprocating engines. In theory, the turbine engine is simpler and directly converts thermal energy (burning and expanding gases) into thrust. Reciprocating engines have many moving parts that convert the thermal energy into mechanical energy, and then finally into thrust by rotating a propeller. Turbine engines are characterized by smooth operation, a high power-to-weight ratio, and they use readily available jet fuel. Also, turbine engines can produce more thrust at high altitudes and high speeds.

The path the air takes through the engine and how power is produced determines the type of engine. Four types of gas turbine engines are made:

- Turbojet
- Turbofan
- Turboprop
- Turboshaft

Turbojets

Regardless of type, all turbine engines share similar parts and operation. This section describes basic turbojet operation. Figure 13-1-1 shows the major parts of a turbojet and how air flows through the engine.

A basic aircraft turbine engine works by bringing atmospheric air into the engine through an air inlet, compressing the air in the compressor section, adding fuel, and burning the air/fuel mixture in the combustion chamber. The turbine section follows, which turns the compressor; the exhaust section directs high-velocity exhaust gases back into the atmosphere. Thrust is produced by increasing the velocity of the air flowing through the engine. In other words, the air leaves the engine at a higher velocity than it entered.

To start the engine, a starter rotates the compressor section. As the compressor's revolutions per minute (r.p.m.) increases, air is brought in through the inlet duct, compressed to a high pressure, and delivered to the combustion section (combustion chamber).

In the combustion chamber, fuel is introduced into the air through spray nozzles and ignited by igniter plugs. The air/fuel mixture in the combustion chamber is then burned in a continuous combustion process that produces a very high temperature. The heated mixture expands, and the velocity increases, as it is directed to the turbine section, forcing the turbines to rotate. The rotating turbine drives the compressor by means of a shaft connecting the turbine and the compressor. The high-velocity excess exhaust exits the exhaust section. The accelerated exhaust gases from the engine provide thrust. This is a basic application of compressing air, igniting the air/fuel mixture, producing power to self-sustain the engine operation, and exhaust for propulsion.

Once the engine reaches a self-sustaining r.p.m., the starter is disengaged, and the igniters are turned off. Combustion continues until turning off the fuel supply shuts down the engine.

The term *turbojet* was originally used to describe any gas turbine engine used in aircraft. As gas turbine technology evolved, other engine types were developed to take the place of the turbojet engine.

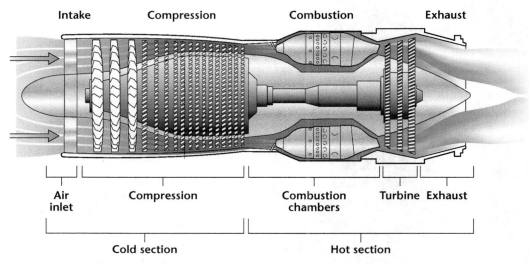

Figure 13-1-1. A gas turbine engine's major components.

Turbofans

Turbojet engines are noisy and use excessive fuel. Because of these problems, pure turbojet engines are not commonly used. Today's large airliner aircraft use turbofan engines. Recent advances in material, engine design, and manufacturing processes have also increased turbofan engine use in small or light aircraft.

The turbofan engine was developed to turn a large fan or set of fans at the front of the engine that can produce much of the total engine thrust. Turbofan engines are designed to create additional thrust by diverting a secondary airflow around the combustion chamber (Figure 13-1-2).

Like other gas turbine engines, the heart of the turbofan engine is a compressor, a combustion chamber that produces hot, high-velocity gases, and a turbine that turns the compressor. These combined sections are referred to as the engine *core* or the *gas generator section.*

As air enters a turbofan engine, it passes through the fan, and splits into separate paths. One path passes through the engine core. The second path flows around or bypasses the engine core. Depending on which path the air takes, air flowing through the engine is referred to as *core air* or *bypass air.* This is why turbofan engines are often referred to as bypass engines.

The amount of air that bypasses the core compared to the amount passing through the core determines a turbofan's *bypass ratio.* Turbofan engines can be classified as low-, medium-, high-, or ultrahigh-bypass, depending the bypass ratio. The amount of air flow is measured in pounds per second (lb/sec), and the

bypass ratio is determined by dividing the fan bypass flow by the core flow. For example the bypass ratio of a turbofan engine with a core flow of 20 lb/sec and a bypass flow of 100 lb/sec is determined as follows:

$$\text{Bypass ratio} = \frac{100 \text{ lb/sec flow fan}}{20 \text{ lb/sec core flow}} = 5:1 \text{ bypass ratio}$$

A turbofan engine takes little additional energy to turn the fan, but the fan can provide significant thrust. Thus, the turbofan bypass air generates great thrust, and improves fuel consumption for the amount of power produced. Much of the noise from a turbojet engine is generated when the hot, high-velocity exhaust gas is reintroduced to the atmosphere. Because much of the thrust from a turbofan is produced from the bypass air, turbofan engines are much quieter than turbojets.

Turboprop

A turboprop engine is a turbine engine that drives a propeller through a reduction gearbox (Figure 13-1-3). As in other turbine engines, the exhaust gases in the turbine section rotate the compressor, and the turbine section also turns the propeller. The turbine connects to an output shaft that drives a reduction gearbox, and the gearbox turns the propeller. Reduction gearing is necessary in turboprop engines because optimum propeller performance is at a much lower r.p.m. than the engine's operating r.p.m.

Turboprop engines are most efficient at aircraft speeds below 400 miles per hour (mph) and at altitudes below 30,000 feet. They also perform well at the low airspeeds required for takeoff and landing, and they are fuel efficient.

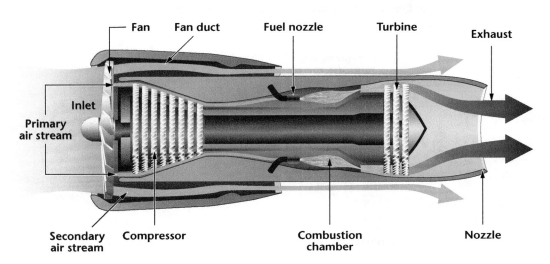

Figure 13-1-2. Example of airflow through a turbofan engine.

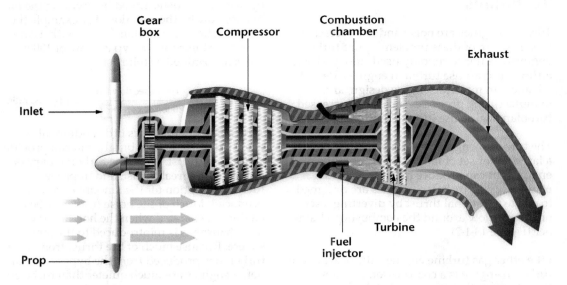

Figure 13-1-3. An example of a turboprop engine.

Most of the combustion energy developed by the gas turbine engine is used to drive the propeller. The rest of the available energy exits the exhaust as thrust.

Turboshaft

Turboshaft engines are similar to turboprop engines, but turboshaft engines deliver power to an output shaft that drives something other than a propeller. Like a turboprop, almost all combustion energy is used to drive an output shaft rather than produce thrust. Many helicopters use a turboshaft gas turbine engine. Turboshaft engines are made in many styles, shapes, and horsepower ranges.

Turboshaft engines are also widely used as auxiliary power units (APUs) on larger aircraft. An APU is used on turbine-powered

aircraft to provide electrical power and bleed air for the aircraft pneumatic systems.

Other Construction Features

Compressor and Turbine Stages

One type of compressor, an axial flow compressor is shown in Figure 13-1-4. This type of compressor has two main elements: rotating blades and stationary vanes (called stators). The blades move the air rearward through the compressor in the same manner as a propeller because of their angle and airfoil contour. The vanes direct the air into the next set of blades. The compressor has multiple rows of blades and vanes. One row of blades and the next set of vanes are referred to as a *stage*.

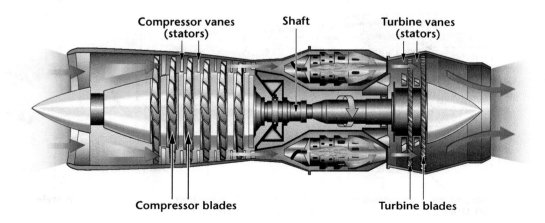

Figure 13-1-4. An example of a six-stage compressor and two-stage turbine.

The turbine assembly consists of a row of stationary vanes, also referred to as a nozzle, followed by a row of rotating turbine blades. As in the compressor, one row of stators and the following set of rotor blades are referred to as a stage.

The exhaust gases leaving the combustion chamber act on the blades of the turbine wheel, causing the assembly to rotate, which then turns the shaft and compressor. The vanes direct the air into the next set of blades. Figure 13-1-4 shows an example of a *six-stage* compressor, linked by a shaft to a *two-stage* turbine. Additional details regarding compressors and turbines are later in this chapter.

Single Spool/Multi-Spool Engines

Turbojet and turbofan engines can have a single spool or multiple spools (split spool). A spool is defined as a compressor and a turbine, connected by a common shaft. Figure 13-1-5 shows a single-spool turbojet engine.

Most turbofan engines have two spools for better efficiency. This means that there are two separate compressors, two turbines and two shafts. These engines incorporate two compressors with their respective turbines and interconnecting shafts, which form two physically independent rotor systems with no mechanical connection to each other. Many two-spool engines have rotors turning in opposite directions. Figure 13-1-6 shows a two-spool turbofan engine.

A two-spool engine has a high-pressure spool and a low-pressure spool. In most engines, the fan and the first few stages of compression is called the low-pressure compressor. The low-pressure compressor is connected to the low-pressure shaft and low-pressure turbine, completing the low-pressure spool. After air passes through the low-pressure compressor, it moves into the high-pressure compressor, which is connected to the high-pressure shaft and high-pressure turbine, which is referred to as the high-pressure spool.

A few turbofans have a three (triple) spool configuration. Typically, the fan is the first stage of compression, followed by the intermediate compressor, and the high-pressure compressor, all of which rotate on separate shafts by separate turbines. Figure 13-1-7 shows a three-spool engine.

Engines can also use a reduction gearbox to turn the fan (Figure 13-1-8). Multiple spools and a fan reduction gearbox allow the larger diameter blades at the front of the engine to

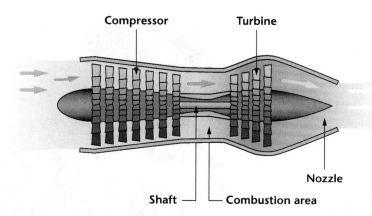

Figure 13-1-5. An example of a single-spool turbojet.

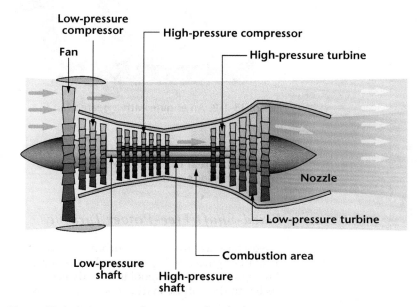

Figure 13-1-6. An example two-spool turbofan.

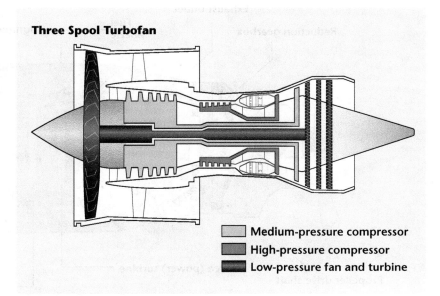

Figure 13-1-7. A three-spool turbofan.

Figure 13-1-8. An engine with a geared fan.

Courtesy of United Technologies Corp., Pratt & Whitney Division.

turn more slowly than the smaller diameter blades at the rear of the compressor, increasing compressor efficiency.

Fixed-Shaft/Free-Power Turbine

Fixed-shaft and free-power turbines are used in shaft engines, turboprops, and turboshafts. An engine where the spool is directly connected to the output shaft is known as a fixed shaft. In a fixed-shaft engine, the compressor, turbine, and reduction gearbox are all turned by the same shaft.

In a turboprop with a free-power turbine, the propeller is driven by a separate turbine through reduction gearing. The propeller is not on the same shaft as the compressor that supplies air to the combustion chamber and the turbine that turns the compressor. The free-power turbine design allows the flight crew

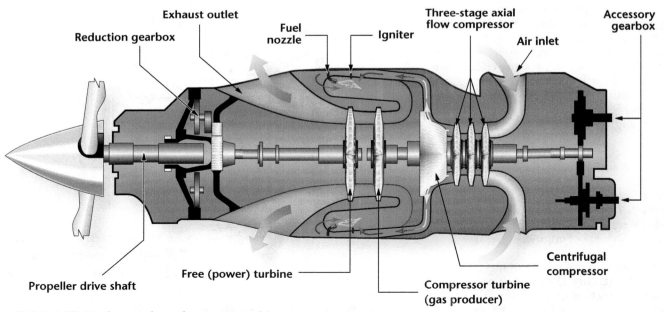

Figure 13-1-9. A PT-6 turboprop has a free-power turbine.

to select a desired propeller governing r.p.m., regardless of basic engine r.p.m. (Figure 13-1-9). The turbine and shaft turning the compressor is referred to as the gas generator spool, and the turbine turning the output shaft is referred to as the free-power turbine. A typical free-power turbine engine has two independent counter-rotating turbines. One turbine drives the compressor, and the other drives the propeller through a reduction gearbox.

The example of a turboprop engine shown earlier (Figure 13-1-3) has airflow entering the front and flowing to and exiting at the back. Compare that to the PT-6 shown in Figure 13-1-9, which has air entering at the rear and flowing forward as it drives the power turbine. Both are turboprops with a free-power turbine, but the PT-6 has a reverse flow.

Spool R.P.M.

Each spool usually has a separate indicator devoted to monitoring its speed of rotation. Depending on the make and model, an N_1 gauge indicates the low-pressure spool or fan speed in turbofan engines. The gas generator or high-pressure spool could be monitored by an N_2 gauge, and *triple-spool engines* have an N_3 gauge. Each engine section rotates at many thousands of r.p.m. The gauges, therefore, are calibrated in percent of r.p.m. rather than actual r.p.m. for ease of display and interpretation.

Section 2

Turbine Engine Terms, Theory, and Operating Principles

Brayton Cycle

A cycle is a process of repeating a series of events. The Brayton cycle describes the events occurring in a turbine engine to produce thrust. This is a variable-volume, constant-pressure cycle of events commonly called the constant-pressure cycle. A more recent term is *continuous combustion cycle*. The four continuous events are intake, compression, expansion (including power), and exhaust. The four events are the same in both cycles; in the Otto cycle engine, the events occur one after another, but in the Brayton cycle, the events occur at the same time. The Brayton and Otto cycles are compared in Figure 13-2-1. Here, it is

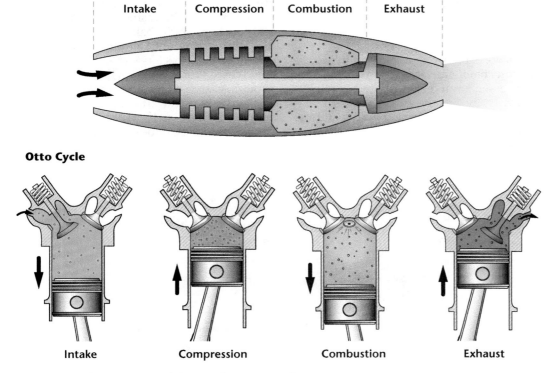

Figure 13-2-1. The Brayton and Otto cycles compared.

clear that in the Brayton cycle, the events are performed continuously and all at the same time, the Otto cycle events are performed in a sequence.

It is important to note that the turbine engine has a separate component designed for each event. Reciprocating engines have intermittent combustion and, therefore, produce intermittent power. Because a turbine engine's combustion is continuous, it produces power continuously.

Bernoulli's principle (whenever a stream of any fluid has its velocity increased at a point, the pressure of the stream at that point is less than the rest of the stream) is applied to gas turbine engines through the design of convergent and divergent air ducts. The convergent duct increases velocity and decreases pressure. The divergent duct decreases velocity and increases pressure. Turbine engines take advantage of this principle to speed up, slow down, and change pressures of the air as it moves through an engine.

In the inlet, outside air enters at ambient pressure and a constant volume. As the air moves through the inlet, it is subjected to changes in temperature, pressure, and velocity. It leaves the intake and enters the compressor at an increased pressure and a decreased velocity.

At the compressor section, air is received from the intake and enters the compressor where it is compressed by mechanical action. It leaves the compressor with a large increase in pressure.

The next step, expansion, takes place in the combustion chamber. Here, fuel is added to the compressed air and once ignited, continues to burn as long as the air/fuel mixture is correct. The burning fuel and air expand from the increase in temperature. Velocity also increases. During combustion, the pres-sure remains relatively constant, but volume and velocity greatly increase. The expanding gases move rearward through the turbine assembly, where the turbine converts the gases' velocity (kinetic energy) to mechanical energy, to turn the compressor.

After the turbine section, the high-velocity gases exit the exhaust section. The exhaust section provides a final acceleration to the air before leaving the engine. Thrust is produced by increasing the velocity of the air flowing through the engine. In other words, thrust is produced because the exhaust exit velocity is greater than the velocity of the air entering the engine inlet.

Newton's 2nd and 3rd Laws

The principles used by a gas turbine engine as it provides force to move an airplane are based on Newton's second and third laws of motion. The third law states that for every action, there is an equal and opposite reaction. The second law states that force = mass × acceleration ($F = m \times a$). Therefore, if the engine accelerates a mass of air (action), it applies a force ($F = m \times a$) on the engine (reaction).

This principle explains how a balloon can fly around a room. If a balloon is inflated, the air pressure inside the balloon is greater than the pressure outside the balloon (Figure 13-2-2). With the stem held closed, the air pressure pushes inside the balloon equally in all directions. Releasing the stem allows air to rush out of the balloon, and the balloon flies around until all the air inside has escaped. This is because when the stem is open, there is no longer anything for the air to push on at that location. On the opposite side of the stem, the air continues to push on an equal area inside the balloon, and the balloon moves in the opposite direction of the escaping air.

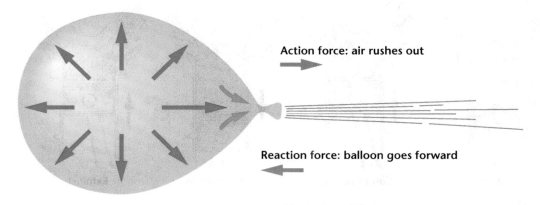

Action force: air rushes out

Reaction force: balloon goes forward

Figure 13-2-2. An inflated balloon demonstrates Newton's laws.

The accelerating air escaping from the balloon nozzle is an action, and according to Newton's third law, a force is applied in the opposite direction, causing the balloon to move. How much force is acting on the balloon depends on the mass of the air being accelerated and the rate of acceleration as illustrated in Newton's second law.

Section 3

Turbine Engine Performance

Basic Thrust Formula

By displacing air in a direction opposite to that in which the aircraft is propelled, thrust can be developed. From Newton's second law, it can be said that if a mass of air is accelerated as it goes through an engine, a force is produced. The equal but opposite force moves the engine in the direction opposite the exhaust. The reaction is thrust, so force = thrust. The formula for thrust can be derived from Newton's second law, which states that force is proportional to the product of mass and acceleration. This law is expressed in the formula

$$F = m \times a$$

where

F = force (thrust) in lbs.

m = mass in lbs./second

a = acceleration in ft./second

In this formula, mass is similar to weight, but it is actually a different quantity. Mass refers to the quantity of matter, and weight refers to the pull of gravity on that quantity of matter. Something that weighs 100 lbs. on earth would be weightless in space, but the units of mass would remain the same. To calculate the acceleration of a mass, the gravitational constant is used as a unit of comparison. The force of gravity on earth, is 32.2 feet per second squared (ft/sec^2) (9.8 meters/sec^2), assuming there is no friction or other resistance to overcome. Using flow rate of the air in pounds per second, times the acceleration, divided by gravity, the formula can be expressed as

$$F = \frac{W_a \times a}{g}$$

where

F = force

W_a = weight of the airflow

a = acceleration

g = gravity

In any formula involving work, time must be considered. It is convenient to have all time factors in equivalent units (i.e., seconds, minutes, or hours). In calculating jet thrust, the term *pounds of air per second* is convenient, because the second is the same unit of time used for the force of gravity.

Acceleration is defined as a change in velocity. The acceleration of the air in a turbine engine can be determined by subtracting the exhaust velocity from the inlet velocity. This can be expressed in the thrust equation as exhaust exit velocity, in feet per second, minus inlet velocity, in feet per second, or as $V_2 - V_1$.

Because the turbojet engine accelerates air, this formula can be used to determine jet thrust:

$$F = \frac{W_a \times (V_2 - V_1)}{g}$$

where

F = force in lbs.

W_a = airflow rate in lbs./second

V_1 = inlet velocity in ft./second

V_2 = exhaust velocity in ft./second

$V_2 - V_1$ = change in velocity; the difference between inlet velocity and jet velocity

g = Acceleration of gravity, 32.2 ft./sec^2

Therefore, the thrust of the engine must be equal to the force required to accelerate the air mass through the engine. The symbol F_n is used for net thrust.

Thrust can be expressed two ways—as net thrust, as shown in the formula or as gross thrust. Gross thrust does not use the initial velocity or the initial velocity is zero such as when the engine is static or not moving. The air is considered to have no inlet velocity, and the velocity of the gas leaving the engine is considered to be the acceleration factor. F_g is the symbol for gross thrust.

If comparing gross thrust and net thrust, net thrust decreases as aircraft speed increases. This is because for any power setting, aircraft speed has little effect on V_2 (exhaust velocity), but V_1 (inlet velocity) increases as airspeed increases. If V_1 increases for the same V_2, the change in velocity decreases, decreasing net thrust. Because gross thrust excludes V_1 or it is assumed that V_1 is zero, gross thrust does not change with an increase in airspeed. The difference between net thrust and gross thrust is referred to as *ram drag*. Ram drag increases with aircraft speed.

As shown in the equation, thrust can be increased two ways—either by increasing the flow rate of the air mass through the engine or by increasing the change in velocity. A large airflow rate results in a high thrust as long as the exit velocity is greater than entrance velocity. This is the design theory behind high-bypass turbofan engines. A large amount of air is moved through the engine each second, with a small increase in air velocity. High thrust can also be produced with a small rate of airflow if the exit velocity is high. Turbojets can produce large amounts of thrust using a moderate airflow rate, if the exit velocity is much greater than the inlet velocity. At higher airspeeds, a rise in pressure above the outside atmospheric pressure occurs at the engine inlet as a result of the aircraft's forward velocity. This is referred to as ram pressure, and it increases the mass flow.

Shaft Horsepower and Equivalent Shaft Horsepower

The power of a turboprop engine is measured in shaft horsepower (SHP). SHP is determined by the r.p.m. and the torque (twisting moment) applied to the propeller shaft. Because turboprop engines are gas turbine engines, some jet thrust is produced by exhaust leaving the engine. This thrust is added to the SHP to determine the total engine power, or equivalent shaft horsepower (ESHP). Jet thrust usually accounts for a small percentage of the total engine power.

Turboprop engines excel during takeoff, climb, and at lower airspeeds. This is because the propeller can accelerate a large mass of air while the airplane is moving at a relatively low airspeed.

Thrust Horsepower

Turbojet and turbofan engines use thrust directly. Turboprop and turboshaft engines deliver torque to an airplane propeller or a helicopter rotor to produce thrust.

The power from a turbojet or turbofan engine is measured in pounds of thrust. SHP is a measurement of useful power delivered to

the propeller shaft. Turboprop and turboshaft engine output is measured in horsepower instead of thrust because the power output is a turning shaft. The two units of measure cannot be directly compared.

However, a comparison can be calculated when an aircraft with a turbojet or turbofan is in flight in the form of thrust horsepower (THP).

The formula for THP is as follows:

$$THP = \frac{\text{thrust} \times \text{aircraft speed (m.p.h.)}}{375 \text{ mile} - \text{pounds per hour}}$$

Note that for this formula to be relevant, the aircraft must be moving.

THP can also be used to determine the thrust produced from an engine turning a propeller. THP can be considered the result of the engine and the propeller working together. If a propeller could be designed to be 100 percent efficient, the thrust and the horsepower output would be the same. However, the efficiency of the propeller varies with the engine speed, attitude, altitude, temperature, and airspeed. Thus, the ratio of the THP and the horsepower delivered to the propeller shaft are never equal. For example, if an engine delivers 1,000 HP to the propeller shaft, and a propeller that is 85 percent efficient is installed, the THP of that engine-propeller combination is 85 percent of 1,000 or 850 THP. The THP determines the performance of the engine-propeller combination.

Turbine Engine Efficiency

Thermal efficiency. Thermal efficiency is a prime factor in gas turbine performance. As in a reciprocating engine, thermal efficiency is the ratio of net work produced by the engine compared to the chemical energy supplied in the fuel. For more information on thermal efficiency, see chapter 11.

TSFC and ESFC. Thrust-specific fuel consumption (TSFC) and equivalent-specific fuel consumption (ESFC) can be used to compare fuel used by different engines. TSFC is used for turbojets and turbofan engines and is calculated by the weight of the fuel flow in pounds per hour, divided by the net thrust the engine is producing. In other words, it is the number of pounds of fuel required per hour to produce one pound of thrust.

ESFC is used for turboprops and turboshafts, except ESHP is used instead of net thrust.

ESFC is used for the turboprop engine and is the fuel flow in pounds per hour divided by a turboprop's ESHP.

Comparisons can be made between the various engines on a specific fuel consumption basis. At low speed, turboprop engines have better economy than turbojet or turbofan engines. However, at high speed, because of losses in propeller efficiency, the turboprop engine's efficiency is limited.

Propulsive efficiency. Propulsive efficiency compares the velocity of the air as it exits the propeller or the exhaust velocity from the engine to the aircraft's speed. The nearer the speed of the aircraft is to the speed of the exhaust, the less kinetic energy is lost, and the higher the propulsive efficiency. Figure 13-3-1 shows a comparison of propulsive efficiency and different types of engines.

Things Affecting Performance

The amount of air passing through the engine, and therefore the amount of thrust being produced, is dependent on three factors:

1. The compressor speed (r.p.m.)
2. The density of the ambient (surrounding) air
3. The forward speed of the aircraft

Variation of thrust with r.p.m. Turbine engines are designed to operate most efficiently at high r.p.m., in the 85 percent to 100 percent range. The thrust increase when going from 90 percent to 100 percent r.p.m.,

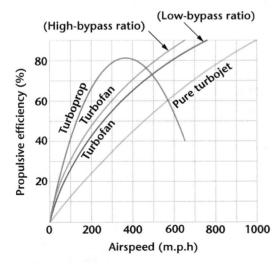

Figure 13-3-1. Propulsive efficiency.

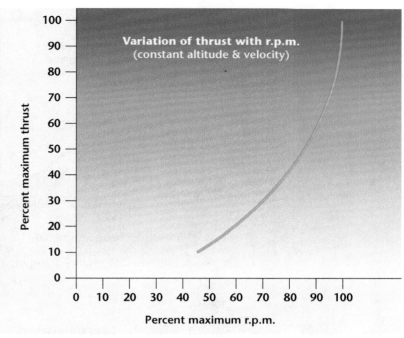

Figure 13-3-2. Variation of thrust with r.p.m.

can produce as much thrust as the total available at 70 percent (Figure 13-3-2).

Variation of thrust with density. Turbine engine thrust varies directly with air density. As air density decreases, so does thrust. In the previous discussion, it was assumed that the state of the air at the inlet to the compressor remained constant. Just like in a reciprocating engine, the density of the air in the inlet affects engine performance. The principal variables that affect turbine engine inlet conditions are the atmospheric pressure, ambient temperature (outside air temperature, or OAT), altitude of the aircraft, and speed of the aircraft.

Air density decreases at high elevations, low atmospheric pressures, high temperatures, low airspeed, or some combination of these factors. Air density increases at high atmospheric pressures, low temperatures, low altitude, high airspeeds, or some combination of those. For information on standard day conditions, see chapter 11.

The density of the air used by the engine has a large effect on how much power an engine produces. As inlet air density decreases, engine thrust is reduced. Increased inlet air density results in higher engine thrust.

Variation of thrust with atmospheric pressure. Changes in atmospheric pressure affect engine thrust. Standard day pressure is 14.69 pounds per square inch (p.s.i.) or 29.92 inches of mercury ("Hg). An increase in atmospheric

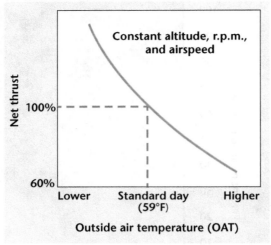

Figure 13-3-3. Effect of OAT on thrust output.

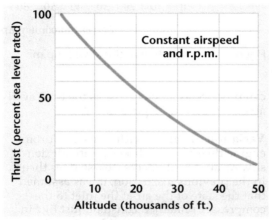

Figure 13-3-4. Effect of altitude on thrust output.

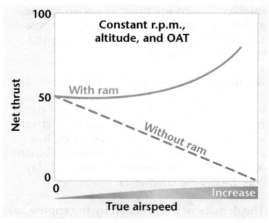

Figure 13-3-5. Effect of airspeed on net thrust.

pressure over standard day conditions results in additional thrust because of the increase in air density. Likewise, atmospheric pressures less than standard day conditions results in an engine producing less thrust as the air is less dense. Changes in temperature also affect thrust. Figure 13-3-3 shows that the

thrust output improves rapidly with a reduction in OAT at constant altitude, r.p.m., and airspeed. The thrust output increases because the air at a lower temperature is more dense. The increase in density causes the mass flow through the engine to increase.

Variation of thrust with altitude. The altitude's effect on thrust, as shown in Figure 13-3-4, can also be discussed as a density and temperature effect. In this case, an increase in altitude causes a decrease in pressure and temperature. Because the temperature lapse rate is less than the pressure lapse rate as altitude is increased, the density is decreased. Although the decreased temperature increases thrust, the effect of decreased density more than offsets the effect of the colder temperature. The net result of increased altitude is a reduction in the thrust output.

Variation of thrust with aircraft speed (airspeed). The effect of airspeed on the thrust of a turbojet engine is shown in Figure 13-3-5.

As airspeed is increased, the ram drag increases rapidly. The exhaust jet velocity remains relatively constant; thus, the effect of the increase in air-speed results in a decrease in net thrust.

Ram recovery. A rise in pressure above existing outside atmospheric pressure at the engine inlet, because of the forward velocity of an aircraft, is referred to as ram recovery or ram effect. As the aircraft speed increases, air is literally *rammed* into the inlet. This compresses the air in the inlet, increasing pressure and density. Because any ram effect causes an increase in inlet pressure over atmospheric, the resulting pressure rise causes an increase in the mass airflow, increasing thrust (Figure 13-3-5).

Section 4

Main Parts of a Turbine Engine

To help build an understanding of turbine engines, how they are alike and how they are different, we can start by looking at the major parts of the engine and its basic construction. In this section we begin where the air enters the engine and move our way through the engine, ending at the exhaust section. Then, we go a little further and take a quick look at

Figure 13-4-1. An example of a turbofan engine inlet.

afterburners and thrust reversers, which are downstream of the normal exhaust exit.

Inlet Section

The inlet duct (Figure 13-4-1) is very important to the engine's overall performance and its ability to produce optimum thrust.

A gas turbine engine uses considerably more air than a reciprocating engine, so the air entrance passage also needs to be much larger. Airflow in a turbine engine is critical when determining engine and aircraft performance, especially at high airspeeds. Any inefficiencies in the inlet duct result in losses through other components of the engine. The inlet design varies according to the type of turbine engine. Many turboprop, APUs, and turboshaft engines use screens that cover the inlet to prevent foreign object damage.

Inlet ducts are designed to uniformly deliver air to the compressor inlet with as little turbulence and pressure variation as possible. The choice of configuration of the entrance to the duct is dictated by the location of the engine on the aircraft and the airspeed, altitude, and attitude at which the aircraft is designed to operate.

The inlet must be able to recover as much of the total pressure of the free airstream as possible. As air molecules are trapped and begin to be compressed in the inlet, much of the pressure loss is recovered. This added pressure at the inlet of the engine increases the pressure and airflow to the engine. This is known as *ram recovery* or *ram effect*.

Turboprop Compressor Inlets

The air inlet on a turboprop is more of a problem than some other gas turbine engines because the propeller drive shaft, the hub, and the spinner must be considered in addition to other inlet design factors (Figure 13-4-2).

Figure 13-4-2. An example of a turboprop engine inlet.

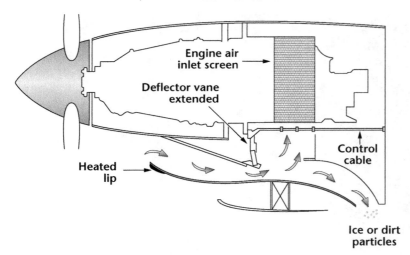

Figure 13-4-3. A turboprop inlet with an inertial separator.

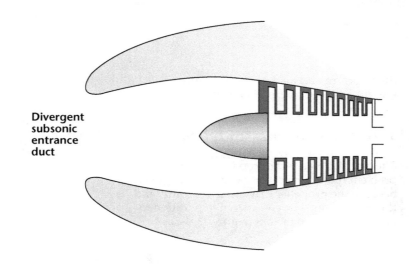

Figure 13-4-4. A divergent inlet duct.

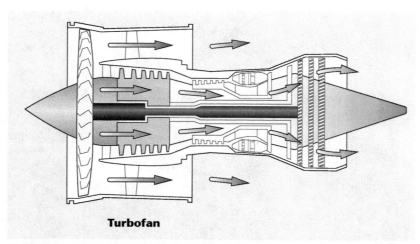

Figure 13-4-5. The air that passes through the inner part of the fan blades becomes the primary (or core) airstream (red), and the air passing through the outer part of the blades becomes the secondary (or bypass) airstream (blue).

Inertial separators are sometimes used to deflect ice or dirt away from the intake, thus acting as a type of particle separator. The air then passes up into the engine, and the ice and dirt are directed overboard through the bottom of the cowl (Figure 13-4-3).

Turbofan Engine Inlets

Turbofan engines are usually made with the fan at the forward end of the compressor. The inlet duct directs air into the fan and the core of the engine. On turbofan engines, the duct must have a sufficiently straight section to ensure smooth, even airflow at the face of the fan. Inlet ducts used on subsonic aircraft use a divergent shape (Figure 13-4-4). The divergent duct slows down the air before entering the fan and increases the static pressure.

The fan on turbofan engines usually consists of one stage of rotating blades (Figure 13-4-5). However, some engines might incorporate multiple stage fans.

The air accelerated by the outer part of the fan blades forms a secondary airstream that is ducted overboard without passing through the engine core. This secondary air (fan flow) produces a large percentage of the thrust in high-bypass engines. The air that passes through the inner part of the fan blades becomes the primary airstream (core flow), and the air passing through the outer part of the blades becomes the secondary airstream (bypass flow).

Compressor

The compressor section of the gas turbine engine has many functions. Its primary function is to supply air in a large enough quantity to satisfy the requirements of combustion. Specifically, to fulfill this purpose, the compressor must increase the pressure of the air received from the inlet duct, and then discharge it to the combustion chamber in the quantity and pressure required.

A secondary function of the compressor is to supply bleed air for various purposes in the engine and aircraft. The bleed air is taken from any of the various pressure stages of the compressor. The exact location of the bleed ports depends on the pressure or temperature required for a job. The ports are small openings in the compressor case next to the stage from which the air is to be bled; thus, varying degrees of pressure are available simply by tapping into the appropriate stage.

At times it might be necessary to cool this high-pressure air. If it is used for cabin pressurization or other purposes for which excess heat would be uncomfortable or detrimental, the air is sent through an air conditioning unit before it enters the cabin.

Bleed air is used in many ways; some are listed here:

- Cabin pressurization, heating, and cooling
- Deicing and anti-icing equipment
- Pneumatic pressure for starting engines
- Auxiliary drive units

Compressor Types

The two principal types of compressors used in gas turbine aircraft engines are centrifugal flow and axial flow. The centrifugal-flow compressor works by receiving air at its center and accelerating it outwardly by centrifugal action. The axial-flow compressor compresses the air as it continues in its original direction of flow, thus avoiding the energy loss caused by turns. Each stage in a compressor is associated with a corresponding rise in pressure. The air then continues on to the combustion section.

Centrifugal flow. The centrifugal-flow compressor consists of an impeller (rotor) and a diffuser (stator), housed in a manifold (Figure 13-4-6). Centrifugal compressors create a high pressure rise per stage. However, centrifugal compressors are limited to two stages because of efficiency losses. The two main functional elements are the impeller and the diffuser.

As the impeller rotates, it draws air into the center and accelerates the air radially outwardly to the diffuser. The diffuser is an annular chamber provided with vanes that form a series of divergent passages. As the air flows through the vanes, because of the divergent passages, the air velocity decreases, and pressure increases (Figure 13-4-7). The air is then routed through an outlet duct or manifold to change the direction of the air one more time, from a radial direction to an axial direction and to the combustion chamber.

The centrifugal compressor can be either of two types—single entry or double entry. The single-entry impeller (Figure 13-4-8) permits convenient ducting directly to the impeller eye (inducer vanes) as opposed to the more

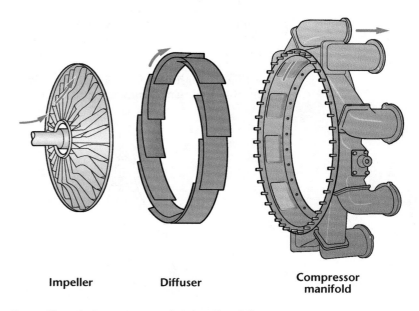

Impeller   Diffuser   Compressor manifold

Figure 13-4-6. Components of a centrifugal-flow compressor.

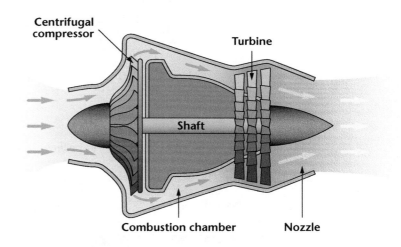

Figure 13-4-7. Airflow through an engine with a centrifugal flow compressor.

Figure 13-4-8. A single-entry impeller.

complicated ducting necessary to reach the back side of the double-entry type (Figure 13-4-9).

Although slightly more efficient in receiving air, the single-entry impeller must have a large diameter to deliver the same quantity of air as the double-entry type. This increases the engine's overall diameter.

Some engines use a two-stage centrifugal compressor as shown in Figure 13-4-10. Engines are generally limited to two stages of centrifugal compressors because energy is lost any time the air changes direction. Ducting the air from one stage to the next requires many turns for the airflow, reducing efficiency.

Axial flow. The axial-flow compressor has two main elements: a rotor and a stator. The rotor has blades fixed on a spindle. These blades impel air rearward in the same manner as a propeller because of their angle and air-foil contour. The rotor, turning at high speed, takes in air at the compressor inlet and moves it through a series of stages made of a set of rotating blades and stator vanes. The action of the rotor-stator combination increases the pressure of the air at each stage and moves it rearward through several stages. With this action, energy is transferred from the compressor to the air in the form of velocity.

The stator has rows of vanes that are attached inside an enclosing case. The stator vanes, which do not rotate, project radially toward the rotor axis and fit closely on either side of each stage of the rotor blades. In some cases, the compressor case, into which the stator

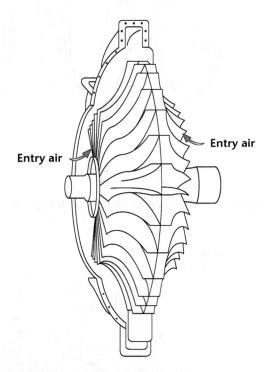

Entry air

Entry air

Figure 13-4-9. A double-entry impeller.

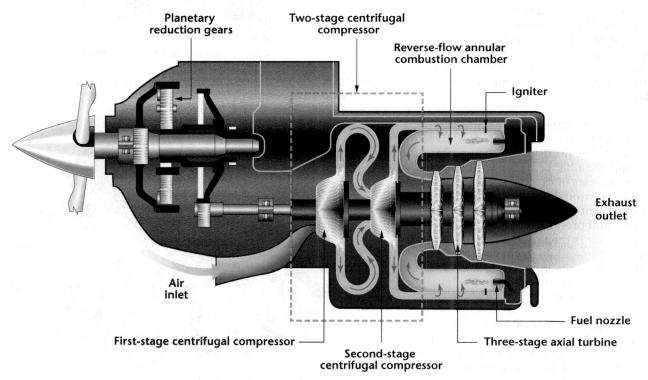

Planetary reduction gears

Two-stage centrifugal compressor

Reverse-flow annular combustion chamber

Igniter

Exhaust outlet

Air inlet

Fuel nozzle

First-stage centrifugal compressor

Second-stage centrifugal compressor

Three-stage axial turbine

Figure 13-4-10. A two-stage centrifugal compressor.

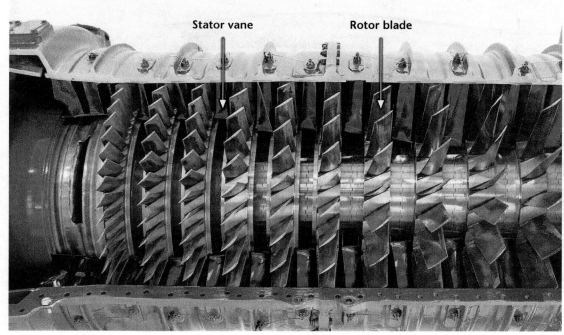

Figure 13-4-11. In an axial-flow compressor, stator vanes do not move, and rotor blades do.

vanes are fitted, is horizontally divided into halves. Many engines have multiple rows of vanes that can vary their angle during engine operation to increase engine performance. Figure 13-4-11 shows the rotor and stator elements of a typical axial-flow compressor.

Stator vanes act as diffusers at each stage, partially converting velocity to pressure. Each consecutive pair of rotor blades and stator vanes constitutes a pressure stage. From inlet to exit, the air flows along an axial path and is compressed at a ratio of about 1.25:1 per stage. The number of rows of blades and vanes (stages) is determined by the amount of air and total pressure rise required. Compressor pressure ratio increases with the number of compression stages.

Compressor Types Advantages and Disadvantages

The advantages and disadvantages of both types of compressors are included in the following lists. Even though each type has advantages and disadvantages, each has its use by engine type and size.

Centrifugal-flow compressor advantages

- High-pressure rise per stage
- Efficiency over wide rotational speed range

- Simple to manufacture and low cost
- Light
- Low starting power requirements

Centrifugal-flow compressor disadvantages

- Large frontal area for an airflow
- Losses in turns between stages

Axial-flow compressor advantages

- High peak efficiencies
- Small frontal area for an airflow
- Straight-through flow, highly efficient
- Increased pressure rise by increasing number of stages, with negligible losses

Axial-flow compressor disadvantages

- Good efficiencies over only narrow rotational speed range
- Difficult to manufacture and high cost
- Relatively heavy
- High starting power requirements (partially overcome by split compressors)

Some engines use both types of compressors, with several stages of an axial-flow compres-

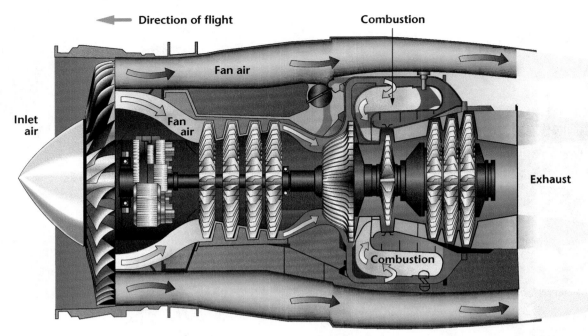

Figure 13-4-12. A four-stage axial compressor, followed by a single-stage centrifugal compressor.

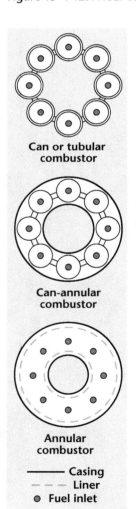

Figure 13-4-13. Three types of combustion chambers.

sor followed by a centrifugal-flow compressor (Figure 13-4-12).

Diffuser

The diffuser is the divergent section of the engine that is after the compressor and before the combustion section. It reduces high-velocity compressor discharge air to a lower velocity and increases its static pressure one last time. This prepares the air for entry into the flame burning area of the combustion section at a lower velocity so that the flame of combustion can burn continuously. If the air passed through the flame area at a high velocity, it could extinguish the flame.

Combustor

The combustion section is between the diffuser and the turbine sections. This section houses the combustion process. The primary function of the combustion section is to burn the air/fuel mixture, thereby adding heat energy to the air. The turbine then extracts much of this energy to drive the compressor. The remaining energy exits the engine exhaust nozzle at a high velocity, providing thrust. To do this efficiently, the combustion chamber must do the following:

- Properly mix the fuel and air to ensure good combustion
- Burn the mixture efficiently
- Deliver the hot gases to the turbine section
- Cool the hot combustion products to a temperature that the turbine can withstand under operating conditions

Three basic types of combustion chambers are used (Figure 13-4-13):

- Can type
- Can-annular type
- Annular type

All types of combustion chambers require a great deal of cooling air. Only about 25 percent of the air in the combustion chamber is used for combustion. The rest of the air flowing through the chamber is used for cooling.

Can Type Combustor

The can combustion chamber was used in early turbine engines. Each of the can-type combustion chambers consists of an outer case or housing, within which is a perforated stainless steel (highly heat resistant) combustion chamber. Each can has a fuel nozzle to supply fuel, and cooling air is supplied for each individual can.

Can-Annular Type Combustor

The basic components of a can-annular combustion chamber are a housing and a liner (Figure 13-4-13), just as in the can type.

Louvers and cooling holes

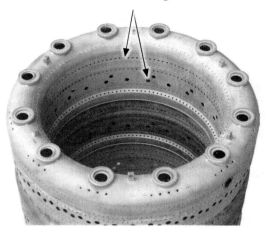

Figure 13-4-14. Combustion chamber louvers and cooling holes (right). The ample cooling air keeps flame away from the metal combustion chamber parts.

Combustion still takes place in the individual cans, but the cooling air can circulate among the different cans.

Annular Type Combustor

Modern turbine engines usually have an annular combustion chamber as shown in Figure 13-4-13. The annular combustion chamber (Figure 13-4-14) uses louvers and holes to prevent the flame from contacting the side of the combustion chamber.

Reverse-flow annular. Some engines incorporate a reverse-flow annular combustion chamber. An example is shown in Figure 13-4-15.

Turbine

The turbine transforms a portion of the kinetic (velocity) energy of the exhaust gases into mechanical energy to drive the compressor and accessories. The exact amount of energy absorbed by each turbine stage is determined by the load the turbine is driving (i.e., compressor size and type, number of accessories, and the load applied by the other turbine stages). These turbine stages can be used to drive a low-pressure compressor (fan), propeller, or shaft.

The turbine section is downstream of the combustion chamber. Specifically, it is directly behind the combustion chamber outlet. The turbine assembly consists of two basic elements: stationary vanes and rotating turbine blades (Figures 13-4-16 and 13-4-17). The stationary vanes are known by a vari-

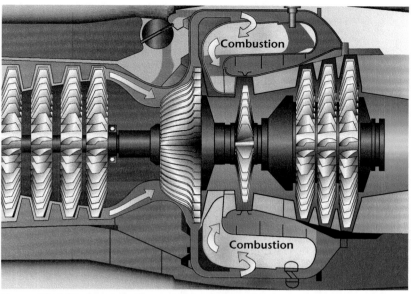

Figure 13-4-15. A reverse-flow annular combustor.

Figure 13-4-16. Turbine inlet guide vanes.

Figure 13-4-17. Turbine blades.

ety of names. Turbine nozzle vanes, turbine vanes, and nozzle guide vanes are commonly used terms.

The first-stage turbine nozzle vanes are directly aft of the combustion chambers and immediately forward of the first-stage turbine blades. The first stage vanes are sometimes referred to as turbine inlet guide vanes. This is the highest temperature that comes in contact with metal components in the engine. The turbine inlet temperature (TIT) must be controlled, or the high heat will damage the turbine vanes.

After the combustion chamber has introduced the heat energy into the mass airflow and delivered it evenly to the turbine nozzles, the

Figure 13-4-18. Rotor elements of the turbine assembly.

nozzles must prepare the mass air flow to drive the turbine rotor. The stator vanes of the turbine nozzles are contoured and set at such an angle that they form several small nozzles discharging gas at extremely high speed; thus, the nozzle converts a varying portion of the heat and pressure energy to velocity energy that can then be converted to mechanical energy through the turbine blades.

The second purpose of the turbine nozzle is to deflect the gases to a specific angle in the direction of turbine blades. Because the gas flow from the nozzle must enter the turbine blade passageway while it is still rotating, it is essential to aim the gas in the general direction of turbine blade rotation.

The rotor element of the turbine section consists essentially of a shaft and a wheel (Figure 13-4-18). The turbine wheel consists of blades attached to a rotating disk. The disk, in turn, is attached to the main power-transmitting shaft of the engine. The exhaust gases leaving the turbine nozzle vanes act on the blades of the turbine wheel, causing the assembly to rotate at a very high speed.

The disk acts as an anchoring component for the turbine blades. Because the disk is attached to the rotor shaft, the blades transmit the energy they extract from the exhaust gases to the shaft. The forward end of the turbine shaft is attached to the compressor. The combustion gases pass through the turbine, causing the turbine to spin. Because the compressor is attached to the turbine, the compressor also spins. Figure 13-4-19 shows exhaust gases traveling through a turbine.

Figure 13-4-19. Air flow through the turbine.

Exhaust Section

The exhaust section receives the gases from the fan or core and delivers the gases back to the atmosphere. Turbine engines use several types of exhaust nozzles, depending on the type of engine.

Turboshaft engines. Turboshaft engines in helicopters can have an exhaust nozzle that forms a divergent duct. This type of nozzle does not provide any thrust; all engine power goes to rotate the rotors.

Turboprop engines. Turboprop exhaust nozzles might provide small amounts of thrust but are mainly used to discharge the exhaust gases from the aircraft. Most of the energy has been used by the turbine section to turn the propeller.

Turbofan engines. In a turbofan engine, the shape of the exhaust duct is designed to increase engine thrust. The core exhaust is directly behind the turbine section. The components of the exhaust section include the exhaust cone, tailpipe, and the exhaust nozzle (Figure 13-4-20).

Using a converging nozzle, the exhaust gases increase in velocity before they are discharged from the exhaust nozzle. Increasing the velocity of the gases increases their momentum and increases the thrust produced.

Fan exhaust can be ducted, in which the engine takes the fan airflow and directs it through a closed duct along the engine. Then, it flows into a common exhaust nozzle. The core exhaust flow and the fan flow mix and

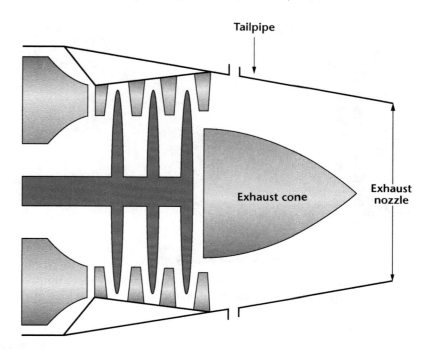

Figure 13-4-20. The parts of an exhaust nozzle.

flow from the engine through this mixed nozzle.

Many engines have two exhaust nozzles—one for the fan airflow and one for the core airflow. These both flow to ambient air separate from each other and have separate nozzles (Figure 13-4-21)

Engines that produce exhaust gas velocities greater than the speed of sound use a convergent-divergent exhaust nozzle as shown in Figure 13-4-22. This nozzle increases the thrust.

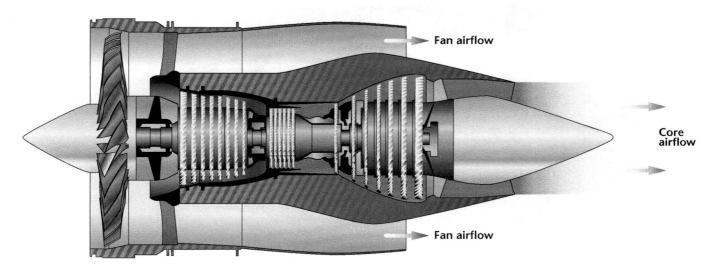

Figure 13-4-21. Path of both core exhaust flow and fan flow from the engine to separate nozzles.

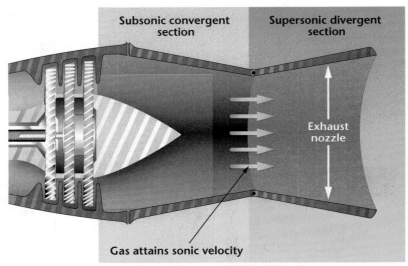

Figure 3-4-22. A convergent-divergent nozzle helps produce more thrust when exhaust gas velocities are greater than the speed of sound.

Thrust Reversers

As aircraft have become heavier with higher landing speeds, the problem of stopping an aircraft after landing has greatly increased. In many instances, the aircraft brakes can no longer be relied on solely to slow the aircraft within a reasonable distance after touch-down.

A thrust reverser is a device fitted in the engine exhaust system that effectively reverses the flow of the exhaust gases. The flow does not reverse through 180°; however, the final path of the exhaust gases is about 45° from straight ahead.

Normally, a jet engine has one of two types of thrust reversers: a target reverser or a cascade reverser (Figure 13-4-23). Target reversers

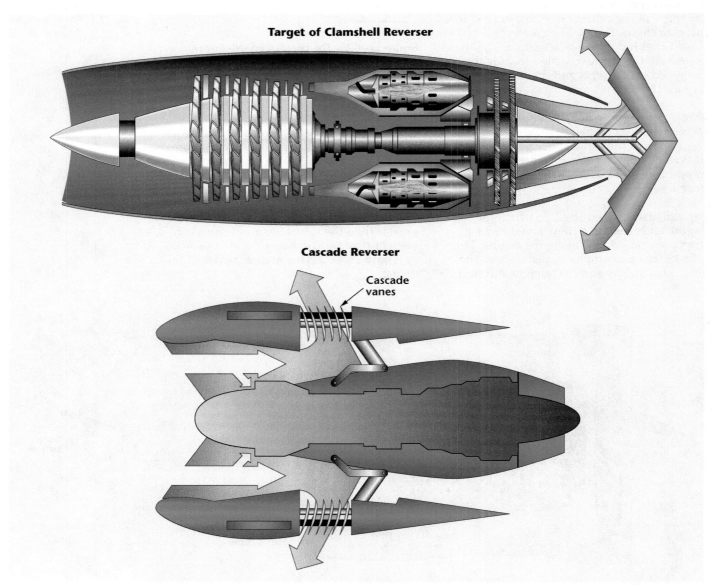

Figure 13-4-23. Thrust reversers block and divert engine exhaust gases (top) or fan air (bottom) in a reverse direction.

are simple clamshell doors that swivel from the stowed position at the engine tailpipe to block all the outflow and redirect some component of the thrust forward.

Cascade reversers are more complex. They are normally used on turbofan engines and are usually designed to reverse only the fan air portion. Blocking doors in the shroud obstruct forward fan thrust and redirect it through cascade vanes for some reverse component.

On most installations, reverse thrust is obtained with the thrust lever at idle, by pulling up the reverse lever to a detent. Doing so positions the reversing mechanisms for operation but leaves the engine at idle r.p.m. Further upward and backward movement of the reverse lever increases engine power. Reverse is canceled by moving the reverse lever to the idle reverse position, then dropping it fully back to the forward idle position. This last movement operates the reverser back to the forward thrust position. Generally, an indication is in the flight deck about the status of the reverser system.

Inadvertent deployment of thrust reversers is a very serious emergency situation. Therefore, thrust reverser systems are designed with this prospect in mind. The systems normally have several lock systems to prevent inadvertent deployment.

A modern cascade vane thrust reverser system consists of a translating cowl, blocker doors, and cascade vanes.

Afterburning/Thrust Augmentation

The term *afterburning* and *thrust augmentation* generally pertain to military engine applications. The terms are used to describe the same system. Normally, this is used to increase the thrust of the engine up to double the original thrust. The required additions to the exhaust nozzle for this system are a flame stabilizer, fuel manifold, flame holder, igniter, and a variable area exhaust nozzle (Figure 13-4-24). After the engine has reached full power under normal operation, the power lever can be advanced to activate the afterburner. This allows more fuel to flow into the exhaust nozzle where it is ignited and burned, adding energy, producing additional thrust.

Thrust Vectoring

Thrust vectoring is the ability of an aircraft's main engines to direct thrust other than parallel to the vehicle's longitudinal axis, allowing the exhaust nozzle to move or change position to direct the thrust in varied directions. Vertical takeoff aircraft use thrust vectoring as takeoff thrust and then change direction to propel the aircraft in horizontal

Figure 13-4-24. A variable area exhaust nozzle used to increase or decrease exhaust flow during afterburn.

Figure 13-4-25. A vectoring nozzle increases flight maneuverability.

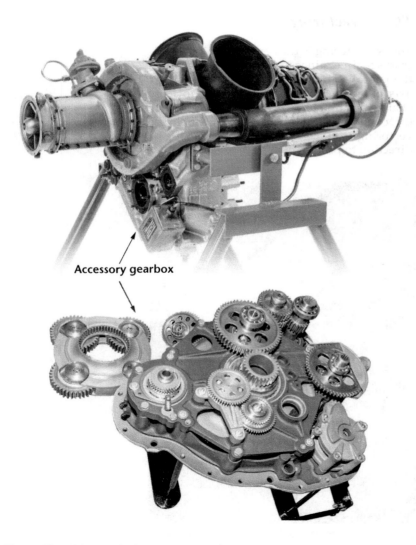

Accessory gearbox

Figure 13-4-26. A typical accessory gearbox.

flight. Military aircraft use thrust vectoring for maneuvering in flight to change direction. Thrust vectoring is generally achieved by relocating the direction of the exhaust nozzle to direct the thrust to move the aircraft in the desired path. This makes the aircraft much more maneuverable in flight (Figure 13-4-25).

Accessory Gearbox

The accessory gearbox of the gas turbine engine (Figure 13-4-26) provides space for mounting accessories needed to operate and control the engine, such as fuel pumps, oil pumps, and other components. Generally, it also includes accessories concerned with the aircraft, such as electric generators and hydraulic pumps.

The accessory gearbox is driven by the engine's high-pressure turbine through an accessory drive shaft (tower shaft) gear coupling that splines with a gear on the high-pressure turbine shaft. The reduction gearing in the case provides suitable drive speeds for each engine accessory or component

Section 5

Turbine Engine Systems Overview

Turbine engine systems are complex and vary widely by manufacturer and model. This section gives an overview of some turbine engine systems—those that support and control the engines themselves. For brevity, many systems have been excluded. Some systems that are included might not describe all parts of a typical system. Components and part nomenclature varies by manufacture and type of engine.

Engine Fuel Systems and Fuel Metering

The fuel metering system is one of the more complex aspects of the gas turbine engine. It must be possible to increase or decrease the power at will to obtain the thrust required for any operating condition. In turbine-powered aircraft, this control is provided by varying the flow of fuel to the combustion chambers. Most turboprop aircraft also use variable-pitch propellers; thus, the selection of thrust is shared by two controllable variables, fuel flow and propeller blade angle.

The quantity of fuel supplied must be adjusted automatically to correct for changes in ambient temperature or pressure because of changes in aircraft altitude, airspeed and changing atmospheric conditions. The engine must operate through acceleration and deceleration without any fuel-control-related problems.

For satisfactory combustion, the fuel system must deliver fuel to the combustion chambers in the right quantity and in the right condition. The fuel nozzles form part of the fuel system and atomize or vaporize the fuel so that it ignites and burns efficiently. The fuel system must also supply fuel so that the engine can be easily started on the ground and in the air. This means that the fuel must be injected into the combustion chambers in a combustible condition during engine starting, and that combustion must be sustained while the engine is accelerating to its normal idling speed.

Another critical condition to which the fuel system must respond occurs during rapid r.p.m. changes. When the engine is accelerated, energy must be furnished to the turbine in excess of that necessary to maintain a constant r.p.m. However, if the fuel flow increases too rapidly, an over rich mixture can be produced. The other extreme, *lean flame-out*, occurs if the fuel quantity is reduced proportionally below the air quantity. The engine must operate through acceleration and deceleration without any fuel-control-related problems at various outside air temperatures, altitudes and airspeeds.

Following is a brief overview of a typical turbofan engine fuel system. Figure 13-5-1 shows the common components of a turbofan engine fuel system.

Fuel is supplied to the engine fuel pump from the aircraft fuel system. Most fuel pumps have a low-pressure stage and a high-pressure stage combined into one unit. The fuel first goes through the low-pressure side of the pump and flows through the oil cooler, which cools the oil and warms the fuel. The fuel then travels back to the fuel pump, passing through the main engine fuel filter and then to the high-pressure side of the pump. The now highly pressurized fuel flows next to the fuel metering valve. The metering valve position is controlled by an electronic control referred to as an *electronic engine control* (EEC) or a *full authority digital electronic engine control* (FADEC). The fuel metering valve regulates fuel flow to the combustion chamber according to the signal received from the EEC or FADEC. Engine controls are described in more detail later in this section.

From the metering valve, the fuel goes to a fuel distribution valve that divides the fuel

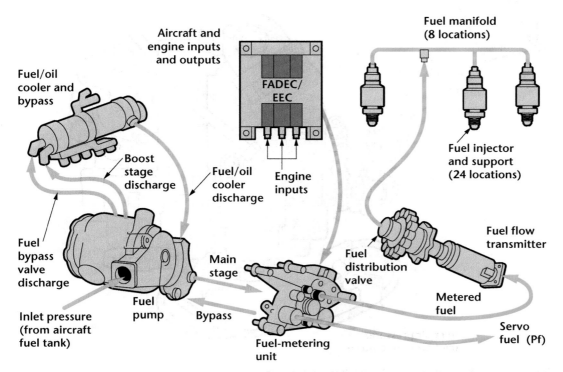

Figure 13-5-1. Turbofan fuel system example.

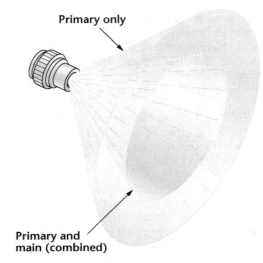

Primary only

Primary and main (combined)

Figure 13-5-2. A duplex nozzle spray pattern.

to individual fuel nozzles. The fuel nozzles distribute fuel inside the combustion chamber. The fuel nozzles inject fuel into the combustion area in a highly atomized, precisely patterned spray so that burning is completed evenly, in the shortest possible time, and in the smallest possible space. It is very important that the fuel be evenly distributed and well centered in the flame area in the combustion chamber. This prevents hot spots

from forming and prevents the flame from burning through the combustion chamber.

Most fuel nozzles produce two spray patterns, one for starting and one for normal operation. This type of fuel nozzle is referred to as a duplex nozzle (Figure 13-5-2).

Turbine Fuel Controls

The fuel control can be thought of as the brains of the engine fuel system, in charge of controlling fuel flow for all aspects of engine operation. Gas turbine engine fuel controls can be divided into three basic groups:

1. Hydromechanical

2. Hydromechanical/electronic

3. FADEC, EEC, or engine control unit (ECU)

Regardless of the type, all fuel controls essentially do the same thing: schedule the fuel flow to match the power requested by the flight crew. Some types sense more engine variables than others. The fuel control can sense many different inputs, such as power lever position, engine r.p.m., compressor inlet pressure and temperature, burner pressure,

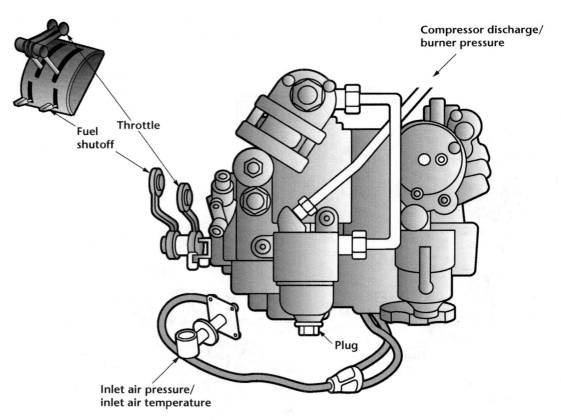

Compressor discharge/ burner pressure

Throttle

Fuel shutoff

Plug

Inlet air pressure/ inlet air temperature

Figure 13-5-3. Example of a hydromechanical fuel control.

compressor discharge pressure, and many more parameters as needed by the engine. These variables affect the amount of thrust that an engine produces for a given fuel flow. By sensing these parameters, the fuel control has a clear picture of what is happening in the engine and can adjust fuel flow as needed.

Hydromechanical fuel control.

Hydromechanical fuel controls are still used on many engines, but their use is becoming limited as more electronic-based controls are used. These fuel controls have two sections—computing and metering—to provide the correct fuel flow for the engine. A pure hydromechanical fuel control has no electronic interface helping to compute or meter the fuel flow. It is installed on and driven by the accessory gearbox. Because of this, it can be used to sense engine speed. Other engine parameters it senses are compressor discharge pressure, burner pressure, and inlet air temperature, inlet air pressure, throttle position, and fuel shutoff valve position. Once the computing section determines the correct amount of fuel flow, the metering section regulates fuel flow to the fuel nozzles. Actual operating procedures for a hydromechanical fuel control are very complicated, and the fuel metering is not as accurate as with an electronic control (Figure 13-5-3).

Hydromechanical/electronic fuel control.

Adding a limited authority electronic control to a basic hydromechanical fuel control was the next step in developing turbine engine fuel controls. Generally, this type of system uses a remotely located EEC, which provides additional information to the hydromechanical fuel control. Fuel flow is still controlled by hydromechanical fuel control as described earlier.

During normal engine operation, an EEC sets thrust, governs speed, acceleration, and deceleration. If the electrical or electronic flight control unit failure occurs, or if the flight crew uses the EEC deactivate switch, the system operates the engine using the hydromechanical control only (Figure 13-5-4).

FADEC fuel control systems.

A FADEC has been developed to control fuel flow on most new turbine engine models (also known as EEC or ECU). A true FADEC system has no hydromechanical fuel control. It uses sensors that feed engine parameter information into the FADEC. The FADEC gathers the needed information to determine the amount of fuel flow and transmits it to a fuel metering valve. The fuel metering valve simply reacts to the commands from the FADEC. The FADEC is the computing section of the fuel delivery system, and the metering valve meters the fuel flow. FADEC systems are used on many types of turbine engines, from APUs to the largest turbofan engines. In addition to controlling fuel flow, the FADEC can control other aircraft systems (Figure 13-5-5).

Ignition System

Because turbine ignition systems are operated mostly for a brief period during the engine-starting cycle, they are, as a rule, more trouble-free than the typical reciprocating engine ignition system. The turbine engine ignition system does not need to be timed to spark at an exact point in the operational cycle. It is used to ignite the air/fuel mixture in the combustor and then it is switched off. Other modes of turbine ignition system operation, such as continuous ignition

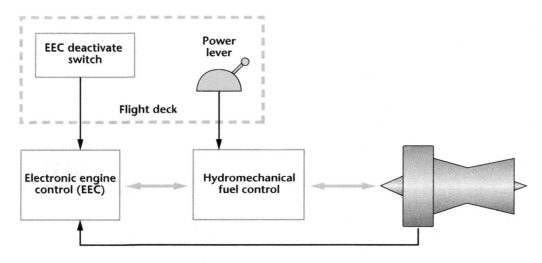

Figure 13-5-4. Hydromechanical/electronic fuel control.

Figure 13-5-5. An engine with a FADEC unit installed.

that work at a lower voltage and energy level, are used for certain flight conditions.

Continuous ignition is used as a precaution during critical operations if the engine flames out. This ignition could relight the fuel and keep the engine from shutting down. Examples of critical flight modes that use continuous ignition are takeoff, landing, and some abnormal and emergency situations.

Most gas turbine engines are equipped with a high-energy, capacitor-type ignition system (consisting of two identical independent ignition units) that are air cooled by fan airflow. Fan air is ducted to the exciter box and then flows around the igniter lead and surrounds the igniter before flowing back into the nacelle area. Cooling is important when continuous ignition is used for some extended period.

Because aircraft often operate in the low temperatures at high altitudes, the systems must be capable of supplying a high-heat-intensity spark. Thus, a high voltage is supplied to arc across a wide igniter spark gap, providing the ignition system with a high degree of reliability under widely varying conditions of

altitude, atmospheric pressure, temperature, fuel vaporization, and input voltage.

A typical ignition system includes two exciter units, two high-tension leads, and two ignitor plugs. Thus, as a safety factor, the ignition system is a dual system that is designed to fire two igniter plugs (Figure 13-5-6).

Capacitor discharge exciter unit. This capacitor-type system provides ignition for turbine engines. The exciter provides a spark of great heat intensity, capable of igniting abnormal fuel mixtures and burning away any foreign deposits on the igniter plug electrodes. The exciter is a dual unit that produces sparks at each of the two igniter plugs (Figure 13-5-7). It produces a continuous series of sparks until the engine starts. The power is then cut off, and the plugs do not fire while the engine is operating other than on continuous ignition for certain flight conditions.

Igniter plugs. The igniter plug of a turbine engine ignition system differs considerably from the spark plug of a reciprocating engine ignition system (Figure 13-5-8). Its electrode must be capable of withstanding a current of much higher energy than the electrode of a conventional spark plug.

Turbine Engine Starters

To start a turbine engine, it is necessary to rotate the high-pressure compressor at a high enough r.p.m. to provide enough air to support combustion in the combustion section. Once ignition and fuel have been introduced and the light-off has occurred, the starter

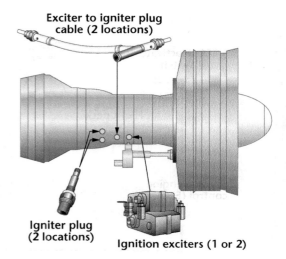

Figure 13-5-6. Turbine ignition system components.

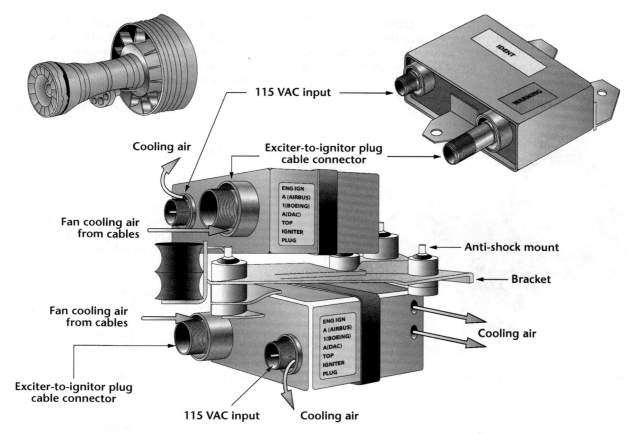

Figure 13-5-7. An exciter.

stays engaged to help the engine until the engine reaches a self-sustaining speed.

The exact sequence of the starting procedure is important because enough air must flow through the engine to support combustion before the air/fuel mixture is ignited.

If the starter is cut off below the self-accelerating speed, the engine would either fail to accelerate to idle speed or might even decelerate because it does not produce enough energy to sustain rotation or to accelerate in the beginning of the starting cycle. The basic types of starters in use for gas turbine engines are the direct cranking electric motor, starter-generator, and air turbine starters. The starter is installed on the accessory gearbox, which turns the high-pressure compressor.

Electric Starting Systems and Starter-Generator Starting System

Two general types of electric starting systems are used for gas turbine aircraft: direct cranking electrical systems and starter-generator systems. Direct cranking electric motors are used mostly on small turbine engines, such as APUs, and some small turboshaft engines.

Figure 13-5-8. An igniter plug.

Many gas turbine aircraft are equipped with starter-generator systems. Starter-generator starting systems are like direct cranking electrical systems except that after functioning as a starter, they have a second series of windings that allow it to switch to a generator after the engine has reached a self-sustaining speed. This saves weight and space on the engine because only one component is needed.

Although the starter-generator is permanently engaged with the engine shaft through drive gears, the direct cranking starter must use some means of disengaging the starter from the shaft after the engine has started (Figure 13-5-9). Starter-generator units are desirable from an economic standpoint, because one unit performs the functions of both starter and generator. Additionally, the total weight of starting system components is reduced and fewer spare parts are required.

Figure 13-5-9. A typical starter-generator.

Air Starting Systems

Air-powered starters are small, lightweight, and designed to provide high starting torque. The typical air turbine starter weighs from one-fourth to one-half as much as an electric starter capable of starting the same engine. It can develop considerably more torque than an electric starter.

The typical air turbine starter consists of an axial flow turbine that turns a drive coupling through a reduction gear and a starter clutch mechanism. The air to operate an air turbine starter is supplied from a ground power unit, APU, or a cross-bleed air start from an engine already operating (Figure

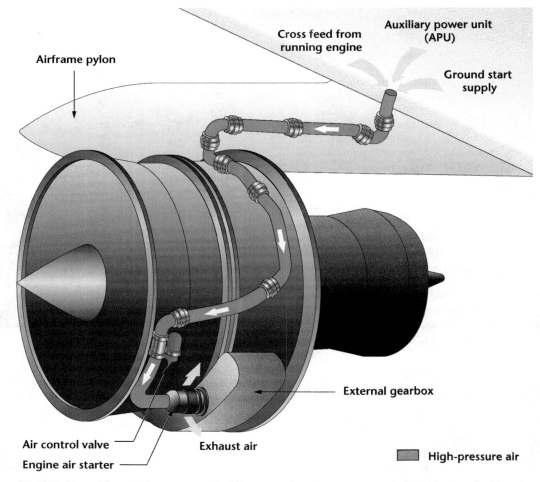

Figure 13-5-10. Air turbine starters are supplied by ground cart, APU, or another engine on the aircraft that is already operating.

13-5-10). Figure 13-5-11 shows a cutaway view of an air turbine starter.

The starter is operated by introducing air of enough volume and pressure into the starter inlet. The air supplied to the starter is controlled with a valve. The air is directed through the rotor blades, causing the turbine rotor to turn.

The clutch assembly engages automatically as soon as the rotor starts to turn but disengages as soon as the drive coupling turns more rapidly than the rotor side.

Turbine Engine Lubrication Systems

Both wet- and dry-sump lubrication systems are used in gas turbine engines. Wet-sump engines store the lubricating oil in the engine, and dry-sump engines use an external tank mounted on the engine or somewhere in the aircraft structure near the engine (Figure 13-5-12).

One of the main functions of the oil system in turbine engines is cooling the bearings by circulating oil around the bearings. The oil carries the heat away.

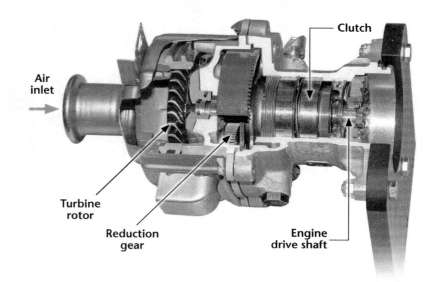

Figure 13-5-11. Cutaway of an air turbine starter.

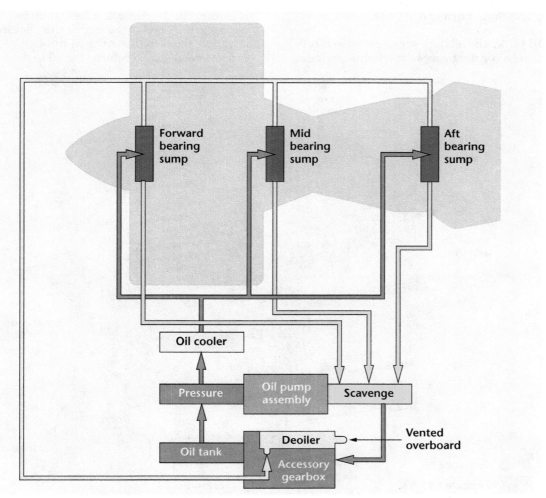

Figure 13-5-12. A simplified example of a dry-sump oil system.

Figure 13-5-13. An externally mounted oil tank.

Turbine Lubrication System Components

The following component descriptions include most found in the various turbine lubrication systems. However, because engine oil systems vary by engine model and manufacturer, not all of these components are necessarily found in any one system.

Oil tank. The oil tank stores the oil and furnishes a constant supply of it to the engine at any aircraft attitude. A typical tank is shown in Figure 13-5-13.

All oil tanks are provided with expansion space. This allows the oil to expand after it absorbs heat from the bearings and gears and it foams from circulating through the system.

Oil pump. The oil pump supplies oil under pressure to the parts of the engine that require lubrication, then circulates the oil through coolers as needed, and returns the oil to the

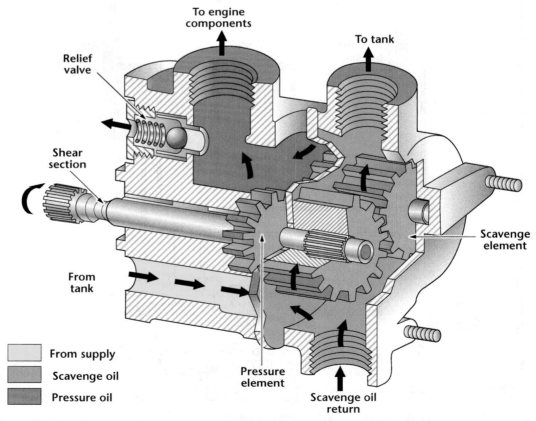

Figure 13-5-14. Cutaway of a gear-type oil pump.

Filter Element

Figure 13-5-15. A cutaway view of a typical turbine oil filter.

Oil filters. Filters (Figure 13-5-15) are an important part of the lubrication system because they remove foreign particles that might be in the oil.

A filter bypass valve prevents the oil flow from being stopped if the filter element becomes clogged. The bypass valve opens whenever a certain pressure is reached. If this occurs, the filtering action is lost, allowing unfiltered oil to be pumped to the bearings. However, this prevents the bearings from receiving no oil at all. Under normal operation, it should never open.

Oil nozzles. Oil jets (or nozzles) are in the pressure lines next to the engine bearings. These nozzles deliver the oil to the bearings in the form of an atomized spray.

Lubrication system breather systems (vents). Breather subsystems remove excess air from the bearing cavities and return the air to the oil tank where it is separated from any oil mixed in the vapor of air and oil by the deaerator. The air is then vented overboard, into the atmosphere.

Oil coolers. Two basic types of oil coolers in general use are air-cooled and fuel-cooled (Figure 13-5-16). Oil coolers are used in the lubricating systems to reduce the temperature of the oil to a degree suitable for recirculation through the system.

oil tank. Many oil pumps consist of a pressure supply element and scavenge elements (Figure 13-5-14). The pressure pump supplies oil to the engine bearings. The scavenge pump returns the oil to the tank after lubricating the bearings.

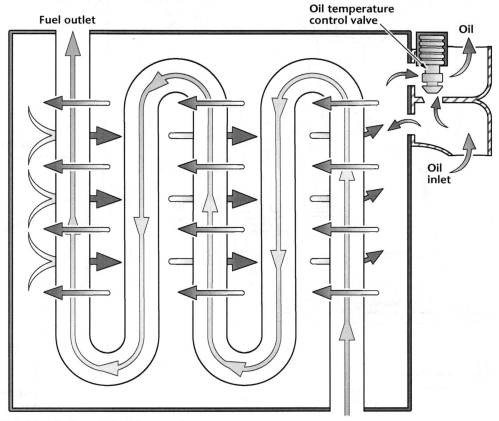

Fuel outlet

Oil temperature control valve

Oil

Oil inlet

Figure 13-5-16. A fuel-cooled oil heat exchanger.

Turbine Engine Cooling

The intense heat generated when fuel and air are burned requires a means of cooling for all internal combustion engines. The burning process in a gas turbine engine is continuous, and nearly all the cooling air must be passed through the inside of the engine. A large amount of air (more than needed for combustion) is admitted to the engine. The surplus air is used to cool the engine's hot sections to acceptable temperatures.

Fan air is often used to cool the ignition system and provide turbine case cooling. Excess air from the compressor is used to cool the combustion chamber, and air bleed from the compressor is used for internal cooling of turbine parts.

Figure 13-5-17 is an example of internal cooling air for the turbine blades and vanes, and Figure 13-5-18 shows an example of combustion chamber cooling.

Air in the combustion chamber can be divided into primary and secondary air. The primary air is used for combustion. The secondary air cools the combustion chamber liners.

Turbine Engine Insulation Blankets

To reduce the temperature of the structure near the exhaust duct and to eliminate the possibility of fuel or oil coming in contact with the hot parts of the engine, it is sometimes necessary to provide insulation on the exhaust duct of gas turbine engines. An example of heat shield construction is shown in Figure 13-5-19.

Engine Noise and Suppression

Noise comes from various places when operating a gas turbine engine. Turbojet and low-bypass turbofans, which are typical designs of early jet engines, produce tremendous noise from the exhaust (Figure 13-5-20). The

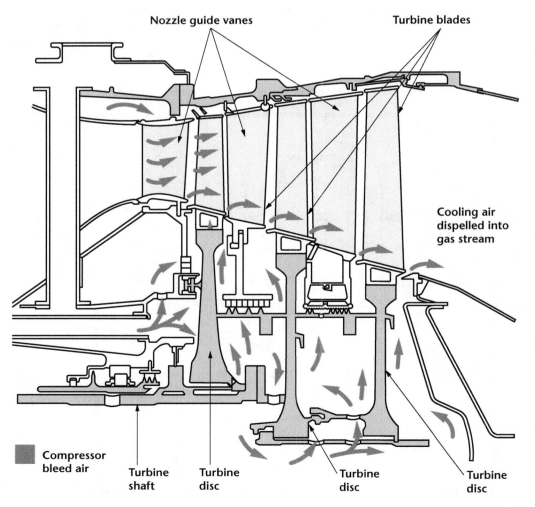

Figure 13-5-17. Turbine blade and vane internal cooling.

Figures 13-5-18 through 13-5-20

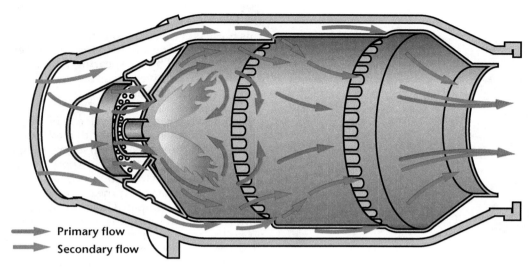

Primary flow
Secondary flow

Figure 13-5-18. Combustion chamber cooling.

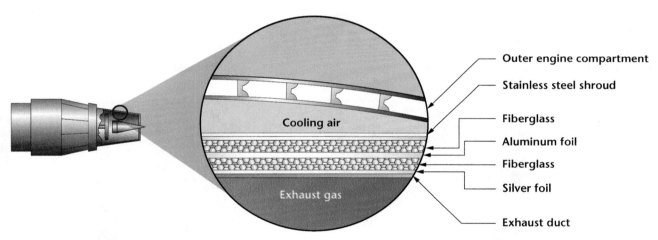

Outer engine compartment
Stainless steel shroud
Fiberglass
Aluminum foil
Fiberglass
Silver foil
Exhaust duct

Cooling air
Exhaust gas

Figure 13-5-19. A typical engine insulation blanket.

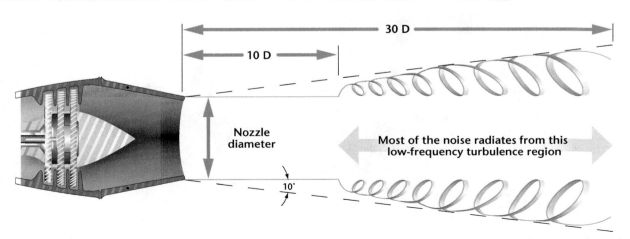

30 D
10 D
Nozzle diameter
Most of the noise radiates from this low-frequency turbulence region
10°

Figure 13-5-20. Noise from engine exhaust is created by the turbulence of a high-velocity jet stream moving through the relatively quiet atmosphere.

noise produced by the engine exhaust is caused by the high turbulence of a high-velocity jet stream moving through a relatively quiet atmosphere. For a distance of a few noz-

Figure 13-5-21. Lobed mixers help reduce noise in older engines.

zle diameters behind the engine, the velocity of the jet stream is high, and there is little mixing of the atmosphere with the jet stream. In this region, the turbulence in the high-speed jet stream is very fine-grain turbulence and produces relatively high-frequency noise. This noise is caused by violent, turbulent mixing of the exhaust gases with the atmosphere and is influenced by the shearing action caused by the relative speeds between the velocity and the atmosphere.

Farther downstream, as the velocity of the jet stream slows down, it mixes with the atmosphere and turbulence of a coarser type begins. Compared with noise from other portions of the jet stream, noise from this portion has a much lower frequency. As the energy of the jet stream finally is dissipated in large turbulent swirls, more of the energy is converted into noise. The noise generated as the exhaust gases dissipate is at a frequency near the low end of the audible range. The lower the frequency of the noise, the greater the distance the noise travels. This means that the low-frequency noises reach an individual on the ground in greater volume than the high-frequency noises and, thus, are more objectionable.

High-frequency noise is weakened more rapidly than low-frequency noise, both by

Figure 13-5-22. Chevrons on the trailing edge of the engine core and fan exhaust exits reduce noise.
Courtesy of NASA

distance and the interference of buildings, terrain, and atmospheric disturbances. A deep-voiced, low-frequency foghorn, for example, can be heard much farther than a shrill, high-frequency whistle, even though both could have the same overall volume (decibels) at their source.

Noise levels vary with engine thrust and are proportional to the amount of work the engine does on the air that passes through it. An engine with relatively low airflow but high thrust from high exhaust gas temperature, pressure, or afterburning produces a high velocity gas stream and, therefore, high noise levels. Larger bypass engines are quieter at the same thrust. Turbofan engines produce less noise than turbojets and low-bypass turbofan engines. The exhaust from the fan is at a relatively low velocity and is cooler. Therefore, it reduces the noise problem.

Many engines use a lobed mixer to help reduce noise (Figure 13-5-21). The mixers break up the single, main jet exhaust stream into several smaller jet streams, changing the frequency of the exhaust stream.

Modern engines frequently incorporate chevrons on the trailing edges of the exhaust to help reduce noise. Figure 13-5-22 shows chevrons on the core and bypass exhaust duct trailing edge. The sawtooth shaped edges smooth the transition of the exhaust into the atmosphere, reducing noise.

Acoustic linings, in both the inlet and exhaust, are also extensively used to reduce noise. This lining material converts acoustic energy into heat. These linings normally consist of a porous skin supported by a honeycomb backing.

Controls and Indication

Fixed-Shaft Tuboprops

Powerplant (engine and propeller) control is achieved with a *power lever* and a *condition lever* for each engine (Figure 13-5-23). No mixture control or r.p.m. lever is used as on piston engine aircraft. On the fixed-shaft, constant-speed, turboprop engine, the power lever is advanced or retreated to increase or decrease forward thrust. The power lever is also used to provide *reverse thrust*. The condition lever sets the desired engine r.p.m. within a narrow range between that appropriate for ground operations and flight.

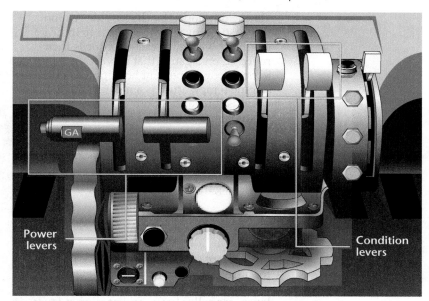

Figure 13-5-23. Engine power controls.

Figure 13-5-24. Engine indication for fixed-shaft turboprops.

Powerplant instrumentation in a fixed-shaft turboprop engine typically consists of the following basic indicators (Figure 13-5-24):

- Torque or horsepower
- Engine temperature
- Fuel flow
- R.P.M.

Torque developed by the turbine section is measured by a torque sensor to indicate engine power output. The torque is then reflected on a gauge that is typically calibrated in horsepower, percent horsepower, or torque. Engine temperature is a measurement of the combustion gas temperature passing through the turbine section. The gauge is usually calibrated in degrees Celsius. Propeller r.p.m. is reflected on a tachometer as a percentage of maximum r.p.m. The fuel flow indicator indicates fuel flow rate in pounds per hour, sometimes in gallons per hour.

Free-Power Turbine

Powerplant (engine and propeller) operation for a free-power turbine is achieved by three sets of controls for each engine: the power lever, propeller lever, and condition lever (Figure 13-5-25). The power lever controls engine power in the range from idle through takeoff power. Forward or aft motion of the power lever increases or decreases gas generator r.p.m. (N_1) and thereby increases or decreases engine power. The propeller lever controls the constant-speed propellers through the primary governor. The condition lever controls the flow of fuel to the engine. The positions are HIGH IDLE and LOW IDLE for ground operations, but condition levers have no metering function. Leaning is not required in turbine engines; this function is performed automatically by a dedicated fuel control unit.

Figure 13-5-25. Engine controls for free-power turbines.

Engine instruments in a split-shaft/free-turbine engine typically consist of these basic indicators (Figure 13-5-26):

- Engine temperature
- Torquemeter
- Propeller tachometer
- N_1 (gas generator) tachometer
- Fuel flow indicator
- Oil temperature/pressure indicator

The indicators are similar to those for a fixed-shaft engine, except two tachometers are needed—one for the propeller and one for the gas generator. This is because in the free-turbine engine, the propeller is not attached physically to the shaft of the gas generator section. The propeller tachometer is read directly in revolutions per minute. The N_1 or gas generator is read in percent of r.p.m.

Prop operation. The thrust provided by the propeller is a function of the angle of attack at which the air strikes the blades and the speed at which this occurs. The angle of attack varies with the propeller's pitch angle.

The so-called *flat pitch* is the blade position offering minimum resistance to rotation and no net thrust for moving the airplane. Forward pitch produces forward thrust—higher pitch angles are required at higher aircraft speeds.

The *feathered* position is the highest pitch angle obtainable (Figure 13-5-27). The feathered position produces no forward thrust. The propeller is generally feathered only if an engine fails in flight; this minimizes drag and prevents the air from turning the propeller as a turbine.

In the *reverse pitch* position, the engine/propeller turns in the same direction as in the normal (forward) pitch position, but the propeller blade angle is positioned to the other side of flat pitch (Figure 13-5-27). In reverse pitch, air is pushed away from the aircraft rather than being drawn over it. Reverse pitch results in braking action, rather than forward thrust of the aircraft. Reverse pitch does not mean reverse rotation of the engine. The engine delivers power just the same, regardless of which side of flat pitch the propeller blades are positioned.

With a turboprop engine, for high-power operation, the power lever is placed somewhere between *flight idle* (in some engines referred to as *high idle*) and maximum. The

Figures 13-5-26 and 13-5-27

Figure 13-5-26. Engine indication for free-power turbines.

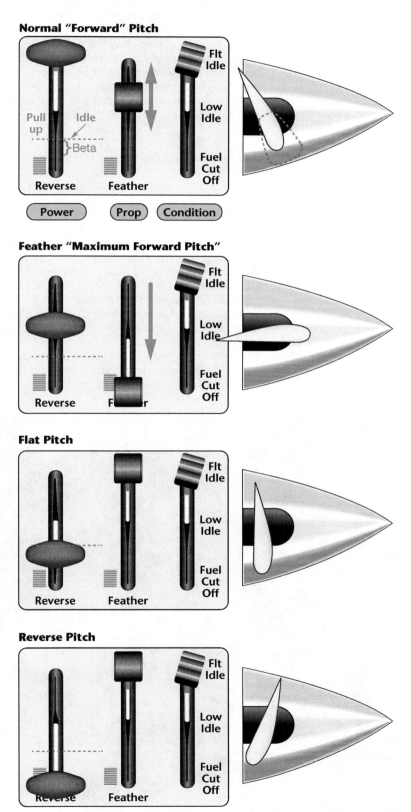

Figure 13-5-27. The normal, feather, flat, and reverse pitches and their corresponding control positions.

power lever directs signals to a fuel control unit to manually select fuel. The propeller governor selects the propeller pitch needed to keep the propeller/engine on speed. This is referred to as the propeller governing or *alpha* mode of operation. When positioned aft of flight idle, however, the power lever directly controls propeller blade angle. This is known as the *beta* range of operation. The beta range of operation consists of power lever positions from flight idle to maximum reverse.

Turbofan Engines

In a jet engine, thrust is determined by the amount of fuel injected into the combustion chamber. The power controls on most turbojet and turbofan-powered aircraft consist of just one thrust lever for each engine because most engine control functions are automatic. The thrust lever is linked to a fuel control that meters fuel flow called for by r.p.m., internal pressures or temperatures, ambient conditions, and other factors, depending on engine model (Figure 13-5-28).

In a jet engine, each major rotating section (spool) has a separate gauge to indicate its rotation speed. An N_1 gauge monitors the low-pressure compressor or fan speed in turbofan engines. The high-pressure compressor r.p.m. is indicated using an N_2 gauge. Triple-spool engines have an N_3 gauge as well. Each engine section rotates at many thousands of r.p.m. The gauges, therefore, are calibrated in percent of r.p.m. rather than actual r.p.m. for ease of display and interpretation.

When operating any turbine engine, monitoring internal temperatures is important. Exceeding temperature limits, even for a few seconds, can result in serious heat damage. As the burned air and fuel exit the combustion chamber and enter the turbine section, the temperature is critical. It is one of the factors that limits the amount of power the engine can produce.

Depending on the engine make and model, gas temperatures can be measured at various places in the engine and can have different names, as in the examples below:

- Exhaust gas temperature (EGT)—EGT is the term used for many aircraft regardless of probe location, and a common reference when discussing turbine engine internal temperature

- Turbine inlet temperature (TIT)

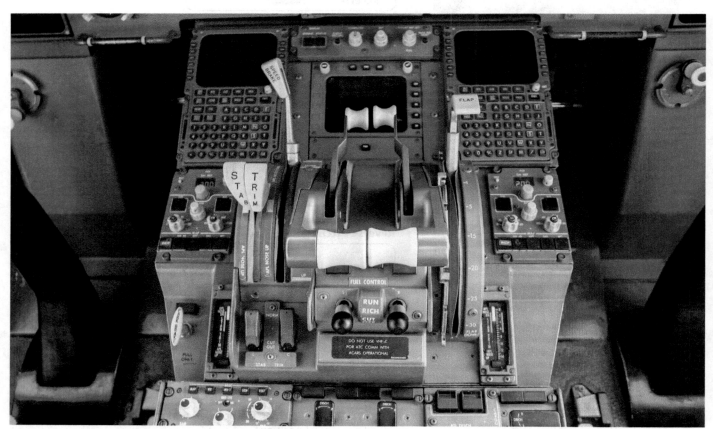

Figure 13-5-28. Thrust levers for a twin-engine aircraft.

- Interstage turbine temperature or inter-turbine temperature (ITT)
- Turbine outlet temperature (TOT)

On some turbine-powered aircraft, engine power is indicated by an engine pressure ratio (EPR) gauge. EPR is the difference between turbine discharge pressure and engine inlet pressure. For example, an EPR setting of 2.24 means that the discharge pressure relative to the inlet pressure is 2.24 : 1. On these airplanes, the EPR gauge is the primary reference used to establish power settings. EPR and other electronic indications for a large, transport category aircraft are shown in Figure 13-5-29.

N_1 (fan/low compressor) is the primary indication of thrust on turbofan engines that do not use EPR. Fuel flow provides a secondary thrust indication. Turbofans also have a high-pressure compressor r.p.m. indicator, N_2, which is used mainly for engine starting and some system functions.

Thrust to Thrust Lever Relationship

Efficiency in a jet engine is highest at high r.p.m. where the compressor is working closest to its optimum conditions. At low r.p.m., the operating cycle is generally inefficient. If the engine is operating at a relatively high r.p.m. and there is a sudden requirement for increased thrust, the jet engine responds immediately, and full thrust is achieved quickly. However, at a low r.p.m., issues can occur if fuel flow is increased too rapidly and airflow through the engine is still relatively low. Therefore, the engine fuel control restricts the fuel flow until the engine is at an r.p.m. at which it can respond to a rapid acceleration demand without distress.

Starting Issues

Turbine engines are extremely heat sensitive. They cannot tolerate an overtemperature condition for more than very few seconds without experiencing serious damage.

After fuel is introduced to the combustion chamber during the start sequence, *light-off*

and its associated heat rise occur very quickly. Engine temperatures can approach the maximum in a matter of seconds before the engine stabilizes and temperatures fall into the normal operating range.

An engine start exceeding maximum starting temperature limits is called a *hot start*. The temperature rise can be preceded by unusually high initial fuel flow, which can be the first indication that the engine start is not proceeding normally. Serious engine damage can occur depending on the how much the temperature limit is exceeded and for how long.

A condition in which the engine is accelerating more slowly than normal is called a *hung start* or *false start*. During a hung start/false start, the engine can stabilize at an engine r.p.m. that is below normal idle r.p.m.

Figure 13-5-29. Turbofan indication on a transport category aircraft.

Aircraft Maintenance and Documentation

Whether it is a training flight, a business professional on a sales call, or an airliner carrying hundreds of people to an exotic port of call somewhere overseas, the goal is for every flight to be safely completed. To ensure that the aircraft has been designed, constructed, and maintained in a condition that results in a safe flight is the goal of the airworthiness program. This chapter explores some of the processes, recordkeeping, forms, and publications in place to keep flying safe.

Section 1

Aircraft Logs

Aircraft logs is an inclusive term that applies to the aircraft logbook and all supplemental records for the aircraft. The aircraft logbook is the record in which all data for the aircraft is recorded. Information gathered in this log is used to determine the aircraft's condition; dates of inspections; and time on airframe, engines, propellers, and some avionics systems. The more comprehensive the logbook, the easier it is to understand the aircraft's history.

Aircraft owners are converting paper logbooks to electronic systems. These systems often store the information in *the cloud* and can be accessed by a variety of devices. This greatly reduces the possibility of logbook information being lost or destroyed. These systems can be set up so that the maintenance facility monitors the aircraft's activity and can notify the owner when an inspection or timed maintenance item is nearing its limit.

Learning Objectives

DESCRIBE
- Aircraft logbooks

EXPLAIN
- Aircraft maintenance requirements
- Required aircraft maintenance records and recordkeeping requirements

DISCUSS
- Forms and publications

Left: Modern maintenance facilities often operate around the clock to keep the business fleet operating on schedule.

Courtesy of Textron Aviation

Section 2

Forms and Publications

Manuals and aircraft documentation are essential tools that provide pertinent information needed to safely fly and maintain aircraft. Their proper use greatly aids in efficiently operating and maintaining all aircraft.

FAA Forms and Publications

The Code of Federal Regulations

The *Code of Federal Regulations* (CFR) is the codification of the general and permanent rules published in the *Federal Register* by the executive departments and agencies of the federal government. Title 14 of the CFR provides rules regarding Aeronautics and Space. The titles are divided into volumes, chapters, subchapters, and parts. The FAA regulates volumes 1, 2, and 3 and provides the rules for the design, certification, operation, and maintenance of aircraft. A fourth volume deals with the U.S. Department of Transportation, and a fifth volume is focused on the National Aeronautics and Space Administration. The regulations that pertain to aviation are sometimes referred to as Federal Aviation Regulations, or FARs (Figure 14-2-1).

When discussing a section of the CFR, generally the title and then part are listed. For example General Operating and Flight rules are in *14 CFR part 91*. Some of 14 CFR part subjects that pertain to certification, maintenance, and operation, are below:

- Part 1 – Definitions and Abbreviations
- Part 21 – Certification Procedures for Products and Parts
- Part 23 – Airworthiness Standards: Normal, Utility, Acrobatic and Commuter Airplanes
- Part 25 – Airworthiness Standards: Transport Category Airplanes
- Part 27 – Airworthiness Standards: Normal Category Rotorcraft
- Part 29 – Airworthiness Standards: Transport Category Rotorcraft
- Part 33 – Airworthiness Standards: Aircraft Engines
- Part 35 – Airworthiness Standards: Propellers
- Part 36 – Noise Standards: Aircraft Type and Airworthiness Certification
- Part 39 – Airworthiness Directives
- Part 43 – Maintenance, Preventive Maintenance, Rebuilding, and Alteration
- Part 45 – Identification and Registration Marking
- Part 47 – Aircraft Registration
- Part 61 – Certification: Pilots, Flight Instructors, and Ground Instructors
- Part 63 – Certification: Flight Crewmembers Other Than Pilots
- Part 65 – Certification: Airmen Other Than Flight Crewmembers
- Part 91 – General Operating and Flight Rules
- Part 107 – Small Unmanned Aircraft Systems
- Part 119 – Certification: Air Carriers and Commercial Operators
- Part 121 – Operating Requirements: Domestic, Flag, and Supplemental Operations
- Part 125 – Certification and Operations: Airplanes Having a Seating Capacity of 20 or More Passengers or a Payload Capacity of 6,000 Pounds or More
- Part 135 – Operating Requirements: Commuter and On Demand Operations and Rules Governing Persons on Board Such Aircraft
- Part 139 – Certification of Airports
- Part 141 – Flight Schools
- Part 145 – Repair Stations
- Part 147 – Aviation Maintenance Technician Schools

Airworthiness Certification

Standard Airworthiness Certificate. The airworthiness process begins when a new aircraft is built. A representative of the FAA issues a Standard Airworthiness Certificate after the aircraft has been inspected, meets the requirements of 14 CFR part 21, and is in condition for safe operation. A Standard Airworthiness Certificate must be displayed in the aircraft so it is legible to the passengers and crew whenever it is operated.

A representative of the FAA issues a Standard Airworthiness Certificate for aircraft type-certificated in the normal, utility,

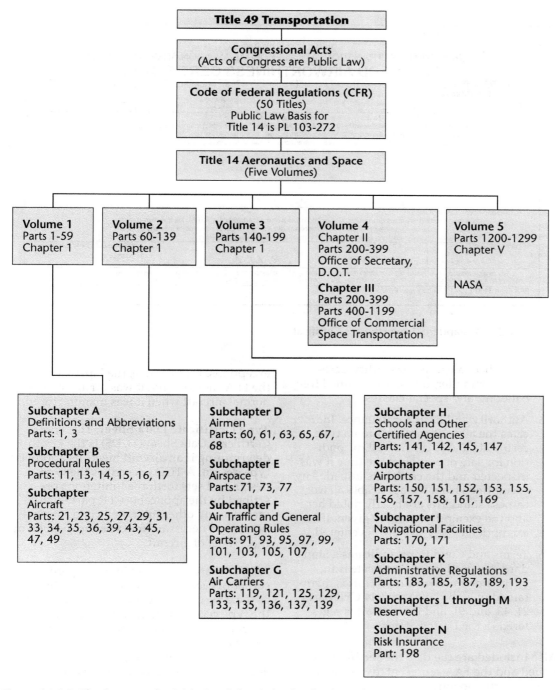

Figure 14-2-1. The framework of title 14 of the *Code of Federal Regulations.*

acrobatic, commuter, transport categories, and manned free balloons. Figure 14-2-2 illustrates a Standard Airworthiness Certificate. An explanation of each item in the certificate follows.

1. Nationality and Registration Marks. The "N" indicates the aircraft is registered in the United States. Registration marks consist of up to five numbers or numbers and letters. In this case, N12345 is the registration number assigned to this aircraft.

2. Manufacturer and Model. Indicates the manufacturer, make, and model of the aircraft.

3. Aircraft Serial Number. The manufacturer's number assigned to the aircraft as part of a series. It is recorded on the aircraft data plate.

4. Category. Indicates the category in which the aircraft must be operated. In this example, it must be operated in accordance with the limitations specified for the NORMAL category.

UNITED STATES OF AMERICA
DEPARTMENT OF TRANSPORTATION-FEDERAL AVIATION ADMINISTRATION

STANDARD AIRWORTHINESS CERTIFICATE

1 NATIONALITY AND REGISTRATION MARKS	2 MANUFACTURER AND MODEL	3 AIRCRAFT SERIAL NUMBER	4 CATEGORY
N12345	Boeing 787	43219	Transport

5 AUTHORITY AND BASIS FOR ISSUANCE
This airworthiness certificate is issued pursuant to 49 U.S.C. 44704 and certifies that, as of the date of issuance, the aircraft to which issued has been inspected and found to conform to the type certificate therefore, to be in condition for safe operation, and has been shown to meet the requirements of the applicable comprehensive and detailed airworthiness code as provided by Annex 8 to the Convention on International Civil Aviation, except as noted herein.
Exceptions:

None

6 TERMS AND CONDITIONS
Unless sooner surrendered, suspended, revoked, or a termination date is otherwise established by the FAA, this airworthiness certificate is effective as long as the maintenance, preventative maintenance, and alterations are performed in accordance with Parts 21, 43, and 91 of the Federal Aviation Regulations, as appropriate, and the aircraft is registered in the United States.

DATE OF ISSUANCE	FAA REPRESENTATIVE	DESIGNATION NUMBER
9 Jan 2015	E.R. White E.R. White	NE-XX

Any iteration, reproduction, or misuse of this certificate may be punishable by a fine not exceeding $1,000 or imprisonment not exceeding 3 years or both.
THIS CERTIFICATE MUST BE DISPLAYED IN THE AIRCRAFT IN ACCORDANCE WITH APPLICABLE FEDERAL AVIATION REGULATIONS.

FAA Form 8100-2 (04-11) Supersedes Previous Edition

Figure 14-2-2. A Standard Airworthiness Certificate.

The other categories are utility, acrobatic, commuter, transport, manned free balloons, and special classes.

5. Authority and Basis for Issuance. Indicates the aircraft conforms to its type certificate and is considered in condition for safe operation at the time it was inspected and the certificate issued. Any exemptions from the applicable airworthiness standards are briefly noted here and the exemption number given. If no exemption exists, "NONE" is entered.
6. Terms and Conditions. Indicates a Standard Airworthiness Certificate is in effect indefinitely if the aircraft is maintained in accordance with 14 CFR parts 21, 43, and 91, and the aircraft is registered in the United States.

Also included are the date the certificate was issued and the FAA representative's signature and office identification.

A standard airworthiness certificate remains valid if the aircraft meets its approved type design; is in a condition for safe operation and maintenance, preventative maintenance; and alterations are performed in accordance with 14 CFR parts 21, 43, and 91.

A representative of the FAA issues a Special Airworthiness Certificate for all aircraft certificated in a classification other than the standard, such as Experimental, Restricted, Limited, Provisional, and Light-Sport Aircraft (LSA). LSA receive a pink Special Airworthiness Certificate; however, there are exceptions. For example, the Piper Cub is in the LSA category, but it was certificated as a normal aircraft when it was manufactured.

Type Certificate Data Sheet. The Type Certificate Data Sheet (TCDS) is the key to determining if an aircraft meets its approved type design. A TCDS describes the type design and sets forth the limitations prescribed by the applicable CFR part. It also includes any other limitations and information found necessary for type certification of that model of aircraft.

All TCDS are numbered in the upper-right corner of each page. This number is the same as the type certificate number. The name of the type certificate holder, together with all the approved models, appears immediately below the type certificate number. The issue date completes this group. This information is within a bordered text box to set it off.

The TCDS is separated into one or more sections. Each section is identified by a Roman numeral followed by the model designation of the aircraft to which the section pertains. The category or categories in which the aircraft can be certificated are shown in parentheses after the model number. Also included is the approval date shown on the type certificate. The data sheet contains the following information:

- Model designation of all engines that the aircraft manufacturer obtained approval for use with this model aircraft.

- Minimum fuel grade to be used.

- Maximum continuous and takeoff ratings of the approved engines, including manifold pressure (when used), rotations per minute (r.p.m.), and horsepower (hp).

- Name of the manufacturer and model designation for each propeller that the aircraft manufacturer obtained approval is shown together with the propeller limits and any operating restrictions peculiar to the propeller or propeller engine combination.

- Airspeed limits in both miles per hour (mph) and knots.

- Center of gravity (CG) range for the extreme loading conditions of the aircraft is given in inches from the datum. The range could also be stated in percent of mean aerodynamic chord (%MAC) for transport category aircraft.

- Empty weight center of gravity (EWCG) range (when established) is given as fore and aft limits in inches from the datum. If no range exists, the word "none" follows the heading on the data sheet.

- Location of the datum.

- Means provided for leveling the aircraft.

- All pertinent maximum weights.

- Number of seats and their moment arms.

- Oil and fuel capacity.

- Control surface movements.

- Required equipment.

- Additional or special equipment required for certification.

- Information concerning required placards.

It is not within the scope of this book to list all the items that can be shown on the TCDS. Those items listed above serve only to acquaint the reader with the type of information generally included on the data sheets. TCDS can be many pages long. The first page of a common TCDS is shown in Figure 14-2-3. The complete TCDS is 13 pages. To see a complete TCDS, go to the FAA's website.

Supplemental Type Certificates (STC). An STC is a document the FAA issues to approve a product (aircraft, engine, or propeller) modification. The STC defines the product design change and states how the modification affects the existing type design.

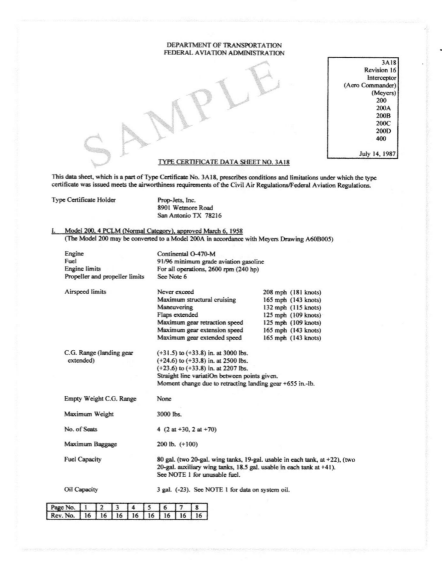

Figure 14-2-3. A sample Type Certificate Data Sheet.

Certificate of Aircraft Registration. Before an aircraft can be flown legally, it must be registered with the FAA Aircraft Registry. The Certificate of Aircraft Registration, which is issued to the owner as evidence of the registration, must be carried in the aircraft at all times (Figure 14-2-4).

Airworthiness Directives (ADs). A primary safety function of the FAA is to require correction of unsafe conditions found in an aircraft, aircraft engine, propeller, or appliance when such conditions exist and are likely to exist or develop in other products of the same design. The unsafe condition could exist because of a design defect, maintenance, or other causes. ADs, under 14 CFR part 39, define the authority and responsibility of the FAA Administrator for requiring the necessary corrective action. ADs are used to notify aircraft owners and other interested persons of unsafe

REGISTRATION NOT TRANSFERABLE

UNITED STATES OF AMERICA DEPARTMENT OF TRANSPORTATION - FEDERAL AVIATION ADMINISTRATION CERTIFICATE OF AIRCRAFT REGISTRATION	This certificate must be in the air-craft when operated.

NATIONALITY AND REGISTRATION MARKS **N505DH**   AIRCRAFT SERIAL NO. **8806**

MANUFACTURER AND MANUFACTURER'S DESIGNATION OF AIRCRAFT

PITTS   S1S

ICAO Aircraft Address Code: **5199999**

ISSUED TO

LINBERGH, DANIEL E.
800 GATEWAY ROAD
OKLAHOMA CITY, OK 73125

This certificate is issued for registra-tion purposes only and is not a certif-icate of title. The Federal Avia-tion Administration does not determine rights of ownership as between private persons.

It is certified that the above described aircraft has been entered on the register of the Federal Aviation Administration. United States of America, in accordance with the Convention on International Civil Aviation dated December 7, 1944, and with the Federal Aviation Act of 1958, and regulations issued thereunder.

DATE OF ISSUE
JUNE 3, 1995   *David Hinson* ADMINISTRATOR

U.S. Department of Transportation
Federal Aviation Administration

AC Form 8050-3(11/93) Supersedes previous editions

Figure 14-2-4. A sample Certificate of Aircraft Registration.

conditions and to specify the conditions under which the product may continue to be oper-ated. ADs are divided into two categories:

- Those of an emergency nature requiring immediate compliance before further flight

- Those of a less urgent nature requiring compliance within a specified time

ADs are regulatory and must be complied with unless a specific exemption is granted. The aircraft owner or operator is responsible to ensure compliance with all pertinent ADs, including those ADs that require recurrent or continuing action. For example, an AD might require a repetitive inspection each 50 hours of operation, meaning the inspection must be performed and recorded every 50 hours of time in service. No provision exists to exceed the maximum hour requirement of an AD unless it is specifically written into the AD.

The regulations at 14 CFR 91.417 require a record to be maintained that shows the current status of applicable ADs, including the method of compliance; the AD number and revision date, if recurring; next due date and time; the signature; type of certificate; and certificate number of the repair station or mechanic who performed the work. For ready reference, many aircraft owners have a chronological listing of the pertinent ADs in the aircraft logs.

Advisory Circular (ACs). ACs are another type of FAA publication and are issued to inform the aviation public of nonregulatory material. Unless incorporated into a regula-tion by reference, the contents of an AC are not binding on the public.

Manufacturers' Published Data/Other

The original equipment manufacturer (OEM) is usually the best source of information for operating and maintaining a product.

Aircraft Flight Manual/Pilot's Operating Handbook

The Airplane Flight Manual (AFM) or the Pilot's Operating Handbook (POH) provides the pilot with the information to properly operate the aircraft. These manuals are usually listed in the aircraft TCDS and, therefore, are required for the aircraft to be considered airworthy.

The typical AFM/POH contains these nine sections: General; Limitations; Emergency Procedures; Normal Procedures; Performance; Weight and Balance/Equipment List; Systems Description; Handling, Service, and Maintenance; and Supplements. Manufacturers also have the option of includ-ing additional sections, such as one on Safety and Operational Tips or an alphabetical index.

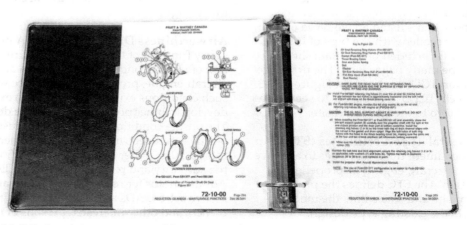

Figure 14-2-5. A maintenance manual for a powerplant.

Maintenance Manual

The manufacturer's aircraft maintenance manual contains complete instructions for maintaining all systems and components installed in the aircraft (Figure 14-2-5). It contains information needed when working on components, assemblies, and systems while they are installed in the aircraft.

Overhaul Manual

The manufacturer's overhaul manual contains brief descriptive information and detailed, step-by-step instructions covering work normally performed on a unit that has been removed from the aircraft.

Structural Repair Manual

The structural repair manual contains the manufacturer's information and instructions for repairing primary and secondary structures. It also contains instructions for typical skin, frame, rib, and stringer repairs, as well as material and fastener substitutions and special repair techniques.

Illustrated Parts Catalog

The illustrated parts catalog presents component breakdowns of structure and equipment in disassembly sequence. Also included are exploded views or cutaway illustrations for all parts and equipment manufactured by the aircraft manufacturer.

Service Bulletins

Throughout the life of a product, manufacturing defects, changes in service, or design improvements often occur. When that happens, the manufacturer frequently creates a service bulletin (SB) to distribute the information to the aircraft's operator. However, SBs are not required *unless* they are referred to in an AD note or if compliance is required as a part of the authorized inspection program.

Minimum Equipment Lists and Operations with Inoperative Equipment

Under 14 CFR, all aircraft instruments and installed equipment (per the Type Certificate) are required to be operative before each departure. Some equipment is considered to be nonessential for completing a safe flight. To allow the aircraft to continue to operate with inoperative, nonessential equipment, there is a process to defer repairs and to fly with inoperable equipment. Using a minimum equipment list (MEL) allows for repairs to certain inoperative items or equipment to be accomplished at a later date (deferred). The MEL is aircraft specific, developed from a master minimum equipment list (MMEL) that the FAA publishes. Operators can develop a MEL that is based on the MMEL and tailor it to their operations. Once the FAA approves a MEL, an aircraft can be operated in a condition other than originally type certificated. The FAA considers an approved MEL to be an STC issued to an aircraft by serial number and registration number. Figure 14-2-6 is an excerpt from a Cessna

```
----------------------------------------------------------------------
| U.S. DEPARTMENT OF TRANSPORTATION                                    |
|                                                                      |
|                                        MASTER MINIMUM EQUIPMENT LIST |
| FEDERAL AVIATION ADMINISTRATION                                      |
| -------------------------------------------------------------------- |
| AIRCRAFT:                            | REVISION NO: 8    | PAGE:     |
|         CESSNA MODELS 310/320        |                   |           |
|                                      | DATE: 11/22/2002  | 30-2      |
| -------------------------------------------------------------------- |
|                        1. | 2. NUMBER INSTALLED                      |
| SYSTEM &                  | --------------------------------------   |
| SEQUENCE          ITEM    | 3. NUMBER REQUIRED FOR DISPATCH          |
| NUMBERS                   | --------------------------------------   |
| ------------------------- |        | 4. REMARKS OR EXCEPTIONS        |
| 30  ICE AND RAIN          |        |                                 |
|     PROTECTION            |        |                                 |
|                           |        |                                 |
| 8.  Static Port Heater  C | 1 | 0  | May be inoperative provided     |
|                           |        | aircraft is not operated in known|
|                           |        | or forecast icing conditions.   |
----------------------------------------------------------------------
```

Figure 14-2-6. An example MMEL.

	UNITED STATES OF AMERICA DEPARTMENT OF TRANSPORTATION - FEDERAL AVIATION ADMINISTRATION **SPECIAL AIRWORTHINESS CERTIFICATE**		
A	CATEGORY/DESIGNATION		
	PURPOSE		
B	MANU- FACTURER	NAME	
		ADDRESS	
C	FLIGHT	FROM	
		TO	
D	N-		SERIAL NO.
	BUILDER		MODEL
	DATE OF ISSUANCE		EXPIRY
	OPERATING LIMITATIONS DATED		ARE PART OF THIS CERTIFICATE
E	SIGNATURE OF FAA REPRESENTATIVE		DESIGNATION OR OFFICE NO.

Any alteration, reproduction or misuse of this certificate may be punishable by a fine not exceeding $1,000 or imprisonment not exceeding 3 years, or both. THIS CERTIFICATE MUST BE DISPLAYED IN THE AIRCRAFT IN ACCORDANCE WITH APPLICABLE TITLE 14, CODE OF FEDERAL REGULATIONS (CFR).

FAA Form 8130-7 (04-11) Previous Edition 07/04 May be Used until Depleted   *SEE REVERSE SIDE*   NSN: 0052-00-693-4000

Figure 14-2-7. Example of a special flight permit.

310/320 MMEL. It indicates that the aircraft can be operated with the static port heater inoperative as long as it is not in icing conditions.

Inoperable equipment is deactivated or removed and an INOPERATIVE placard placed near the appropriate switch, control, or indicator.

Yet another way to operate an aircraft with inoperative equipment is with a special flight permit. This permit authorizes an aircraft to be operated if it does not meet applicable airworthiness requirements but is safe for a specific flight. Special flight permits are a Category or Designation of a Special Airworthiness Certificate (Figure 14-2-7). Special flight permits, often referred to as ferry permits, are issued for the following purposes:

- Flying the aircraft to a base where repairs, alterations, or maintenance are to be performed, or to a point of storage

- Delivering or exporting the aircraft

- Flight testing new production aircraft

- Evacuating aircraft from areas of impending danger

- Conducting customer demonstration flights in new production aircraft that have satisfactorily completed production flight tests

Radio Station License

A radio station license is required if the aircraft is equipped with radios, and the aircraft is planned to be flown outside the boundaries of the United States. A radio station license is *not* required for aircraft that are operated domestically.

Documents Required on the Aircraft

The FAA and the FCC require the following documents to be on the aircraft. A common acronym used to help remember these documents is ARROW (Table 14-2-1).

A	Airworthiness certificate	FAA Form 8100-2, Standard Airworthiness Certificate, or FAA Form 8130-7, Special Airworthiness Certificate (as applicable)
R	Registration certificate	FAA Form 8050-3, Certificate of Registration
R	Radio station license (not required if operated in the U.S.)	FCC Form 605, Quick-Form Application for Authorization in the Ship, Aircraft, Restricted and Commercial Operator, and General Mobile Radio Services, available on FCC website at www.fcc.gov (if required by the type of operation)
O	Operating limitations	FAA-approved Airplane Flight Manual (AFM) and/or Pilot's Operating handbook (POII), and/or limitations attached to FAA Form 8130-7
W	Weight and balance	Documentation provided by aircraft manufacturer, maintenance and modification records

Table 14-2-1. ARROW helps you remember the documents that must be on an aircraft.

Section 3

Aircraft Maintenance

Maintenance is defined as the inspection, overhaul, repair, preservation, and replacement of parts but excludes preventive maintenance. Regular and proper maintenance and inspection ensures that an aircraft meets an acceptable standard of airworthiness throughout its operational life.

Purpose of Inspection

Inspections are examinations to determine the condition of an aircraft or component. An inspection system consists of several processes, including reports made by mechanics, the pilot, or crew flying an aircraft, and regularly scheduled inspections of an aircraft. This process is designed to keep the aircraft in the best possible condition.

Regularly scheduled inspections help ensure airworthiness (Figure 14-3-1). Operating failures and malfunctions of equipment are appreciably reduced if excessive wear or minor defects are detected and corrected early. The importance of inspections and properly using records concerning these inspections cannot be overemphasized.

Inspection Classifications

Preflight/Postflight Inspections

Pilots are required to follow a checklist in the POH or AFM when operating aircraft. The first section of the checklist is titled *Preflight*

Figure 14-3-1. Inspections help ensure airworthiness.

Inspection. The preflight inspection checklist includes a *walk-around* section listing items that pilots are to visually check for general condition as they walk around the airplane (Figure 14-3-2). Also, pilots must ensure that fuel, oil, and other items required for flight are at the proper levels and not contaminated. Pilots are also responsible to review the aircraft maintenance records and other required paperwork to verify that the aircraft is indeed airworthy.

After each flight, the pilot or mechanic should conduct a postflight inspection to detect any problems that might require repair or servicing before the next flight.

Figure 14-3-2. Pilots conduct walkaround inspections and other reviews and inspections before a flight.

Annual/100-Hour Inspections

With some exceptions, all aircraft operating under 14 CFR part 91 flight rules must have a complete inspection annually. Aircraft that are used for commercial purposes or flight instruction for hire must have this complete inspection every 100 hours. Aircraft operating under 14 CFR parts 135 and 121 (air carriers) have different inspection requirements.

Annual inspection. Aircraft flown for business or pleasure and not flown for compensation or hire must be inspected at least annually. The inspection is performed by a certificated airframe and powerplant (A&P) mechanic who holds an inspection authorization (IA) rating, by the aircraft manufacturer, or by a certificated and appropriately rated repair station. The aircraft may not be operated unless the annual inspection has been performed in the preceding 12 calendar months. A period of 12 calendar months extends from any day of a month to the last day of the same month the following year. An aircraft overdue for an annual inspection may be operated under a Special Flight Permit issued by the FAA for flying the aircraft to a location where the annual inspection can be performed. However, all applicable ADs that are due must be complied with before the flight.

100-hour inspection. Aircraft used for commercial purposes or flight instruction for hire, such as shown in Figure 14-3-3, must be inspected every 100 hours. They must be approved for return to service. Additionally, an aircraft used for flight instruction for hire, when provided by the person giving the flight instruction, must also have received a 100-hour inspection. This inspection must be performed by an FAA-certificated A&P mechanic, an appropriately rated FAA-certificated repair station, or the aircraft manufacturer. An annual inspection may be substituted for a required 100-hour inspection. The 100-hour limitation may be exceeded by no more than 10 hours for traveling to a location at which the required inspection can be performed. Any excess time used for this purpose must be included in computing the next 100 hours of time in service.

The annual and 100-hour inspection requirements do not apply to large (over 12,500 pounds) airplanes, turbojets, or turbopropeller-powered multiengine airplanes or to aircraft for which the owner complies with a progressive inspection program.

Progressive Inspections

Because the scope and detail of an annual and 100-hour inspection are very extensive and could keep an aircraft out of service for a considerable time, alternative inspection programs designed to minimize down time may be used. A progressive inspection program allows an aircraft to be inspected progressively. The scope and detail of an annual inspection is essentially divided into segments or phases (typically four to six). Completing all the phases in a cycle satisfies the requirements of an annual inspection and 100-hour inspection. The advantage of such a program is that any required segment may be completed overnight and thus enable the aircraft to fly daily without missing any revenue-earning potential.

Figure 14-3-3. Aircraft used for hire must be inspected every 100 hours of operation.

Progressive inspection programs include routine tasks, such as engine oil changes, and detailed items, such as flight control cable inspection. Routine tasks are performed each time the aircraft comes in for a phase inspection, and detailed item inspections focus on specific areas. Detailed inspections are typically done once each cycle. A cycle must be completed within 12 months or for aircraft requiring a 100-hour inspection, within 100 hours of operation.

Continuous Inspections

Continuous inspection programs are like progressive inspection programs, except that they apply to large or turbine-powered aircraft and are, therefore, more complicated. Like progressive inspection programs, they require approval by the FAA. The approval may be sought according to the type of operation and the CFR parts under which the aircraft is operated. The maintenance program for commercially operated aircraft must be detailed in the approved operations specifications (OpSpecs) of the commercial certificate holder.

In the past, airlines or operators called their continuous inspections letter checks (such as A, B, C, and D) or some other type of interval system. Some operators might still use these terms. Others might use something like 1A, 2A, 3A, and 4A instead. Others use what they refer to as A check intervals (1–5) or C check intervals (1–5).

Altimeter and Transponder Inspections

Aircraft that are operated in controlled airspace under instrument flight rules (IFR) must have each altimeter and static system tested in accordance with procedures described in 14 CFR part 43, Appendix E, within the preceding 24 calendar months. Transponders must also have each transponder checked in the preceding 24 months. All these checks must be conducted by appropriately certified persons.

Emergency Locator Transmitter (ELT).
An ELT (Figure 14-3-4) is required by 14 CFR 91.207 and must be inspected within 12 calendar months after the last inspection of and involving the following:

- Proper installation
- Battery corrosion
- Operating the controls and crash sensor
- The presence of a sufficient signal radiated from its antenna

ELT installation

Figure 14-3-4. An ELT must be inspected every 12 months.

The ELT must be attached to the airplane so as to minimize the probability of the transmitter being damaged from impact in a crash. Fixed and deployable automatic transmitters must be attached to the airplane as far aft as practicable. Batteries used in the ELTs must be replaced or recharged if the batteries are rechargeable in these cases:

- When the transmitter has been in use for more than 1 cumulative hour
- When 50 percent of the battery useful life or, for rechargeable batteries, 50 percent of useful life of the charge has expired

An expiration date for replacing or recharging the battery must be legibly marked on the outside of the transmitter and entered in the aircraft maintenance record. This does not apply to batteries that are essentially unaffected during storage intervals, such as water-activated batteries.

Special Inspections

Within the service life of an aircraft, occasions can arise when out-of-the ordinary care and use of an aircraft could affect its airworthiness. In such situations, special inspection procedures, also called conditional inspections, are followed to determine if the aircraft structure has been damaged. The procedures below are general and are intended to inform readers of the areas to be inspected. As such, they are not all-inclusive. Below are some typical types of special inspections.

Hard or overweight landing inspection.
The structural stress induced by a landing depends on the gross weight at the time and on the severity of impact. The hard landing inspection is for hard landings at or below the maximum design landing limits. An over-

weight landing inspection must be performed when an airplane lands at a weight more than the maximum design landing weight.

Severe turbulence inspection/over G.

When an aircraft encounters severe turbulence in flight, the air load on the wings exceeds the normal wing load supporting the aircraft weight. The turbulence tends to accelerate the aircraft while its inertia acts to resist this change. If the combination of turbulence velocity and airspeed is too severe, the induced stress can cause structural damage.

A special inspection is performed after a flight through severe turbulence.

Lightning strike.
Although lightning strikes to aircraft are extremely rare, if a strike has occurred, carefully inspect the aircraft to determine the extent of any damage. When lightning strikes an aircraft, the electrical current must be conducted through the structure and be allowed to discharge or dissipate at controlled locations. These controlled locations are primarily the aircraft's static discharge wicks or, on more sophisticated aircraft, null field dischargers.

When surges of high-voltage electricity pass through good electrical conductors, such as aluminum or steel, damage is likely to be minimal or nonexistent. When surges of high-voltage electricity pass through nonmetallic structures, such as a fiberglass radome, engine cowl or fairing, glass or plastic window, or a composite structure that does not have built-in electrical bonding, burning and more serious damage to the structure could occur. Visual inspection of the structure is required. Look for evidence of degradation, burning, or erosion of the composite resin at all affected structures, electrical bonding straps, static discharge wicks, and null field dischargers.

Bird strike.
If the aircraft was hit by birds during flight, the external areas of the airplane are inspected in the general area of the bird strike (Figure 14-3-5). If the initial inspection shows structural damage, the internal structure of the airplane must also be inspected. Also, an inspection of the hydraulic, pneumatic, and any other systems around the bird strike might be needed.

Fire damage.
Inspecting aircraft structures that have been subjected to fire or intense heat can be relatively simple if visible damage is present. Visible damage requires repair or replacement. If there is no visible damage, the structural integrity of an aircraft might still have been compromised. Because most structural, metallic components of an aircraft have undergone some sort of heat treatment process during manufacture, an exposure to high heat not encountered in normal operations could severely degrade the design strength of the structure.

Flood damage.
Like aircraft damaged by fire, aircraft damaged by water can range from minor to severe. This depends on the level of the flood water, whether it was fresh or salt water, and the time between the flood occurrence and when repairs were initiated. Many parts might have to be replaced, especially interior carpeting, seats, side panels, and instruments. Because water serves as an electrolyte that promotes corrosion, all traces of water and salt must be removed before the aircraft can again be considered airworthy.

FAR Legal Requirements for Completing Inspections

The regulations calling for the inspections discussed above are scattered through several parts of 14 CFR. Generally, the requirements are in either 14 CFR part 91 General Operating and Flight Rules or 14 CFR part 43 Maintenance, Preventive Maintenance, Rebuilding, and Alteration. The location and basic requirements for completing these inspections follow.

Annual/100-Hour Inspections

The requirements for annual and 100-hour inspections are in 14 CFR part 91. Although this regulation establishes that the inspections must be completed, it supplies no details on conducting the inspection. To find out what needs to be done in the inspection, section 91.409 refers to part 43. The scope and detail of items to be included in annual and 100-hour inspections are included as an excerpt of Appendix D to part 43 (Figure 14-3-6).

Figure 14-3-5. Damage from a bird strike should be inspected.

Appendix D to Part 43—Scope and Detail of Items (as Applicable to the Particular Aircraft) To Be Included in Annual and 100-Hour Inspections

(a) Each person performing an annual or 100-hour inspection shall, before that inspection, remove or open all necessary inspection plates, access doors, fairing, and cowling. He shall thoroughly clean the aircraft and aircraft engine.

(b) Each person performing an annual or 100-hour inspection shall inspect (where applicable) the following components of the fuselage and hull group:

(1) Fabric and skin—for deterioration, distortion, other evidence of failure, and defective or insecure attachment of fittings.

(2) Systems and components—for improper installation, apparent defects, and unsatisfactory operation.

(3) Envelope, gas bags, ballast tanks, and related parts—for poor condition.

(c) Each person performing an annual or 100-hour inspection shall inspect (where applicable) the following components of the cabin and cockpit group:

(1) Generally—for uncleanliness and loose equipment that might foul the controls.

(2) Seats and safety belts—for poor condition and apparent defects.

(3) Windows and windshields—for deterioration and breakage.

(4) Instruments—for poor condition, mounting, marking, and (where practicable) improper operation.

(5) Flight and engine controls—for improper installation and improper operation.

(6) Batteries—for improper installation and improper charge.

(7) All systems—for improper installation, poor general condition, apparent and obvious defects, and insecurity of attachment.

(d) Each person performing an annual or 100-hour inspection shall inspect (where applicable) components of the engine and nacelle group as follows:

(1) Engine section—for visual evidence of excessive oil, fuel, or hydraulic leaks, and sources of such leaks.

(2) Studs and nuts—for improper torquing and obvious defects.

(3) Internal engine—for cylinder compression and for metal particles or foreign matter on screens and sump drain plugs. If there is weak cylinder compression, for improper internal condition and improper internal tolerances.

(4) Engine mount—for cracks, looseness of mounting, and looseness of engine to mount.

(5) Flexible vibration dampeners—for poor condition and deterioration.

(6) Engine controls—for defects, improper travel, and improper safetying.

(7) Lines, hoses, and clamps—for leaks, improper condition and looseness.

(8) Exhaust stacks—for cracks, defects, and improper attachment.

(9) Accessories—for apparent defects in security of mounting.

(10) All systems—for improper installation, poor general condition, defects, and insecure attachment.

(11) Cowling—for cracks, and defects.

(e) Each person performing an annual or 100-hour inspection shall inspect (where applicable) the following components of the landing gear group:

(1) All units—for poor condition and insecurity of attachment.

(2) Shock absorbing devices—for improper oleo fluid level.

(3) Linkages, trusses, and members—for undue or excessive wear fatigue, and distortion.

(4) Retracting and locking mechanism—for improper operation.

(5) Hydraulic lines—for leakage.

(6) Electrical system—for chafing and improper operation of switches.

(7) Wheels—for cracks, defects, and condition of bearings.

(8) Tires—for wear and cuts.

(9) Brakes—for improper adjustment.

(10) Floats and skis—for insecure attachment and obvious or apparent defects.

(f) Each person performing an annual or 100-hour inspection shall inspect (where applicable) all components of the wing and center section assembly for poor general condition, fabric or skin deterioration, distortion, evidence of failure, and insecurity of attachment.

(g) Each person performing an annual or 100-hour inspection shall inspect (where applicable) all components and systems that make up the complete empennage assembly for poor general condition, fabric or skin deterioration, distortion, evidence of failure, insecure attachment, improper component installation, and improper component operation.

(h) Each person performing an annual or 100-hour inspection shall inspect (where applicable) the following components of the propeller group:

(1) Propeller assembly—for cracks, nicks, binds, and oil leakage.

(2) Bolts—for improper torquing and lack of safetying.

(3) Anti-icing devices—for improper operations and obvious defects.

(4) Control mechanisms—for improper operation, insecure mounting, and restricted travel.

(i) Each person performing an annual or 100-hour inspection shall inspect (where applicable) the following components of the radio group:

(1) Radio and electronic equipment—for improper installation and insecure mounting.

(2) Wiring and conduits—for improper routing, insecure mounting, and obvious defects.

(3) Bonding and shielding—for improper installation and poor condition.

(4) Antenna including trailing antenna—for poor condition, insecure mounting, and improper operation.

(j) Each person performing an annual or 100-hour inspection shall inspect (where applicable) each installed miscellaneous item that is not otherwise covered by this listing for improper installation and improper operation.

Figure 14-3-6. 14 CFR part 43, Appendix D contains the scope and detail of items to be included in the annual/100-hour inspection.

A properly written inspection checklist includes all the items listed in Appendix D. Although the scope and detail of annual and 100-hour inspections are identical, they have two significant differences. One difference involves persons authorized to conduct them. A certified A&P maintenance technician can conduct a 100-hour inspection, but an annual inspection must be conducted by a certified A&P maintenance technician with inspection authorization (IA). The other difference involves authorized overflight of the maximum 100 hours before inspection. An aircraft may be flown up to 10 hours beyond the 100-hour limit if necessary to fly to a destination where the inspection is to be conducted.

Progressive Inspections

Each registered owner or operator of an aircraft that wants to use a progressive inspection program must submit a written request to the FAA Flight Standards District Office that has jurisdiction over the applicant's area. The regulations at 14 CFR 91.409(d) establish procedures to be followed for progressive inspections.

Altimeter Inspections

As seen before, the altimeter inspection is another case where part 91 establishes the requirements for the inspection, the time in which it must be completed, and then refers to part 43 appendix for the scope and details of the actual inspection.

Transponder Tests and Inspections

Transponders are yet another case where part 91 establishes the requirements for the inspection and then refers to part 43 appendix for the scope and details.

Certification Requirements for Completing Inspections

As the regulations in the CFR specify what inspection must be made, they also designate what personnel are accepted to perform that work. To find what certifications the technician or the repair station needs to complete the work, see the text of each regulation. For a summary of inspections and who must do the work, see Table 14-3-1.

Repairs, Alterations, Preventive Maintenance

This chapter, so far, has emphasized the role of inspections in maintaining airworthiness. However, to complete this study, it must pres-

Inspection type	Person authorized to complete the work
Preflight inspection	Pilot
Annual inspection	A certificated mechanic holding an inspection authorization, a certificated airframe repair station, or the manufacturer of the aircraft to supervise or conduct the inspection
100-hour inspection	A certificated mechanic, a certificated airframe repair station, or the manufacturer of the aircraft to supervise or conduct the inspection
Progressive inspection	A certificated mechanic holding an inspection authorization, a certificated airframe repair station, or the manufacturer of the aircraft to supervise or conduct the progressive inspection
Continuous inspection	A certificated mechanic holding an inspection authorization, a certificated airframe repair station, or the manufacturer of the aircraft.
Altimeter certification	The manufacturer of the airplane, or helicopter, on which the tests and inspections are to be performed, a certificated repair station, or a certificated mechanic with an airframe rating (static pressure system tests and inspections only)
Transponder certification	A certificated repair station, a holder of a continuous airworthiness maintenance program, or the manufacturer of the aircraft on which the transponder to be tested is installed, if the transponder was installed by that manufacturer.

Table 14-3-1. Inspection types and who is authorized to complete the work.

ent the role of repairs, alterations, and preventive maintenance, which are not necessarily associated with inspections.

Repairs and Alterations

Repairs are generally considered something that restore an aircraft to at least its original condition. This can include replacing parts, or operations such as riveting or welding (Figure 14-3-7). An alteration, on the other hand, is a change from its original condition.

Part 43, Appendix A helps explain the different types of maintenance items and establishes who is authorized to complete the work and return the aircraft to service. The first division established is between items that are considered major repairs and those that are minor repairs.

Major repair means one of the following:

1. A repair that, if improperly done, could appreciably affect weight, balance, structural strength, performance, powerplant operation, flight characteristics, or other qualities regarding airworthiness

2. A repair that is not done according to accepted practices or cannot be done by elementary operations

By defining major repairs, and giving specific examples, it stands to reason that anything that is not an established major repair is a minor repair.

The same logic is applied to major alterations. Appendix A defines major alterations and provides an extensive list of items that fall into that category. A major alteration is an alteration not listed in the aircraft, aircraft engine, or propeller specifications:

1. That might appreciably affect weight, balance, structural strength, performance, powerplant operation, flight characteristics, or other qualities regarding airworthiness

2. That is not done according to accepted practices or cannot be done by elementary operations

Again, it is assumed that anything that is not specified as a major alteration is a minor alteration.

To determine if it is a repair or alteration, keep in mind that a repair basically returns the aircraft to its previous or unaltered condition (e.g., replacing magnetos, an exhaust sys-

Figure 14-3-7. Repairing an accessory gearbox (top) and parts (bottom).

tem, tires, or brakes). Even replacing an entire engine (although it is a big job) is a repair if it is the one specified for that aircraft. An alteration, on the other hand, *always changes or modifies* the aircraft from its previous state (e.g., installing winglets, or an engine that is *not* listed in the aircraft TCDS).

Preventive Maintenance

Preventive maintenance is regarded as simple or minor preservation operations and replacing small standard parts, not involving complex assembly operations. A few examples of preventive maintenance items are listed below. The full list in 14 CFR part 43 appendix A(c) is in Figure 14-3-8.

- Remove, install, and repair landing gear tires
- Service landing gear wheel bearings (for example, cleaning and greasing)
- Service landing gear shock struts (for example, adding oil, air, or both)

Appendix A to Part 43 - Major Alterations, Major Repairs, and Preventive Maintenance

(c) Preventive maintenance. Preventive maintenance is limited to the following work, provided it does not involve complex assembly operations:

(1) Removal, installation, and repair of landing gear tires.
(2) Replacing elastic shock absorber cords on landing gear.
(3) Servicing landing gear shock struts by adding oil, air, or both.
(4) Servicing landing gear wheel bearings, such as cleaning and greasing.
(5) Replacing defective safety wiring or cotter keys.
(6) Lubrication not requiring disassembly other than removal of nonstructural items such as cover plates, cowlings, and fairings.
(7) Making simple fabric patches not requiring rib stitching or the removal of structural parts or control surfaces. In the case of balloons, the making of small fabric repairs to envelopes (as defined in, and in accordance with, the balloon manufacturers' instructions) not requiring load tape repair or replacement.
(8) Replenishing hydraulic fluid in the hydraulic reservoir.
(9) Refinishing decorative coating of fuselage, balloon baskets, wings tail group surfaces (excluding balanced control surfaces), fairings, cowlings, landing gear, cabin, or cockpit interior when removal or disassembly of any primary structure or operating system is not required.
(10) Applying preservative or protective material to components where no disassembly of any primary structure or operating system is involved and where such coating is not prohibited or is not contrary to good practices.
(11) Repairing upholstery and decorative furnishings of the cabin, cockpit, or balloon basket interior when the repairing does not require disassembly of any primary structure or operating system or interfere with an operating system or affect the primary structure of the aircraft.
(12) Making small simple repairs to fairings, nonstructural cover plates, cowlings, and small patches and reinforcements not changing the contour so as to interfere with proper air flow.
(13) Replacing side windows where that work does not interfere with the structure or any operating system such as controls, electrical equipment, etc.
(14) Replacing safety belts.
(15) Replacing seats or seat parts with replacement parts approved for the aircraft, not involving disassembly of any primary structure or operating system.
(16) Trouble shooting and repairing broken circuits in landing light wiring circuits.
(17) Replacing bulbs, reflectors, and lenses of position and landing lights.
(18) Replacing wheels and skis where no weight and balance computation is involved.
(19) Replacing any cowling not requiring removal of the propeller or disconnection of flight controls.
(20) Replacing or cleaning spark plugs and setting of spark plug gap clearance.
(21) Replacing any hose connection except hydraulic connections.

(22) Replacing prefabricated fuel lines.
(23) Cleaning or replacing fuel and oil strainers or filter elements.
(24) Replacing and servicing batteries.
(25) Cleaning of balloon burner pilot and main nozzles in accordance with the balloon manufacturer's instructions.
(26) Replacement or adjustment of nonstructural standard fasteners incidental to operations.
(27) The interchange of balloon baskets and burners on envelopes when the basket or burner is designated as interchangeable in the balloon type certificate data and the baskets and burners are specifically designed for quick removal and installation.
(28) The installations of anti-misfueling devices to reduce the diameter of fuel tank filler openings provided the specific device has been made a part of the aircraft type certificate data by the aircraft manufacturer, the aircraft manufacturer has provided FAA-approved instructions for installation of the specific device, and installation does not involve the disassembly of the existing tank filler opening.
(29) Removing, checking, and replacing magnetic chip detectors.
(30) The inspection and maintenance tasks prescribed and specifically identified as preventive maintenance in a primary category aircraft type certificate or supplemental type certificate holder's approved special inspection and preventive maintenance program when accomplished on a primary category aircraft provided:
(i) They are performed by the holder of at least a private pilot certificate issued under part 61 who is the registered owner (including co-owners) of the affected aircraft and who holds a certificate of competency for the affected aircraft (1) issued by a school approved under § 147.21(e) of this chapter; (2) issued by the holder of the production certificate for that primary category aircraft that has a special training program approved under § 21.24 of this subchapter; or (3) issued by another entity that has a course approved by the Administrator; and
(ii) The inspections and maintenance tasks are performed in accordance with instructions contained by the special inspection and preventive maintenance program approved as part of the aircraft's type design or supplemental type design.
(31) Removing and replacing self-contained, front instrument panel-mounted navigation and communication devices that employ tray-mounted connectors that connect the unit when the unit is installed into the instrument panel, (excluding automatic flight control systems, transponders, and microwave frequency distance measuring equipment (DME)). The approved unit must be designed to be readily and repeatedly removed and replaced, and pertinent instructions must be provided. Prior to the unit's intended use, and operational check must be performed in accordance with the applicable sections of part 91 of this chapter.

Figure 14-3-8. Part 43 provides a complete list of preventive maintenance items.

- Replace defective safety wire or cotter keys
- Lubricate items not requiring disassembly other than removing nonstructural items (for example, cover plates, cowling, and fairings)
- Replenish hydraulic fluid in the hydraulic reservoir
- Apply preservative or protective material to components where no disassembly of any primary structure or operating system is involved, and where such coating is not prohibited or contrary to good practices
- Replace safety belts
- Replace bulbs, reflectors, and lenses of position and landing lights
- Replace or clean spark plugs and set spark plug gap clearance

The most significant difference in preventive maintenance items compared to all other maintenance items is the provision that allows pilots to complete this work. Part 43 states, "Except for holders of a sport pilot certificate, the holder of a pilot certificate issued under part 61 may perform preventive maintenance on any aircraft owned or operated by that pilot which is not used under part 121, 129, or 135 of this chapter." Note that this permission is granted *only* when the pilot is the owner or operator of the aircraft.

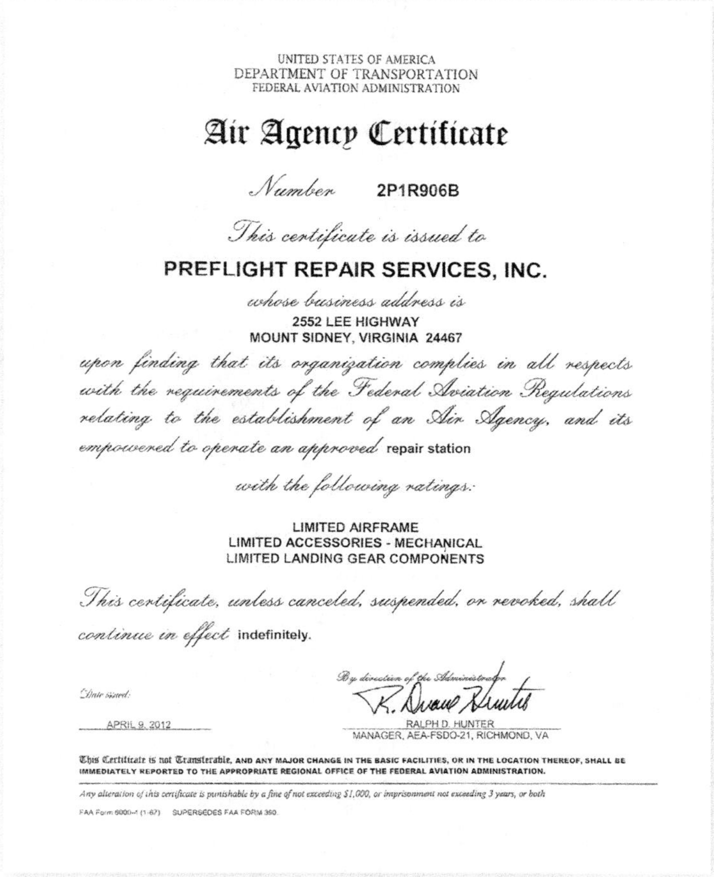

UNITED STATES OF AMERICA
DEPARTMENT OF TRANSPORTATION
FEDERAL AVIATION ADMINISTRATION

Air Agency Certificate

Number **2P1R906B**

This certificate is issued to

PREFLIGHT REPAIR SERVICES, INC.

whose business address is

2552 LEE HIGHWAY
MOUNT SIDNEY, VIRGINIA 24467

upon finding that its organization complies in all respects with the requirements of the Federal Aviation Regulations relating to the establishment of an Air Agency, and its empowered to operate an approved repair station

with the following ratings:

LIMITED AIRFRAME
LIMITED ACCESSORIES - MECHANICAL
LIMITED LANDING GEAR COMPONENTS

This certificate, unless canceled, suspended, or revoked, shall continue in effect indefinitely.

Date issued: APRIL 9, 2012

By direction of the Administrator
RALPH D. HUNTER
MANAGER, AEA-FSDO-21, RICHMOND, VA

This Certificate is not Transferable, AND ANY MAJOR CHANGE IN THE BASIC FACILITIES, OR IN THE LOCATION THEREOF, SHALL BE IMMEDIATELY REPORTED TO THE APPROPRIATE REGIONAL OFFICE OF THE FEDERAL AVIATION ADMINISTRATION.

Any alteration of this certificate is punishable by a fine of not exceeding $1,000, or imprisonment not exceeding 3 years, or both

FAA Form 8000-4 (1-67) SUPERSEDES FAA FORM 390.

Figure 14-4-1. A sample Air Agency Certificate that was issued under Part 145.

Section 4

Legal Requirements for Completing Maintenance

With inspections, several people or organizations are allowed to complete each type of inspection. Maintenance is much the same. Section 43.3 establishes who may perform maintenance items. Nine different persons may perform maintenance.

> **NOTE:** According to 14 CFR part 1, the FAA definition of a person is "an individual, firm, partnership, corporation, association, joint-stock association, or governmental entity. It includes a trustee, receiver, assignee, or similar representative of any of them."

1. Certified mechanic per part 65.
2. Certified repairman per part 65.
3. Person working under the supervision of a certified mechanic or repairman.
4. Holder of repair station certificate (Figure 14-4-1).
5. Holder of an air carrier certificate.
6. Holder of pilot certificate (other than a sport pilot certificate) may perform preventive maintenance on an aircraft he or she owns or operates. This does not apply to aircraft operated under parts 121, 129, or 135.

   NOTE: Preventive maintenance is identified in appendix A, paragraph C of this part.
7. Pilot of a rotorcraft (when operated under part 135 and in remote areas) may perform specific preventive maintenance actions. These actions may be accomplished only under the following conditions:
   - The mechanical difficulty or malfunction occurred enroute to or in the remote area.

- The pilot has been satisfactorily trained and is authorized in writing by the certificate holder to perform the required maintenance.

- There is no certificated mechanic available.

- The certificate holder has procedures to evaluate the work performed when a decision for airworthiness is required.

- The work done is listed in paragraph (c) or Appendix A of this chapter.

8. Holder of part 135 certificate may allow pilots of aircraft with nine or less passenger seats to remove and reinstall cabin seats and stretchers, and cabin mounted medical oxygen bottles. These actions may only be accomplished under the following conditions:

- The pilot has been satisfactorily trained and is authorized in writing by the certificate holder to perform the required maintenance

- The certificate holder has written procedures available to the pilot to evaluate the work performed

9. Manufacturer may inspect and rebuild any item it has manufactured.

Section 5

Owner/Operator Responsibilities for Inspection and Maintenance

The primary responsibility for maintaining an aircraft in an airworthy condition falls on the aircraft owner or operator. These responsibilities are clearly established by the regulations in 14 CFR part 91. Certain inspections must be performed on the aircraft, and the owner must maintain the airworthiness of the aircraft during the time between required inspections by having any defects corrected.

The registered owner/operator of an aircraft is responsible for the following:

- Having a current Standard Airworthiness Certificate and a Certificate of Aircraft Registration in the aircraft

- Maintaining the aircraft in an airworthy condition, including compliance with all applicable ADs and ensuring that maintenance is properly recorded

- Keeping abreast of current regulations about the operation and maintenance of the aircraft

However, for any flight, the pilot in command has final responsibility for airworthiness. Section 91.7 clearly states:

(a) No person may operate a civil aircraft unless it is in an airworthy condition.

(b) The pilot in command of a civil aircraft is responsible for determining whether that aircraft is in condition for safe flight. The pilot in command shall discontinue the flight when unairworthy mechanical, electrical, or structural conditions occur.

Part 91 has other guidance regarding maintenance and inspections, and as mentioned earlier, it references other regulations where information on these subjects is. The general requirements in section 91.403 refer to both part 39 (Airworthiness Directives) and part 43 (Maintenance). The four regulations are below:

(a) The owner or operator of an aircraft is primarily responsible for maintaining that aircraft in an airworthy condition, including compliance with part 39 of this chapter.

(b) No person may perform maintenance, preventive maintenance, or alterations on an aircraft other than as prescribed in this subpart and other applicable regulations, including part 43 of this chapter.

(c) No person may operate an aircraft for which a manufacturer's maintenance manual or instructions for continued airworthiness has been issued that contains an airworthiness limitations section unless the mandatory replacement times, inspection intervals, and related procedures specified in that section or alternative inspection intervals and related procedures set forth in an operations specification approved by the Administrator under part 121 or 135 of this chapter or in accordance with an inspection program approved under section 91.409(e) have been complied with.

(d) A person must not alter an aircraft based on a supplemental type certificate unless the owner or operator of the aircraft is the holder of the supplemental type certificate or has written permission from the holder.

The regulations also establish that the owner or operator of the aircraft is responsible to have the aircraft inspected and maintained in accordance with part 43. The language in section 91.405 is below.

Each owner or operator of an aircraft—

(a) Shall have that aircraft inspected as prescribed in subpart E of this part and shall between required inspections, except as provided in paragraph (c) of this section, have discrepancies repaired as prescribed in part 43 of this chapter;

(b) Shall ensure that maintenance personnel make appropriate entries in the aircraft maintenance records indicating the aircraft has been approved for return to service;

(c) Shall have any inoperative instrument or item of equipment, permitted to be inoperative by section 91.213(d)(2) of this part, repaired, replaced, removed, or inspected at the next required inspection; and

(d) When listed discrepancies include inoperative instruments or equipment, shall ensure that a placard has been installed as required by section 43.11 of this chapter.

The aircraft's owner or operator must understand their role in returning the aircraft to service following maintenance and inspection. The requirements are in section 91.407, which states:

(a) No person may operate any aircraft that has undergone maintenance, preventive maintenance, rebuilding, or alteration unless—

 1. It has been approved for return to service by a person authorized under section 43.7 of this chapter; and

 2. The maintenance record entry required by section 43.9 or section 43.11, as applicable, of this chapter has been made.

(b) No person may carry any person (other than crewmembers) in an aircraft that has been maintained, rebuilt, or altered in a manner that may have appreciably changed its flight characteristics or substantially affected its operation in flight until an

appropriately rated pilot with at least a private pilot certificate flies the aircraft, makes an operational check of the maintenance performed or alteration made, and logs the flight in the aircraft records.

(c) The aircraft does not have to be flown as required by paragraph (b) of this section if, prior to flight, ground tests, inspection, or both show conclusively that the maintenance, preventive maintenance, rebuilding, or alteration has not appreciably changed the flight characteristics or substantially affected the flight operation of the aircraft.

Keeping these requirements in mind, it is clear that the pilot may have the final say as to the airworthiness of the airplane he or she is about fly, but the owner or operator is responsible for maintaining the aircraft in airworthy condition.

Section 6

Maintenance Records

Whenever maintenance, preventive maintenance, rebuilding, or alteration work occurs on an aircraft, airframe, aircraft engine, propeller, appliance, or component part, a maintenance record entry must be created (Figure 14-6-1). The importance of compliance with this requirement cannot be overemphasized. Complete and organized maintenance logs for an aircraft can have significant (and usually positive) effect during the buy/sell nego-

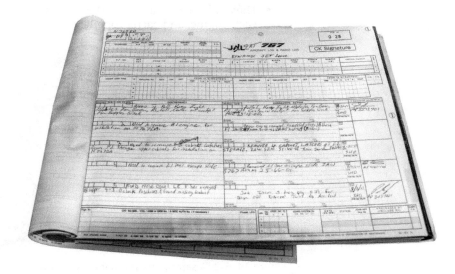

Figure 14-6-1. A maintenance logbook for a large aircraft.

tiations of an aircraft. On the other hand, poorly organized and incomplete logs can have a detrimental effect on the selling price of an aircraft. Aircraft maintenance records fall into one of two categories: (1) temporary or (2) permanent.

Temporary records are defined by 14 CFR sections 91.417(a)(1) and (b)(1). The owner must keep temporary records until the work is repeated, superseded, or 1 year has passed since the work was performed. These are typically records referring to maintenance, preventive maintenance, alteration, and all inspections. They include a description of the work performed (or reference to the FAA-accepted data); the date it was completed; and the name, signature, and certificate number of the person doing the return to service.

Permanent records are defined by 14 CFR sections 91.417(a)(2) and (b)(2). The owner must retain these records while he or she operates the aircraft. They are transferred with the aircraft at the time of sale. Typically, these are documents relating to total time in service, current status of life-limited parts, time since last overhaul, current inspection status, current status of applicable AD notes, and major alteration forms as required by 14 CFR section 43.9.

Aircraft Maintenance Record Entries

Aircraft logbooks enable the aircraft owner to keep records of the entire aircraft in chronological order including inspections; tests; repairs; alterations; AD compliance; SBs; and equipment additions, removals, or exchanges.

Permanent records include the following:

- The total time in service of the airframe, each engine, and each propeller

- The current status of life-limited parts of each airframe, engine, propeller, rotor, and appliance

- The time since last overhaul of all items installed on the aircraft that are required to be overhauled on a specified interval

- The identification of the current inspection status of the aircraft, including the time since the last inspection required by the inspection program under which the aircraft and its appliances are maintained

- The current status of applicable ADs, including for each the method of compliance, the AD number, revision date, and if the AD involves recurring action, the time and date when the next action is required

- A copy of each Form 337 approving major alterations to each airframe, engine, propeller, rotor, and appliance

Each time maintenance, including preventive maintenance, is performed on an aircraft, an appropriate entry must be added to the maintenance records (Figure 14-6-2).

According to 14 CFR part 43, any person who maintains, rebuilds or alters an aircraft, airframe, aircraft engine, propeller, or appliance must make an entry containing all the following:

- A description of the work or some reference to data acceptable to the FAA

- The date the work was completed

- The name of the person who performed the work

- If the work was approved for return to service, the signature, certificate number, and kind of certificate held by the person approving the aircraft for return to service

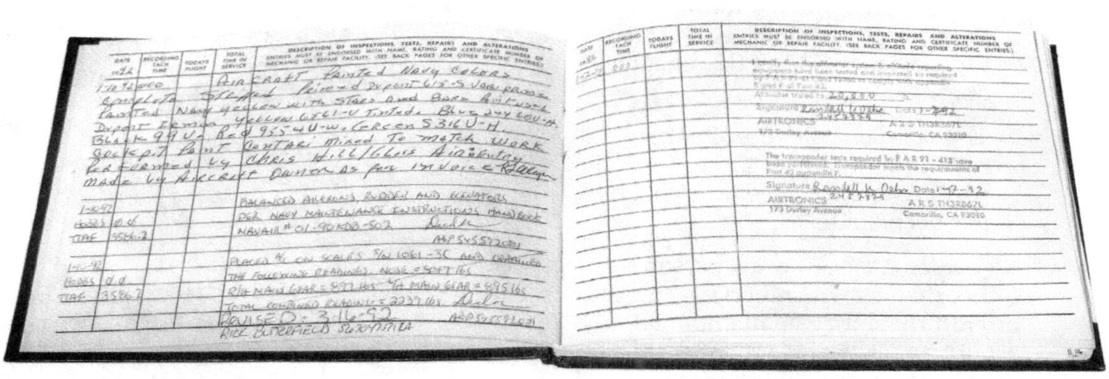

Figure 14-6-2. A sample maintenance logbook.

According to CFR part 43, when a mechanic approves or disapproves an aircraft for return to service after an annual, 100-hour, or progressive inspection, an entry must be made consisting of the following:

- Aircraft time in service
- The type of inspection
- The date of inspection
- The signature, certificate number, and kind of certificate held by the person approving or disapproving the aircraft for return to service
- A signed and dated listing of discrepancies and unairworthy items

FAA Form 337, Major Repair and Alteration

Form 337 (Figure 14-6-3) is used when major repairs or alterations are performed on an aircraft. This form provides aircraft owners and operators with a record of major repairs and major alterations, indicating details of the repair or alteration and approvals. A copy of the form is also provided to the FAA for inclusion in the aircraft records at the FAA Registration Branch.

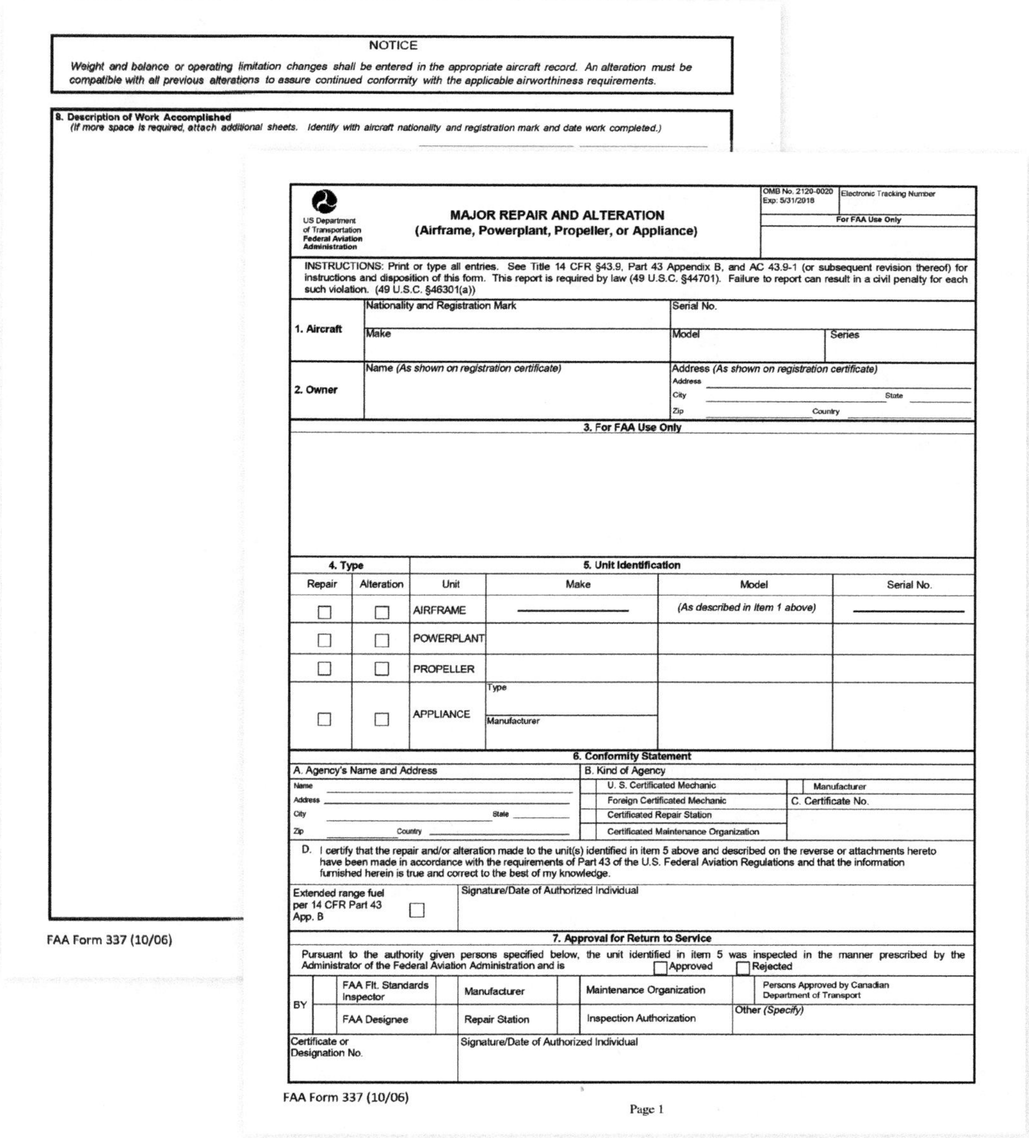

NOTICE

Weight and balance or operating limitation changes shall be entered in the appropriate aircraft record. An alteration must be compatible with all previous alterations to assure continued conformity with the applicable airworthiness requirements.

8. Description of Work Accomplished
(If more space is required, attach additional sheets. Identify with aircraft nationality and registration mark and date work completed.)

FAA Form 337 (10/06)

US Department of Transportation
Federal Aviation Administration

MAJOR REPAIR AND ALTERATION
(Airframe, Powerplant, Propeller, or Appliance)

OMB No. 2120-0020
Exp: 5/31/2018

Electronic Tracking Number

For FAA Use Only

INSTRUCTIONS: Print or type all entries. See Title 14 CFR §43.9, Part 43 Appendix B, and AC 43.9-1 (or subsequent revision thereof) for instructions and disposition of this form. This report is required by law (49 U.S.C. §44701). Failure to report can result in a civil penalty for each such violation. (49 U.S.C. §46301(a))

1. Aircraft	Nationality and Registration Mark	Serial No.	
	Make	Model	Series
2. Owner	Name *(As shown on registration certificate)*	Address *(As shown on registration certificate)* Address, City, State, Zip, Country	

3. For FAA Use Only

4. Type		**5. Unit Identification**			
Repair	Alteration	Unit	Make	Model	Serial No.
☐	☐	AIRFRAME		*(As described in item 1 above)*	
☐	☐	POWERPLANT			
☐	☐	PROPELLER			
☐	☐	APPLIANCE	Type / Manufacturer		

6. Conformity Statement

A. Agency's Name and Address	B. Kind of Agency	
Name	U. S. Certificated Mechanic	Manufacturer
Address	Foreign Certificated Mechanic	C. Certificate No.
City, State	Certificated Repair Station	
Zip, Country	Certificated Maintenance Organization	

D. I certify that the repair and/or alteration made to the unit(s) identified in item 5 above and described on the reverse or attachments hereto have been made in accordance with the requirements of Part 43 of the U.S. Federal Aviation Regulations and that the information furnished herein is true and correct to the best of my knowledge.

Extended range fuel per 14 CFR Part 43 App. B ☐	Signature/Date of Authorized Individual

7. Approval for Return to Service

Pursuant to the authority given persons specified below, the unit identified in item 5 was inspected in the manner prescribed by the Administrator of the Federal Aviation Administration and is ☐ Approved ☐ Rejected

BY	FAA Flt. Standards Inspector	Manufacturer	Maintenance Organization	Persons Approved by Canadian Department of Transport
	FAA Designee	Repair Station	Inspection Authorization	Other *(Specify)*

Certificate or Designation No.	Signature/Date of Authorized Individual

FAA Form 337 (10/06)

Page 1

Figure 14-6-3. Sample FAA Form 337.

Abbreviations and Acronyms

AC	Advisory Circular	EGT	exhaust gas temperature	LOX	liquid oxygen
AC	alternating current	EICAS	engine indicating and crew alerting system	LSA	light sport aircraft
ACM	air cycle machine	ELT	emergency locator transmitter	MAP	manifold air pressure
AD	ashless dispersant			mb	millibar
ADC	air data computer	emf	electromotive force	MEL	minimum equipment list
ADF	automatic direction finder	EPR	engine pressure ratio	MEMS	microelectromechanical systems
AD	Airworthiness Directive	ESFC	equivalent-specific fuel consumption	MHz	megahertz
ADS-B	automatic dependent surveillance–broadcast	ESHP	equivalent shaft horsepower	MMEL	master minimum equipment list
AFM	airplane flight manual	EWCG	empty weight center of gravity	m.p.h.	miles per hour
AGL	above ground level			MSL	mean sea level
AIMS	aircraft in-flight monitoring system	FAA	Federal Aviation Administration	N_1	low-pressure turbine speed
AISI	American Iron and Steel Institute	FADEC	full authority digital engine control	N_2	high-pressure turbine speed
AOA	angle of attack	fhp	friction horsepower	NAS	national airspace system
APU	auxiliary power unit	FS	flap station	NC	nacelle station
AS	aileron station	FS	fuselage station	NC	normally closed
ASI	airspeed indicator	FSDO	Flight Standards District Office	NDB	nondirectional radio beacon
ATC	air traffic control			NFPA	National Fire Protection Association
AVGAS	aviation gasoline	ft.	feet		
BDC	bottom dead center	ft-lb	foot-pound	Ni-Cad	nickel-cadmium
bhp	brake horsepower	gal	gallon	NiMH	nickel metal hydride
BITE	built-in test equipment	gpm	gallons per minute	NO	normally open
BL	buttock line or butt line	GPS	global positioning system	OAT	outside air temperature
BS	body station	GPU	ground power unit	OBOGS	onboard oxygen generating system
BSFC	brake specific fuel consumption	HMDG	hydraulic motor-driven generator	OBS	omni bearing selector
BTU	British thermal unit	hp	horsepower	OEM	original equipment manufacturer
C	Celsius	HRD	high-rate-of-discharge		
CAT	carburetor air temperature	HSI	horizontal situation indicator	PFC	primary flight computer
CDI	course deviation indicator			POH	pilot's operating handbook
CFR	Code of Federal Regulations	HSS	horizontal stabilizer station	PPS	powerplant station
CG	center of gravity	IA	inspection authorization	p.s.i.	pounds per square inch
CHT	cylinder head temperature	IFR	instrument flight rules	PSU	passenger service unit
CO_2	carbon dioxide	ihp	indicated horsepower	PTU	power transfer unit
DC	direct current	ILS	instrument landing system	RAT	ram air turbine
DG	directional gyro	in.	inch	RLG	ring laser gyro
DME	distance measuring equipment	in-lb	inch-pound	RMI	radio magnetic indicator
DPDT	double-pole, double-throw	IR	infrared	r.p.m.	revolutions per minute
DPST	double-pole, single-throw	ITT	interturbine temperature	RRTNM	radar round trip nautical mile
ECAM	electronic centralized aircraft monitor	KOH	potassium hydroxide	SAE	Society of Automotive Engineers
ECS	environmental control system	lb.	pound	SB	service bulletin
		lb-ft	pound-feet	SFC	specific fuel consumption
ECU	engine control unit	lb-in	pound-inch	SHP	shaft horsepower
EEC	electronic engine control	LED	light-emitting diode	SLA	sealed lead acid
		Li-ion	lithium-ion	SPDT	single-pole, double-throw

SPST	single-pole, single-throw	**TIT**	turbine inlet temperature	**VSI**	vertical speed indicator
STC	Supplemental Type Certificates	**TOT**	turbine outlet temperature	**VSS**	vertical stabilizer station
TACAN	tactical navigation	**T-R**	transformer-rectifier	**W**	watt
TAT	total air temperature	**TSFC**	thrust-specific fuel consumption	**WAAS**	wide area augmentation system
TCDS	Type Certificate Data Sheet	**TXV**	thermal expansion valve	**WL**	water line
TDC	top dead center	**UHF**	ultra high frequency	**WOW**	weight on wheels
TEL	tetraethyl lead	**UV**	ultraviolet	**WWI**	World War I
THP	thrust horsepower	**V**	volt	**WWII**	World War II
		VHF	very high frequency		
		VOR	VHF omnirange		

Index